D1217438

Astronomy Notes

2020 Edition

NICK STROBEL

XanEdu

Copyright © 2020 by Nick Strobel.

All rights reserved

Printed in the United States of America

ISBN 13: 978-1-97507-641-2

No part of this book may be reprinted in any manner without written permission from the publisher.

4750 Venture Drive, Suite 400
Ann Arbor, MI 48108
800-562-2147
www.xanedu.com

Contents

Preface

I wrote this textbook for the introductory astronomy course at Bakersfield College, a community college in southern California. The course is a one-semester general education class primarily intended for non-science majors. A general education science course gives a survey of a particular field of science with the main goal of showing how science works. Therefore, the book covers just the primary concepts at a basic level with a minimum of mathematics. I focus on *how* astronomers figure out how the universe and its numerous parts work. I strive to show the student the thinking process behind the scientific discoveries. Astronomy is the oldest of the sciences and it provides a fascinating way to show the process of science to the non-scientist.

The textbook will probably present a new way of thinking and viewing the world to the non-science major student. That is the main goal of a college general education science course. Throughout the text, I draw connections between different parts of astronomy to show how one process of understanding or technique of measurement is used in a variety of seemingly very different areas of astronomy. If after studying this textbook, the reader has an understanding of the scientific method and is able to take a recent news item about something in astronomy and see how it connects with other parts of astronomy, then I will consider the text successful.

The main content is in the central 5-inch wide block of text on the page. I use the remaining outermost 3 inches of the page for brief notes—pointers to the first usage of vocabulary terms, to the introduction of a particular concept, or to a particularly important point. You are encouraged to make additional notes in the margins that will help you understand the material such as brief summaries, marks flagging a topic that you need clarification, or whatever else your heart desires!

Textbook Website

This hardcopy version of *Astronomy Notes* has black-and-white versions of the illustrations. The nice color photographs and animations are found in the web version of the textbook. The text website's URL (the address you type in your web browser) is:

`https://www.astronomynotes.com`

I recommend that you start your use of the textbook's website by selecting the top link called "How to Navigate in this website" in the top left of the homepage. That will introduce you to the setup of the website. The bottom half of the homepage gives a brief overview of the website and links to each of the chapters.

The web version also has links to other astronomy sites embedded within the text material. Sometimes a set of links is also placed at the end of a section. Unfortunately, information on the internet is not ranked by quality or accuracy. Bad or junk material looks the same as the good, respectable stuff. The other websites I have chosen are of excellent quality and from reputable sources. However, sites on the web will frequently change addresses. I tried to select stable sites, but if you find a link does not work, please let me know. My email address is `strobel@astronomynotes.com`.

New Edition

This edition has additional diagrams in several of the chapters and improvements in the explanations to clarify concepts based on student feedback. There are also numerous updates from discoveries made since the previous edition, including gravitational wave detection events, the Rosetta mission, New Horizon mission, the Event Horizon Telescope, the Planck mission, exoplanets, dark matter, and many others. The page at `https://www.astronomynotes.com/updates-2019.htm` gives more details of the updates.

We have learned new things since the previous update, but the methods we use and the reasons for finding about those things has not changed. Since this book focusses on the "how we know" and "why it matters" (concepts) rather than the "what we know" (facts), I have been able to keep the textbook from becoming a huge encyclopedia.

How to Read the Textbook

Reading a science textbook requires a different method than the usual sequential page-by-page method you use for a novel or other book! Your mind will need to have some sort of framework or place holders to store the information presented in a chapter. So you need to create that framework *first* before you get to the meat of the material. Read the "headlines" first—the chapter title and the section titles. Scan the notes in the outermost column and look up the definitions of the vocabulary terms in boldface type in the glossary. Then read the Review Questions at the end of each section.

Note that all of this is done *before* you even read the chapter material! Only after you have built the framework will your mind be ready for the substance of the textbook. After you have read a section, then answer the Review Questions at the end. If you cannot answer a question, then read through the section again to get the answer.

At first glance this technique may seem to take longer than simply reading the text page-by-page. However, it vastly improves comprehension of the material and actually saves time in the long run. Rather than having to read the chapter several times and memorizing the wrong things, you can get the *correct understanding* of the material by reading the chapter once. Your study time is much more efficient with this method and you will do better on the exams. No need to cram for an exam (and fail it!) if you "study read" the chapters.

Final Word

Give yourself extra time to learn this material. I suspect you will find there is much more material to learn in your astronomy class and more study time required than what you thought it would take when you signed up for it (just about every student has said that to me). In California, students learn about astronomy in a small unit (perhaps up to two or three weeks) in the third and/or fifth grade. If they are lucky, they review the material and learn a little more in junior high/middle school in another one-to-three week unit of a general science class. The order of the planets, a few facts about them, and a few of the famous constellations are memorized. I suspect it is pretty much the same in other states.

In college you have a full term (quarter or semester) or two devoted to the subject! It is also at a deeper, more abstract level. Ideas and concepts are more important than facts. If you have not had a science course for a while, it will take your mind some time to "switch gears" from the elementary astronomy exposure you had long ago. Finally, talk with your astronomy instructor frequently, even if you just need to double-check your understanding of the concepts. Most astronomy instructors (including myself) are lonely during their office hours and would be happy to have an inquisitive student to talk to!

Nick Strobel — Bakersfield, CA, May 2019

Chapter 1

Introduction to Astronomy

Hello, explorer! You are about to start a journey that will take you to the farthest reaches of space and the innermost depths of matter and from the earliest beginning of time to the future billions of years from now. Introductory astronomy classes have the daunting task of introducing students to the wonders of the entire universe in one short course, often just one semester or one quarter long. Though the places and events you will encounter will sometimes be mind-boggling, I hope you will find it such a fascinating experience that you will want to learn more about those places in another course or in your own free time in the library or in your backyard with binoculars or telescope (or even better, at star parties on a mountain far from the city lights with your local astronomy club).

The first part of this chapter takes you on a tour of the universe in space and time to give you some context—"set the stage and introduce the characters", some familiar and others quite obscure but still vital to the play. It is like a travel brochure you read before your vacation trip. One word of warning: a lot of numbers and facts are presented in the first section but do not try to memorize them. What is important is to get a sense of the relative scale of things.

In grade school you probably memorized a lot of facts about the planets and stars and when you were older you wondered, "but how do they know that?" In the following chapters you will learn how astronomers measure the distances, sizes, and ages of these objects and determine what they are like and what makes them appear the way they do. This textbook emphasizes the techniques and process astronomers use to find out about the universe around us and the unifying principles operating "behind the scenes". Facts will be given as examples of what is found when those techniques are used or as examples of a particular effect of a physical principle in operation.

The second part of the chapter presents a brief description of the philosophy and method of science and the role astronomy plays in our attempts to understand the universe scientifically. At the end is a discussion of the non-science often confused with astronomy called astrology. The vocabulary terms are in boldface.

1.1 A Sense of Scale

1.1.1 Size

You probably already know that the universe is big but most people do not realize how B I G it really is. Many astronomy classes start off with a tour of the universe based on the excellent short film called *Powers of Ten* by Charles and Ray Eames. The film starts with a man and woman in a city park and then expands the field of view by ten times every ten seconds until it reaches the bounds of the observable

1

universe. After zooming back to the man and woman in the park, the field of view is reduced by ten times every ten seconds until one proton in a carbon atom in the man's hand fills the screen. The film is longer than one might first expect because of all of those powers of ten that must be counted to include all of the things astronomy covers.

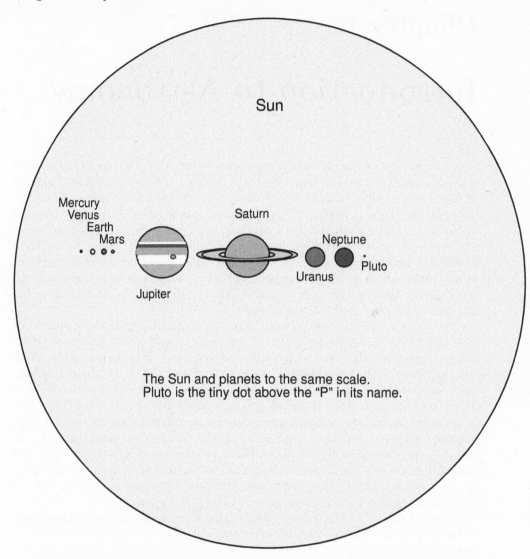

The Sun and planets to the same scale.
Pluto is the tiny dot above the "P" in its name.

solar system scale model

Another way to give you a sense of the distances between things is to use a proportional ("scaled") model. In such a model, everything is reduced by the same amount, so all parts of the model *relative to each other* are of the same proportional size. (In the same way a good trail map you use for hiking or the road map you use for driving is a flat scaled model of the terrain you are moving over.) To create a scale model, divide all of the actual distances or sizes by the same scale factor (in the example below the scale factor is 8,431,254,000), so the scaled distance = (actual distance)/(scale factor).

For our scale model, let us use a yellow mini-basketball about 16.51 centimeters (6.5 inches) across to represent the Sun and then pace out how far the tiny planets would be in this scale model. Since the real Sun is 1,392,000 kilometers (865,000 miles) across, the scale model has all of the planets and distances reduced by an amount equal to (139,200,000,000 / 16.51) = 8,431,254,000 times. The largest planet, Jupiter, would be only 1.7 centimeters across (a dime) and about 92.3

meters away. Our little Earth (a grain of sand) would be closer: "only" 17.7 *meters* (about 18 big steps) away. Our Sun is much larger than the planets, and, yet, it is just a typical star! Here is a scaled model of our solar system:

Scaled Model of the Solar System

Object	Diameter (km)	Distance (million km)	Scaled Size (cm)	Scaled Distance (m)
Sun	1,392,000		16.51	
Mercury	4880	57.910	0.058 (*tiny!* grain of sand)	6.9 (7 big steps)
Venus	12,104	108.16	0.14 (grain of sand)	12.8 (13 big steps)
Earth	12,742	149.6	0.15 (grain of sand)	17.7 (18 big steps)
Mars	6780	228.0	0.08 (almost 1 mm)	27.0 (27 big steps)
Jupiter	139,822	778.4	1.7 (a dime)	92.3 (92 big steps)
Saturn	116,464	1,427.0	1.4 (a button)	169.3 (169 big steps)
Uranus	50,724	2,869.6	0.6 (button snap)	340.4 (340 big steps)
Neptune	49,248	4,496.6	0.6 (button snap)	533.3 (533 big steps)
Pluto	2274	5,913.5	0.03 (small piece of dust)	701.4 (701 big steps)
Oort Cloud		11,200,000		1,328,400 (1,328 km)
Proxima Centauri	375,840	40,493,000	4.5 (handball)	4,802,700 (4,803 km)

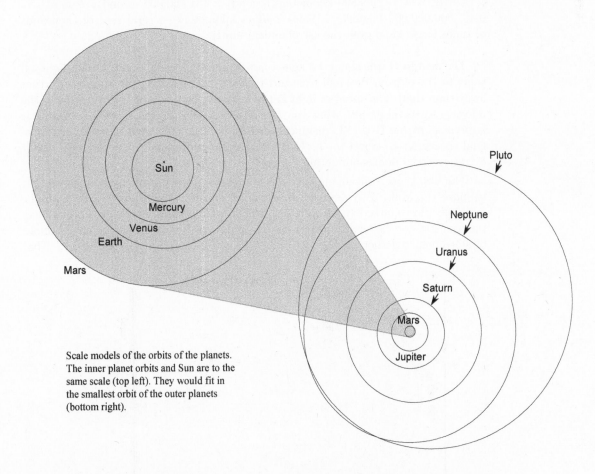

Scale models of the orbits of the planets. The inner planet orbits and Sun are to the same scale (top left). They would fit in the smallest orbit of the outer planets (bottom right).

I will usually use the metric system in this text. This system is used by every major country in the world except the United States. The United States will eventually adopt this system. Readers in the U.S. can multiply the kilometer numbers by 0.6 to get the number of miles and multiply the centimeter numbers by 0.4 to get the number of inches.

The Oort Cloud is a huge spherical cloud of trillions of comets surrounding the Sun that is about 7.5 to 15 *trillion* kilometers across. In our scale model, the middle of the Oort Cloud would be about the distance between Los Angeles and Denver. *the nearest star* Proxima Centauri is the *closest* star to us outside of the solar system (remember that the Sun is a star too!). Proxima Centauri would be from Los Angeles to beyond the tip of the state of Maine on this scale model (from Los Angeles to New Glasgow, Nova Scotia to be more precise!). In our fastest rocket ships (neglecting the Sun's gravity) it would take almost 70,000 years to reach Proxima Centauri!

Instead of using ridiculously small units like kilometers, astronomers use much larger distance units like an **astronomical unit** to describe distances between the planets and a **light year** to describe distances between the stars. An **astronomical** **astronomical unit** **unit** = the average distance between the Earth and the Sun, or about 149.6 million kilometers. For example, Jupiter is (778.4 million km)/(149.6 million km) = 5.203 astronomical units from the Sun. A **light year** is how far light will travel in **light year** one *year*. The distance D something travels in a given time interval t is found by multiplying the speed v by the time interval. In compact math notation this is: $D = v \times t$. You can find out how many kilometers a light year is by multiplying the *speed* of light by a *time* interval of one year:

1 light year = (299,800 kilometers/second) × (31,560,000 seconds/year) = 9,461,000,000,000 kilometers (9.461 *trillion* kilometers—several tens of thousands of times larger than even the astronomical unit!).

The nearest star is about 4.3 light years away which means that it takes light 4.3 years to travel from Proxima Centauri to Earth. The rest of the stars are further away than that! The speed of light is the fastest speed possible for *anything* in the universe to travel despite what you may see in science fiction movies or books. It is because of the H-U-G-E distances and l-o-n-g times it would take extraterrestrial spacecraft to travel to the Earth that many astronomers are skeptical about extraterrestrial beings abducting humans.

the Galaxy The Sun is one star among over 200 *billion* stars gravitationally bound together to make the Milky Way Galaxy. Below is an artist's view of our galaxy with the Sun's position marked (note that our *entire* solar system would be smaller than the smallest dot visible in the picture!). A galaxy is a very large cluster of billions of stars held together by the force of their mutual gravity on each other. That

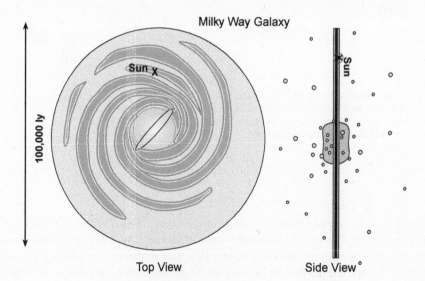

Milky Way Galaxy

100,000 ly

Sun X

Sun

Top View   Side View

definition is a loaded one that will be unpacked and examined in more detail in later chapters, but for now let us continue on our brief tour of the universe. The Milky Way is a flat galaxy shaped like a pancake with a bulge in the center. Stars and gas are clumped in spiral arms in the flat disk part of the Galaxy. Many stars are also found in between the spiral arms. Our solar system is in one of the spiral arms of Milky Way and is about 27,000 light years from the center of the galaxy. The entire Milky Way is about 100,000 light years across. In our scaled model with the Sun 16.51 centimeters across, the Milky Way would be about 112 million kilometers across or about 38% of the size of the Earth's orbit around the Sun. Recall that Pluto's orbit is only 1.4 kilometers across on this scale—the Galaxy is MUCH larger than our solar system!

galaxy is millions of times the size of the solar system

Let's reduce our scale model even more so that our galaxy is the size of the mini-basketball. The closest other galaxy is a small irregularly-shaped one about 13 centimeters away from the Sun toward the direction of the Milky Way's center. It is about the size of a cooked, fat breakfast sausage link in our scale model. Appropriately, the Milky Way is in the process of gobbling up this galaxy. Two famous satellite galaxies of the Milky Way called the Large Magellanic Cloud and Small Magellanic Cloud are about 30 centimeters and 35 centimeters away, respectively. The Large Magellanic Cloud is about the size of a tennis ball and the Small Magellanic Cloud is about the size of a ping pong ball. The Andromeda Galaxy (M 31)

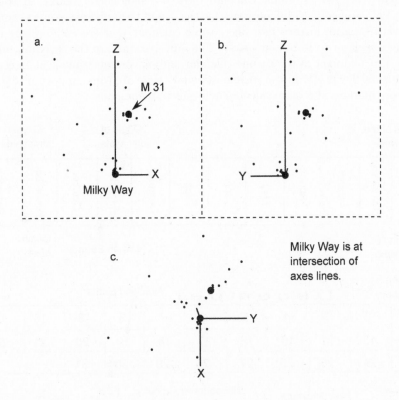

is the closest large galaxy to the Milky Way: a ball 19 centimeters in diameter (a volleyball) about 4.8 meters away. The Milky Way and the Andromeda Galaxy are at either end of a group of about 30 galaxies gravitationally bound together in the Local Group. The Local Group can be roughly divided into two clumps each with a large spiral galaxy and several satellite dwarf galaxies. Three views of the Local Group, each viewed from a position 90 degrees different from the rest, are shown above. The Milky Way is the large dot at the intersection of the x,y,z axes and the

the Local Group

Andromeda Galaxy is the other large dot.

The closest large cluster of galaxies is called the Virgo cluster (toward the direction of the Virgo constellation). The Virgo cluster has over 1000 galaxies in it and is roughly 50 meters away in our scale model. Notice that compared to their size, the galaxies are relatively close to one another. Stars *inside* a galaxy are relatively very far apart from one another compared to the sizes of the stars. You will see that the relative closeness of the galaxies to each other has a significant effect on the development of galaxies.

The Local Group and Virgo cluster are part of a larger long, narrow group called the Local SuperCluster, sometimes called the Virgo Supercluster since the Virgo cluster is close to the middle. The Local Group is close to one edge of the Local SuperCluster. In our scale model with the Milky Way the size of a mini-basketball, the Local Supercluster is about 190 meters long and the entire observable universe is about 49.5 *kilo*meters in diameter.

1.1.2   Time

24 "cosmic days" = 1 billion real years

Now let's try to get a feel for the time scales. I will use another scale model, but instead of reducing distances, I will shrink down time. The scale model is called the "cosmic calendar" in which every second in the "cosmic calendar" corresponds to 475 real years (so 24 cosmic calendar days = 1 billion real years). If you use the classical number of 15 billion years for the age of the universe, you can squeeze the universe's entire history into one cosmic calendar year (recent measurements place the age closer to 14 billion years). The universe starts in the early morning of January 1 at midnight in the cosmic calendar and our present time is at December 31 at 11:59:59.99999 PM in the cosmic calendar. Here are some important dates in this super-compressed cosmic calendar relevant to us humans:

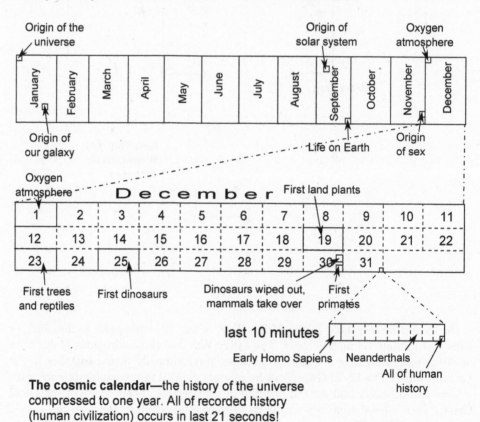

The cosmic calendar—the history of the universe compressed to one year. All of recorded history (human civilization) occurs in last 21 seconds!

Origin of the universe—Jan. 1.

Origin of our galaxy—Jan. 24.

Solar system origin—Sept. 9.

Earth Solidifies—Sept. 14.

Life on Earth—Sept. 30.

Sexual reproduction advent—Nov. 25.

Oxygen atmosphere—Dec. 1.

Cambrian explosion (600 mil years ago when most complex organisms appear, fish, trilobites)—Dec 17.

Land plants & insects—Dec. 19, 20.

First amphibians—Dec. 22.

First reptiles & trees—Dec. 23.

First dinosaurs—Dec. 25.

KT impact, mammal age, birds—10:00 AM Dec 30.

First primates—Dec. 30 late evening.

Australopithicenes (Lucy, etc.)—10:00 P.M. Dec. 31.

Homo habilis—11:25 P.M. Dec. 31.

Homo erectus—11:40 P.M. Dec. 31.

Early Homo sapiens—11:50 P.M.

Neanderthal man—11:57 P.M. Dec. 31.

Cro-Magnon man—11:58:38 P.M.

Homo sapiens sapiens—11:58:57 P.M. Dec. 31.

Human history—11:59:39

Ancient Greeks to now—last five seconds.

Average human life span—0.15 second.

It is rather surprising that we have been able to discover so much about the long term evolution of the universe and the things in it, especially when you consider that we have only been seriously observing the universe for about 100 years, which is only a very slight fraction of the universe's lifetime. About 100 years ago is when photography was first used in astronomy, making truly systematic observation programs possible. How can astronomers say that the Sun will go through a red giant phase in about 5 billion years from now with confidence? Is it hubris to confidently talk about the Earth's formation process 4.6 billion years ago?

To give you an idea of the difficulties in studying long timespans consider this analogy: An alien comes to Earth to search for life and to understand how it evolved. ET has a camera and has just 14 seconds to take as many photographs as possible. Fifteen seconds is the same proportion of a human lifetime as the 100 years is to the universe's age (14 seconds/human lifetime = 100 years/universe age). ET returns home and her colleagues try to understand Earth from this 14-second period of snapshots. They won't see any important evolutionary changes. How will they determine the dominant life form? They could use a variety of criteria: 1) Size: leads them to choose whales or elephants; 2) Numbers: choose insects; 3) amount of land space controlled by one species: choose automobiles.

Suppose they somehow decide humans are dominant. They now have further problems. There is considerable diversity among the humans (though to ET with 10 tentacles, 200 eyes, and a silicon outer shell, the humans all look alike!). ET and colleagues try to systematically classify the humans. The humans come in a variety of sizes. In a coarse classification scheme, they break the sizes down into small, medium, and large. They also come in variety of optical colors for their outer shell: red, black, brown, yellow, and white. There appears to be 2 separate sexes (ET is both male and female). After some false starts with theories that used hair length and eye color, they are ready to ask themselves, "Do small, brown, female humans evolve into large, red, male humans?" "Do the small stay small and the large stay large?" "Why is there a tendency for small humans to be with one or two large humans?" With the three characteristics [size (3 divisions), color (5 divisions), and sex (2 divisions)], ET has $3 \times 5 \times 2$ different combinations and 30×30 possible evolutionary schemes to consider! Well, the universe has a lot more characteristics and, therefore, many more combinations to consider!

Vocabulary

astronomical unit   light year

Review Questions

1. The fastest plane can travel at about 4400 kilometers/hour. How long would

it take to travel to the Sun? Convert your answer to the number of days and then the number of years. (The time it takes to travel a given distance = (distance travelled)/speed, or in the notation used in the chapter: $t = D/v$.)

2. Compared to the distances between the planets in the solar system, how far apart are the stars from each other? For this comparison find out how many **astronomical units** there are between two typical stars (e.g., the Sun and Proxima Centauri). Is the answer closer to 10, 100, 1000, 10000, 100,000, 500,000, or 1,000,000?

3. How far away is the nearest star outside of the solar system in kilometer units and light year units?

4. In a manner similar to how the light year is defined, define a "car day" as how far a car will travel in one day (24 hours) moving at a speed of 105 kilometers/hour (= 65 miles/hour). How far would a "car day" be in kilometers? How many "car days" across is your home state? (Specify if it is the north-south size or the east-west size.)

5. How many kilometers would a light year be if it was discovered that the speed of light was two times slower than previously thought?

6. Where is our solar system in the Milky Way Galaxy?

7. How old is the Earth compared to the age of the universe?

8. How many times older is the Earth than the first civilizations?

1.2   Science in General

Scientific knowledge is based on observations of nature. From observations of many different events and situations, scientists try to find patterns and create generalizations as to the underlying fundamental processes involved. Then they experiment again to see if the right guess was made of what the rule is that nature follows under a given situation. *Experiments determine scientific truth.*

controlled experiments   The scientist usually learns about nature by using controlled experiments in which only one thing at a time is varied to determine whether or not a particular situation, feature, or circumstance can be determined to be the *cause* of an observed effect. The experiments can be repeated by anyone as many times as they want to verify that the effect is reproducible. The astronomer cannot do controlled experiments. They cannot even examine things from a variety of angles. What astronomers do is collect light and other radiation from celestial objects and use all of the information and their creativity to interpret the signals from afar. They look for the experiments nature has set up and hone on a few basic characteristics at a time.

1.2.1   Scientific Models and Scientific Theories

model

Scientists will create **models** (simplified views of reality) to help them focus on the basic fundamental processes. In this context a **model** is an abstract construct or idea that is a simplified view of reality, not something made out of paper, wood, or plastic (or some good-looking person). "Theory" in the scientific use of the word is different than the everyday language usage today. Most people today use "theory" as just a hunch, guess, belief, or proposal. Science uses the original meaning of "**theory**":   a logical, systematic set of principles or explanation that has been verified—has stood up against attempts to prove it false. Scientific models and theories must make testable predictions. Like any scientist, the astronomer makes observations, which suggest hypotheses. These speculations are made into predictions of what may be observed under slightly different observing and/or analysis

theory

circumstances. The astronomer returns to the telescope to see if the predictions pan out or if some revision needs to be made in the theory. Theory and observation play off each other.

Often the evidence for a particular hypothesis is indirect and will actually support other hypotheses as well. The goal is to make an observation that conclusively disproves one or more of the competing theories. Currently unresolvable questions may be resolved later with improved observations using more sophisticated/accurate equipment. Sometimes new equipment shows that previously accepted theories/hypotheses are wrong!

Scientific models and theories must make testable predictions. If an explanation is offered that has no concrete test that could disprove the explanation in principle, it is not a scientific one. This characteristic of scientific explanations is often the distinguishing one between scientific and other types of theories or beliefs (religious, astrological, conventional wisdom, etc.). Do understand that a scientific theory can be *incorrect* but still be considered a *good* scientific theory because it makes a testable prediction of what will happen under a given set of observing or analysis circumstances.

testable predictions

1.2.2   A Definition of Scientific Truth

The discussion up to now has been based on a couple of closely-tied assumptions. We assume that there *are* fundamental rules that nature follows and that there is only one real way that nature is and that nature operates. There are rules and nature (the physical world) always follows them. If we did not assume that, then it would be a waste of time to try to understand nature. These assumptions are discussed more fully in the scientific method chapter (chapter 2).

two assumptions of science

Explanations and theories that correctly predict new results from new observations or experiments bring us closer to a true understanding of nature and the rules by which it operates. This true understanding of nature is what I call "scientific truth" in this text to distinguish it from other definitions of truth as in religious truth, for example. Scientific truths are based on clear observations of physical reality and can be tested through observation. Certain religious truths are held to be true no matter what. That is okay as long as it is not considered to be a *scientific* truth. Some things like love, honor, honesty, and compassion are known to be right or true without the test of experiments. Confusion between the religious and scientific types of explanation has been, and still continues to be, a major source of a huge amount of conflict between some people.

finding the rules

observations are the key

Another source of friction between science and religion is when science proponents confuse "absence of evidence" with "evidence of absence". The process or *methodology* of science restricts itself to natural causes. Scientists limit themselves to just matter, energy, and their interactions. This does not necessarily mean that scientists deny the existence of God or of things beyond the physical realm because they understand the self-imposed limitation of the scientific method. Science can never prove the existence of God nor can science ever *disprove* the existence of God. Yes, it is possible to be a scientist and a devout member of a spiritual faith—I know of many scientists who are serious practitioners of their religion. In fact, several significant advancements in science were made by clergy. In chapter 4 you will find several examples of scientists who were guided by their spiritual faith. A couple of other examples not mentioned in that chapter are Gregor Mendel (the Austrian monk whose research with pea plants became the foundation of genetics) and Georges Lemaitre (the Belgian Roman Catholic priest who developed the Big Bang theory from Einstein's General Relativity). Not all scientists are believers in a spiritual faith just as not all non-scientists are believers in a spiritual faith. For more on the compatibility of science and religion, see the textbook's website supple-

self-imposed restriction of science

science not prove or disprove existence of God

mentary material for chapter 1 called "Science-Religion interface and interaction".

Since this is a science textbook, I will focus on the scientific type of explanations. Whether or not you, the reader, chooses to *believe* what is discussed here is up to you. However, I want you to *understand* the physical principles discussed here and be able to apply them to various situations. The scientific method for finding scientific truth is discussed in more depth in chapter 2.

1.3   Value of Astronomy in the Scientific Endeavor

Even though astronomers cannot do controlled experiments and they are confined to observing the universe from locations near the Earth, the universe gives us a vast number of different phenomena to observe. Many of these things cannot be reproduced in Earth laboratories. There are gas clouds in such a rarefied state that they give off radiation not seen on Earth. Some objects are so dense that their gravitational fields bend light so much that it is prevented from leaving the object! Many things that are unlikely or impossible on Earth are routinely observed in the cosmos. Many of the scientific theories in other fields make predictions of what would happen under very extreme circumstances. Sometimes those extreme circumstances are the only situations distinguishing two or more contradictory theories. Unfortunately, the scientists of those other disciplines cannot test their "wild" ideas—is it hogwash or reality? Astronomy allows those theories to be tested. Very subtle and easily missed but crucial processes may be missed by observers focussing on the Earth, but the astronomer can see those processes magnified to easily noticeable levels in some other celestial object.

testing theories

In addition you will see later that the light coming from far-away objects in all parts of the universe tells us about the laws of physics (the rules of nature governing how physical things interact with each other) there. Astronomers find that the laws of physics discovered here on the Earth are the same throughout the cosmos. The fact that nature makes nearly an infinite variety of things from the same types of material here on the Earth and has those things interact with each other in so many different ways using the same rules we see followed here on the Earth is awe-inspiring.

universality of physical laws

Now back to the long term evolution side of the coin. We actually have a time machine! Not the H.G. Wells variety or G. Roddenberry's Guardian of Forever but something much simpler due to the large distances and finite speed of light (300,000 kilometers/second!). It takes time for radiation from a celestial object to reach the Earth. Therefore, when you examine an object at a large distance from us, you see it as it *was*. The farther away the object is, the longer it took the radiation to reach the Earth, and the further back in time you observe it. The Sun is 150 million kilometers from us, so you see the Sun as it was 8-1/3 minutes ago. The farthest object you can see without a telescope is the Andromeda galaxy about 2.8×10^{19} kilometers from the Earth, so you see it as it was almost 3 million years ago. Recall that a **light year** is how far light travels in one year (about 9.46×10^{12} kilometers). Therefore, the Andromeda galaxy is almost 3 million light years away from us. (The speed of light is the key in the relationship between space and time, a fact used by Albert Einstein in developing his Relativity theories that are described later in this text.)

To study the evolution of long-lived objects like stars (with lifetimes of millions to billions of years) or galaxies, astronomers observe the objects of interest at different distances from the Earth so the objects are seen at different epochs. Therefore, the objects are seen at various different ages or evolutionary stages. Since light from remote objects can take millions to billions of years to reach the Earth, astronomers find out about the laws of physics at different times. What they find is that the universe has used the same laws of physics throughout its 14-billion year lifetime (and presumably will continue using those same rules). Pretty amazing!

same laws followed throughout all time

1.4 Astrology

Perhaps even harder to distinguish are the false claims by those who say they are scientific from the claims arrived at using proper research methods. Much of the television and internet media are awash in pseudoscience claims that are wrapped in a technical/scientific-looking veneer in an attempt to give them some legitimacy. Pseudoscience (fake or bogus science) says it is scientific but does not follow the rigorous error-correction process of true science, particularly peer review. A couple of places in astronomy where pseudoscience claims are commonly made are astrology and UFOs as alien spacecraft. Astrology is dealt with here in this section and UFOs are dealt with in the Pseudoscience vs. science article posted on the textbook's website.

Many astronomy students take the class believing they are going to "learn about the stars and planets." You will learn about these things! However, quite often when I probe a little more what people mean by that phrase "learn about the stars and planets", I find out that many people are thinking about **astrology**—a belief system in which the positions of the planets among the stars are thought to hold the key to understanding what you can expect from life. I find that even many of those who have a four-year college degree (including some college professors!) are thinking this when I tell them that I teach *astroNOMY*. Astronomy is a science, astrology is NOT. Today the two subjects are very different from one another, but hundreds of years ago astronomy and astrology were very similar to one another.

astrology

1.4.1 History of Astrology

Astrology began about 4000 years ago in the religions of Babylonia that believed the future of the nation and ruling class depended on the planets, Sun, and Moon and their motions. Astrology spread through most of the western world when the Greeks became the world power and incorporated the Babylonian culture into their own. The application of astrology expanded to all social classes—the planets were believed to influence every person, not just the ruling class. Eventually, people came to believe that the position of the Sun, Moon, and planets at a person's birth was especially significant.

While most astrologers were developing ways to predict the future of human events by careful observations of the sky, early *astronomers* were developing ways to predict the motions of the planets, Sun, and Moon. Most early astronomers were motivated by the idea that if they could accurately predict the motions of the planets then they would be able to accurately predict the future of persons. Astronomy broke away from astrology and became a science when astronomers became more interested in explaining what made the planets move the way they do and not in divining the future and interactions of individuals.

1.4.2 The Horoscope

The horoscope is a chart showing the positions of the planets, Sun, and Moon in the sky at a person's birth. Their positions are located in the **zodiac**—a narrow belt of constellations centered on the ecliptic. The **ecliptic** is the path the Sun takes through the stars throughout the year (as opposed to the arc it travels from sunrise to sunset). The zodiac is divided into 12 signs named after the constellations through which the Sun, Moon, and planets passes. Your "sign" is the zodiac sign which the Sun was in at your birth.

zodiac
ecliptic

different   constellation sizes

Right away you run into a problem with the zodiac constellations—some are large (like Scorpio or Virgo) and others are small (like Aries and Cancer). Because the rate that the Sun moves along the ecliptic is nearly constant, the Sun spends more time in the large zodiac constellations than in the small ones. It does not matter whether you use the ancient constellation boundaries or the modern boundaries recognized by the International Astronomical Union (though, the IAU boundaries have the Sun spending part of its time in the non-zodiac constellation Ophiuchus!). However, the dates listed in the newspaper for the horoscope signs are

Ophiuchus ignored

all 30 or 31 days long (even for tiny Aries) and the horoscopes do not include the constellation Ophiuchus. (However, the astrologers can simply counter that with their constellation/zodiac boundaries are different from the astronomical ones.)

zodiac sign one month off

Because of an effect called precession, the zodiac constellations slide westward along the ecliptic, making a complete circuit in about 26,000 years. Since the zodiac signs were named over 2000 years ago, the stars have moved by about 1/12 of the zodiac (about one sign's worth). Your "sign" is about one month off! (The different sizes of the constellations prevents me from making a more definite statement.) For example, if your sign is a Sagittarius, then the Sun was actually located in the constellation Scorpio when you were born. Actually, for part of the Sagittarius timeframe, the Sun is in Ophiuchus, so perhaps that is not a good example. (Some astrologers today do take precession into account all the while continuing to use the old labels for the sun signs for the sake of their clients—the subjectivity, training, and cultural context of a given astrologer make it hard to make a blanket statement.)

The horoscope includes the position of each planets in the zodiac and where they are with respect to the person on the Earth at the time of his/her birth. Because of this, creating a horoscope is a bit complicated. There are some standard rules (most of which have not changed for thousands of years despite the dramatic improvements in our understanding of how the planets and stars move), but how much emphasis an astrologer will give to each rule in developing the horoscope, depends on the creativity of the astrologer. This lack of objectivity is one reason why astrologers cannot agree on the right prediction for any given person. *Unlike astronomy, astrology does not have clear objective observations of nature (experiments) determine the truth.*

A recent (December 2010/January 2011) furor over the astrology signs being a month off is not the problem with astrology despite what the mass media has latched onto. Some modern astrologers have taken precession into account (check with your favorite one) when they cast their horoscopes for their clients and they do not use the constellation boundaries set by the IAU in the 1930s. So an astrology "constellation" or "zodiac sign" doesn't match the astronomy constellation. If you believe what has been said in the mass media, then it would be a simple matter of just re-labeling a person with a different sign and just continue using the horoscope to predict the future or personality of someone. The real problem remains! The next section talks about testing astrology.

1.4.3   Testing Astrology

There is no known *physical* force from the planets that can have any effect on a person at the moment of birth. The only possible force would be gravity but the gravitational pull of the obstetrician delivering the baby is greater than the gravity from any of the planets! The Earth's gravity on the baby is tens of thousands of times stronger than the gravity on the baby from the Sun or Moon. Astrologers are forced to invoke mystical forces for which there is NO physical proof.

Many people read their horoscope in the newspaper not to get a prediction of what will happen to them, but, rather, to get advice on what they should do in the day (in the United States the horoscope columns focus on who to date and how best to gain money). A person who is serious about using astrology to guide their actions should consult several horoscope columns every day to be sure they have the most accurate information. Unfortunately, that person would find out that the horoscopes for him/her are not consistent with one another even though the horoscopes are phrased as vaguely as they are. Astrology is not as systematic as it claims to be.

Many tests comparing the birthdates of national or state leaders have found the birthdates to be randomly distributed among the twelve signs. If astrology could determine a person's future or his/her personality, then the leaders should have birthdates in one or two signs. Other tests on the birthdates of those who *re-enlist* in the Marines have also found a completely random distribution of birthdates among all of the signs. (I do not say this in a disparaging way. Surely, you'll agree that it takes a particular type of personality to do well in the Marines and to want to re-enlist. There's good reason why their advertising slogan is "The Few. The Proud.") A recent episode of NOVA (on PBS) showed a researcher testing astrology by giving each person in a college class of astrology believers their own individual authentic horoscope. Not surprisingly, they found some event in their day that fitted their horoscope. The students then gave their horoscope to the person sitting behind them. To their surprise or dismay, the students discovered the substituted horoscopes were just as good! (Yes, the students had birthdays spread throughout the year.) There are numerous cases of twins or triplets having different personalities and life events even though their birth times and places were very close to one another.

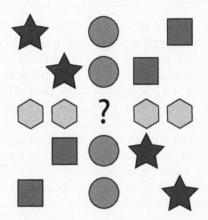

Usually, those who seek out astrologers just want some guidance of any kind. If they feel the horoscope interpretation was prepared just for them, then they will find agreement with reality. Astrology cannot be proven wrong—testable predictions cannot be made because if someone is already convinced of the validity of the horoscope or astrologer's prediction, they will use their natural creativity to "fill in the gaps" and to make sense of contradictions: to reinterpret the prediction to fit what happened.

As an example of this, consider reading your horoscope (it is in the *entertainment* section of my local newspaper) in the morning. It tells you that "you're going to have a bad day—the 'stars' are not aligned for you today—so watch out!" You drive to work or school and when your light turns green, someone in the cross traffic runs through their red light. The horoscope is coming true! You continue on and someone very rudely cuts right in front of you. You think your horoscope was right on despite the fact that in *[insert your town and/or state]*, people are always running red lights and people are always cutting off others. (Don't think that that other driver was giving you a friendly salute.) You concentrate on the bad things during that day.

Now consider reading your horoscope another morning and it says something like "Congratulations! This is your day—the 'stars' are aligned for you today." You drive to work and someone runs that red light, but no problem—that's not unusual. Someone else cuts right in front of you, but, no problem, that was just one person. All the rest of the people were so courteous today. Yes, your horoscope is correct. You concentrate on the good things during that day.

In a more rigorous test of this, Michel Gaugelin (a French researcher) sent a horoscope of a mass murderer to 150 people but told each one that the horoscope was prepared just for him or her. Over ninety percent of them said they could see themselves in that horoscope. If a person is already convinced ahead of time of the validity of something like a horoscope or a psychic's prediction, then he or she will be easily able to use his or her natural problem-solving capabilities and creativity to make sense of the vague, even contradictory statements. The Australian researcher Geoffrey Dean substituted phrases in the horoscopes of 22 people that were opposite of the original phrases in the horoscopes. Ninety-five percent of time they said the horoscope readings applied to them just as well as to the people to whom the original phrases were given. An astrologer relies on her client's ability to create meaning in even random data and to fill in the gaps of incomplete information if some context is given (or if the creative client makes up a context himself). The astrologer's predictions will always be "correct", not testable as a scientific theory or prediction must be.

1.4.4   Further Testing of Astrology

What other tests of astrology can you come up with? Perhaps you might try setting up a study of astrology predictions with your classmates and friends. Ask them about what happened to them yesterday and then compare that to what the horoscope in the newspaper said should have happened. Should you look at their horoscope before you ask them what happened? Would that bias how you interpret what they tell you or would it help you ask appropriate questions to jog their memory? If your astronomy class is large enough and everyone in the class is involved in the study, you will probably have several people sharing the same zodiac sign and comparisons can be made. Be sure to keep track of both positive and negative results. You will need to decide how much of the horoscope prediction should be valid (the whole thing or at least one point?). Your astronomy professor may have other suggestions for possible tests.

Further Reading

Articles I recommend you read about astrology and fortune telling are given below. They were originally published in the magazines *Skeptical Inquirer* and *The Zetetic* and are reprinted in the book *The Outer Edge* published by the Committee for the Scientific Investigation of Claims of the Paranormal in 1996.

- Hyman, Ray. "'Cold Reading': How to Convince Strangers That You Know All About Them," *The Outer Edge*, p. 70. (Originally in *The Zetetic*, Spring/Summer 1977.)

- Frazier, Kendrick. "Double-Blind Test of Astrology Avoids Bias, Still Refutes the Astrological Hypothesis," *The Outer Edge*, p. 40. (Originally in *Skeptical Inquirer*, Spring 1986.)

- Kurtz, Paul and Fraknoi, Andrew. "Scientific Tests of Astrology Do Not Support Its Claims," *The Outer Edge*, p. 36. (Originally in *Skeptical Inquirer*, Spring 1985.

Vocabulary

astrology   ecliptic   model

theory   zodiac

Review Questions

1. What is the scientific method? Give a description of each of its parts. (See chapter 2 for more on this).

2. How are controlled experiments helpful in understanding the rules of nature?

3. What is a scientific **model** and what must the model be able to do to be useful?

4. How can an incorrect scientific theory still be considered a good scientific theory?

5. What distinguishes a scientific truth from a religious truth?

6. In what way can scientists use astronomical observations to find the correct explanations for physical events here on the Earth?

7. How do we know that the laws of physics on the Earth are the same throughout the rest of the universe?

8. How do we know that the laws of physics are the same throughout time?

9. How is astrology different from astronomy?

10. Why is astrology not considered a science?

Chapter 2

Method for Finding Scientific Truth

In your astronomy course, you will cover a lot of explanations as to how the universe and its constituent parts work. All of these explanations were arrived at by using the scientific method in one form or another. One goal of this text is to give you some familiarity with the process of science and how its tools are used to find out about the physical reality around us. Hopefully you will find the method of science a useful one to use in your future to understand the physical universe. The scientific method and the tools of science are powerful tools of knowledge, but there are limits to its applicability and certainty.

There is confusion of what is "scientific" and what is "non-scientific" in the popular media today and undoubtedly you've heard testimonies of one science expert or group contradicting the testimony of another science expert or group. What is the truth? How do we know? How do we tell the difference between mere opinions and real accurately predictive explanations? We will use astronomy as a vehicle to arrive at an answer to these important questions. With all the material we cover in this course, it will help to keep the approach of the two-year-old (or rebellious teenager) in mind. Ask yourself, "How do you know that's right?" and "Why does that happen that way?" What follows is a close adaptation of a chapter from Ronald Pine's book *Science and the Human Prospect*. I recommend that this book be a part of your personal library.

2.1 A Scientific Theory Is...

What distinguishes a scientific theory from a non-scientific theory is that a scientific theory must be refutable in principle; a set of circumstances must potentially exist such that if observed it would logically prove the theory wrong.

Here is a simplified version of the logic of the scientific method: we begin the encounter with nature by making observations and then through some creative process a **hypothesis** (a model or idea) is generated about how some process of nature works. On the basis of this hypothesis, an experiment is logically deduced that will result in a set of particular observations that should occur, under particular conditions, if the hypothesis true. If those particular observations do not occur, then we are faced with several possibilities: our hypothesis needs to be revised, the experiment was carried out incorrectly, or the analysis of the results from that experiment was in error.

The actual process often involves a great deal of insight and creativity. Keep in mind, though, that this interpretive process may have biased the outcome or

hypothesis

17

conclusions. This point will be addressed later. For now, simply note that without a disconfirmation being possible in principle, a belief is not acceptable as even a potential *scientific* hypothesis. *There must be a possible concrete test.*

This refutability and the testable predictions of a "good" or useful scientific theory should extend even further. A scientific theory must make testable or refutable predictions of what should happen or be seen under a given set of *new, independent,* observing or analysis circumstances from the particular problem or observation the theory was originally designed to explain. For example, the seeming contradiction between Uranus' predicted position from Newton's celestial mechanics was explained by the presence of a previously unknown planet, Neptune, whose position was predicted from Newton's celestial mechanics. Astronomers found Neptune just where the theory said it should be. Newton's theory was not originally developed to explain Uranus' or Neptune's motions and it was tested via telescopic observations.

Summary

- A scientific theory must be testable. It must be possible in principle to prove it wrong.

- Experiments are the sole judge of scientific truth.

- Scientific method: observations →hypothesis/theory →experiment (test) →revision of theory

- A "good" or useful scientific theory will make testable predictions of what should happen under new circumstances that are independent of the original problem or observation for which the theory was developed.

2.2   Other Features of a Successful Scientific Theory

This particular section draws from another philosopher of science, Philip Kitcher, particularly his book titled *Abusing Science: The Case Against Creationism* (see p. 46-48). Kitcher gives some other features of a scientific theory in addition to the testability requirement already mentioned. A successful or useful scientific theory will also be a unified theory, solving problems by using the same pattern of reasoning or problem-solving strategy again and again You will see in this book that Newton's theories are applied in the same way to explain the motions and features of a wide variety of celestial objects and physics students use them to understand an even wider range of phenomena.

Finally, a good or successful theory will also be fruitful in opening up new and profitable areas of research. Newtons theories led to improvements in our understanding of hydrodynamics, chemistry, optics, electricity and magnetism, thermodynamics, etc. "A flourishing science is incomplete... A good theory should be productive; it should raise new questions and presume that those questions can be answered without giving up its problem-solving strategies" (Kitcher p. 48).

Summary

- A "good" or useful scientific theory solves problems by using the same pattern of reasoning or problem-solving strategy again and again.

- A "good" or useful scientific theory is fruitful in opening up new and profitable areas of research.

2.3   Correlations May Not Prove the Cause

Often the observation of a **correlation** (a mutual relationship) between two observables is used to proclaim a *cause-effect* relationship between them. For example, suppose that there was a possible correlation between sex education in schools and a recent rise in venereal disease and teenage pregnancy. One could say that sex education has caused the rise in VD and teen pregnancy, but the scientist cannot say that without a more detailed investigation.

After all, there are many other factors that could be the real cause of this problem. A rise in the population of teenagers is possible, causing every activity related to teenagers to go up: automobile accidents or purchasing particular types of clothing and albums. Few would claim that sex education in schools has been the cause of increased purchases of acne lotion. There could be an increase in the population of particular types of teenagers, those in an area of the country where sex education is not taught or where early sexual experimentation is encouraged by various social or family pressures. There are many variables possible to produce that correlation. *Correlation does not prove causation.* A correlation between sex education and teen sex problems does not prove a causal connection, and, by itself, it does not give us a clear indication in which direction there may be a connection. For all we know at this point, an increase in teen sex problems has led to an increase in sex education classes!

Another example is the correlation between smoking and lung cancer occurrences. After a couple of decades of study the government decided in the 1970s that there was a causal connection between smoking and lung cancer and changed the warning label from "Caution, smoking *may* be hazardous to your health" to "Caution, smoking *is* hazardous to your health". A 1950s study only controlled the basic environmental variable—lung cancer for smokers living in the cities vs. lung cancer for smokers living in the country. This study was roundly criticized and rightly so. There were many other important factors that needed to be looked at such as diet, healthy or unhealthy occupations, stressful occupations, or genetic factors.

By the 1970s, more careful studies each incorporating tighter and tighter controls based on possible oversights of the previous studies had proven to the government's satisfaction the causal connection between smoking and lung cancer. By the 1980s other diverse corroborating factors had been identified—from the effects of secondhand smoke to chemical analysis of cigarette smoke revealing over 200 toxic substances, including radioactivity.

Despite all of this study, we really cannot say that cigarette smoking has been *proven* to be the principal cause of lung cancer. A scientific proof is not known with absolute logical certainty. A controlled study can never be completely controlled—there are just too many possible variables. The link between smoking and lung cancer cannot be known in the sense of "known beyond any logical or conceivable doubt." The point is, however, can we say we know that cigarette smoking is a principal cause of lung cancer beyond a "reasonable doubt"? Is it rational if we claim to know something even if we are not absolutely sure that we know something? Can we distinguish between what is "conceivably" true and what is "reasonably" true?

A humorous example of the difference between a correlation and a cause-effect relationship is the Coalition to ban Dihydrogen Monoxide. Links to select sites are given on the text's website.

correlation

Summary

- A correlation between two things does NOT prove one thing *causes* the other. The second thing could cause the first or some other underlying factor could cause the correlation.

- Scientists have to be very careful to rule out other possible underlying factors before concluding one thing *causes* something else.

- Though scientific proofs are not known with absolute certainty, enough evidence can be accumulated to be reasonably certain.

2.4   The Problem of Induction

problem of induction

Science has the **problem of induction:** *No matter how much evidence we have for a conclusion, the conclusion could still conceivably be false.* The best we can say is that it is "unlikely" that our conclusion is false when we are using inductive reasoning. Here's an example: suppose there is a barrel filled with 100 apples and the first apple I pull out off the top is very rotten. Few would wager from this single apple that we know *all* the apples in the barrel are rotten. However, small amounts of evidence need not always be weak. A biologist might be willing on the basis of this one apple to wager that all of the apples are likely to be rotten, if other information were provided like what temperature the apples were stored, and for how long, because of her general knowledge of bacteria and their ability

paradigm

to spread rapidly. If we have some world view or **paradigm** (a framework of a general consensus of belief of how the world works), we can do a lot of hypothetical work with just a few observations.

But without anything else to go on, concluding that all the apples are rotten from a single positive case is a very weak inductive inference. To make the inductive inference stronger, more apples need to be sampled. If I pull out 4 more apples off the top and all of them are also rotten, we'd now have a better basis for concluding

induction by enumeration

that all the apples are rotten. This is called **induction by enumeration.**   In general, *the more positive cases in favor of a hypothesis, the stronger the hypothesis is.* But how about the apples at the bottom? A stronger case could be made by choosing a **representative sample**—a sample that matches in characteristics the

representative sample

total population of things under investigation. In the case of the barrel of apples, a representative sample could be gathered by selecting one from the top, one from the very bottom, one from each side of the barrel, and one from the middle. If all five are rotten, this would strengthen the hypothesis considerably. *A small representative sample is much stronger logically than is a large unrepresentative one.* Five representative apples are better than 20 just off the top.

If you found that another 45 were rotten, would you bet your life savings that all the remaining 50 were rotten? Probably not, since it is still possible that some, even many, of them are not rotten. If you found that another 49 were also rotten, would you bet your life savings that the last remaining apple was rotten? Most people would, but they'd still have a lot of anxiety as the last apple was pulled from the barrel because it was still possible that the hypothesis, "all the apples are rotten," was false. Hypotheses can only be confirmed, not logically proven to be true. Understand that *it is possible to deduce true conclusions* (the 5th apple will be rotten) *from premises that may be false* (all the apples are rotten). Because we can deduce true predictions from a false theory, no matter how long a theory has been successful in making predictions, it cannot be known to be true absolutely. It could be found to be false tomorrow.

Critics of science often attempt to use this logical window to repudiate many scientific conclusions. They also often commit the logical fallacy of appealing to ignorance, arguing that because the theory cannot be proved absolutely true, it must be false. But absence of evidence for absolute proof is not evidence of absence of truth. Critics of science fail to recognize the positive aspect of this logical doubt. Without room for doubt, there would be no room for self-correction, and we would be left with a cluttered clash of irrefutable beliefs.

In another logical fallacy, the appeal to ignorance has been used to argue *for* the existence of things like the Loch Ness monster, Bigfoot, space aliens in flying saucers, etc. by saying one cannot prove they do not exist. See the textbook website for an article by Steven Hales on how it is still possible to prove a negative using inductive reasoning beyond a reasonable doubt.

Summary

- No matter how much evidence we have for a conclusion, the conclusion could still conceivably be false.

- The more positive cases in favor of a hypothesis, the stronger the hypothesis is.

- The most logically sound samples are those that are representative of the entire set.

- It is possible to make true conclusions from false assumptions.

- A hypothesis can only be confirmed but it cannot be proven absolutely true.

- Even though a scientific hypothesis cannot be proven absolutely true, that does not mean that it must be false.

2.5   Science as a Human Endeavor

I probably will not analyze fully the evidence for every claim made in this textbook but keep in mind that this critical attitude lies behind all the explanations presented. Science does not claim to know all the answers. It does, however, claim to provide us with a method of test and interaction by which we can become more and more intimate with the physical universe.

Because science is done by human beings, many aspects of our humanity also play a role in scientific discovery: artistic creation and imagination, political manipulation and personal exploitation, wishful thinking, bias, egocentricity, critical review, and premature skeptical rejection. At its best, however, there is only one absolute truth: that there are no absolute truths. Every solution to a mystery creates new mysteries. Science is a game that never ends, a game whose completion would render life boring. Science then involves a logical process that is fallible, and it involves much more than just a logical process. Every scientist and the science of a time are subject to the forces of human nature and culture. Scientists are forced to make many assumptions; some are conscious and some are not.

2.5.1   Assumptions of Scientists

Let's take a brief look at some these assumptions or philosophical backdrop. Many scientists today will claim they are interested in *how* things work, not *why* they work as they do, because a scientist's task is to conduct experiments, make observations, and find mathematical connections. Influenced by a philosophical tradition known as **positivism,** these scientists will want to know what atoms will do, for instance, not what they are. Or, rather than trying to understand why gravity is attractive and not repulsive, these scientists figure out how the gravitational attraction affects the interaction of objects.

positivism

Another position held by many (but not all) scientists consciously or unconsciously is known as **materialism.**   Metaphysical materialism states that there is no evidence that anything called "mind" exists and that all that exists are concrete material things, forces, and empty space. However, the scientific method does

materialism

not depend necessarily upon making this assumption. Some have argued that recent developments in physics and neurophysiology warrant a reexamination of this question.

idealism

Some scientists have even held a position that is a form of classical **idealism,** believing that the universe can be best understood by assuming that "thought" or "consciousness" is the most fundamental reality. Certain mathematical concepts are ideas in the mind of God and that any physical reality, such as the motion of a planet, must conform to these ideas.

2.5.2   Materialism: Methodology vs. Philosophy

Let's look at the materialism assumption a bit more closely since it is a source of major conflict (in the United States at least). For this section, I use material from Eugenie C Scott's book *Evolution vs. Creationism: An Introduction.*

Modern day scientists purposefully limit themselves to explaining natural phenomena using only natural causes. We have learned a lot about our world, our universe, by adopting a *methodology* of materialism, limiting ourselves to just matter, energy and their interactions. Adopting a materialistic *methodology* when doing science does not necessarily lead to metaphysical or *philosophical* materialism. There have been many theist (not atheist!) scientists who practiced a materialistic methodology and this continues even today.

Why do scientists limit themselves to materialistic explanations? Several reasons: The empiricism of modern science, the testing of explanations, relies on the regularity of nature, that nature does follow rules or laws (see section 2.6.1). Otherwise, we could not trust observations as evidence. How would we know if the observation was not the result of some supernatural whim? Controlled, repeatable experimentation would not be possible and any conclusions from them would not be reliable without assuming that supernatural entities are not intervening to violate natural regularities or laws. (Pennock quoted in Scott p. 249) Secondly, relying on supernatural explanations is a cop-out or a dead-end to deepening our understanding of the natural world. There would be no reason to continue looking for a natural explanation. When confronted with a very hard puzzle due to an inadequate theory or technology, we do not throw up our hands and say, "God did it" and leave it at that—end of inquiry. No, if a natural cause for something is not known, the scientific approach is to say, "I do not know *yet*" and keep on looking. Finally, the "methods of science are inadequate to test explanations involving supernatural forces" (Scott p. 50). It is hard to do controlled experiments if one of the control variables is an omnipotent force. The scientist usually learns about nature by using controlled experiments in which only one thing at a time is varied to determine whether or not a particular situation, feature, or circumstance can be determined to be the cause of an observed effect. Well, as any theologian will tell you, you cannot control God, "the More". You cannot put God in a box (or test tube).

Summary

- Science provides a way of testing and interacting with the physical universe that will better our understanding of the physical universe.

- Science is a human effort and is subject to all of the best and worst of cultural biases existing at the time.

- Most scientists are interested in *how* things work, not *why* things work they way they do.

- Though the assumption is not necessary for science, many scientists assume that science needs to consider only the physical, concrete objects around us.

- Some scientists assume that thought or consciousness is the most fundamental reality.

- Philosophical (metaphysical) materialism is a sub-set of methodological materialism. Many theist scientists use the methodology of materialism to study nature but do not deny the existence of the non-material.

2.6   Ways of Finding the Truth

Some science critics claim that science is absolute and dogmatic in terms of how it approaches the best way of knowing something. Much of our personal knowledge is based upon **testimony.** Someone may tell me that Bogus Basin, just 30 minutes from Boise, ID, has great skiing. If I believe this even though I have only skied at Snoqualmie or Stevens Pass, my belief is based on testimony. Sometimes the testimony is based on **authority,** as would be the case if an Olympic gold medalist told me about Bogus Basin. Many religions claim that **revelation** is a valid method of knowing, whereby important truths about life, impossible to find out any other way, are disclosed to human beings by a divine being or God. Mystics, in general, claim that after years of special training it is possible to know some very important things about life and the universe "intuitively" or in a **mystical vision** while in a deep state of meditation. Mystical visions are not necessarily revelation, because the visions not only involve personal effort and training but also do not necessarily involve divine aid or God.

testimony

authority
revelation

mystical vision

2.6.1   Science's Way of Finding the Truth

Science assumes the position of **empiricism,** because *observational experience is necessary,* either indirectly via robot sensors and cameras or directly through human senses to understand the physical universe. *The experience must be objective and communicable or describable in public language.* Another way of knowing often opposed to empiricism, but historically greatly influenced by the discovery and development of mathematics, is called rationalism. The rationalist has a great faith in the logical power of the human mind and is skeptical about the universal validity of our observational perceptions. Some things are so clear logically or mathematically that we just know that they are true, like the absence of round squares on the dark side of the Moon. We know that round squares are impossible. The rationalist believes that we can know some things about life ahead of time, so to speak; we can know some things that no conceivable experience will contradict.

empiricism

It is difficult for many people today to imagine that the Earth is moving and not the Sun. We do not experience ourselves moving at 1,000 miles per hour; instead we "observe" the Sun to move. That a belief is inconsistent with our common observational experience is not by itself a conclusive argument that it is false. Empirical scientists do believe in the ability of the human mind to figure things out. Any fundamental inconsistency between common sense and reason is seen as nature's way of taunting us, of revealing one of her important secrets. The confidence in the logical and mathematical powers of human thinking has been a key ingredient in the development of modern science.

2.6.2   Theory Must Agree with Reality

The modern scientific method synthesizes rationalism and empiricism. The logic of the rationalist is combined with the observational experience of the empiricist. There is an overwhelming consensus, though, that empiricism is the main emphasis. *No matter how much logical deduction and mathematical analysis is used, at some point the world must be checked for the confirmation of a belief.* Historically, however, spurred on by the power of mathematics and the tendency to conclude that we know something even though complete empirical observations are not available, rationalism has played both a constructive and creative role in development of science. The criticism of those who are too rationalistic and who create ivory-tower fantasies from speculative logic, overlooks the fact that many great discoveries have been made by scientists sitting at desks, following the elegant trails of mathematical equations. Creative ideas are the result of a complex web of influences. *The key is to have ideas with which to make connections.*

Of course, not all ideas are fruitful in making connections. Nor have great scientists been immune from detrimental rationalistic tendencies. Tycho Brahe was the best observational astronomer of the sixteenth century. Mathematically, he knew that one of the implications of his extremely accurate observations of planetary motions was that the Sun was the center of motion of all the planets, which further implied that the universe was very large and that the stars were an immense distance away. He could not bring himself to accept this radical conclusion, however, and accepted instead a more traditional view for his time because God would not be foolish to "waste" all that space!

Johannes Kepler, who used Tycho's data to finally solve the problem of planetary motion, was motivated by his belief that the Sun was the most appropriate object to be placed in the center of the universe because it was the material home or manifestation of God. Galileo, in spite of his brilliant astronomical observations and terrestrial experiments, failed to see the importance of Kepler's solution of planetary motion because it did not involve using perfect circles for the motion of the planets.

Summary

- Possible ways of knowing: testimony, authority, revelation, mystical visions, scientific method.

- Observational experience is a crucial part of scientific knowledge.

- The experience must be objective and communicable in public language.

- Scientific theories must logically agree with known physical truths or well-established physical laws.

- No matter how much logical deduction and mathematical analysis is used, the scientific theory must be checked against the real world to confirm the theory.

- However, the exploration of the implications of a logical train of thought is a vital part of the scientific process.

- The best ideas are those that enable us to make connections between rational theories and the physical world.

2.7   Is the Scientific Method the Only Way to Truth?

Must science assume some ideas dogmatically? Must we assume that the scientific method, a synthesis of reason and experience, is the only avenue to truth? The mystics claim that some simple acts of knowing cannot be described by an objective language. Consider the experience of seeing a death on the highway. Does a cold scientific description, "the cause of the cessation of bodily function was due to a rapid deceleration," accurately convey the truth? What about our own deaths? There seems to be much more to the truth that we will die someday than can be described in the statement "I am mortal." Are there subjective truths that cannot be described in an objective language?

2.7.1   Ideas Change, Physical Laws Do Not

Most scientists today accept an assumption that can be traced to the ancient Greeks: *Whatever they are, the basic truths of the universe are "laws" that do **not** change— only our ideas about them do.* Scientific objectivity presupposes that there is one truth, a collective truth, and our personal beliefs or the beliefs of scientists of a particular time either match these truths or they do not. Most scientists assume that beliefs about what is real do not affect what is real (i.e., *philosophical realism*). Truth results only when our beliefs about what is real *correspond* to what is real.

realism

2.7.2   Perception Changes Reality?

This traditional assumption may not, however, be essential to science. Some quantum physicists have proposed that the points of view implied by our experiments can affect the nature of reality: instead of assuming that there is only reality, there can be "complementary" realities. And reputable physicists and medical researchers are not only re-examining this traditional scientific assumption, but also are wondering candidly if a person's state of mind may have a bearing on whether he or she is prone to diseases such as cancer and whether cures and remissions are possible using a mental therapy. The belief that there is only one reality can itself be subjected to scientific scrutiny. There could be multiple realities or none at all! Even if controversial, these ideas are at least discussed.

2.7.3   Value of Examining Assumptions

Although we may be caught at any given time within a web of many assumptions, science at its best does not rely on many assumptions. Science also assumes that the more we think critically about our beliefs, the more likely we are to know the truth. There are cynics, however, who believe that critical thinking is not a marvelous human characteristic at all. They argue that critical thinking makes life more complicated and distracts us from discovering the simple solutions to life's problems. There are also nihilists who argue that our so-called intelligence and our ability to be aware of the details of the universe are an evolutionary dead end, that far from producing the good life, our awareness and rationality are the cause of our craziness.

Defenders of science often argue that even if some assumptions are necessary in the application of scientific method, these assumptions are validated by the record of success. However, there is a major logical problem with this justification. It simply raises the problem of induction again. It is circular reasoning to attempt to vindicate inductive reasoning by asserting that so far inductive reasoning has worked, because this vindication itself is an inductive argument. It is logically possible for the scientific method to completely fail tomorrow even though it has been successful for centuries. Is it reasonable to continue to believe in the scientific method as helpful for our future? Can science be self-corrective? Philosophers believe these abstract questions are important because they are intimately related to our more personal concerns about who we are, where we have come from, and what may be in store for us in terms of the survival of our species on this fragile fragment of the universe.

2.7.4   Peer Review

It is possible to arrive at various interpretations of the same data or facts and to develop various explanations of the underlying causes at work. Our culture, egos, and personal beliefs provide a filter through which we interpret the data and develop explanations. Because scientists have a "realism" perspective and because culture and egos can affect the interpretations of the data, scientists are willing to have their ideas and explanations closely examined and tested by others, particularly by their peers, in a process called "peer review". "[Science] values testability and critical evaluation, because thus far it appears that the more we think critically about our beliefs, the more likely we are to know the truth" (Pine, ch 2). Peer review works best if the ones who critically analyze an explanation have an alternate explanation and try to poke holes in the other persons explanation. (Sometimes that "poking" is pretty brutal!) This peer review happens at science conferences and in the pages of science journals. A scientist will not try to have his/her opinion advanced by political means or legislated by politicians.

Summary

- A basic assumption of science: fundamental physical laws do exist in the universe and do not change. Our understanding of those laws may be incorrect or incomplete.

- Recent developments in our knowledge of the universe seem to challenge this basic assumption. Our perception *may* affect the physical laws or events.

- Scientists must be aware of the assumptions they make and how those assumptions affect our understanding of the universe.

- Scientists must be willing to have their ideas and explanations closely examined and tested by others, particularly by their peers, in a process called "peer review".

Chapter 3

Astronomy Without a Telescope

Now that you have some feeling for the scales of time and space that astronomy encompasses and some of the difficulties caused by being Earth-bound (well, okay: solar-system bound!), let's take a look at what is up there in the sky beyond the clouds. In this chapter, you will learn where to find the key points on the night sky, how to use the coordinate system that astronomers use, how the Sun's position among the stars changes and how that affects the temperature throughout the year, and about the phases of the Moon and eclipses. At the end of the chapter, you will learn about the motions of the planets among the stars. All of the things in this chapter, you can observe without a telescope. You just need to observe the objects carefully and notice how things change over time. The vocabulary terms are in boldface.

3.1   Celestial Sphere Defined

Imagine the sky as a great, hollow, sphere surrounding the Earth. The stars are attached to this sphere—some bigger and brighter than others—which rotates around the stationary Earth roughly every 24 hours. Alternatively, you can imagine the stars as holes in the sphere and the light from the heavens beyond the sphere shines through those holes. This imaginary sphere is called the **celestial sphere**, and has a very large radius so that no part of the Earth is significantly closer to any given star than any other part. Therefore, the sky always looks like a great sphere centered on your position. The celestial sphere (and, therefore, the stars) appears to move westward—stars rise in the east and set in the west.

celestial sphere

Even though it is now known that this ancient model of a stationary Earth is incorrect, you can still use this model because it is a convenient way to predict the motions of the stars and planets relative to a location on the Earth. A star's apparent brightness is actually determined by its distance, as well as, its physical size and temperature. It is also now known that the stars apparent motion around us is due to the Earth rotating once every 24 hours on its axis. The stars are stationary and the Earth rotates from west to east. This rotational motion makes the stars *appear* to move from east to west around us. The celestial sphere model is used by planetaria to simulate the night sky. I hope you will be able to distinguish between the convenience of the celestial sphere model and the way things really are.

Why a sphere? The Earth is spherical! This was known much earlier than Columbus' time. Sailors had long known that as a ship sailed away from the shore it not only diminished in apparent size, but it also appeared to sink into the water.

27

The simplest explanation to use was that the Earth was curved (particularly, since those ships did come back without falling off some edge!). They also knew that if one traveled in a north-south direction, some stars disappeared from view while others appeared. The difference in the height of a star's height above the north or south horizon is directly proportional to the difference in the north-south distance of observers looking at the star at the same time. The simplest explanation said that the Earth is round, not flat. Pythagoras noted that the shadow of the Earth falling on the Moon during a lunar eclipse was always curved and the amount of the curvature was always the same. The only object that always casts a circular shadow regardless of its orientation is a sphere. This Pythagorean argument is passed on to us through the writings of Aristotle.

Vocabulary
celestial sphere

Review Questions

1. How does the sky *appear* to move around us?
2. What motion of the Earth produces the *apparent* motion of the stars around us?

3.2   Angles

To measure distances on the imaginary celestial sphere, you use "angles on the sky" instead of meters or kilometers. There are 360° in a full circle and 90° in a right angle (two perpendicular lines intersecting each other make a right angle). Each degree is divided into 60 minutes of arc. A quarter viewed face-on from across the length of a football field is about 1 arc minute across. Each minute of arc is divided into 60 seconds of arc. The ball in the tip of a ballpoint pen viewed from across the length of a football field is about 1 arc second across.

arc minute
arc second

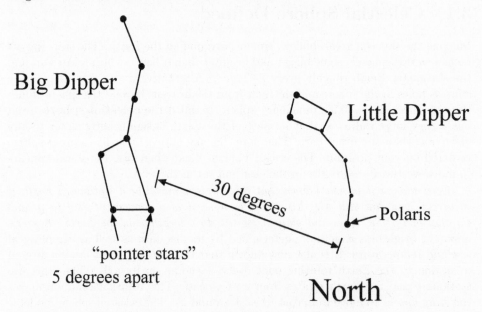

The Sun and Moon are both about 0.5° = 30 arc minutes in diameter. The pointer stars in the bowl of the Big Dipper are about 5° apart and the bowl of the Big Dipper is about 30° from Polaris, the North Star that is very close to the North Celestial Pole (described in the next section). Some angles using your hand held at arm's length are described in the figure below. The arc from the north point on the horizon to the point directly overhead to the south point on the horizon is 180°, so any object directly overhead is 90° above the horizon and any object "half-way up" in the sky is about 45° above the horizon.

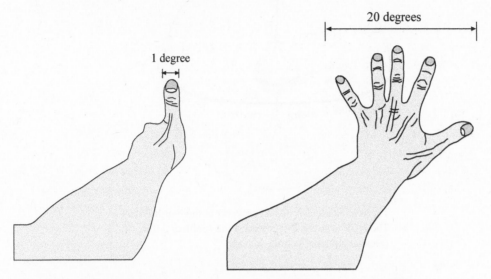

Some simple angular distances using your hand held at arm's length. Your thumb is about 1 degree across, your clenched fist is about 10 degrees across and your spread out fingers are about 20 degrees across.

Review Questions

1. How many degrees is 30 arc minutes?

2. How many degrees is 10 arc seconds?

3. How many Moon diameters would it take to span the distance from a point on the eastern horizon to a point directly opposite on the western horizon?

3.3   Reference Markers

Now for some reference makers: The stars rotate around the **North and South Celestial Poles**. These are   the points in the sky directly above the geographic north and south pole, respectively.   The Earth's axis of rotation intersects the celestial sphere at the celestial poles.   The number of degrees the celestial pole is above the horizon is equal to the latitude of the observer. Fortunately, for those in the northern hemisphere, there is a fairly bright star real close to the North Celestial Pole (Polaris or the North star). Another important reference marker is the **celestial equator:** an imaginary circle around the sky directly above the Earth's equator. It is always 90° from the poles. *All the stars rotate in a path that is parallel to the celestial equator.* The celestial equator intercepts the horizon at the points directly east and west *anywhere* on the Earth.

If you joined Santa last Christmas at the north pole (90° N latitude), you would have seen Polaris straight overhead and the celestial equator on your horizon. The point straight overhead on the celestial sphere for any observer is called the **zenith** and is always 90° from the horizon.   The arc that goes through the north point on the horizon, zenith, and south point on the horizon is called the **meridian.** The positions of the zenith and meridian *with respect to the stars* will change as the celestial sphere rotates and if the observer changes locations on the Earth, but

North and South Celestial Poles

celestial equator
motion of stars

zenith
meridian

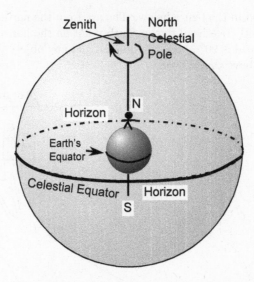

The celestial sphere for an observer at the North Pole.
The NCP is straight overhead at the zenith and the
celestial equator is on the horizon.

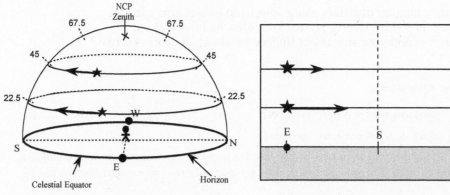

Stars motion at North Pole. Stars rotate parallel to
the Celestial Equator, so they move parallel to the
horizon here---they never set! Altitudes of 1/4,
1/2, and 3/4 the way to zenith are marked.

Your view from the North Pole. Stars move
parallel to the horizon. The Celestial Equator
is on the horizon.

those reference marks do *not* change *with respect to the observer's horizon.* Any celestial object crossing the meridian is at its highest altitude (distance from the horizon) during that night (or day). The angle the star paths make with respect to the horizon as they rise up or set down = 90 degrees minus the observer's latitude. At the north pole, the latitude = 90 degrees so the stars paths make an angle of 90 minus 90 degrees = 0 degrees with respect to the horizon—i.e., they move parallel to the horizon as shown in the north pole figure above. For locations further south you will see in the figures below that the stars will rise up (and then set down) at steeper angles as you get closer to the equator.

During daylight, the meridian separates the morning and afternoon positions of the Sun. In the morning the Sun is "ante meridiem" (Latin for "before meridian") or east of the meridian, abbreviated "a.m.". At local noon the Sun is right on the meridian (the reason why this may not correspond to 12:00 on your clock is discussed a little later in this chapter). At local noon the Sun is due south for northern hemisphere observers and due north for southern hemisphere observers (though observers near the Earth's equator can see the local noon Sun due north or due south at different times of the year for reasons given in the next section). In the afternoon the Sun is "post meridiem" (Latin for "after meridian") or west of the meridian, abbreviated "p.m".

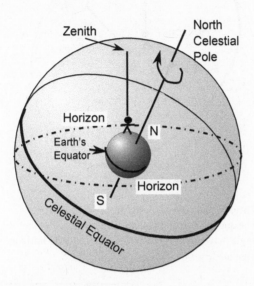

The celestial sphere for an observer in Fairbanks. The NCP is a little lower down and the celestial equator is higher. The zenith is still straight overhead.

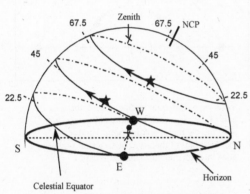

Stars motion at Fairbanks. Stars move parallel to the Celestial Equator, so they move at a shallow angle with respect to the horizon here. Many are still circumpolar.

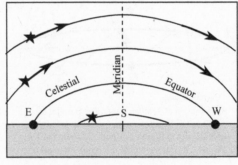

Your view from Fairbanks. For each degree closer to the Earth's equator you move, the Celestial Equator moves higher by one degree. The Celestial Equator goes through due East and due West.

For each degree you move south with Santa in his sleigh, the North Celestial Pole (NCP from here on) moves 1 degree away from the zenith toward the north and the highest point of the celestial equator's curved path in the sky moves up one degree from the southern horizon. This effect has *nothing* to do with the distance between a celestial object or marker and you at different points on the Earth (remember that the celestial sphere has a practically infinite radius). In fact, observers on a spherical world only ten miles across would see the same effect! The picture above shows the celestial sphere for the far northern city of Fairbanks in Alaska. Since it is 25° *south* of the north pole, the NCP is 25° away from (*north of*) the zenith for Fairbanks observers.

position of NCP and cel. eq. as your horizon changes

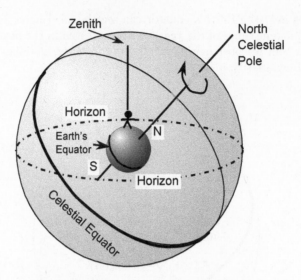

The celestial sphere for an observer in Seattle.
The angle between the zenith and the NCP = the
angle between the celestial equator and the horizon.
That angle = 90° − observer's latitude.

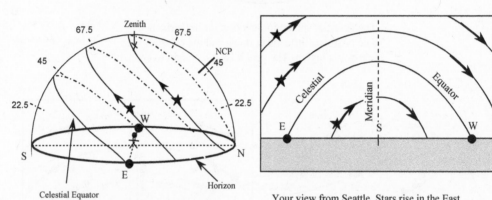

Stars motion at Seattle. Stars rotate parallel to
the Celestial Equator, so they move at an angle
with respect to the horizon here. Altitudes of 1/4,
1/2, and 3/4 the way up to the zenith are marked.

Your view from Seattle. Stars rise in the East
half of the sky, reach maximum altitude when
crossing the meridian (due South) and set in
the West half of the sky. The Celestial Equator
goes through due East and due West.

NCP position and your
latitude

latitude

longitude

By the time you reach your hometown, the NCP has moved away from the zenith
so it is now a number of degrees above the horizon equal to your **latitude** on the
Earth. Remember that your position on the Earth is specified by a **latitude** and
a **longitude** coordinate. The **latitude** is the number of degrees north or south of
the Earth's equator. On a map or globe, lines of latitude run horizontally, parallel
to the equator. The **longitude** is the number of degrees east or west of the 0°
longitude line (the "prime meridian" on the Earth) that runs through Greenwich
England. On a map or globe, lines of longitude run vertically, perpendicular to the
equator. The celestial sphere for observers in Seattle and any other observer at the
same latitude (47°N) on the Earth is shown above.

For another more detailed example, let's choose Los Angeles at latitude 34°
N. The number of degrees the NCP is above the horizon equals your latitude, so,
therefore, the NCP is now 34 degrees above the north horizon. The diagram for
latitude 34° N is shown above. Notice that finding the angle of the NCP above
the horizon provides a very easy way of determining your latitude on the Earth (a

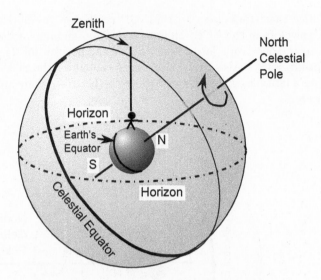

The celestial sphere for an observer in Los Angeles.
The Earth's rotation axis pierces the celestial sphere
at the north and south celestial poles.

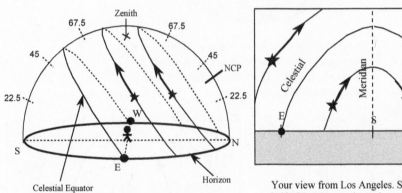

Stars motion at Los Angeles. Stars rotate parallel to
the Celestial Equator, so they move at angle with
respect to the horizon here. Altitudes of 1/4, 1/2,
and 3/4 the way up to zenith are marked.

Your view from Los Angeles. Stars rise in the East
half of the sky, reach maximum altitude when
crossing the meridian (due South) and set in
the West half of the sky. The Celestial Equator
goes through due East and due West.

fact used by navigators even today!). Because the Earth's equator is 90° away from
the north pole, the number of degrees the **celestial equator** is above the opposite
horizon on the meridian will always be 90° – your latitude. In Los Angeles the
celestial equator will arc up to $90 - 34 = 56$ degrees above the *southern* horizon at
the point it crosses the meridian. It still intercepts the horizon exactly at the east
and west points. The stars rise in the east part of the sky, move in arcs parallel
to the celestial equator reaching maximum altitude when they cross your meridian,
and set in the west part of the sky. The star paths make an angle of $90 - 34 = 56$
degrees with respect to the horizon.

    *stars move parallel to cel.
eq.*

    If you are in the northern hemisphere, celestial objects north of the celestial
equator are above the horizon for more than 12 hours because you see more than
half of their total 24-hour path around you. Celestial objects on the celestial equator
are up 12 hours and those south of the celestial equator are above the horizon for
less than 12 hours because you see less than half of their total 24-hour path around
you. The opposite is true if you are in the southern hemisphere.

    how long a star will be up

circumpolar

Notice that stars closer to the NCP are above the horizon longer than those farther away from the NCP. Those stars within an angular distance from the NCP equal to the observer's latitude are above the horizon for 24 hours—they are **circumpolar** stars. Also, those stars close enough to the SCP (within a distance = observer's latitude) will never rise above the horizon. They are also called **circumpolar** stars.

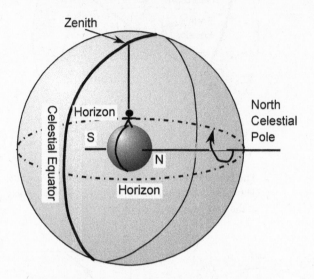

The celestial sphere for an observer on the Equator. The angle between the NCP and the horizon = observer's latitude. The Celestial Equator goes through the zenith.

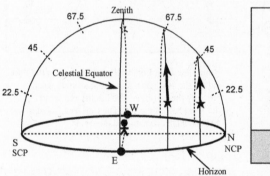

Stars motion at the Equator. Stars rotate parallel to the Celestial Equator, so they move perpendicular to the horizon here. All stars are visible for 12 hours. Both celestial poles are visible on the horizon.

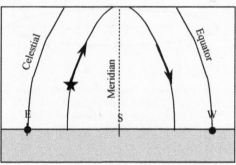

Your view from the Equator. Stars rise and set perpendicular to the horizon (a star south of the Celestial Equator is shown here). The Celestial Equator reaches zenith and goes through due East and due West on the horizon.

special case of the equator

To warm Rudolph's frozen nose, Santa heads down to the equator (0° latitude). At the equator, you see the celestial equator arcing from exactly east to the zenith to exactly west. The NCP is on your northern horizon. At the equator you see one-half of *every star's* total 24-hour path around you so *all* stars are up for 12 hours. All of the stars rise and set perpendicular to the horizon (at an angle = 90 − 0 = 90°).

Continuing southward, you see the NCP disappear below the horizon and the SCP rise above the southern horizon one degree for every one degree of latitude south of the equator you go. The arc of the celestial equator moves to the north, but the arc still intercepts the horizon at the exactly east/west points. The angle of the SCP above the *southern* horizon equals your south latitude and the angle of the celestial equator above the *northern* horizon on the meridian is now 90° – your latitude.

Here is a summary of the positions of the celestial reference marks (note that "altitude" means the number of degrees above the horizon):

- Meridian always goes through directly North, zenith, and directly South points.

  celestial sphere reference marks

- Altitude of zenith = 90° (straight overhead) always.

- Altitude of celestial pole = observer's latitude. Observers in northern hemisphere see NCP; observers in southern hemisphere see SCP.

  important one to remember!

- Altitude of celestial equator on meridian = 90° minus the observer's latitude.

  celestial equator is 90° from celestial poles

- Celestial equator always intercepts horizon at exactly East and exactly West points.

- Angle celestial equator (and any star path) makes with the horizon = 90 minus the observer's latitude.

- Stars move parallel to the celestial equator.

- Circumpolar object's distance from celestial pole = observer's latitude.

Vocabulary

celestial equator	circumpolar	latitude
longitude	meridian	North Celestial Pole
South Celestial Pole	zenith	

Review Questions

1. How do the positions of the celestial equator, celestial poles, zenith, and meridian depend on the latitude of the observer?

2. Would their position with respect to the horizon change if the Earth were only 200 miles in diameter? How about 80,000 miles in diameter? Why is that?

3. During a night, how do the stars move? What angle does their nightly path make with respect to the horizon? How does it depend on latitude?

4. What reference point is a celestial object on when it is at its highest position above the horizon?

5. Why do observers in the northern hemisphere see celestial objects above the celestial equator for more than 12 hours?

6. For northern hemisphere observers, which celestial object would be above the horizon for the greatest amount of time: one that is on the celestial equator, one that is 30° above the celestial equator, one that is 70° above the celestial equator, or one that is 40° below the celestial equator? Which one would be above the horizon the greatest amount of time for southern hemisphere observers? Explain your answer.

3.4   Motion of Our Star the Sun

Now that you have your bearings, let's take a look at the position and motion of the closest star to us, the Sun. Every day the Sun rises in an easterly direction, reaches maximum height when it crosses the meridian at local noon, and sets in a westerly direction. It takes the Sun on average 24 hours to go from noon position to noon position the next day. The "noon position" is when the Sun is on the meridian on a given day. Our clocks are based on this **solar day**. The exact position on the horizon of the rising and setting Sun varies throughout the year (remember though, the celestial equator always intercepts the horizon at exactly East and exactly West). Also, the time of the sunrise and sunset changes throughout the year, very dramatically so if you live near the poles, so the solar day is measured from "noon to noon".

solar day

noon to noon

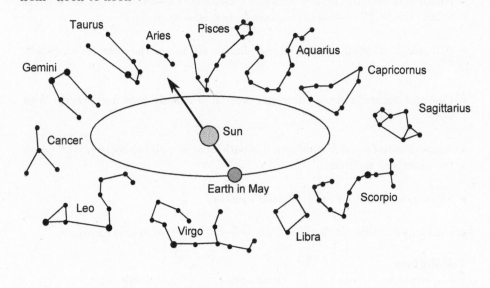

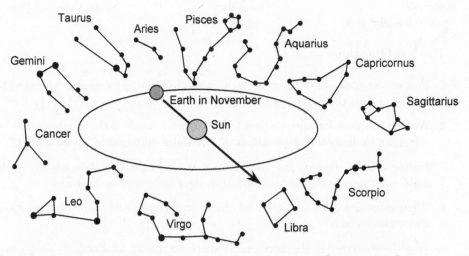

As the Earth moves around the Sun, the Sun **appears** to drift among the zodiac constellations along the path called the **ecliptic.** The ecliptic is the projection of the Earth's orbit onto the sky.

The Sun appears to drift eastward with respect to the stars (or lag behind the stars) over a year's time. It makes one full circuit of 360° in 365.24 days (very close to 1° or twice its diameter per day). This drift eastward is now known to be caused by the motion of the Earth around the Sun in its orbit. The apparent yearly path of the Sun through the stars is called the **ecliptic**. This circular path is tilted 23.5° with respect to the celestial equator because the Earth's rotation axis is tilted by 23.5° with respect to its orbital plane. Be sure to keep distinct in your mind the difference between the slow drift of the Sun along the ecliptic during the year and the fast motion of the rising and setting Sun during a day.

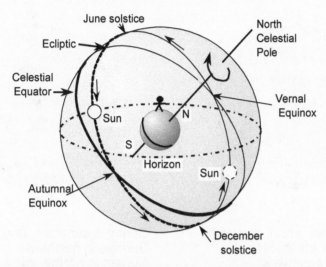

The Sun moves among the stars along the ecliptic, completing one 360° path in one year. The ecliptic is tilted by 23.5° with respect to the celestial equator. The Sun's position on the celestial sphere in August (full circle) and in February (dashed circle) is shown.

The ecliptic and celestial equator intersect at two points: the **vernal (spring) equinox** and **autumnal (fall) equinox**. The Sun crosses the celestial equator moving northward at the vernal equinox around March 21 and crosses the celestial equator moving southward at the autumnal equinox around September 22. When the Sun is on the celestial equator at the equinoxes, everybody on the Earth experiences 12 hours of daylight and 12 hours of night for those two days (hence, the name "equinox" for "equal night"). The day of the vernal equinox marks the beginning of the three-month **season** of spring on our calendar and the day of the autumn equinox marks the beginning of the **season** of autumn (fall) on our calendar. On those two days of the year, the Sun will rise in the exact east direction, follow an arc right along the celestial equator and set in the exact west direction. When the Sun is above the celestial equator during the other days of the seasons of spring and summer, you will have more than 12 hours of daylight. The Sun will rise in the northeast, follow a long, high arc north of the celestial equator, and set in the northwest. Where exactly it rises or sets and how long the Sun is above the horizon depends on the day of the year and the latitude of the observer. When the Sun is below the celestial equator during the other days of the seasons of autumn and winter, you will have less than 12 hours of daylight. The Sun will rise in the southeast, follow a short, low arc south of the celestial equator, and set in the southwest. The exact path it follows depends on the date and the observer's latitude.

Make sure you understand this. No matter where you are on the Earth, you will see 1/2 of the celestial equator's arc. Since the sky appears to rotate around you in 24 hours, anything on the celestial equator takes 12 hours to go from exact east to exact west. Every celestial object's diurnal (daily) motion is parallel to the celestial equator. So for northern observers, anything *south* the celestial equator takes less

ecliptic

vernal (spring) equinox

autumnal (fall) equinox

season

arc of Sun's path in a day changes with the days of the year

position relative to cel. eq. determines how long the Sun is up

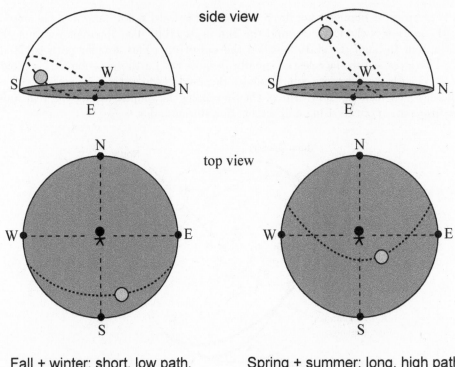

side view

top view

Fall + winter: short, low path.
Sunrise in southeast
Sunset in southwest

Spring + summer: long, high path
Sunrise in northeast
Sunset in northwest

than 12 hours between rise and set, because most of its rotation arc around you is hidden below the horizon. Anything *north* of the celestial equator takes more than 12 hours between rising and setting because most of its rotation arc is above the horizon. For observers in the southern hemisphere, the situation is reversed. However, remember that everybody anywhere on the Earth sees 1/2 of the celestial equator so *at the equinox*, when the Sun is on the celestial equator, you see 1/2 of its rotation arc around you, and therefore you have 12 hours of daylight and 12 hours of nighttime everyplace on the Earth.

On the textbook website are animations of the Sun's motion for two different locations on Earth (Los Angeles, CA and Fairbanks, AK) at the solstices and equinoxes. With the animations can choose a side view and a top view.

sun motion animations *special cases*

The geographic poles and equator are special cases. At the geographic poles the celestial equator is right along the horizon and the full circle of the celestial equator is visible. Since a celestial object's diurnal path is parallel to the celestial equator, stars do not rise or set at the geographic poles. On the equinoxes the Sun moves along the horizon. At the North Pole the Sun "rises" on March 21st and "sets" on September 22. The situation is reversed for the South Pole. On the equator, observers see one half of every object's full 24-hour path around them, so the Sun and every other star is above the horizon for exactly 12 hours for every day of the year.

summer solstice **winter solstice**

Since the ecliptic is tilted 23.5° with respect to the celestial equator, the Sun's maximum distance from the celestial equator is 23.5°. This happens at the solstices. For observers in the northern hemisphere, the farthest northern point above the celestial equator is the **summer solstice**, and the farthest southern point is the **winter solstice**. The word "solstice" means "sun standing still" because the Sun stops moving northward or southward at those points on the ecliptic. The Sun reaches winter solstice around December 21 and you see the least part of its diurnal path all year—this is the day of the least amount of daylight and marks the

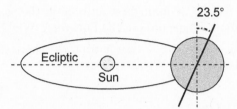

Earth's rotation axis is tilted by 23.5° with
respect to the ecliptic (its orbital plane).

beginning of the **season** of winter for the northern hemisphere. On that day the
Sun rises at its furthest south position in the southeast, follows its lowest arc south
of the celestial equator, and sets at its furthest south position in the southwest.
The Sun reaches the summer solstice around June 21 and you see the greatest
part of its diurnal path above the horizon all year—this is the day of the most
amount of daylight and marks the beginning of the **season** of summer for the
northern hemisphere. On that day the Sun rises at its furthest north position in
the northeast, follows its highest arc north of the celestial equator, and sets at its
furthest north position in the northwest. The seasons are opposite for the southern

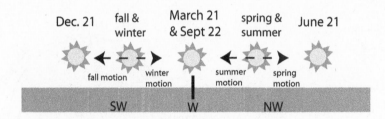

Sunset position changes throughout the
year. Note: change "W" (west) to "E" (east)
for the sun*rise* position.

hemisphere (eg., it is summer in the southern hemisphere when it is winter in the
northern hemisphere). The Sun does not get high up above the horizon on the
winter solstice. The Sun's rays hit the ground at a shallow angle at mid-day so   shadow lengths
the shadows are long at mid-day. On the summer solstice the mid-day shadows are
much shorter because the Sun is much higher above the horizon. See the textbook
website for the link to a powerful animation of the Sun's motion that you can
manipulate to change the time of year and latitude of the observer and to see how
the shadows change with the position of the Sun.

Vocabulary

autumnal (fall) equinox	ecliptic	season
solar day	summer solstice	vernal (spring) equinox
winter solstice		

Review Questions

1. How does the Sun move with respect to the stars during the year?

2. Why does everyone have 12 hours of daylight on the equinoxes?

3. Why is the length of daylight in the northern hemisphere so short on December
   21?

4. When will the Sun be at its highest altitude in the year in Los Angeles or Seattle? How about Singapore (on the Equator)? Why?

5. On what date is the Sun above the horizon the shortest amount of time for the *Southern* Hemisphere? Why?

3.5   Coordinates

Early astronomy concentrated on finding accurate positions of the stars and planets. This was due in part to the influence of astrology, but later, accurate positions came to be important for determining the physical characteristics of the stars and planets. Accurate positions for the stars was also crucial for commercial and military navigation (navigation by the stars has only recently been replaced by the use of satellite systems such as the Global Positioning System). But probably of more importance to you is where to point your telescope or binoculars to find that cool object talked about in the newspaper or astronomy magazine.

There are a couple of popular ways of specifying the location of a celestial object. The first is what you would probably use to point out a star to your friend: the altitude-azimuth system. The **altitude** of a star is how many degrees above the horizon it is (anywhere from 0 to 90 degrees). The **azimuth** of a star is how many degrees along the horizon it is and corresponds to the compass direction.

altitude
azimuth

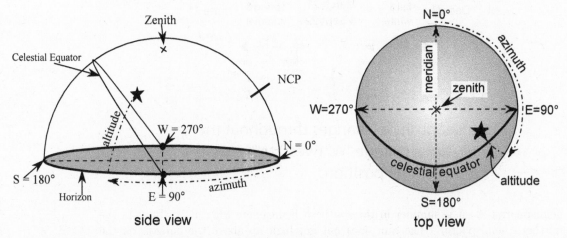

A star's position in the altitude-azimuth coordinate system. The azimuth=120° and the altitude=50°. The azimuth is measured in degrees clockwise along the horizon from due North. The azimuths for the compass directions are shown in the figure. The altitude is measured in degrees above the horizon. The star's altitude and azimuth changes throughout the night and depends on the observer's position (here at the intersection of the N-S line and E-W line). The star's position does not depend on the location of the NCP or Celestial Equator in this system.

Azimuth starts from exactly North = 0° azimuth and increases clockwise: exactly East = 90°, exactly South = 180°, exactly West = 270°, and exactly North = 360° = 0°. For example, a star in the southwest could have an azimuth between 180° and 270°. Since stars change their position with respect to your horizon throughout the night, their altitude-azimuth position changes. Also, observers at different locations looking at the same star at the same time will see it at a different altitude-azimuth position. A concise summary of this coordinate system and the numbers involved is given at the end of this section.

fixed system

The second way of specifying star positions is the equatorial coordinate system. This system is very similar to the longitude-latitude system used to specify positions on the Earth's surface. This system is *fixed* with respect to the stars so, unlike the altitude-azimuth system, a star's position does not depend on the observer's location or time. Because of this, astronomers prefer using this system. You will find this system used in astronomy magazines and in most sky simulation computer software.

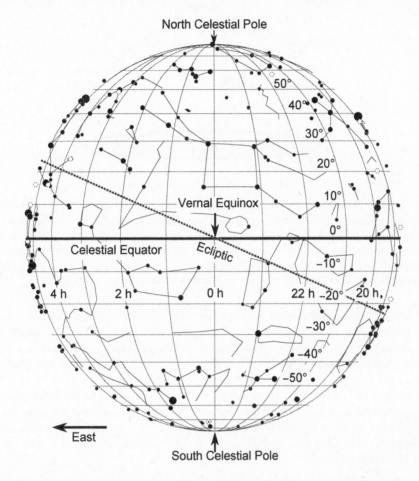

The lines on a map of the Earth that run north-south are lines of **longitude** and when projected onto the sky, they become lines of **right ascension.** Because the stars were used to measure time, right ascension (RA) is measured in terms of hours, minutes, and seconds instead of degrees and increases in an easterly direction. For two stars one hour of RA apart, you will see one star cross your meridian one hour of time before the other. If the stars are not circumpolar, you will see one star rise one hour before the other. If they were 30 minutes of RA apart, you would see one rise half an hour before the other and cross your meridian half an hour before the other. Zero RA is where the Sun crosses the celestial equator at the vernal equinox. The full 360° of the Earth's rotation is broken up into 24 hours, so one hour of RA = 15° of rotation. The lines of RA all converge at the celestial poles so two stars one hour of RA apart will not necessarily be 15° in *angular separation* on the sky (only if they are on the celestial equator will they be 15° apart).

right ascension

uses time units

The lines on a map of the Earth that run east-west parallel to the equator are lines of **latitude** and when projected onto the sky, they become lines of **declination.** Like the latitude lines on Earth, declination (dec) is measured in degrees away from the celestial equator, *positive* degrees for objects *north* of the celestial equator and *negative* degrees for objects *south* of the celestial equator. Objects on the celestial equator are at 0° dec, objects half-way to the NCP are +45°, objects at the NCP are +90°, and objects at the SCP are −90°. Polaris's position is at RA 2^{h}31^m and dec 89° 15′ (the tic mark, ′, after the number "15" is the abbreviation for

declination
angle from cel. eq.

arc minutes, see section 3.2). A concise summary of this coordinate system and the numbers involved is given at the end of this section (see also the diagram below).

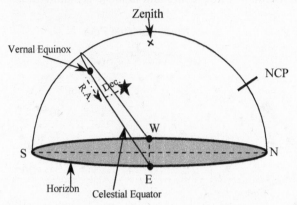

A star's position in the equatorial coordinate system. The right ascension (R.A.)=1 hr 30 min and the declination (Dec.)=15°. The right ascension is measured in hours, minutes, and seconds in the easterly direction from the vernal equinox position on the celestial equator. The declination is measured in degrees above the celestial equator. The star's R.A. and Dec. does NOT change throughout the night—its equatorial coordinate position is fixed with respect to the stars. The star's position does depend on the location of the NCP and Celestial Equator in this system.

precession

An effect called **precession** causes the Sun's vernal equinox point to slowly shift westward over time, so a star's RA and dec will slowly change by about 1.4° every century (a fact ignored by astrologers), or about 1 minute increase in a star's RA every twenty years. This is caused by the gravitational pulls of the Sun and Moon on the Earth's equatorial bulge (from the Earth's rapid rotation) in an effort to reduce the tilt of the Earth's axis with respect to the ecliptic and the plane of the Moon's orbit around the Earth (that is itself slightly tipped with respect to the ecliptic). Like the slow wobble of a rapidly-spinning top, the Earth responds to the gravitational tugs of the Sun and Moon by slowly wobbling its rotation axis with a period of 26,000 years.

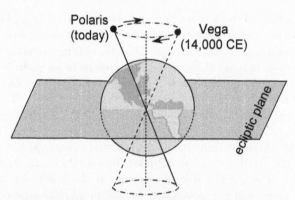

The Earth's rotation axis precesses (wobbles)
with a period of 26,000 years.

This motion was first recorded by Hipparchus in 100 B.C.E. who noticed differences between ancient Babylonian observations and his own. When the Babylonians were the world power in 2000 B.C.E., the vernal equinox was in the constellation Aries and the star Thuban (in Draco) was the closest bright star to the NCP (see the sky chart below). At the time of Jesus Christ the vernal equinox had shifted to the constellation Pisces and the star Kochab (in the bowl of the Little Dipper) was the closest bright star to the NCP. Now the star Polaris is close to the NCP and the vernal equinox is close to the border between Pisces and Aquarius (in 2600 C.E. it will officially be in Aquarius) which is what a popular song of years ago refers to with the line "this is the dawning of the Age of Aquarius". In the year 10,000 C.E., the bright star in the tail of Cygnus, Deneb will be the pole star and Vega (in Lyra) will get its turn by the year 14,000 C.E. Horoscopes today are still based on the 4,000-year old Babylonian system so even though the Sun is in Aries on my birthday, the zodiac sign used for my horoscope is Taurus. I guess it's hard to keep up with all of the changes in the modern world!

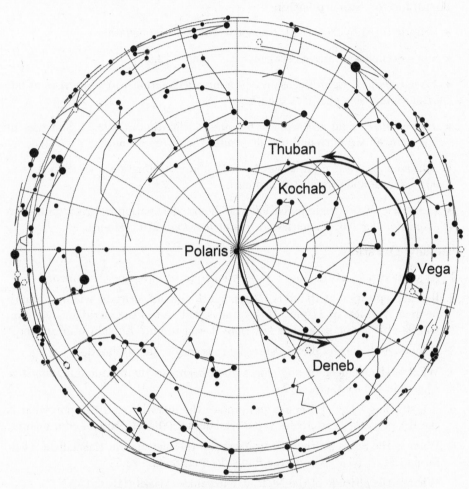

The path of the precession of the Earth's rotation axis.
It takes 26,000 years to complete a full 360° wobble.

Vocabulary

altitude	azimuth	declination
precession	right ascension	

Formulae

- **Altitude** varies from 0 to 90°. Vertical position of object.

- **Azimuth** increases clockwise from 0° to 360°. Exact N = 0°, exact E = 90°, exact S = 180°, exact W = 270°. Horizontal position of object.

- **Right ascension** varies from 0 to 24 *hours,* so every hour corresponds to a rotation angle of 15°. Horizontal position of object measured in time units.

- **Declination** varies from −90° (at SCP) to +90° (at NCP). Celestial equator declination = 0°. Vertical position of object.

- *Meridian altitude* of any object = 90° − (observer's latitude) + declination degrees. If declination is negative, then addition of declination becomes a subtraction.

Formulae for Sun's position

- Ecliptic tilted by 23.5° with respect to the celestial equator.

- Sun's declination ranges between −23.5° and +23.5°.

- *Vernal equinox*: right ascension = 0 hours; declination = 0°; Sun rises at 90° azimuth and sets at 270° azimuth.

- *June solstice*: right ascension = 6 hours; declination = +23.5°; Sun rises at *less than* 90° azimuth and sets at *greater than* 270° azimuth.

- *Autumnal equinox*: right ascension = 12 hours; declination = 0°; Sun rises at 90° azimuth and sets at 270° azimuth.

- *December solstice*: right ascension = 18 hours; declination = −23.5°; Sun rises at *greater than* 90° azimuth and sets at *less than* 270° azimuth.

Review Questions

1. At what two azimuths does the celestial equator intercept the horizon?

2. If a star's position at 10 pm is 110° azimuth and 40° altitude, will its azimuth be greater or less at 11 pm? If the star is still east of the meridian at 11 pm, will its altitude be greater or less than it was 10 pm? Explain your answer.

3. Why do astronomers prefer using right ascension and declination?

4. What is the azimuth of *any object* when it crosses the meridian at *any time of year* in the southern sky?

5. If a star has a RA of 5 hours and crosses the meridian at 10:45 pm, what is the RA of a star that crosses the meridian at 1:00 am? Explain your answer.

6. What is the Sun's altitude when it crosses the meridian in Bakersfield, California (lat. = 35.5° N) and the Sun's declination is +23.5°?

7. What is the altitude of the NCP at Fairbanks, Alaska (lat. = 65° N)?

8. How do the positions of the equinoxes and solstices with respect to the horizon depend on the latitude?

9. What is the maximum altitude of the Sun on the vernal equinox for people on the equator? What is the Sun's azimuth and right ascension at that time?

10. What will the Sun's declination be on the following dates: June 21, March 21, September 22, and December 21?

11. What will the Sun's approximate declination be on the following dates: April 10, July 20, and October 31? Explain your answer.

12. If the Sun sets 10° away from exact West on October 20, what is the sunset azimuth?

13. If the Sun rises 12° away from exact East on April 19, what is the sunrise azimuth?

14. What causes precession?

15. How does precession affect the positions of the stars?

16. If a star on the celestial equator has a RA of 5 hours 33 minutes, what would you estimate its RA to be in 20 years and in 200 years? Explain your answer. (Remember that the Earth spins about 15°/hour.)

17. Which star is the current pole star? Which star was the pole star 2,000 years ago? Which star will be the pole star 8,000 years from now?

18. Are modern horoscopes based on the current motion of the Sun and planets with respect to stars?

3.6 Time and Seasons

3.6.1 Solar and Sidereal day

The fact that our clocks are based on the solar day and the Sun appears to drift eastward with respect to the stars (or lag behind the stars) by about 1° per day means that if you look closely at the positions of the stars over a period of several days, you will notice that according to our clocks, the stars rise and set 4 minutes *earlier* each day. Our clocks say that the day is 24 hours long, so the stars move around the Earth in 23 hours 56 minutes. This time period is called the **sidereal day** because it is measured with respect to the stars. This is also the true rotation rate of the Earth and stays the same no matter where the Earth is in its orbit—the sidereal day = 23 hours 56 minutes on every day of the year. One month later (30 days) a given star will rise 2 hours earlier than it did before (30 days × 4 minutes/day = 120 minutes). A year later that star will rise at the same time as it did today.

sidereal day

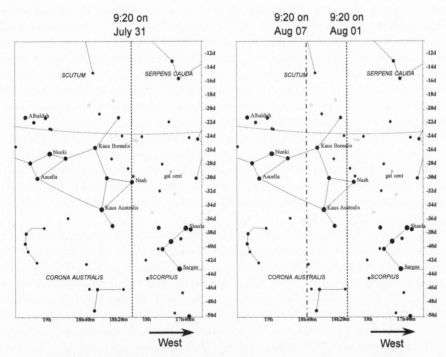

A star will rise and cross your meridian 4 minutes **earlier** than it did the night before because of the Earth's motion around the Sun. One week from now it will rise and cross your meridian 28 minutes **earlier** than it does tonight. During a night the stars move from east to west due to the Earth's rotation.

Another way to look at it is that the Sun has made one full circuit of 360° along the ecliptic in a year of 365.24 days (very close to 1° per day). The result is that between two consecutive meridian crossings of the Sun, the Earth has to rotate nearly 361°, not 360°, in 24 hours. This makes the length of time for one solar day to be a little more than the true rotation rate of 23 hours 56 minutes with respect to the background stars.

3.6.2 Solar and Sidereal Time as Viewed from Space

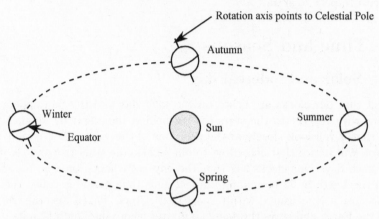

Earth's rotation axis always pointed to Celestial Poles. As Earth moves around Sun sometimes one hemisphere is tilted toward the Sun and sometimes away. The seasons shown are for the Northern hemisphere. The southern hemisphere's seasons are opposite to those shown.

Let's jump to a more modern view and take a position off the Earth and see the Earth revolving around the Sun in 365.24 days and rotating on its axis every 23 hours 56 minutes. The Earth's rotation plane is tilted by 23.5° from its orbital plane which is projected against the background stars to form the ecliptic. Note that the Earth's rotation axis is always pointed toward the Celestial Poles. Currently the North Celestial Pole is very close to the star Polaris. The figure above shows this view of the Earth's nearly circular orbit from slightly above the orbital plane (hence the very elliptical appearance of the orbit).

Imagine that at noon there is a huge arrow that is pointing at the Sun and a star *directly* in line behind the Sun (see the figure on the next page). The observer on the Earth sees the Sun at its highest point above the horizon: on the arc going through the north-zenith-south points, which is called the **meridian**. The observer is also experiencing **local noon**. If the Sun were not there, the observer would also see the star on the meridian.

Now as time goes on, the Earth moves in its orbit and it rotates from west to east (both motions are counterclockwise if viewed from above the north pole). One sidereal day later (23 hours 56 minutes) or one true rotation period later, the arrow is again pointing toward the star. The observer on the Earth sees the star on the meridian. But the arrow is *not* pointing at the Sun! In fact the Earth needs to rotate a little more to get the arrow lined up with the Sun. The observer on the Earth sees the Sun a little bit *east* of the meridian. Four minutes later or one degree of further rotation aligns the arrow and Sun and you have one solar day (24 hours) since the last time the Sun was on the meridian. The geometry of the situation also shows that the Earth moves about 1° in its orbit during one sidereal day. That night the Earth observer will see certain stars visible like those in Taurus, for example. (Notice that the Earth's rotation axis is still pointed toward Polaris.) A half of

spin rate = 360° /sidereal day

orbit rate = 360° /#days in one orbit

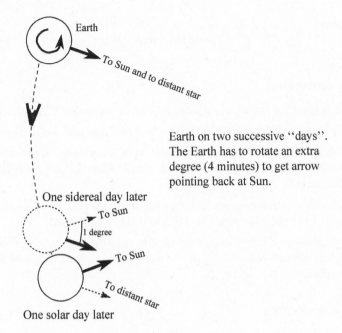

Earth on two successive "days". The Earth has to rotate an extra degree (4 minutes) to get arrow pointing back at Sun.

a year later Taurus will not be visible but those stars in Scorpius will be visible. (Again, notice that the Earth's rotation axis is still pointed toward Polaris.) *The extra angle any planet must rotate on its axis to get the Sun back to the meridian equals the angle amount the planet moved in its orbit in one <u>sidereal</u> day.*

key concept

The amount of time it takes to spin the extra angle = (extra angle amount)/(spin rate). For the Earth, the spin rate = 360°/23.9333 hours = 15°/hour or 1°/4 minutes. Notice that I converted 23 hours 56 minutes to a decimal fraction of hours before I did the division. The amount of time between the solar day and sidereal day = (1 degree)/(1 degree/4 minutes) = 4 minutes.

The Earth's sidereal day is always 23 hours 56 minutes long because the number of degrees the Earth spins through in a given amount of time stays constant. If you are a careful observer, you will notice that the solar day is sometimes slightly longer than 24 hours and sometimes slightly shorter than 24 hours during the year. The reason for this is that the Earth's orbit around the Sun is elliptical and that the Sun's motion is not parallel to the celestial equator. The effects of this are explained fully in the **Equation of Time** section below. The value of 24 hours for the solar day is an *average* for the year and is what our time-keeping system is based on.

The precession of the Earth's rotation axis introduces another difference between sidereal time and solar time. This is seen in how the year is measured. A year is defined as the orbital period of the Earth. However, if you use the Sun's position as a guide, you come up with a time interval about 20 minutes shorter than if you use the stars as a guide. The time required for the constellations to complete one 360° cycle around the sky and to return to their original point on the sky is called a **sidereal year**. This is the time it takes the Earth to complete exactly one orbit around the Sun and equals 365.2564 solar days.

sidereal year

The slow shift of the star coordinates from precession means that the Sun will not be at exactly the same position with respect to the celestial equator after one sidereal year. The **tropical year** is the time interval between two sucessive vernal equinoxes. It equals 365.2422 solar days and is the year our calendars are based on. After several thousand years the 20 minute difference between sidereal and tropical years would have made our summers occur several months earlier if we used a calendar based on the sidereal year.

tropical year

Vocabulary

local noon   sidereal day   sidereal year
tropical year

Review Questions

1. Which is used for our clocks—sidereal day or solar day? Why?

2. Why is there a difference between the sidereal day and solar day?

3. If the Earth rotated twice as quickly as it does now, what would be the difference in minutes between the solar and sidereal days? Explain how you got your answer.

4. If the Earth's year was twice as long as it is now, what would be the difference in minutes between the solar and sidereal days? Explain!

5. Mars rotates once every 24.623 hours (its sidereal day) and it orbits the Sun once every 686.98 solar earth days. Show how to find out how long a solar day is on Mars.

3.6.3   Time Zones

People east of you will see the Sun on their meridian before you see it on yours. Those in Denver, Colorado will see the Sun on their meridian about 52 minutes before people in Los Angeles will see the Sun on their meridian. Denver residents experience local noon about 52 minutes before those in Los Angeles. That is because Denver is at longitude 105° West longitude while Los Angeles is at 118° West longitude (or 13° difference). For each one degree difference in longitude a person is from you, the time between his local noon and yours will increase by 4 minutes.

time zone

It used to be that every town's clocks were set according to their local noon and this got very confusing for the railroad system so they got the nation to adopt a more sensible clock scheme called **time zones**. Each person within a time zone has the same clock time. Each time zone is 15 degrees wide in longitude, corresponding to 15 degrees × 4 minutes/degree = 60 minutes = 1 hour worth of time. Those in the next time zone east of you have clocks that are 1 hour ahead of yours. The Pacific timezone is centered on 120° W longitude, the Mountain timezone is centered on 105° W longitude, etc.

3.6.4   Equation of Time

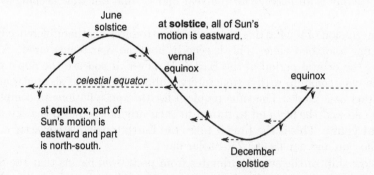

There is a further complication in that the actual Sun's drift against the stars is not uniform. Part of the non-uniformity is due to the fact that on top of the general eastward drift among the stars, the Sun is moving along the ecliptic northward or southward with respect to the celestial equator. Thus, during some periods the Sun appears to move eastward faster than during others. Apparent solar time is based on the component of the Sun's motion *parallel to* the celestial equator. This effect alone would account for as much as 9 minutes difference between the actual Sun and a fictional **mean Sun** moving uniformily along the celestial equator.

Another effect to consider is that the Earth's orbit is elliptical so when the Earth is at its closest point to the Sun (at **perihelion**), it moves quickest. When at its farthest point from the Sun (at **aphelion**), the Earth moves slowest. Remember

mean Sun

perihelion
aphelion

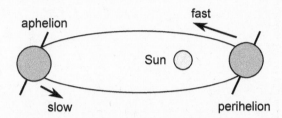

Earth's orbital speed depends on its distance from the Sun. The change in the orbital speed produces variations in the length of the solar day. (Orbit shape is greatly exaggerated here.)

that a solar day is the time between meridian passages of the Sun. At perihelion the Earth is moving rapidly so the Sun appears to move quicker eastward than at other times of the year. The Earth has to rotate through a greater angle to get the Sun back to local noon. This effect alone accounts for up to 10 minutes difference between the actual Sun and the mean Sun (figure top of next page).

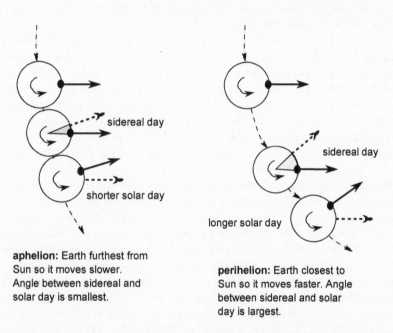

aphelion: Earth furthest from Sun so it moves slower. Angle between sidereal and solar day is smallest.

perihelion: Earth closest to Sun so it moves faster. Angle between sidereal and solar day is largest.

However, the maximum and minimum of these two effects do not coincide so the combination of the two (called the **Equation of Time**) is a complicated relation shown in the figure on the next page. The Equation of Time explains why, according to your clock, the earliest sunset and latest sunrise is not at the winter solstice. Yet, the shortest length of daylight is at the winter solstice. Rather than resetting our clocks every day to this variable Sun, our clocks are based on a uniformly moving Sun (the **mean Sun**) that moves at a rate along the celestial equator of 360°/365.2564 per day. Aren't you glad that your watch keeps track of time for you?

Equation of Time

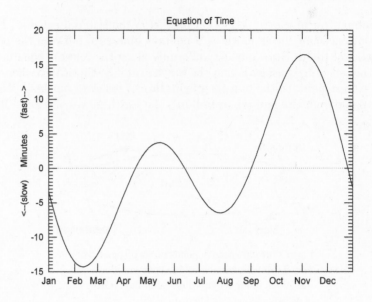

3.6.5 Seasons

The seasonal temperature depends on the amount of heat received from the Sun in a given time. To hold the temperature constant, there must be a balance between the amount of heat gained and the amount radiated to space. If more heat is received than is lost, your location gets warmer; if more heat is lost than is gained, your location gets cooler. What causes the amount of energy reaching a given location during the day to change throughout the year?

Two popular theories are often stated to explain the temperature differences of the seasons: 1) the different distances the Earth is from the Sun in its elliptical orbit (varying from 147.1 million kilometers at perihelion and 152.1 million kilometers at aphelion); and 2) the tilt of the Earth's axis with respect to its orbital plane.

why distance theory is wrong

If the first theory were true, then both the north and south hemispheres should experience the same seasons at the same time. They don't. Using the scientific method discussed in chapters 1 and 2, you can reject the distance theory.

A popular variation of the distance theory says that the part of the Earth tilted toward the Sun should be hotter than the part tilted away from the Sun because of the differences in distances. If you continue along with this line of reasoning, then you conclude that the night side of the Earth is colder than the daylight side because the night side is farther away from the Sun. This ignores the more straightforward reason that the night side is directed opposite the Sun, so the Sun's energy does not directly reach it. But let's examine the tilt-distance model a little more. The 23.5° tilt of the Earth means that the north pole is about 5080 kilometers closer than the south pole toward the end of June. This is much, much smaller than the 152 million kilometer distance between the Sun and the Earth's center at that time. The amount of energy received decreases with the *square* of the distance.

also why distance theory is wrong

If you calculate $(152,000,000 + 5080)^2/(152,000,000 - 5080)^2$, you will find that the north pole would get slightly over 1/100th of one *percent* more energy than the south pole. This is much too small a difference to explain the large temperature differences! Even if you compare one side of the Earth with the opposite side, so you use the Earth's diameter in place of the 5080 kilometers in the calculation above, you get 3/100th of one *percent* difference in energy received. Clearly, distance is not the reason for the large temperature differences. Notice that I used the aphelion value for the distance between the Earth and Sun. That is because the Earth is near aphelion during the northern hemisphere's summer! This is known by measuring the apparent size of the Sun. You can safely assume that the Sun's actual size does not vary with a period that depends on the orbital period of a planet thousands of times smaller than it, or that it would choose the Earth's orbital period as its pulsation cycle. Earth reaches perihelion in the first week of January (during the north hemisphere's winter!) and aphelion in the first week of July (during the north hemisphere's summer!). The distance theory predicts the opposite seasons from what's observed in the north hemisphere.

Even though the distance model (in any variation) is incorrect, it is still a "good" scientific theory in that it makes testable predictions of how the temperature should change throughout the year and by how much. However, what annoys scientists, particularly astronomy professors, is ignoring those predictions and the big conflicts between predictions and what is observed. Let's take a look at a model that correctly predicts what is observed.

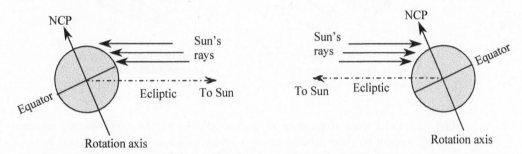

The Earth's rotation axis is tilted by 23.5° with respect to the ecliptic and is always pointed to the celestial poles as the Earth moves around the Sun. Sometimes the northern hemisphere is tilted away from the Sun and the Sun's rays hit the northern hemisphere at a shallow angle. This is winter in the northern hemisphere (summer in the southern hemisphere). Sometimes the northern hemisphere is tilted toward the Sun and the Sun's rays hit the northern hemisphere at a sharp angle. This is summer in the northern hemisphere (winter in the southern hemisphere). The rotation axis itself wobbles (precesses) with a period of about 26,000 years, so the celestial pole directions slowly change. However, from year-to-year, this effect is too small to notice without sensitive equipment.

The tilt theory correctly explains the seasons but the reason is a little more subtle *tilt theory* than the distance theory's explanation. Because the Earth's rotation axis is tilted, the north hemisphere will be pointed toward the Sun and will experience summer while the south hemisphere will be pointed away from the Sun and will experience winter. During the summer the sunlight strikes the ground more directly (closer to *angle of sunlight* perpendicular), concentrating the Sun's energy. This concentrated energy is able to heat the surface more quickly than during the winter time when the Sun's rays hit the ground at more glancing angles, spreading out the energy. Also, during the

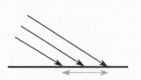

Same energy but more spread out, means less heating.

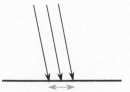

Same energy but more concentrated, means greater heating.

summer the Sun is above the horizon for a longer time so its energy has more time *amount of daylight* to heat things up than during the winter. Like baking something in the oven, the land and water do not heat up instantaneously, so our hottest days are usually after the summer solstice and coldest days are usually after the winter solstice. That is also why the hottest part of the day is usually in the afternoon.

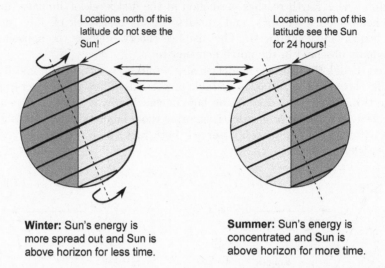

Locations north of this latitude do not see the Sun!

Locations north of this latitude see the Sun for 24 hours!

Winter: Sun's energy is more spread out and Sun is above horizon for less time.

Summer: Sun's energy is concentrated and Sun is above horizon for more time.

The rotational axes of most of the other planets of the solar system are also tilted with respect to their orbital planes so they undergo seasonal changes in their temperatures too. The planets Mercury, Jupiter, and Venus have very small tilts (3° or less) so the varying distance they are from the Sun may play more of a role in any seasonal temperature variations. However, of these three, only Mercury has significant differences between perihelion and aphelion. Its extremely thin atmosphere is not able to retain any of the Sun's energy. Jupiter's and Venus' orbits are very nearly circular and their atmospheres are very thick, so their temperature variations are near zero.

Mars, Saturn, and Neptune have tilts that are similar to the Earth's, but Saturn and Neptune have near zero temperature variation because of their very thick atmospheres and nearly circular orbits. Mars has large temperature changes because of its very thin atmosphere and its more eccentric orbit places its southern hemisphere closest to the Sun during its summer and farthest from the Sun during its winter. Mars' northern hemisphere has milder seasonal variation than its southern hemisphere because of this arrangement. Since planets move slowest in their orbits when they are furthest from the Sun, Mars' southern hemisphere has short, hot summers and long, cold winters.

Uranus' seasons should be the most unusual because it orbits the Sun on its side—its axis is tilted by 98°! For half of the Uranian year, one hemisphere is in sunlight and the other is in the dark. For the other half of the Uranian year, the situation is reversed. The thick atmosphere of Uranus distributes the solar energy from one hemisphere to the other effectively, so the seasonal temperature changes are near zero. Pluto's axis is also tilted by a large amount (122.5°), its orbit is the most elliptical of the planets, and it has an extremely thin atmosphere. But it is always so far from the Sun that it is perpetually in deep freeze (only 50° above absolute zero!).

Vocabulary

aphelion	Equation of Time	mean Sun
perihelion	time zone	

Review Questions

1. How many minutes difference is there between your local noon and somebody's

local noon 3 degrees longitude *east* of you? Will their local noon occur before or after yours?

2. The Eastern Standard Time zone is 3 hours ahead of the Pacific Standard Time zone. The Pacific timezone meridian is at 120° W longitude. What is the longitude of the Eastern Time zone meridian?

3. Is the Sun's drift eastward greater at the solstices or the equinoxes? Why is that?

4. Is the solar day longer at perihelion or aphelion? Why is that?

5. What causes the temperature differences between the seasons? How so?

6. If you shine a flashlight on a flat tabletop, which gives you a smaller concentrated beam: one directed perpendicular to the tabletop or one directed parallel to the tabletop? Which one produces the longer shadow of a pencil on the tabletop?

7. How would the fact that the Sun's angular size is largest around January 4 contradict the popular theory that the Earth's distance from the Sun in its elliptical orbit causes the seasons?

3.7   Motions of the Moon

The moon moves rapidly with respect to the background stars. It moves about 13° (26× its apparent diameter) in 24 hours—slightly greater than its own diameter in one hour! Its rapid motion has given it a unique role in the history of astronomy. For thousands of years it has been used as the basis of calendars. Isaac Newton got crucial information from the Moon's motion around the Earth for his law of gravity.

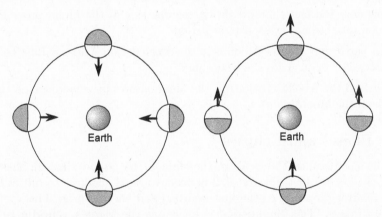

Moon's rotation period = its orbital period. It keeps one side facing the Earth. We never see far side of Moon (shaded).

How it would be IF Moon did not rotate. Sometimes we would see far side of Moon.

If you watch the Moon throughout the year, you will see the same face of the Moon all of the time. It's the "man in the moon", "woman in the moon", "rabbit in the moon" etc. One thing this shows you is that the Moon turns exactly once on its axis each time that it goes around the Earth. Later on you will find out how tidal forces have caused this face-to-face dance of the Earth and Moon. The Moon drifts eastward with respect to the background stars (or it lags behind the stars). It returns to the same position with respect to the background stars every 27.323 days. This is its **sidereal period**.

one spin per orbit

sidereal period

Vocabulary
sidereal period

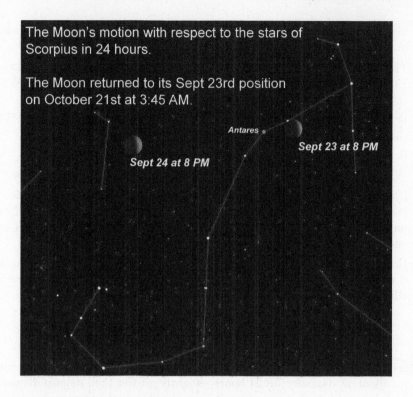

The Moon's motion with respect to the stars of Scorpius in 24 hours.

The Moon returned to its Sept 23rd position on October 21st at 3:45 AM.

Antares

Sept 24 at 8 PM

Sept 23 at 8 PM

Review Questions

1. How does the Moon move with respect to the stars?

2. How does the fact that we always see one side of the Moon prove that the Moon rotates once every orbital period?

3. In a particular year the Moon is in the constellation Aries on June 1st. What date will it be in Aries the next time?

4. Why did the Apollo missions to the Moon always have landings on the same side of the Moon?

3.7.1 Phases and Eclipses

One of the most familiar things about the Moon is that it goes through phases from new (all shadow) to first quarter (1/2 appears to be in shadow) to full (all lit up) to third quarter (opposite to the first quarter) and back to new. This cycle takes about 29.53 days. This time period is known as the Moon's **synodic period**. Because the Moon moves through its phases in about four weeks, the phases of new moon, first quarter, full moon, and third quarter occur nearly one week apart from each other.

The phases are due to how the Sun illuminates the Moon and the relative positioning of the Earth, Moon, and Sun. The figure at the top of the next page shows that as the Moon orbits the Earth, the fraction of its illuminated side *that you can see from the Earth* changes. From high above the Earth and Moon orbit, you can see that the Moon is *always* half lit by the Sun and the lit half (the illuminated side, or day side) *always* faces the light source—the Sun. The other half (night side) faces away from the Sun. The figure on the next page combines two view points. The half-lit moon on the inner circle around the Earth is the Moon as viewed from high above the Earth and Moon orbit. The outer ring of Moon pictures in various phases is the view of the Moon *as we would see it from the Earth*. Of course, this drawing is *not* to scale. Notice that the waning gibbous, third quarter, and waning

synodic period

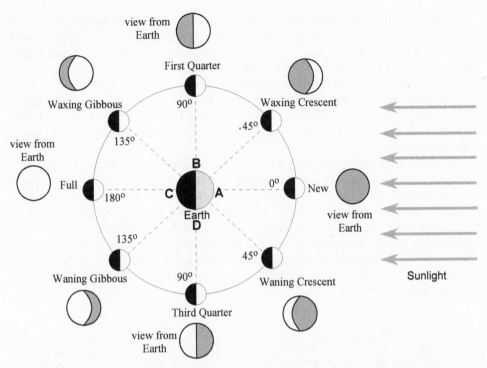

view from
Earth

First Quarter

Waxing Gibbous 90° Waxing Crescent

135° .45°

view from
Earth

B

Full C A 0° New

180° Earth D

view from
Earth

135° 45°

Waning Gibbous 90° Waning Crescent

Third Quarter

Sunlight

view from
Earth

The Sun-Moon angle is the angle defined by Sun->Earth->Moon with Earth (where *you* are) as the angle vertex. As the Sun-Moon angle increases we see more of the sunlit part of the Moon. Note that if this drawing were to scale, then the Moon would be half this size and its orbit would be about **22 times** larger in diameter and the Sun would be about 389 **times** farther away than the Moon!

crescent phases as seen from Earth are lit on the *left* side. The Waxing vs. Waning diagram a few pages over shows how this can be even though the Sun in the figure here is on the right side (one rotates the picture 180°, so the observer at D is facing up).

You will observe only a small fraction of the Moon's *illuminated* side when it is close to the Sun. In fact, the smaller the angular distance between the Moon and the Sun, the less of its illuminated side you see. When the angular distance is less than 90° separation, *you on the Earth will see* less than half of the Moon's illuminated (day) side and it will look like a a curved sliver of light—the *crescent phase*. You will see mostly the night side of the Moon. Because the Moon is spherical, the boundary between light and shadow (night) is curved. Note that the figure of the phase angles above shows just *one* of the angles possible for the crescent phase (at 45°). When the angle is within about 6° you see it in a *new phase* and is the beginning of the phase cycle. Sometimes that angle = 0° and you have a **solar eclipse**—the Moon is in new phase *and* it is covering up the Sun. The Earth's shadow always points *directly away* from the Sun (and it tapers down to a point). At new phase the Moon is in the *same* direction as the Sun as seen from the Earth, so the Earth's shadow can*not* be why you just see the night side of the Moon.

At 90° angular separation you see half of the Moon's illuminated side and the phase is called a *quarter phase* because you can see a quarter of the Moon's entire surface. The quarter phase a week after the new phase is called *first quarter* and the quarter phase a week before new phase is *third quarter*.

The greater the angular distance is between the Moon and the Sun, the more of the Moon's illuminated side you can see *from the Earth*. When the angular distance is *more* than 90° separation, you on the Earth will *more* than half of the Moon's illuminated (day) side—the *gibbous phase*. You will see a small amount of

angle of Sun

crescent phase

new phase
solar eclipse

1st and 3rd quarter phase

gibbous phase

the Moon's night side. "Gibbous" means a shape that is convex (bulges outward) at both sides. Again, note that the phase pictures show just *one* of the angles possible for the gibbous phase (at 135°). Also, note again that the Moon is always half lit up by the Sun. How much of the lit side (day side) we see *from the Earth* depends on where the Moon is in its orbit around the Earth.

Around 180° angular separation, you on the Earth see the entire illuminated (day) side of the Moon—the *full phase*. Sometimes (about twice a year) the Sun-Moon angle is exactly 180° and you see the Earth's shadow covering the Moon—a **lunar eclipse**.

Usually a descriptive term is added to the crescent and gibbous phases. If the amount of illuminated side you can see increases with time, it is *waxing* as in *waxing crescent* or *waxing gibbous*. The daylit side of the Moon will be facing toward the west (toward the right for observers in the northern hemisphere and toward the left for southern hemisphere observers). If the illuminated fraction decreases with time, it is *waning* as in *waning crescent* or *waning gibbous*. The daylit side of the Moon will be facing toward the east (toward the left for observers in the northern hemisphere). Readers in the southern hemisphere need to reverse "left" and "right" in the figure below.

full phase

lunar eclipse

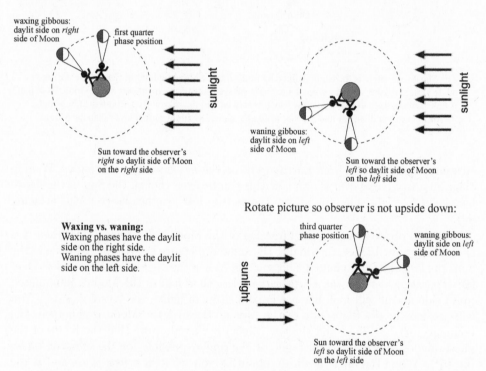

The figures on the next two pages show the geometries for Waxing Crescent and Waxing Gibbous phases. The crescent phase is close to the sun (at a small angle) on our sky and the lit part is closest to the sun. The view from space shows that the Earth's shadow is no where near the Moon. The Earth's shadow does not create the Moon phases! Also on the next two pages are the "Orrery to ground view" figures for the Waxing Crescent and *Waning* Gibbous phases. They show a technique you can use to figure out how a Moon phase will look from from the Earth when you start from an "orrery" or space view of the Moon, i.e., how to translate from the orrery (space) view of the Moon in its orbit around the Earth to the ground-based view.

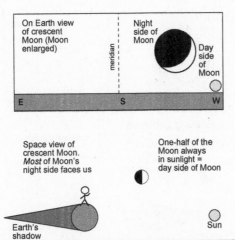

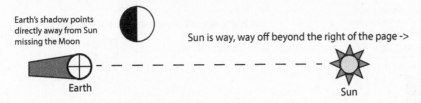

Space view of
crescent Moon.
Most of Moon's
night side faces us

One-half of the
Moon always
in sunlight =
day side of Moon

Earth's
shadow

Sun

Orrery to ground view: Waxing Crescent example

Step 1: Viewed from high above Earth, shade half the Moon with lit half facing the Sun

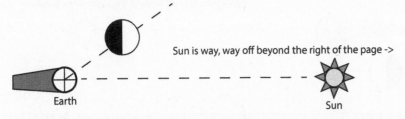

Earth's shadow points
directly away from Sun
missing the Moon

Sun is way, way off beyond the right of the page ->

Earth

Sun

Step 2: Draw line from Earth center to Moon

Sun is way, way off beyond the right of the page ->

Earth

Sun

Step 3: Place observer on Earth in direction of the Moon. The person is raising his ***RIGHT*** hand. ***If*** observer's head is pointed toward the bottom of the page in your drawing, rotate Earth-Moon-Sun drawing 180º. Draw line perpendicular (90º) to Earth-Moon line.

In this example, observer's head already pointed
toward top of page, so no need to rotate drawing.

Sun is way, way off beyond the right of the page ->

Earth

Sun

Step 4: Focus attention on half of Moon facing *Earth*. (Side facing away from Earth has been grayed out.) If less than half of side facing Earth is lit => crescent (or new). If more than half of side facing Earth is lit => gibbous (or full)

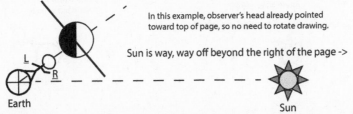

half of
Moon
facing Earth

here the dark is
on the left

here the light is
on the right

What we see on Earth
is a waxing crescent

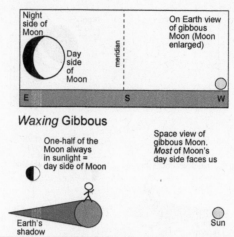

Waxing Gibbous

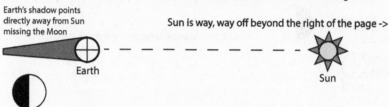

Orrery to ground view: *Waning* Gibbous example

Step 1: Viewed from high above Earth, shade half the Moon with lit half facing the Sun

Earth's shadow points
directly away from Sun
missing the Moon

Sun is way, way off beyond the right of the page ->

Step 2: Draw line from Earth center to Moon

Sun is way, way off beyond the right of the page ->

Step 3: Place observer on Earth in direction of the Moon. The person is raising his ***RIGHT*** hand.
If observer's head is pointed toward the bottom of the page in your drawing, rotate
Earth-Moon-Sun drawing 180°. Draw line perpendicular (90°) to Earth-Moon line.

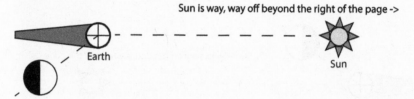

Observer's head in step 2 drawing would have
pointed down toward bottom of page, so
rotate drawing 180°.

oberver now
pointed upward
toward top of page

<- Sun is way, way off beyond the left of the page

Step 4: Focus attention on half of Moon facing *Earth*. (Side facing away from Earth has been
grayed out.) If less than half of side facing Earth is lit => crescent (or new). If more than
half of side facing Earth is lit => gibbous (or full)

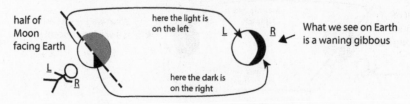

half of
Moon
facing Earth

here the light is
on the left

here the dark is
on the right

What we see on Earth
is a waning gibbous

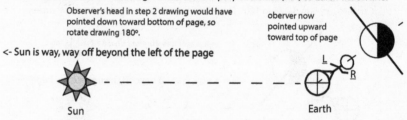

You can use the illustration of the lunar phases at the beginning of this section to find out the time of day when the Moon will be visible. The Sun is at the right of the figure so a person at position (A) on the Earth (e.g., Los Angeles, CA) sees the Sun on the meridian. *When an object is on the meridian, your part of the Earth is pointing directly toward that object.* The Earth rotates in the counterclockwise direction (A to B to C to D). A person at position (B) (e.g., Sao Mateus in the Azores) sees the Sun setting since he is one-quarter turn (6 hours) ahead of the person at position (A). The person at position (C) (e.g., Zahedan, Iran) is at the midnight position (half a turn, 12 hours, ahead of position (A)) and the person at position (D) (e.g., Sydney, Australia) is experiencing sunrise (three-quarters of a turn, 18 hours, ahead of position (A)). If the Moon was at its new phase position, person (D) would see the new moon rising, person (A) would see the new moon on the meridian, and person (B) would see the new moon setting within a few minutes of sunset.

meridian direction

If the Moon was at its first quarter position, person (A) would see the Moon beginning to rise, person (B) would see the Moon on his meridian at sunset, and person (C) would the first quarter moon setting because it is already midnight at her position. The figure below illustrates these views.

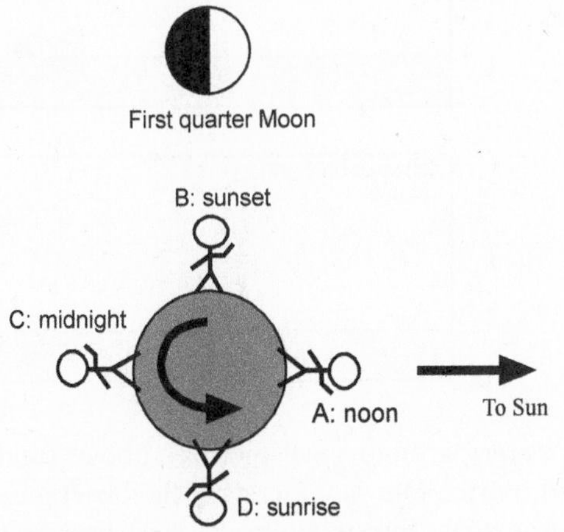

First quarter Moon

B: sunset

C: midnight

A: noon

To Sun

D: sunrise

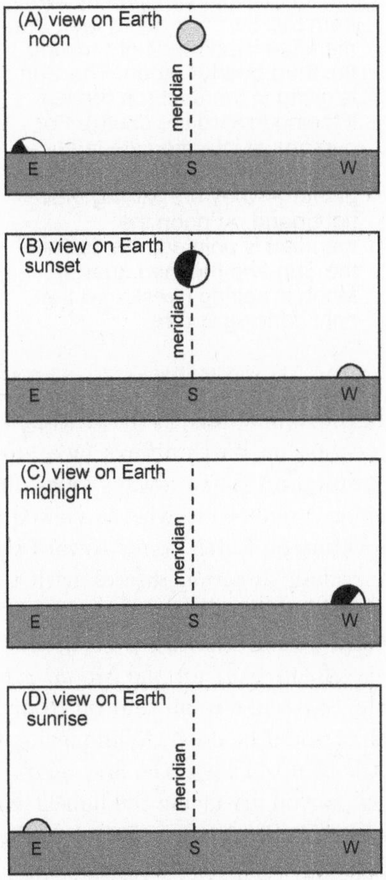

Four people six hours apart from each other. At local noon the meridian is pointed right toward the Sun. Six hours later the meridian is pointed right toward the first quarter Moon. The Sun is setting in the west (on the right if facing toward the south). For persons at intermediate latitudes north, we are looking at the *back* of them—they are raising their right hand. At midnight the meridian is pointed directly away from the Sun and the first quarter Moon is setting (west = on the right if facing south).

(A) view on Earth noon

meridian

E   S   W

(B) view on Earth sunset

meridian

E   S   W

(C) view on Earth midnight

meridian

E   S   W

(D) view on Earth sunrise

meridian

E   S   W

Using the same method, you can see that the full moon is rising for person (B) at sunset, is on the meridian at midnight for person (C) opposite the Sun, and is setting for the person (D) at sunrise. Now try to figure out when the third quarter moon will rise, cross the meridian, and set using this method. Remember that each of the persons A, B, C, D are each six hours apart from each other. Also, remember person (D) is facing *down* in the orrery view on the left side of the figure above and if the person is facing south, the Sun will be rising on his *left*. The textbook website includes animations for a waxing crescent and a waxing gibbous phase.

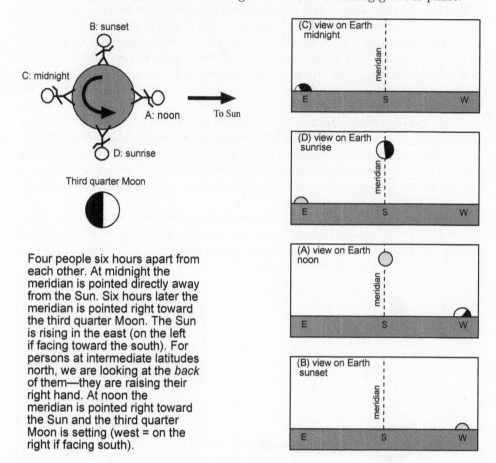

Four people six hours apart from each other. At midnight the meridian is pointed directly away from the Sun. Six hours later the meridian is pointed right toward the third quarter Moon. The Sun is rising in the east (on the left if facing toward the south). For persons at intermediate latitudes north, we are looking at the *back* of them—they are raising their right hand. At noon the meridian is pointed right toward the Sun and the third quarter Moon is setting (west = on the right if facing south).

In the first quarter and third quarter orrery-ground view pictures above (and in the animations on the textbook website), notice four key facts: 1) the observer's location on Earth always faces directly toward the Sun at noon; 2) the observer's location on Earth always faces directly away from the Sun at midnight; 3) Earth spins counter-clockwise as viewed from above the north pole; and 4) the observer's location on Earth points toward the meridian (due South) at any given time, so the meridian direction rotates with the observer (the stick figures are pointed in the meridian direction).

If you are having a hard time visualizing this, try using a white ball (e.g., a styrofoam ball) for the Moon, a bright light bulb for the Sun, and your head for the Earth in a room shut off from other lights. When your eyes are facing the bulb, that would be noon. While facing the bulb, move the ball to your left ear so half of it is lit up. That is the first quarter phase. If you move your head counterclockwise 90° so you are facing the half-lit ball, you will see the bulb out of the corner of your right eye (in the "west" direction). That would be sunset. Move the ball around so it is opposite the bulb but out of the shadow of your head. You should see all of it lit up—a full phase. If you face the same direction that you faced the half-lit ball, the full phase ball would be visible out of the corner of your left eye (in the "east" direction). As you turn your head counterclockwise, you will see the ball "rise" and the bulb "set". When you face the full-lit ball, that would be midnight. How would you simulate a third quarter phase?

The table below gives a summary of approximately when the Moon is visible and where to look (the crescent and gibbous phases are in between the table values). You may be surprised to find out that the Moon is sometimes visible in broad daylight!

Moon Phase	Time ahead/behind the Sun	Moon Rises (eastern sky)	Moon Crosses Meridian (southern sky)	Moon Sets (western sky)
New	within a few minutes	Sunrise	Noon	Sunset
First Quarter	6 hrs behind	Noon	Sunset	Midnight
Full	12 hrs behind	Sunset	Midnight	Sunrise
Third Quarter	6 hrs *ahead*	Midnight	Sunrise	Noon

The phase diagram seems to show that a solar and lunar eclipse should happen *every month* but eclipses actually happen only twice a year. You can see why if you look at the Moon's orbit from close to edge-on. The Moon's orbit is tilted by 5° with respect to the Earth's orbital plane (the ecliptic). In order for an eclipse to occur, the Moon must be in the ecliptic plane AND exactly at the new or full phase. Usually, the Moon crosses the ecliptic plane at another phase instead of exactly at new or full phase during its approximately month-long orbit around the Earth.

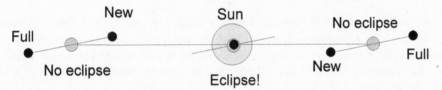

Side view of Moon's orbit and Earth's orbit

Earth-Moon system at three points in their orbit around the Sun. Usually the Moon is above or below the ecliptic at the new or full phase, but twice a year it crosses the ecliptic when it is behind or in front of the Earth to produce an eclipse!

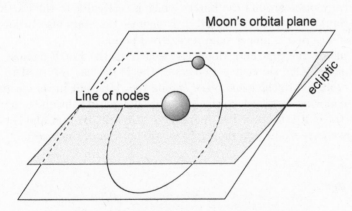

The Moon's orbit is tilted by 5° with respect to the ecliptic (the Earth's orbital plane). The **line of nodes** is the intersection of the two planes.

During a year the Moon's orbit is oriented in very nearly the same direction in space (see the figure on the next page). The position of the Earth and Moon with respect to the Sun changes while the Moon's orbit direction is approximately fixed. So in one month the Moon will be *below* the ecliptic at full phase and *above* the ecliptic at full phase about six months later. Though the Moon crosses the

why eclipses are rare

ecliptic twice a month, an eclipse will happen only when it is exactly at full or new phase when it crosses the ecliptic. *The tilt of the Moon's orbit explains why eclipses happen only twice a year.*

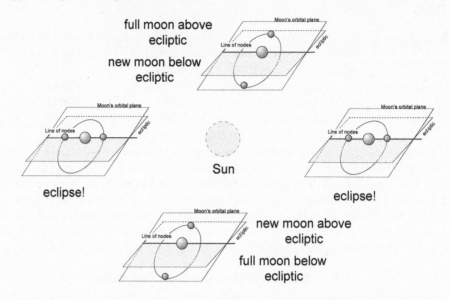

why the eclipse dates change

The direction of the Moon's orbit slowly shifts (precesses) over time. Because the Moon's orbit precesses, eclipses will occur on different dates in successive years. However, even if there was no precession, eclipses would still happen only twice a year. The figure on the next page shows another complication—the elliptical orbit of the Moon around the Earth means that the new moon can occur at different distances from the Earth and the Moon's shadow may not reach the Earth if it is too far away.

Why are the synodic and sidereal periods not equal to each other? For a reason similar to the reason why the solar day and sidereal day are not the same. Remember that a solar day was slightly longer than a sidereal day because of the Sun's apparent motion around the Earth (which is really due to the Earth's motion around the Sun). The Sun's eastward drift against the stars also means that the Moon's synodic period is longer than its sidereal period.

At new moon, the Sun and Moon are seen from the Earth against the same background stars. One sidereal period later, the Moon has returned to the same place in its orbit and to the same place among the stars, but in the meantime, the Sun has been moving eastward, so the Moon has not yet caught up to the Sun. The Moon must travel a little over two more days to reach the Sun and establish the new moon geometry again (see the figure at the bottom of the page).

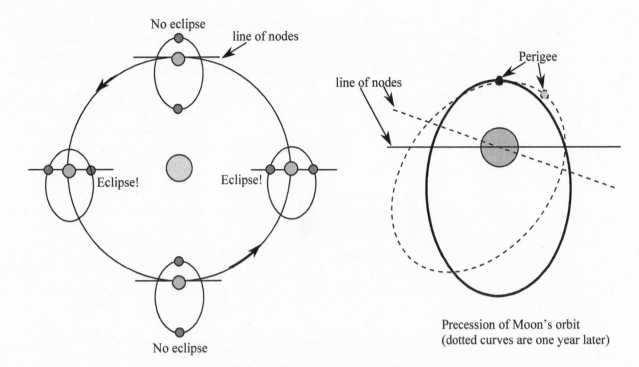

Precession of Moon's orbit
(dotted curves are one year later)

Top view of Moon's orbit and Earth's orbit

The Earth-Moon system at four points in their orbit around the Sun. The **line of nodes** is the intersection of the Moon's orbit with the ecliptic (Earth's orbit). The Moon crosses the ecliptic twice a month. An eclipse happens when the Moon is in either new or full phase **AND** at the line of nodes. The Moon's orbit is slightly elliptical (exaggerated a lot in this picture) and the Moon may not be exactly on the line of nodes so a solar eclipse may or may not be total.

The Moon's orbit precesses so the line of nodes shifts by about 19.3° in one year and the perigee (closest point to Earth) of the Moon's orbit shifts by about 40.7° in one year. The line of nodes completes one full precession in 18.61 years. This precession explains why eclipses occur at different dates in successive years.

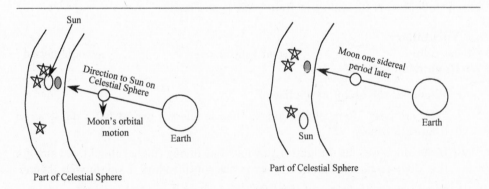

The Moon in orbit around the Earth and how it appears projected onto the Celestial Sphere. At new moon phase (left), the Moon is close to the Sun. One sidereal period later the Moon is projected against the same background stars, but the Sun has moved eastward during that sidereal period. The Moon is not yet in new moon phase. It will have to move about another two days in its orbit to catch up to the Sun.

The modern model has the Moon going around the Earth with the Sun far away. At different positions in its orbit you see different phases all depending on the relative positions of the Earth-Moon-Sun. Another possible model was presented by highly-esteemed Harvard seniors at their graduation (see the figure below). They seriously proposed that the dark part of the Moon is the result of portions of the Moon lying in the shadow of the Earth. Many other people have also explained the phases with this Earth shadow model, but I will call this the "Harvard model" below.

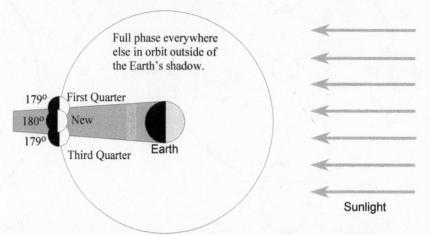

The "Harvard" shadow theory says that the Earth's shadow (the umbra is drawn here) causes the lunar phases. The theory predicts that all of the phases except full phase should happen with the Moon *behind* the Earth at Sun-Moon angles very nearly equal to 180 degrees. For example, first and third quarter phases are predicted to be at a Sun-Moon angle of about 179° but the observed angles are very nearly 90 degrees. If this drawing were to scale, the Moon would be half this size and its orbit would be about 22 **times** larger in diameter and the Earth's shadow length would be increased by the same factor.

Since the Moon would need to be opposite the Sun for it to be in the Earth's shadow, the "Harvard model" predicts Sun-Moon angles that are very different from the observed angles. In addition, the model predicts that the Moon would need to be one-half a rotation (or 12 hours) away from the Sun. The Moon should rise 12 hours after sunrise (i.e., at sun*set*), cross the meridian 12 hours after the Sun (i.e., at midnight), and set 12 hours after sunset (i.e., at sun*rise*) for all of the phases except full. How is this different from what is observed?

Vocabulary

lunar eclipse   solar eclipse   synodic period

Review Questions

1. Why does the Moon have phases?

2. Why are New Moon phases longer than a sidereal period (27.3 days) apart from each other?

3. If the Moon was full 7 nights ago, what time of day (night) should you look for the Moon to be up high in the sky in the south today? Explain your answer.

4. What are the positions of the Earth-Moon-Sun during an eclipse?

5. What would the Sun-Moon angular separation be for the New Moon if the Earth's shadow caused the lunar phases? How about Gibbous phase?

6. What are the real angular separations for New and Gibbous phase?

7. About how much difference in time is there between moonset and sunset at first quarter phase? Does the Moon set before or after the Sun at that phase?

8. About how much difference in time is there between moonset and sunset at new phase?

9. If the Earth's shadow caused the lunar phases, what would be the difference in time between moonrise and sunrise at new and first quarter phases?

10. About when will the Waxing Crescent Moon be on the meridian? Explain your answer.

11. The Moon is low in the western sky at sunrise, what is its phase? Explain!

12. Why do we not have eclipses every month?

3.7.2 Eclipse Details: Lunar Eclipse

Let's explore a little more about lunar and solar eclipses. Remember that an eclipse happens when an object passes through another object's shadow. Any shadow consists of two parts: an **umbra** which is the region of total shadow and the **penumbra** which is the outer region of partial shadow. If the Moon were to pass through the Earth's umbra, an observer on the Moon would not be able to see the Sun at all—she would observe a solar eclipse! At the same time an observer on the Earth would see a total lunar eclipse. The Earth's shadow is pretty big compared to the Moon so a total lunar eclipse can last up to about 1 hour 45 minutes. umbra
penumbra

If the Moon only passed through the outer part of the shadow (the penumbra), then the observer on the Moon would see the Sun only partially covered up—a partial solar eclipse. The observer on the Earth would see the Moon only partially dimmed—a partial lunar eclipse.

During a total lunar eclipse you see another interesting effect—the Moon turns a coppery (or bloody) red. (Nice color images from two different lunar eclipses are posted on the textbook's website.) The reason why some sunlight reaches the Moon despite the fact that the Moon is in the Earth's umbra is that the sunlight **refracts** or bends as it passes through the Earth's atmosphere. Dust particles in the Earth's atmosphere remove much of the bluer colors in the sunlight so only the redder colors make it to the Moon. The amount of dust determines the deepness of the red colors. The dust in the air is also why the Sun appears redder at sunset on Earth. The observer on the Moon would see a reddish ring around the Earth even at mid-eclipse! refraction

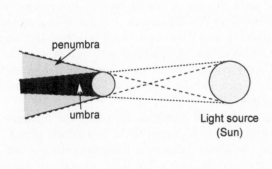

Refraction of sunlight through atmosphere

3.7.3 Eclipse Details: Solar Eclipse

The Moon's shadow also has an umbra and penumbra, but its shadow is much smaller than the Earth's. Only if the Moon is in the ecliptic plane when it is exactly New Moon will the Moon's shadow hit the Earth. Where the umbra hits

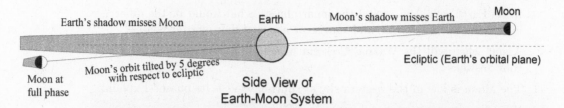

Earth's shadow misses Moon   Earth   Moon's shadow misses Earth   Moon

Moon at full phase   Moon's orbit tilted by 5 degrees with respect to ecliptic   Ecliptic (Earth's orbital plane)

Side View of Earth-Moon System

Total Solar Eclipse August 21, 2017
Nick Strobel

the Earth, you will see a total solar eclipse. Where the penumbra hits the Earth, you will see a partial solar eclipse.

In a total solar eclipse the bright disk of the Sun is completely covered up by the Moon and you can see the other parts of the Sun like the corona, chromosphere, and prominences. Unfortunately, only the tip of the Moon's umbra reaches the Earth (the tip hitting the Earth is at most 270 kilometers [168 miles] in diameter) and it zips along the Earth's surface at over 1600 kph (1000 mph) as the Moon moves around the rotating Earth. This means that a total solar eclipse can last a maximum of only 7.5 minutes. Usually total solar eclipses last only 2–3 minutes. Because of the orbital motion of the Moon and the rotation of the Earth, the umbra makes a long, narrow path of totality.

Sometimes the umbra does not reach the Earth at all (only the penumbra) even though the Moon is on the ecliptic *and* it is exactly in New Moon phase. A
annular eclipse
bright ring will be visible around the Moon when it is lined up with the Sun— an **annular eclipse** (because of the annulus or ring of light around the Moon). What do you think this implies about the shape of the Moon's orbit? (See figure next page) NASA publishes excellent information about upcoming eclipses on the web. See the textbook's website for the links, a sequence of images of the May 20, 2012 annular eclipse, and videos of the November 2012 and August 2017 total solar eclipses.

Vocabulary

annular eclipse	penumbra	refraction
umbra		

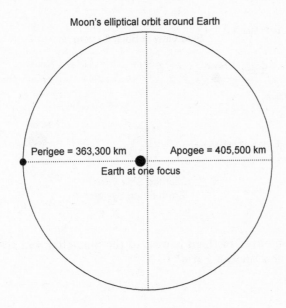

Moon's elliptical orbit around Earth

Perigee = 363,300 km   Apogee = 405,500 km
Earth at one focus

Review Questions

1. What are the two parts of a shadow and in which part is the Sun partially visible?

2. Why does a new phase occur every month but a lunar eclipse occurs only twice a year?

3. Why is the path of totality of a solar eclipse different each time? Why does the latitude of the path vary?

4. Why does the Moon turn orange-red during a total lunar eclipse?

5. Would a person on the Moon ever experience an annular solar eclipse? Explain your answer.

6. Why don't we have just annular solar eclipses or just total solar eclipses when the Moon and Sun are exactly lined up?

3.8   Planetary Motions

There are other celestial objects that drift eastward with respect to the stars. They are the planets (Greek for "wanderers"). There is much to be learned from observing the planetary motions with just the naked eye (i.e., no telescope). There are 5 planets visible without a telescope, Mercury, Venus, Mars, Jupiter, and Saturn (6 if you include Uranus for those with sharp eyes!). All of them move within 7° of the ecliptic. That tells you something about the orientation of the planet orbit planes with respect to the ecliptic—the figure on the next page shows how flat the solar system is when viewed along the ecliptic plane. The planet positions, of course, do change as they orbit the Sun, but the orbit orientations remain the same.

The arrow pointing to Polaris in the solar system picture is tilted by 23.5° because the Earth's rotation axis is tilted by 23.5° with respect to the ecliptic. As viewed from the Earth, two of the planets (Mercury and Venus) are never far from the Sun. Venus can get about 48° from the Sun, while Mercury can only manage a 27.5° separation from the Sun on the Earth's sky. This tells you something about the size of their orbits in relation to the Earth's orbit size—their orbits are smaller and inside the Earth's orbit. When Venus and/or Mercury are east of the Sun, they will set *after* sunset so they are called an "evening star" even though they are not

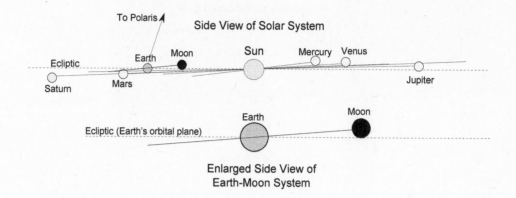

stars at all. When either of them is west of the Sun, they will rise *before* sunrise and they are called a "morning star".

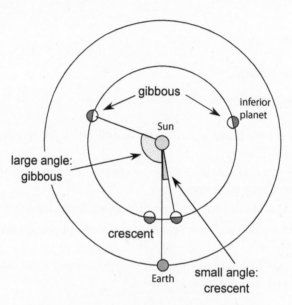

The inferior planets (Venus and Mercury) go
through a complete set of phases. The phase
depends on the planet-Sun-Earth angle.

stars vs. planets   Planets produce no visible light of their own; you see them by reflected sunlight. True stars produce their own visible light. The planets inside the Earth's orbit are called the "inferior" planets because their distance from the Sun is less than (or inferior to) the Earth's distance from the Sun. Their closeness to the Sun enables us to see them go through a complete set of phases. The figure above shows how the phase of the inferior planets depends on the planet-Sun-Earth angle. The figure on the next page gives more details of the inferior planet phases. When the planet is at the "tangent point" (where a line drawn from Earth to the planet's orbit intersects the orbit at only one point), it is at maximum separation from the Sun as seen from Earth and it appears to be in quarter phase. When the planet is farther from Earth than the tangent point, we see it in a gibbous phase and when it is closer to us than the tangent point, we see the planet in a crescent phase.

Because they can get between us and the Sun, Venus and Mercury can be seen in a crescent or new phase. This also explains why the planets outside the Earth's orbit, called the "superior planets", are never seen in a crescent or new phase. When

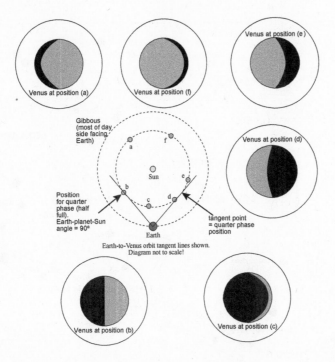

Venus is in crescent phase, it is the brightest object in the sky besides the Moon and the Sun. Even though you see a small fraction of its sunlit side, it is so close to us that you see it appear quite bright. At these times, Venus is bright enough to create a shadow! The fact that you can see Venus and Mercury also in gibbous and nearly full phase proved to be a critical observation in deciding between a Earth-centered model and a Sun-centered model for the solar system.

Because Mercury and Venus are closer to the Sun than we are (i.e., their orbits are inside the Earth's orbit), they are never visible at around midnight (or opposite the Sun). The superior planets can be visible at midnight. At midnight you are pointed directly away from the Sun so you see solar system objects above the horizon that are further out from the Sun than we are.

Ordinarily the planets "wander" eastward among the stars (though staying close to the ecliptic). But sometimes a strange thing happens—a planet will slow down its eastward drift among the stars, halt, and then back up and head westward for a few weeks or months, then halt and move eastward again. The planet executes a loop against the stars! When a planet is moving backward it is said to be executing **retrograde motion**. Perhaps it seemed to the ancients that the planets wanted to take another look at the stars they had just passed by.

retrograde motion

The figure on the next page shows Mars' retrograde loop happening at the beginning of 1997. Mars' position is plotted every 7 days from October 22, 1996 (the position on November 12, 1996 is noted) and the positions at the beginning and end of the retrograde loop (February 4 and April 29, 1997) are noted. What causes retrograde motion? The answer to that question involved a long process of cultural evolution, political strife, and paradigm shifts. You will investigate the question when you look at geocentric (Earth-centered) models of the universe and heliocentric (Sun-centered) models of the universe in the next chapter.

Vocabulary

retrograde motion

Review Questions

1. How do the planets move with respect to the stars?

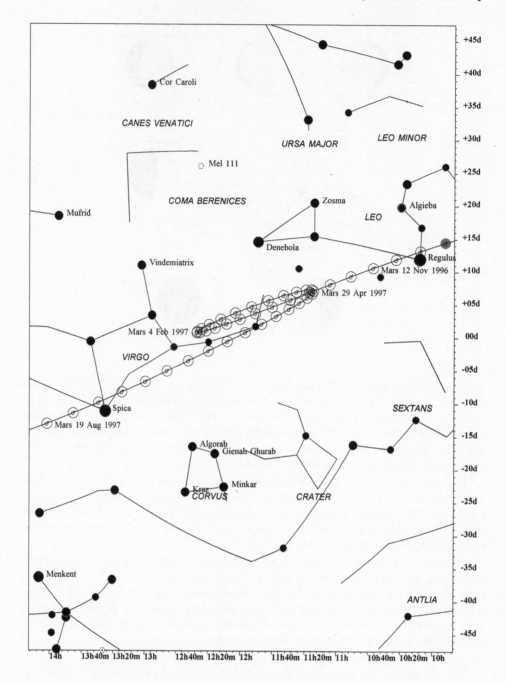

2. What does the fact that all of the planets visible without a telescope move within 7° of the ecliptic imply about the alignment of their orbital planes? What would an edge-on view of our solar system look like?

3. Why are Venus, and Mercury never seen at midnight while the other planets can be visible then?

4. What phase would Venus be in when it is almost directly between us and the Sun? Where would it be in its orbit if we see in a gibbous phase?

5. Are the planet motions random all over the sky or are they restricted in some way?

Chapter 4

History of Astronomy

This chapter covers the development of western astronomy and modern science. I focus on the rise of modern science in Europe, from the ancient Greeks to Isaac Newton. Other cultures were also quite interested and skilled in astronomy (the Mayans, Egyptians, peoples of India and China come immediately to mind), but the Greeks were the first ones to try to explain how the universe worked in a logical, systematic manner using models and observations. Modern astronomy (and all of science) has its roots in the Greek tradition. If you would like a more thorough discussion of the history of astronomy than what I will present here, please take a look at *Science and the Human Prospect* by Ronald Pine. I will give dates of when certain persons lived and worked to give you some reference points in the long history of astronomy. Don't worry about memorizing the dates. What is more important is to see the development of ideas and methods of modern science.

In this chapter and the next, I include atlases of the world from the time periods discussed in the text. You can see from these pictures that as people explored places beyond their home, their view and knowledge of the world and universe expanded and improved. Very often, revolutionary leaps in the understanding of how the universe works happened at the same time that explorers were sparking people's imaginations with their stories of the fascinating new places they had been too. The vocabulary terms are in boldface.

4.1 Philosophical Backdrop

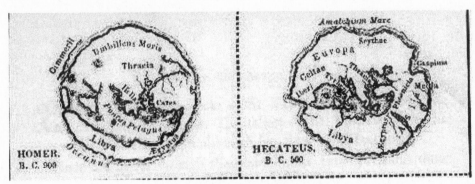

Ancient Greek views of the world
Images courtesy of Jim Siebold

By the 7th Century B.C.E. a common viewpoint had arisen in Greece that the universe is a rational place following universal, natural laws and we are able to figure

71

out those laws. Open inquiry and critical evaluation was highly valued. The emphasis was on the process of learning about the universe rather than attaining the goal. But people eventually got tired of learning and wanted absolute answers. Science is not able to give absolute, certain answers (recall the discussion in section 2.4). There was disagreement among the experts and there came to be a crisis in their confidence of a rational, knowable universe that led to the rise of the Sophists.

Socrates

The *Sophists* taught that an absolute truth and morality are myths and are relative to the individual. Since truth and morality were just cultural inventions for the Sophists, they said a person should conform to the prevailing views, rather than resolutely holding to some belief as an absolute one. *Socrates* (lived 470–399 B.C.E.) disagreed with the Sophists, teaching that we can attain real truth through collaboration with others. By exploring together and being skeptical about "common sense" notions about the way things are, we can get a correct understanding of how our world and society operate. This idea of being skeptical so that a truer understanding of nature can be found is still very much a part of modern science.

Plato

Socrates' student, *Plato*, developed Socrates' ideas further. Plato taught that there are absolute truths—mathematics is the key. While statements about the physical world will be relative to the individual and culture, mathematics is independent of those influences: $2 + 2 = 4$ always, here on Earth or on the far side of the galaxy. Plato had Four Basic Points:

1. There is certainty.

2. Mathematics gives us the power of perception.

3. Though the physical applications of mathematics may change, the thoughts themselves are eternal and are in another realm of existence.

4. Mathematics is thought and, therefore, it is eternal and can be known by anyone. [Today mathematical ideas are viewed as free creations of the human mind. They are the tools used to map the world. Experience is the key. Although absolute certainty is not possible, you can still attain accurate knowledge and reasonable beliefs about the world.]

math is key

Out of Plato's teachings grew the belief that when one studies mathematics, one studies the mind of God. Mathematical symmetries are the language of universal design and harmony. Their faith in order caused the Greeks to try to find explanation for the seemingly unordered planets (particularly retrograde motion). Their faith in an ordered universe compelled them to make precise observations and they were sustained by their belief in the power of reason. In one form or another, modern scientists still have this faith in an ordered universe and the power of human reason.

paradigm

Pythagorean Paradigm

The Greeks were guided by a paradigm that was first articulated by Pythagoras before Socrates' time. A **paradigm** is a general consensus of belief of how the world works. It is a mental framework you use to interpret what happens around you. It is what could be called "common sense". The **Pythagorean Paradigm** had three key points about the movements of celestial objects:

1. The planets, Sun, Moon and stars move in perfectly circular orbits;

2. The speed of the planets, Sun, Moon and stars in their circular orbits is perfectly uniform;

3. The Earth is at the exact center of the motions of the celestial bodies.

4.2   Plato's Homework Problem

Plato gave his students a major problem to work on. Their task was to find a geometric explanation for the apparent motion of the planets, especially the strange

Plato (lived 427–347 BCE)   Pythagoras (lived c569–475 BCE)
Images courtesy of JJ O'Connor and EF Robertson
University of Saint Andrews, Scotland

retrograde motion. One key observation: as a planet undergoes retrograde motion (drifts westward with respect to the stars), it becomes brighter. Plato and his students were, of course, also guided by the Pythagorean Paradigm. This meant that regardless of the scheme they came up with, the Earth should be at the unmoving center of the planet motions. One student named *Aristarchus* violated that rule and developed a model with the Sun at the center. His model was not accepted because of the obvious observations against a moving Earth.

Some of the observations that convinced the Greeks that the Earth was not moving are

Earth as center proofs

1. The Earth is not part of the heavens. Today the Earth is known to be just one planet of eight (plus 5 dwarf planets at the time of writing) that orbit an average star in the outskirts of a large galaxy, but this idea gained acceptance only recently when telescopes extended our vision.

2. The celestial objects are bright points of light while the Earth is an immense, nonluminous sphere of mud and rock. Modern astronomers now know that the stars are objects like our Sun but very far away and the planets are just reflecting sunlight.

3. The Greeks saw little change in the heavens—the stars are the same night after night. In contrast to this, they saw the Earth as the home of birth, change, and destruction. They believed that the celestial bodies have an immutable regularity that is never achieved on the corruptible Earth. Today astronomers know that stars are born and eventually die (some quite spectacularly!)— the length of their lifetimes are much more than a human lifetime so they appear unchanging. Also, modern astronomers know that the stars do change positions with respect to each other, but without a telescope, it takes hundreds of years to notice the slow changes.

4. Finally, our senses show that the Earth appears to be stationary! Air, clouds, birds, and other things unattached to the ground are not left behind as they would be if the Earth was moving. There should be a strong wind if the Earth

were spinning as suggested by some radicals. There is no strong wind. If the Earth were moving, then anyone jumping from a high point would hit the Earth far behind from the point where the leap began. Furthermore, they knew that things can be flung off an object that is spinning rapidly. The observation that rocks, trees, and people are not hurled off the Earth proved to them that the Earth was not moving. Today we have the understanding of inertia and forces that explains why this does not happen even though the Earth is spinning and orbiting the Sun. That understanding, though, developed about 2000 years after Plato.

instrumentalism

Plato taught that since an infinite number of theories can be constructed to account for the observations, you can never empirically answer what the universe is really like. He said that we should adopt an **instrumentalist** view: scientific theories are just tools or calculation devices and are *not* to be interpreted as real (mathematics was reality). Any generalizations you make may be shown to be false in the future and, also, some of the false generalizations can actually "work"—an incorrect theory can explain the observations (see chapter 2).

Aristotle (lived 384–322 BCE)
Image courtesy of JJ O'Connor and EF Robertson
University of Saint Andrews, Scotland

Aristotle

Aristotle was a student of Plato and had probably the most significant influence on many fields of studies (science, theology, philosophy, etc.) of any single person in history. He thought that Plato had gone too far with his instrumentalist view of theories. Aristotle taught a **realist** view: scientific, mathematical tools are not merely tools—they characterize the way the universe actually is. At most *one* model is correct. The model he chose was one developed by another follower of Plato, Eudoxus. The planets and stars were on concentric crystalline spheres centered on the Earth. Each planet, the Sun, and the Moon were on their own sphere. The stars were placed on the largest sphere surrounding all of the rest.

realism

geocentric *universe*

Aristotle chose this model because most popular and observational evidence supported it and his physics and theory of motion necessitated a **geocentric** (Earth-centered) universe. In his theory of motion, things naturally move to the center of the Earth and the only way to deviate from that is to have a force applied to the object. So a ball thrown parallel to the ground must have a force *continually* pushing it along. This idea was unchallenged for almost two thousand years until Galileo showed experimentally that things will not move or *change their motion* unless a force is applied. Also, the crystalline spheres model agreed with the Pythagorean paradigm of uniform, circular motion (see the previous section).

A slight digression: Another conclusion drawn from Aristotle's teachings was that the Earth was unique with its own set of physical laws that were different from how things worked in the heavens. The Earth was a *world* and filled with change and decay while the planets, Moon, and Sun were perfect, unchanging and essentially ornaments on the sky, not worlds that could be explored. (Imagine the transformation of our viewpoint when we discovered using telescopes that those wandering points of light are worlds like the Earth and then later discovered other planets orbiting other stars!) Now, to return to the motions of the planets...

old view: Earth different than rest of universe

Astronomers continued working on models of how the planets moved. In order to explain the retrograde motion some models used **epicycles**—small circles attached to larger circles centered on the Earth. The planet was on the epicycle so it executed a smaller circular motion as it moved around the Earth. This meant that the planet's distance from us changed and if the epicyclic motion was in the same direction (e.g., counter-clockwise) as the overall motion around the Earth, the planet would be closer to the Earth as the epicycle carried the planet backward with respect to the usual eastward motion. This explained why planets are brighter as they retrogress.

epicycle

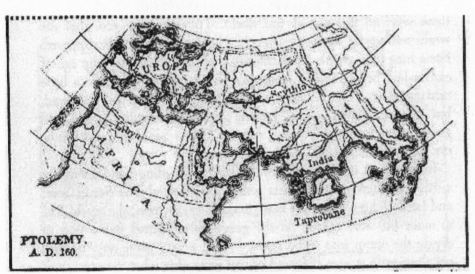

Ptolemy's view of the world
Images courtesy of Jim Siebold

4.2.1 Ptolemy's Geocentric Universe

Ptolemy set out to finally solve the problem of the planets motion. He combined the best features of the geocentric models that used epicycles with the most accurate observations of the planet positions to create a model that would last for nearly 1500 years. He added some refinements to explain the details of the observations: an "eccentric" for each planet that was the true center of its motion (not the Earth!) and an "equant" about which each planet moved uniformly in relation to (not the Earth!). The diagram on the next page shows his model.

Claudius Ptolemy (lived 85–165 CE)
Image courtesy of Albert Van Helden
Rice University

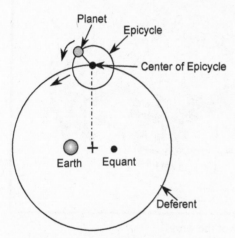

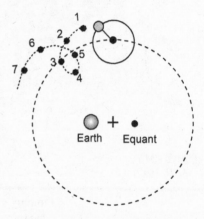

Center of epicycle moves counter-
clockwise on deferent and epicycle
moves counterclockwise. Epicycle
speed is uniform with respect to equant.
The combined motion is shown at right.

Deferent motion is in direction of point 1
to 7 but planet's epicycle carries it on
cycloid path (points 1 through 7) so that
from points 3 through 5 the planet moves
backward (retrograde).

These refinements were incompatible with Aristotle's model and the Pythagorean paradigm—a planet on an epicycle would crash into its crystalline sphere and the motion is not truly centered on the Earth. So Ptolemy adopted an instrumentalist view—this strange model is only an accurate calculator to predict the planet motions but the reality is Aristotle's model. This apparent contradiction between reality and a calculation device was perfectly fine in his time. Our modern belief that models must characterize the way the universe actually is is a tribute to the even longer-lasting influence of Aristotle's realism. Ptolemy was successful in having people adopt his model because he gathered the best model pieces together, used the most accurate observations and he *published* his work in a large 13-volume series called the "Almagest", ensuring that his ideas would last long after he died.

4.3   Renaissance

Our view of the history of astronomy will now skip almost 1500 years to the next major advances in astronomy. Europe was beginning to emerge from a long period of instability in the Middle Ages. During the Middle Ages the Islamic civilization had flourished in the Arabic countries. They had preserved and translated the Greek writings and adopted the Greek ideals of logic and rational inquiry. Islamic astronomers were careful observers of the sky and created accurate star catalogs and tables of planet motions. Many of the names of the bright stars in our sky have Arabic names (e.g., Deneb, Alberio, Aldebaran, Rigel to name a few). However, advances in the *explanations* of the motions of the stars and planets were made by astronomers in Europe starting in the 16th century.

Martin Waldseemuller's world map of 1507
Image courtesy of Jim Siebold

By the 16th century the following paradigm had developed: Man is God's special creation of the physical universe; the Earth is the center of a mathematically-planned universe and we are given the gift of reading this harmony. The Greek ideal of finding logical, systematic explanations to physical events was rediscovered and celebrated thanks to trading with islamic nations. Along with this came an unbounded faith in the power of reason to solve physical problems. This time in history is called the Renaissance (french for "rebirth").

Scientists use a guiding principle called **Occam's Razor** to choose between two or more models that accurately explain the observations. This principle, named after the English philosopher, William of Occam, who stated this principle in the mid-1300's, says: *the best model is the simplest one—the one requiring the fewest assumptions and modifications in order to fit the observations.* Guided by Occam's Razor some scientists began to have serious doubts about Ptolemy's geocentric model in the early years of the Renaissance.

Occam's Razor

keep it simple!

Nicolaus Copernicus (lived 1473–1543 CE)
Image courtesy of JJ O'Connor and EF Robertson
University of Saint Andrews, Scotland

4.3.1 Copernicus' Heliocentric Universe

One such astronomer, *Nicolaus Copernicus*, found many deficiencies in the Ptolemaic model. He felt that any model of the planet motions must account for the observations and have circular, uniform motion. The Ptolemaic model did not do that. Also, the Ptolemaic model was not elegant and, therefore, "un-Godlike". During the years between Ptolemy and Copernicus, many small epicycles had been added to the main epicycles to make Ptolemy's model agree with the observations. By Copernicus' time, the numerous sub-epicycles and offsets had made the Ptolemaic model very complicated. Surely, God would have made a cleaner more elegant universe!

universe should be elegant

Copernicus was strongly influenced by neoplatonism (beliefs that combined elements of Christianity and Plato's teachings) in developing a model to replace Ptolemy's. This led him to believe that the Sun is a material copy of God—God is the creative force sustaining life and the Sun gives us warmth and light. He adopted Aristarchus' **heliocentric** (Sun-centered) model because he felt that God should be at the center of the universe. Copernicus' model had the same accuracy as the revised Ptolemaic one but was more elegant.

heliocentric universe

Copernicus retained the Aristotelian notion that planets were striving to fulfill the goal of perfect (circular) motion. His model still used small epicycles to get the details of the retrograde loops correct, though they were only a minor feature. He used trigonometry to describe the distances of the planets from the Sun relative to the **astronomical unit** (average Earth-Sun distance), but he did not know the numerical value of the astronomical unit. He found that the planets farther from the Sun move slower. The different speeds of the planets around the Sun provided a very simple explanation for the observed retrograde motion.

still use circular orbits

astronomical unit

Retrograde motion is the projected position of a planet on the background stars as the Earth overtakes it (or is passed by, in the case of the inner planets). The figure on the next page illustrates this. Retrograde motion is just an optical illusion! You see the same sort of effect when you pass a slower-moving truck on the highway. As you pass the truck, it appears to move backward with respect to the background trees and mountains. If you continue observing the truck, you will eventually see

retrograde motion explained

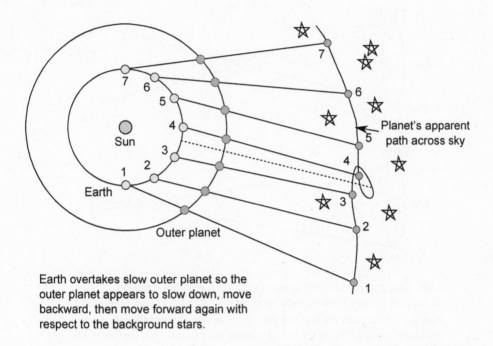

Earth overtakes slow outer planet so the outer planet appears to slow down, move backward, then move forward again with respect to the background stars.

that the truck is moving forward with respect to the background scenery. The relative geometry of you and the other object determines what you see projected against some background.

Copernicus thought his model was reality but other people used his model as a more convenient calculation device only. If the Earth were moving around the Sun, then the stars should appear to shift due to our looking at them from different vantage points in our orbit (a "parallactic shift"). The parallax effect can be illustrated when you look at your thumb at arm's length with one eye and then the other—your thumb appears to shift position!

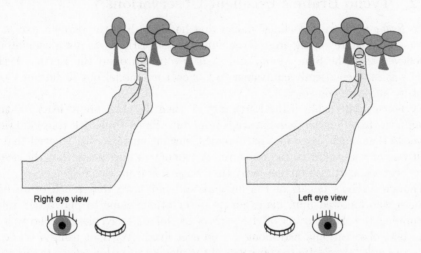

Parallax effect illustrated with your thumb. Notice how your thumb held at arm's length appears to shift with respect to background objects when you look at it with one eye and then the other eye.

Now imagine that the Earth at opposite points in its orbit is your left and right eye and the nearby star is your thumb and you have the situation illustrated below. However, no parallactic shift was observed in the stars. If there was actually a

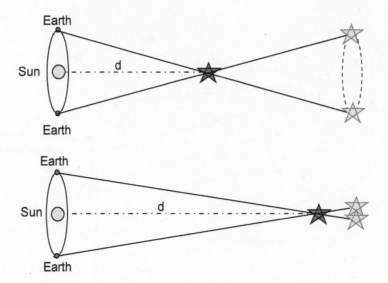

Stars near enough to us will appear to change positions on the sky
as we look at them from opposite sides of our orbit around the Sun. As the
distance d between the star and the Sun increases, the **parallactic shift**
becomes smaller. Before the use of telescopes, astronomers were unable to
observe the tiny parallactic shifts of even the nearest stars. Therefore, many
of them concluded that the Earth does not orbit the Sun.

very small parallactic shift, then the stars would have to be *very far away*. Copernicus' contemporaries felt that God would not waste that much space! They argued that, therefore, there must be no parallactic shift at all—the Earth is not in motion. Astronomers now know that the stars are indeed very far away and telescopes must be used to detect the small parallactic shifts.

4.3.2   Tycho Brahe's Excellent Observations

Tycho Brahe revived Heroclides' model that had the all of the planets, except the stationary Earth, revolving around the Sun. Because Brahe was not a neoplatonist, he believed that the Sun, Moon, and stars revolved around the Earth. Tycho's model was mathematically equivalent to Copernicus' model but it did not violate Scripture and common sense.

Tycho calculated that if the Earth moved, then the stars are at least 700 times farther away from Saturn than Saturn is from Sun. Since Tycho felt that God would not waste that much space in a harmonious, elegant universe, he believed that the Earth was at the center of the universe. Astronomers now know that the nearest star is over 28,500 times farther away than Saturn is from the Sun!

Though Tycho's beliefs of the universe did not have that much of an effect on those who followed him, his exquisite observations came to play a key role in determining the true motion of the planets by Johannes Kepler. Tycho was one of the best observational astronomers who ever lived. Without using a telescope, Tycho was able to measure the positions of the planets to within a few arc *minutes*— a level of precision and accuracy that was at least ten times better than anyone had obtained before!

Tycho Brahe (lived 1546–1601 CE)
Image courtesy of Joseph Dauben
Lehman College (CUNY)

Vocabulary

astronomical unit | epicycle | geocentric
heliocentric | instrumentalism | Occam's Razor
paradigm | Pythagorean paradigm | realism
retrograde motion

Review Questions

1. What two basic kinds of models have been proposed to explain the motions of the planets?

2. What is the Ptolemaic model? What new things did Ptolemy add to his model?

3. Why are epicycles needed in Ptolemy's model?

4. Why was the Ptolemaic model accepted for more than 1000 years?

5. In what ways was the Ptolemaic model a good scientific model and in what ways was it not?

6. What is the Copernican model and how did it explain retrograde motion?

7. Why did Copernicus believe in his model?

8. Why did Copernicus not know the absolute distance between various planets and the Sun in his model? Explain what he would have needed to know to get the absolute distances.

9. What important contributions did Tycho Brahe make to astronomy?

4.4 Battle with the Church

In the 16th century the hierarchical structure of the Church's authority was inextricably bound with the geocentric cosmology. "Up" meant ascension to greater perfection and greater control. God and heaven existed outside the celestial sphere. There was a gradation of existence and control from perfect existence to the central imperfect Earth. God delegated power to angels to control the planet movements and to guide the various earthly events. Plants and animals existed to serve humans and humans were to serve God through the ecclesiastical hierarchy of the Church.

Giordano Bruno (lived 1548–1600 C.E.) revived Democritus' (a contemporary of Socrates) view that the Sun was one of an infinite number of stars. This infinite sphere was consistent with the greatness of God. Bruno believed in a heliocentric universe. He believed that God gave each of us an inner source of power equal to all others, so there was no justification for domination and servitude. His model had definite political ramifications that threatened the Church's political authority.

4.4.1   Galileo

One of Galileo's telescopes
Image courtesy of Joseph Dauben
Lehman College (CUNY)

Galileo Galilei (lived 1564–1642 CE)
Image courtesy of Albert Van Helden
Rice University

Galileo Galilei was the first person known to have used the telescope for astronomical observations (starting in 1609). The telescope was originally used as a naval tool to assess the strength of the opponent's fleet from a great distance. He found many new things when he looked through his telescope:

1. The superior light-gathering power of his telescope over the naked eye enabled him to see many, many new fainter stars that were never seen before. This made Bruno's argument more plausible.

2. The superior resolution and magnification over the naked eye enabled him to see pits and craters on the Moon and spots on the Sun. This meant that the Earth is not only place of change and decay!

3. With his superior "eye" he discovered four moons orbiting Jupiter. These four moons (Io, Europa, Ganymede, and Callisto) are called the Galilean satellites in his honor. In this system Galileo saw a mini-model of the heliocentric system. The moons are not moving around the Earth but are centered on

Galileo's drawing of the Moon as seen
through one of his telescopes.
Image courtesy of Joseph Dauben
Lehman College (CUNY)

Jupiter. Perhaps other objects, including the planets, do not move around
the Earth.

4. He also made the important discovery that Venus goes through a complete
   set of phases. The gibbous and full phases of Venus are impossible in the
   Ptolemaic model but possible in Copernican model (and Tychonic model too!).
   In the Ptolemaic model Venus was always approximately between us and the
   Sun and was never found further away from the Earth than the Sun. Because
   of this geometry, Venus should always be in a crescent, new, or quarter phase.
   The only way to arrange Venus to make a gibbous or full phase is to have it
   orbiting the Sun so that, with respect to our viewpoint, Venus could get on
   the other side of, or behind, the Sun (see the figure at the end of section 3.8).

For Galileo the clear observations against Aristotle's geocentric universe was
a powerful weapon against the hierarchical structure of the seventeenth century
Church. Galileo argued that the heliocentric model is not a mere instrument but
is reality. He stated that his *observations* showed that. From the discussion in
chapter 2, you can argue that Galileo went too far in what conclusions he could
draw from his observations. A scientific model cannot be proven correct, only
disproven. A model that survives repeated tests is one that is *consistent with the
available data.* His observations were consistent with the heliocentric model, but
could also be explained with a geocentric model like Tycho's. But for Galileo,
the observations were enough—he was convinced of the heliocentric system before
he used his telescope and his observations confirmed his belief. More convincing
evidence of the Earth's motion around the Sun would have to wait until 1729
when *James Bradley* (lived 1693–1762 C.E.) discovered that a telescope has to be
slightly tilted because of the Earth's motion, just as you must tilt an umbrella in
front of you when walking quickly in the rain to keep the rain from hitting your
face. The direction the telescope must be tilted constantly changes as the Earth
orbits the Sun. Over a century later, *Friedrich W. Bessel* (lived 1784–1846 C.E.)
provided further evidence for the Earth's motion by measuring the parallax of a
nearby star in the late 1830s. The measurements of Bradley and Bessel required
technology and precision beyond that of Galileo's time. The telescope tilt angle
is less than half an arc minute and the parallax angle of even the nearest star is
less than one arc *second*. Recall from section 3.2 how tiny is an arc second, so you

Earth motion evidence
James Bradley
aberration of starlight

Friedrich Bessel
stellar parallax

can understand why the people of Copernicus' time or Galileo's time could easily discount the heliocentric idea.

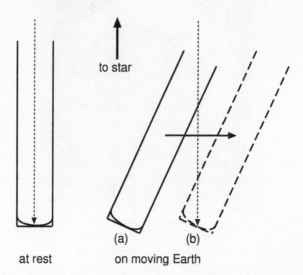

to star

(a)   (b)

at rest   on moving Earth

Aberration of starlight: If the telescope is moving then the telescope must be tipped so that light entering the telescope at position (a) will reach the bottom of the telescope when the bottom gets to position (b).

used experiments

    Galileo also made advances in understanding how ordinary objects move here on the Earth. He set up experiments to see how things move under different circumstances. He found that Aristotle's view of how things move was wrong. Galileo's observations contradicted the long-unchallenged physics of Aristotle, who taught that in order for something to keep moving at even a constant speed, a force must be continually applied. Aristotle also thought that something falling will fall at a constant speed and that heavier things will always fall more quickly than lighter

forces change motion

things. Galileo discovered that an object's motion is *changed* only by having a force act on it. He also discovered that objects falling to the ground will *accelerate* as they fall and that all objects, regardless of size, would fall with the *same* acceleration in the absence of air drag.

proofs of Earth's rotation

    Galileo's studies of how forces operate also provide the foundation to prove that Earth spins on its axis. Although the stars and Sun appear to rise and set every night or day, they are actually stationary. Evidence of the Earth's rotation (from west to east) is seen with the deflection of objects moving in north-south direction caused by the differences in the linear speed of the rotation at different latitudes. All parts of the Earth take 23 hours 56 minutes to turn once, but the higher latitudes

coriolis effect

are closer to the Earth's rotation axis, so they do not need to rotate as fast as regions nearer the equator. A moving object's west-east speed will stay at the original value it had at the start of its motion (unless some force changes it). If the object is also changing latitudes, then its west-east speed will be different than that for the part of the Earth it is over. Therefore, moving objects appear to be deflected to the right in the northern hemisphere and to the left in the southern hemisphere. This

Gustave-Gaspard Coriolis

is called the *coriolis effect* after *Gustave-Gaspard Coriolis* (lived 1792–1843 C.E.) who deduced the effect in 1835 to explain why cannonballs shot long distances kept missing their target if the cannon was aimed directly at its target. See section 9.2.7 for applications (and illustrations) of the coriolis effect to planet atmospheres.

Jean-Bernard-Léon Foucault
Foucault pendulum

    Jean-Bernard-Léon Foucault (lived 1819–1868) gave the first laboratory demonstration of the Earth's spin in 1851. A large mass suspended from a long wire mounted so that its perpendicular plane of swing is not confined to a particular direction, will rotate in relation to the Earth's surface. The only forces acting on the ball are gravity and the wire tension and they lie in the plane of oscillation. There are no forces acting on the ball perpendicular to the oscillation plane, so the

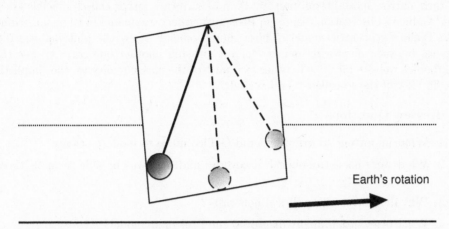

Earth's rotation

Foucault pendulum: No forces perpendicular to the oscillation plane so the plane remains fixed in space while the Earth rotates beneath it.

oscillation direction in space does not change. However, it does rotate *relative to* the Earth's surface because the Earth is rotating under the swinging pendulum. The pendulum appears to rotate westward with a period that depends on the latitude: rotation period $= (23^h\ 56^m)/\sin(\text{latitude})$, where "sin" is the trigonometric sine function. The coriolis effect and the Foucault pendulum are both based on Galileo's discovery that an object's motion (speed and/or direction) are changed *only* if there is a force acting on it.

Galileo is often considered the father of modern science because his ideas were not derived from thought and reason alone. He used the guidance of nature (experiments). This marked a revolutionary change in science—observational experience became the key method for discovering nature's rules. His arguments for the heliocentric model and the critical role of objective observation of nature in science got him into trouble with the Church. The struggle between Galileo and the Church was not a battle between science and religion but was part of a larger battle over different conceptions of the proper routes to knowledge, God, and world view.

first modern scientist

Galileo's intent was to improve the Church by giving a truer understanding of how God actually worked in the physical universe and by allowing greater access to God for more people. Galileo loved to debate and had the bad habit of ridiculing those he disagreed with. Some of those he ridiculed were powerful political figures in the Church. He wrote a book detailing the arguments for and against his model of the universe in a way that ridiculed the official view of the Church. It was written in Italian (the language of everyday discourse), rather than the scholarly Latin, so even non-scholars were exposed to his scathing arguments against the geocentric universe. He may have had more success in getting greater acceptance of his different views of God and research if his style was different but perhaps his ideas needed just such a champion at that time.

This section is titled "Battle with the Church" but that is perhaps a bit misleading when you take a careful look at what really happened between Galileo and church authorities. The disagreement between Galileo and some church figures is often cast as a battle between science (reason, the "good guy") and religion (faith, the "bad guy") in the popular media today but science historians know that the debate was not quite so clear cut—both sides were right on some points and wrong on others; reality is often messier than what is portrayed in the media. For example, Galileo's argument that his observations showed that the heliocentric model is

real history vs. popular history

correct and that the Earth cannot be the center of the universe was only partly correct. While some reactionary church officials thought Galileo was a heretic because of their narrow more literal interpretation of scripture, other church officials knew that Galileo's observation disproved Ptolemy's geocentric model but not something like Tycho's geocentric model. Those church officials knew the philosophical difference between disproving one model vs. proving another one correct. See the textbook's website for links to other examples of the messy reality vs. the simplistic media view of the so-called "Galileo affair".

Review Questions

1. What important contributions did Galileo make to modern science?

2. What were his astronomical discoveries and why was he able to make those discoveries?

3. Why did he get into political hot water?

4. What observation finally disproved the Ptolemaic model?

5. Why is Galileo sometimes referred to as the first "modern scientist"?

6. What evidence is there that the Earth is rotating and that it is revolving around the Sun?

4.5   Kepler's Laws of Planetary Motion

Johannes Kepler (lived 1571–1630 CE)

Image courtesy of JJ O'Connor and EF Robertson
University of Saint Andrews, Scotland

Johannes Kepler was hired by Tycho Brahe to work out the mathematical details of Tycho's version of the geocentric universe. Kepler was a religious individualist. He did not go along with the Roman Catholic Church or the Lutherans. He had an ardent mystical neoplatonic faith. He wanted to work with the best observational data available because he felt that even the most elegant, mathematically-harmonious theories must match reality. Kepler was motivated by his faith in God to try to discover God's plan in the universe—to "read the mind of God." Kepler shared the Greek view that mathematics was the language of God. He knew that all previous models were inaccurate, so he believed that other scientists had not yet "read the mind of God."

Since an infinite number of models are possible (see Plato's Instrumentalism above), he had to choose one as a starting point. Although he was hired by Tycho to work on Tycho's geocentric model, Kepler did not believe in either Tycho's model or Ptolemy's model (he thought Ptolemy's model was mathematically ugly). His neoplatonic faith led him to choose Copernicus' heliocentric model over his employer's model.

Kepler tried to refine Copernicus' model. After years of failure, he was finally convinced with great reluctance of a revolutionary idea: God uses a different mathematical shape than the circle. This idea went against the 2,000 year-old Pythagorean paradigm of the perfect shape being a circle! Kepler had a hard time convincing himself that planet orbits are not circles and his contemporaries, including the great scientist Galileo, disagreed with Kepler's conclusion. He discovered that *planetary orbits are ellipses with the Sun at one focus*. This is now known as **Kepler's 1st law.**

Kepler's 1st law: *elliptical orbits*

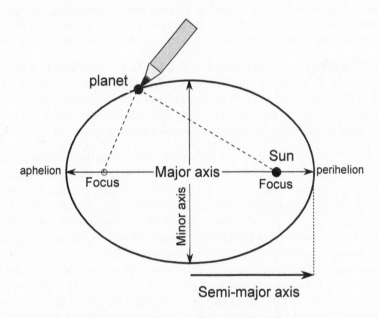

Drawing an **ellipse**: loop string around thumb tacks at each **focus** and stretch string tight with a pencil while moving the pencil around the tacks. The Sun is at one focus.

An ellipse is a squashed circle that can be drawn by punching two thumb tacks into some paper, looping a string around the tacks, stretching the string with a pencil, and moving the pencil around the tacks while keeping the string taut. The figure traced out is an ellipse and the thumb tacks are at the two foci of the ellipse. An oval shape (like an egg) is not an ellipse: an oval tapers at only one end, but an ellipse is tapered at both ends (Kepler had tried oval shapes but he found they did not work).

There are some terms I will use frequently in the rest of this book that are used in discussing any sort of orbit. Here is a list of definitions:

1. *Major axis*—the length of the longest dimension of an ellipse.

2. **Semi-major axis**—one half of the major axis and equal to the distance

semi-major axis

from the center of the ellipse to one end of the ellipse. It is also the average distance of a planet from the Sun at one focus.

3. *Minor axis*—the length of the shortest dimension of an ellipse.

perihelion

4. **Perihelion**—point on a planet's orbit that is closest to the Sun. It is on the major axis.

aphelion

5. **Aphelion**—point on a planet orbit that is farthest from the Sun. It is on the major axis directly opposite the perihelion point. The aphelion + perihelion = the major axis. The semi-major axis then, is the average of the aphelion and perihelion distances.

focus

6. **Focus**—one of two points along the major axis such that the distance between it and any point on the ellipse + the distance between the other focus and the same point on the ellipse is always the same value. The Sun is at one of the two foci (nothing is at the other one). The Sun is NOT at the center of the orbit!

As the foci are moved farther apart from each other, the ellipse becomes more eccentric (skinnier). See the figure on the next page. A circle is a special form of an ellipse that has the two foci at the same point (the center of the ellipse).

eccentricity

7. The **eccentricity** (e) of an ellipse is a number that quantifies how elongated the ellipse is. It equals 1 − (perihelion)/(semi-major axis). Circles have an eccentricity = 0; very long and skinny ellipses have an eccentricity close to 1 (a straight line has an eccentricity = 1). The skinniness an ellipse is specified by the semi-*minor* axis. It equals the **semi-major** axis $\times \sqrt{(1 - e^2)}$.

Planet orbits have small eccentricities (nearly circular orbits) which is why astronomers before Kepler thought the orbits were exactly circular. This slight error in the orbit shape accumulated into a large error in planet positions after a few hundred years. Only very accurate and precise observations can show the elliptical character of the orbits. Tycho's observations, therefore, played a key role in Kepler's discovery and is an example of a fundamental breakthrough in our understanding of the universe being possible only from greatly improved observations of the universe.

Most comet orbits have large eccentricities (some are so eccentric that the aphelion is around 100,000 astronomical units (abbreviated as "A.U.") while the perihelion is less than 1 A.U.!). The figure on the next page illustrates how the shape of an ellipse depends on the **semi-major axis** and the **eccentricity.** The eccentricity of the ellipses increases from top left to bottom left in a counter-clockwise direction in the figure but the semi-major axis remains the same. Notice where the Sun is for each of the orbits. As the eccentricity increases, the Sun's position is closer to one side of the elliptical orbit, but the semi-major axis remains the same.

Kepler's 2nd law:
variable speed

To account for the planets' motion (particularly Mars' motion) among the stars, Kepler found that the planets must move around the Sun at a variable speed. When the planet is close to perihelion, it moves quickly; when it is close to aphelion, it moves slowly. This was another break with the Pythagorean paradigm of uniform motion! Kepler discovered another rule of planet orbits: *a line between the planet and the Sun sweeps out equal areas in equal times.* This is now known as **Kepler's 2nd law.**

angular momentum

Later, scientists found that this is a consequence of the conservation of **angular momentum** (see appendix A, the first application). The angular momentum of a planet is a measure of the amount of orbital motion it has and does NOT change as the planet orbits the Sun. It equals the (planet mass) × (planet's transverse speed) × (distance from the Sun). The transverse speed is the amount of the planet's orbital velocity that is in the direction perpendicular to the line between the planet

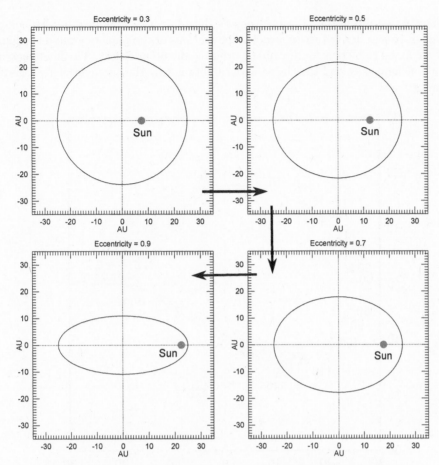

Four ellipses with the **same** *semi-major axis* (25 AU) but **different** *eccentricities.* As the eccentricity increases (direction of arrow), the Sun (at a *focus*) moves farther from the center. The difference between the *perihelion* and *aphelion* increases as well. The ellipse with eccentricity=0.3 looks almost circular. All of the planet orbits have eccentricities **less than** 0.3—this is why it was so hard to discover that planet orbits are ellipses, rather than circles.

and the Sun. If the distance decreases, then the speed must increase to compensate; if the distance increases, then the speed decreases (a planet's mass does not change).

Finally, after several more years of calculations, Kepler found a simple, elegant equation relating the distance of a planet from the Sun to how long it takes to orbit the Sun (the planet's sidereal period). *(One planet's sidereal period/another planet's sidereal period)*^{2} *= (one planet's average distance from Sun/another planet's average distance from Sun)*^{3}. Recall that the semi-major axis is the average distance from the Sun (average of perihelion and aphelion). If you compare the planets to the Earth (with an orbital period = 1 year and a distance = 1 astronomical unit = 1 A.U.), then you get a very simple relation: *(a planet's sidereal period in years)*^{2} *= (semi-major axis of its orbit in A.U.)*^{3}. This is now known as **Kepler's 3rd law**. A review of exponents and square roots is available in appendix B.

Kepler's 3rd law: *distance and period*

math review: appendix B

For example, Mars' orbit has a semi-major axis of 1.52 A.U., so $1.52^3 = 3.51$ and this equals 1.87^2. The number 1.87 is the number of years it takes Mars to go around the Sun. This simple mathematical equation explained all of the observations throughout history and proved to Kepler that the heliocentric system is real. Actually, the first two laws were sufficient, but the third law was very important for Isaac Newton and is used today to determine the masses of many different types of celestial objects. Kepler's third law has many uses in astronomy! Although Kepler derived these laws for the motions of the planets around the Sun, they are found to be true for any object orbiting any other object. The fundamental nature of these rules and their wide applicability is why they are considered "laws" of nature.

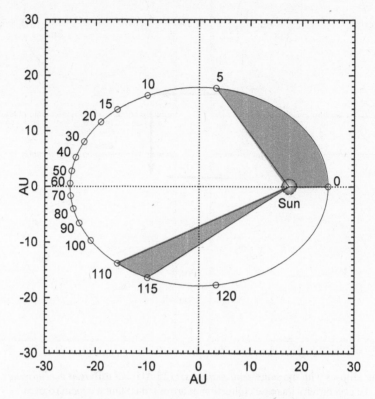

An elliptical orbit with the Sun at one focus (not the center!). Positions are given for different times (in years). Planet speeds up when close to the Sun and slows down when moving away (the line between the planet and Sun sweeps out equal areas in equal intervals of time). The planet's average distance from the Sun (orbit semimajor axis) is 25 AU, so its orbital period is 125 years (derived from $25^3 = 125^2$).

Vocabulary

angular momentum	aphelion	eccentricity
ellipse	focus	Kepler's 1st law
Kepler's 2nd law	Kepler's 3rd law	perihelion
semi-major axis		

Review Questions

1. What shape are planet orbits and where is the Sun with respect to the orbit?

2. What happens to a planet's orbital speed as it approaches its *farthest* point from the Sun and as it approaches its closest point? How is it related to **angular momentum**?

3. How were Kepler's laws of planetary motion revolutionary or a radical break from earlier descriptions of planetary motion?

4. A moon's closest distance from a planet is 300,000 km and its farthest distance is 500,000 km. What is the **semi-major axis** of its elliptical orbit?

5. How will the semi-minor axis compare with the semi-major axis for an ellipse with eccentricity = 0.1, 0.5, 0.8, 0.99? Find the value of (semi-minor/semi-major) for each of the eccentricities.

6. How will the perihelion compare with the aphelion for an ellipse with eccentricity = 0.1, 0.5, 0.8, 0.99? Find the value of (perihelion/aphelion) for each of the eccentricities. [Hint: using the relation that the perihelion + aphelion = 2× semi-major axis and a little algebra, you can find that (perihelion/aphelion) = $(1-e)/(1+e)$.]

7. How is the average distance between a planet and the Sun related to the planet's orbit period?

8. Which planet has a shorter period—one with a large average distance, or one with a small average distance?

9. What is the semi-major axis of an asteroid orbiting the Sun with a period of 64 years? (Kepler's third law works for *any* object orbiting the Sun.)

4.6 Logic of Discovery? Beliefs and Objectivity

Often a mathematical idea or model is discovered with no apparent application to the physical world until many years later. This aspect of pure, basic scientific research is not popular among government officials who want practical applications NOW! How are scientific discoveries made? There are several views about how we make discoveries and why humans are able to do this.

Kepler believed that there is a *creationary resonance* between the human mind and the laws of nature. In this view God creates humans with the gift of reading the mathematical harmonies of God's mind. It is only a matter of time for someone to discover God's plan. A more modern view held by some says that there is an *evolutionary resonance* between the human mind and the laws of nature. Given the infinite variety of paths of evolution, it is inevitable that creatures will eventually evolve capable of reading the laws of nature. In this view, scientific progress is inevitable.

creationary resonance

evolutionary resonance

Is creativity actually a logical process in disguise? It is a common belief today that one's religious/philosophical beliefs are merely along for the inevitable revolutionary ride and are not necessary to make revolutionary scientific advances. Some believe that there are many technically-capable paths by which the universe can be modeled. Kepler's neoplatonism was not logically necessary for the discovery of the planetary laws of motion, but, historically, it may have been absolutely necessary for his time and place.

Every age has its paradigms. Though scientists try to be objective, philosophical considerations do intrude on the scientific, creative process. That is not a bad thing because these beliefs are crucial in providing direction to their inquiries and fuel for the creativity mill. Scientists have faith that there is some order in the universe and this faith keeps them striving to solve the cosmic problems.

Facts have little meaning without ideas to interpret them. Because science is a human discipline, there is no machine-like objectivity. Often crucial facts supporting an idea come after a commitment is made to the idea. So is science then all based on an individual's whim; relative to the scientist's time and place? The self-corrective enterprise of science is messier than most science textbooks would have you believe. Besides the inevitable cultural prejudices, scientists have, in principle, an infinite number of conceivable ideas to choose from. How do you separate reasonable ideas from the infinite number of merely conceivable ideas?

Sure, there are cultural biases, but science does make us confront the real world—reality kicks back. You can ignore the discrepancies between nature's truth (observations) and your theories of what should happen only for so long. Experiments are the sole judge of scientific truth—nature eventually wins. The ideas are crucial to understanding the world but they eventually yield to the facts. Science makes us confront the world.

4.7   References

For further reading, here are some of my references that cover the development of science using historical records. They also cover science's philosophical underpinnings using the tools of philosophy.

1. Owen Barfield *Saving the Appearances* pp. 46–54.

2. Paul K. Feyerabend "Galileo and the Tyranny of Truth" in *The Galileo Affair: A Meeting of Faith and Science* ed. Coyne, Heller, Zycinski (Vatican City: 1985), pp. 155–166 and other papers from that symposium held at the Vatican.

3. Thomas S. Kuhn *The Copernican Revolution: Planetary Astronomy in the Development of Western Thought* (Cambridge, Mass: Harvard Univ. Press, 1957).

4. Ronald Pine *Science and the Human Prospect* (Wadsworth Publ. Co: Belmont, CA, 1989) esp. ch. 5: pp. 130–162.

5. A prelude to Copernicus is Owen Gingerich's *Scientific American* article "Astronomy in the Age of Columbus", Nov. 1992, pp. 100–105.

6. Lawrence M. Principe *Science and Religion*, video lectures available from the Teaching Company's "The Great Courses" (recorded 2006). See https://www.thegreatcourses.com/courses/science-and-religion.html .

7. Steven L Goldman *Science Wars: What Scientists Know and How They Know It*, video lectures available from the Teaching Company's "The Great Courses" (recorded 2006). See https://www.thegreatcourses.com/courses/science-wars-what-scientists-know-and-how-they-know-it.html .

Chapter 5

Newton's Law of Gravity

Isaac Newton (lived 1641–1727)
Image courtesy of Andrew McNab

This chapter covers the revolutionary advancements due to probably the most brilliant scientist who ever lived: *Isaac Newton* (lived 1641–1727). His greatest contributions were in all branches of physics. Kepler's discoveries about elliptical orbits and the planets' non-uniform speeds made it impossible to maintain the idea of planetary motion as a natural one requiring no explanation. Newton had to answer some basic questions: What keeps the planets in their elliptical orbits? On our spinning Earth what prevents objects from flying away when they are thrown in the air? What keeps you from being hurled off the spinning Earth? Newton's answer was that a fundamental force called "gravity" operating between all objects made them move the way they do.

Newton developed some basic rules governing the motion of all objects. He used these laws and Kepler's laws to derive his unifying Law of Gravity. I will first discuss his three laws of motion and then discuss gravity. Finally, several applications in astronomy will be given. This chapter uses several math concepts that are reviewed in appendix B. If your math skills are rusty, study appendix B and don't hesitate to ask your astronomy instructor for help. The vocabulary terms are in boldface.

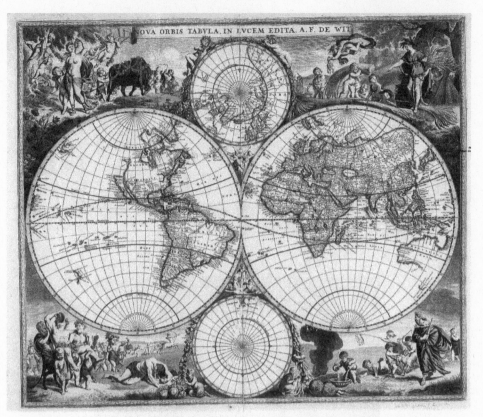

Nova orbis tabula by De Wit in 1688. The world at the time of Isaac Newton.
Image courtesy of The Hargrett Rare Book and Manuscript Library
University of Georgia Libraries

5.1   Newton's Laws of Motion

In order to accurately describe how things move, you need to be careful in how you describe the motion and the terms you use. Scientists are usually very careful about the words they use to explain something because they want to accurately represent nature. Language can often be imprecise and as you know, statements can often be misinterpreted. Because the goal of science is to find the single true nature of the universe, scientists try to carefully choose their words to accurately represent what they see. That is why scientific papers can look so "technical" (and even, introductory astronomy textbooks!)

When you think of motion, you may first think of something moving at a uniform *speed*. The *speed* = (the distance travelled)/(the time it takes). Because the distance is in the top of the fraction, there is a direct relation between the speed and the distance: the greater the distance travelled in a given time, the greater is the speed. However, there is an inverse relation between time and speed (time is in the bottom of the fraction): the *smaller* the time it takes to cover a given distance, the *greater* the speed must be.

To more completely describe all kinds of changes in motion, you also need to consider the *direction* along with the speed. For example, a ball thrown upward at the same speed as a ball thrown downward has a different motion. This inclusion of direction will be particularly important when you look at an object orbiting a planet or star. They may be moving at a uniform speed while their direction is constantly changing. The generalization of *speed* to include *direction* is called **velocity.** The term **velocity** includes both the numerical value of the speed and the direction something is moving.

velocity

Rene Descartes (lived 1596–1650 CE)
Image courtesy of Albert Van Helden
Rice University

Galileo conducted several experiments to understand how something's velocity can be changed. He found that an object's velocity can be changed only if a force acts on the object. The philosopher *René Descartes* used the idea of a greater God and an infinite universe with no special or privileged place to articulate the concept of **inertia:** *a body at rest remains at rest, and one moving in a straight line maintains a constant speed and same direction unless it is deflected by a "force".* Newton took this as the beginning of his description of how things move, so this is now known as **Newton's 1st law of motion.** A **force** causes a *change* in something's velocity (an **acceleration**).

Newton's 1st law: inertia
Descartes

force *changes velocity*

An **acceleration** is a change in the speed and/or direction of motion in a given amount of time: **acceleration**= (the velocity change)/(the time interval of the change). Something at rest is not accelerating and something moving at constant speed in a straight line is not accelerating. In common usage, acceleration usually means just a change in speed, but a satellite orbiting a planet is constantly being accelerated even if its *speed* is constant because its direction is constantly being deflected. The satellite must be experiencing a force since it is accelerating. That force turns out to be gravity. If the force (gravity) were to suddenly disappear, the satellite would move off in a straight line along a path tangent to the original circular orbit.

acceleration: *change in speed and/or direction*

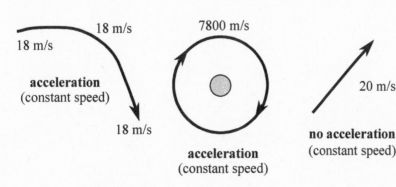

A rock in your hand is moving horizontally as it spins around the center of the Earth, just like you and the rest of the things on the surface are. If you throw the rock straight up, there is no change in its *horizontal* motion because of its inertia. You changed the rock's *vertical* motion because you applied a vertical force on it. The rock falls straight down because the Earth's gravity acts on only the rock's *vertical* motion. If the rock is thrown straight up, it does not fall behind you as the Earth rotates. Inertia and gravity also explain why you do not feel a strong wind as the Earth spins—as a whole, the atmosphere is spinning with the Earth.

Newton's first law of motion is a *qualitative* one—it tells you when something will accelerate. Newton went on to *quantify* the amount of the change that would be observed from the application of a given force. In **Newton's second law of motion,** he said that the force applied = mass of an object × acceleration. **Mass** is the amount of material an object has and is a way of measuring how much inertia the object has. For a given amount of force, more massive objects will have a smaller acceleration than less massive objects (a push needed to even budge a car would send a pillow flying!). For a given amount of acceleration, the more massive object requires a larger force than a less massive object.

Newton's 2nd law: *force = **mass** × acceleration*

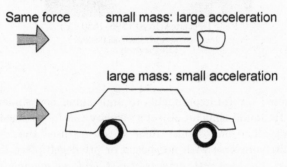

Force = mass × acceleration

Newton also found that for every action force ON an object, there is an equal but opposite force BY the object (**Newton's third law of motion**). For example, if Andre the Giant is stuck on the ice with Tom Thumb and he pushes Tom Thumb to the right, Andre will feel an equal force from Tom pushing him to the left. Tom will slide to the right with great speed and Andre will slide to the left with smaller speed since Andre's mass is larger than Tom's.

Newton's 3rd law: *action = −reaction*

Another example: an apple falls to the Earth because it is pulled by the force of the Earth's gravity on the apple and the acceleration of the apple is large. The apple also exerts a gravitational force on the Earth of the *same amount*. However, the *acceleration* the Earth experiences is vastly smaller than the apple's acceleration since the Earth's mass is vastly larger than the apple's—you will ordinarily refer to the apple falling to the Earth, rather than the Earth moving toward the apple or that they are falling toward each other.

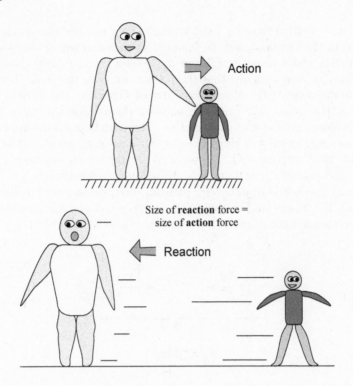

Size of **reaction** force =
size of **action** force

Vocabulary

acceleration	force	inertia
mass	Newton's 1st law	Newton's 2nd law
Newton's 3rd law	velocity	

Formulae

Newton's 2nd law: Force = mass × acceleration: $F = m \times a$.

Review Questions

1. What 2 things can change for an acceleration?

2. If you give a bowling ball a push FAR away from any gravitational effects, what will it do? If you throw a feather (again far out in space) at the same speed as the bowling ball, how will its speed compare to the bowling ball after 5 minutes?

3. Let's say you're twirling a ball on a string and the string breaks. What path does the ball take and why is that?

4. How do you know gravity acts on an orbiting satellite?

5. How does a force exerted on an object relate to the object's mass or acceleration? Given the same force will a boulder accelerate more than a regular marble? Why?

6. Why would you need to apply more force to a bowling ball than a feather (far out in space) so that they would be traveling at the same speed after 10 minutes?

5.2 Universal Law of Gravity

Using Kepler's third law and his own second law, Newton found that the *amount* of the attractive force, called gravity, between a planet and Sun a distance d apart is Force = k_p × (planet mass) / $(d)^2$, where k_p is a number that is the same for all the planets. In the same way he found that the **amount** of the gravity force between the Sun and a planet is Force = k_s × (Sun mass) / $(d)^2$. Using his third law of motion, Newton reasoned that these forces must be the same (but acting in the opposite directions). He derived his **Law of Gravity**: the force of gravity = G× (mass #1) × (mass #2)/(distance between them)^2 and this force is directed toward each object, so it is always attractive. The term G is a universal constant of nature. If you use the units of kilograms (kg) for mass and meters (m) for distance, $G = 6.673 \times 10^{-11} \mathrm{m}^3/(\mathrm{kg\,sec}^2)$. If you need a refresher on exponents, square & cube roots, and scientific notation, then please study appendix B.

Spherically symmetric objects (eg., planets, stars, moons, etc.) behave as if all of their mass is concentrated at their centers. So when you use Newton's Law of Gravity, you measure the distance between the *centers* of the objects.

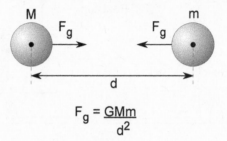

$$F_g = \frac{GMm}{d^2}$$

In a bold, revolutionary step, Newton stated that his gravity law worked for *any* two objects with mass—it applies for any motions on the Earth, as well as, any motions in space. He unified celestial and terrestrial physics and completed the process started by Copernicus of removing the Earth from a unique position or situation in the universe. His law of gravity also explained Kepler's 1st and 2nd laws.

5.2.1   Characteristics of Gravity

Newton's Law of Gravity says a lot about this force in a very compact, elegant way. It says that *any* piece of matter will feel it whether it is charged or not (this sets it apart from electrical and magnetic forces that affect only charged objects). Gravity depends only on the masses of the two attracting objects and their distance from each other. It does not depend on their chemical composition or density. A glob of peanut butter the mass of the Sun will have the same gravitational effect on the Earth as the Sun does. Gravity is always attractive, never repulsive (this is another way it is different from electrical and magnetic forces).

Because the masses are in the top of the fraction, more mass creates more gravity force. This also means that more massive objects produce greater accelerations than less massive objects. Since distance is in the bottom of the fraction, gravity has an *inverse* relation with distance: as distance *increases*, gravity *decreases*. However, gravity never goes to zero—it has an infinite range (in this respect it is like the electrical and magnetic forces). Stars feel the gravity from other stars, galaxies feel gravity from other galaxies, galaxy clusters feel gravity from other galaxies, etc. The always attractive gravity can act over the largest distances in the universe.

There is no way to get rid of the *force* of gravity. If you want to prevent a body from producing a gravitational *acceleration* on an object, you need to use a second body, with the same amount of gravity pull as the first body, in a way that its gravity pulling on the object is in the opposite direction. The resulting *accelerations* due to the forces from the two bodies will cancel each other out.

Newton's Law of Gravity

math review: appendix B

center-to-center distance

always attractive

more mass, more gravity

greater distance, less gravity

infinite range

Review Questions

1. What basic fundamental assumption did Newton make about the laws of nature on the Earth and in space?

2. Why is gravity often the most important force in astronomical interactions?

3. What things does gravity depend on?

4. How does gravity vary with distance between objects and with respect to what do you measure the distances?

5. What would happen to the orbit of Io (one of Jupiter's moons) if all of the hydrogen and helium in Jupiter were converted to silicon and oxygen? Explain your answer.

6. What would happen to the Earth's orbit if the Sun suddenly turned into a black hole (of the same mass)? Why?

7. How would *anti*matter respond to gravity? (Hint: antimatter has mass just like ordinary matter.)

8. What important laws of planet motion can be derived from Newton's law of gravity?

9. Use Newton's laws of motion and gravity to answer the two questions given in the figure below.

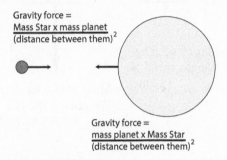

Gravity force =
$$\frac{\text{Mass Star} \times \text{mass planet}}{(\text{distance between them})^2}$$

Gravity force =
$$\frac{\text{mass planet} \times \text{Mass Star}}{(\text{distance between them})^2}$$

1. Which has greater force?
2. Which has greater acceleration?

5.3   Mass vs. Weight

Though the terms **weight** and **mass** are used interchangeably in common language, in science there is a distinct difference between the two terms. The **weight** of an object = force of gravity felt by that object but the **mass** of an object is the amount of matter the object has. Mass is a measure of the object's resistance to acceleration: a push on a skateboard will make it roll away quickly but the same push on a more massive car will barely budge it.

    An object's weight depends on the pull of the gravitating object but the object's mass is independent of the gravity. For example, Joe Average weighs himself on the Earth's surface and then on the Moon's surface. His *weight* on the Moon will be about six times less than on the Earth but the number of atoms in his body has not changed so his *mass* is the same at the two places. In the old English unit system, there is a "pound" of force and "pound" of mass. On only the Earth's surface, an object's pound of mass = the number of pounds of force felt by the object due to the Earth's gravity.

    In the metric system there is no confusion of terms. A **kilogram** is a quantity of *mass* and a **newton** is a quantity of *force*. One kilogram (kg) = 2.205 pounds

weight: *force*
mass: *inertia*

mass stays the same

kilogram
newton

of mass and 4.45 newtons (N) = 1 pound of force. If someone uses "pounds", be sure you understand if s/he means force or mass!

How do you do that?

To find something's weight in newtons, you multiply the mass in kilograms by the acceleration of gravity in the units of meters/seconds^2. For example: Joe Average has a mass of 63.5 kg and he feels a force of gravity on the Earth = 63.5 kg $\times$ 9.8 m/s^2 = 623 kg m/s^2 = 623 N. His weight is 623 N. The other value in the preceding equation, 9.8 m/s^2, is the acceleration due to gravity close to the Earth's surface. Joe Average's weight at other places in the universe will be different but his mass will remain the same.

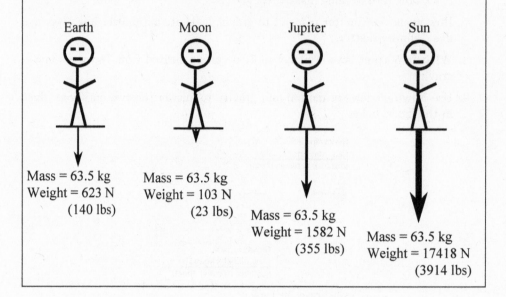

Earth

Mass = 63.5 kg
Weight = 623 N
(140 lbs)

Moon

Mass = 63.5 kg
Weight = 103 N
(23 lbs)

Jupiter

Mass = 63.5 kg
Weight = 1582 N
(355 lbs)

Sun

Mass = 63.5 kg
Weight = 17418 N
(3914 lbs)

Vocabulary

kilogram   mass   newton
weight

Review Questions

1. What is the difference between *mass* and *weight*?

2. When the astronauts landed on the Moon, how were they able to stay on the ground?

3. On the Moon, the astronauts weighed about six times less than they did on the Earth. Compare the amount of gravity on the Moon's surface with that on the Earth's surface. If objects fall with an acceleration of about 10 meters/second^2 on the Earth, how much would the acceleration be on the Moon's surface? Explain your answer.

4. If Joe Astronaut has a mass of 40 kilograms on the Earth, how much mass would he have on an asteroid with 10 times less surface gravity than the Earth's surface gravity? Explain your answer.

5.4 Inverse Square Law

Newton's *law of gravity* describes a force that decreases with the SQUARE of the distance. For every factor of 2 the distance increases, the gravitational attraction *decreases* by a factor of $2 \times 2 = 4$; for every factor of 3 increase in distance, the gravity decreases by a factor of $3 \times 3 = 9$ (not by $3 + 3 = 6$!); for every factor of 4 increase in distance, the gravity decreases by a factor of $4 \times 4 = 16$ (not by $4 + 4 = 8$!), etc. See appendix B for a review of "factor" and "times". Some more examples are given in table 5.1. Notice how quickly an inverse square force gets very small.

math review: appendix B

distance	inverse	inverse square
1	$1/1 = 1$	$1/1^2 = 1$
2	$1/2 = 0.5$	$1/2^2 = 1/4 = 0.25$
3	$1/3 = 0.33$	$1/3^2 = 1/9 = 0.11$
4	$1/4 = 0.25$	$1/4^2 = 1/16 = 0.0625$
7	$1/7 = 0.14$	$1/7^2 = 1/49 = 0.02$
10	$1/10 = 0.1$	$1/10^2 = 1/100 = 0.01$
100	$1/100 = 0.01$	$1/100^2 = 1/10,000 = 0.0001$

Table 5.1: A comparison of inverse and inverse square relations

Example: Joe Average has a mass of 63.5 kilograms, so he weighs 623 newtons (=140 pounds) on the Earth's surface. If he moves up 1 Earth radius (= 6378 kilometers) above the surface, he will be two times farther away from the Earth's center (remember that distances are measured from *center-to-center!*), so his weight will be *four* times less, or $623/4$ newtons $= 155.8$ newtons ($= 140/4$ pounds); NOT two times less, or $623/2$ newtons $= 311.5$ newtons. If he moves up another Earth radius above the surface, he will be three times farther away than he was at the start, so his weight will drop by a factor of *nine* times, NOT 3 times. His weight will be $623/9$ newtons $= 69.22$ newtons ($= 140/9$ pounds); NOT $623/3$ newtons $= 207.7$ newtons. His mass will still be 63.5 kilograms (see the figure below).

Let us generalize this for any situation *where the masses do not change:* the force of gravity at distance A = (the force of gravity at distance B) $\times$ (distance B / distance A)^2. Notice which distance is in the top of the fraction! To use this relation, have the gravity at distance A represent the unknown gravity force you are trying to find and the gravity at distance B represent the reference gravity force felt at the reference distance B.

inverse square law

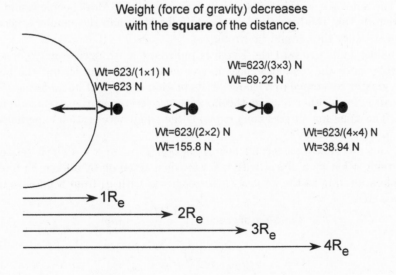

Weight (force of gravity) decreases
with the **square** of the distance.

Wt=623/(1×1) N
Wt=623 N

Wt=623/(3×3) N
Wt=69.22 N

Wt=623/(2×2) N
Wt=155.8 N

Wt=623/(4×4) N
Wt=38.94 N

1R$_e$

2R$_e$

3R$_e$

4R$_e$

How do you do that?

Let's find where the weight values in the inverse square law figure came from.
For Mr. Average's case the reference weight is his weight on the surface of the Earth
= 623 N. His weight at 6378 kilometers above the surface is

gravity at A = 623 × [6378 / (2 × 6378)]^2 = 623 × 1/2^2 = 623 × 1/4 = 155.8 N.
When he is at two Earth radii above the surface, the

gravity at A = 623 × (6378/(3 × 6378))^2 = 623 × 1/3^2 = 623 × 1/9 = 69.22 N.

Formulae

Inverse Square Law: Gravity at A = gravity at B × (distance B / distance A)^2.

Review Questions

1. Why is gravity called an "inverse square force"?

2. What is the difference between a simple inverse relation and an inverse square relation?

3. If the Earth was 3 A.U. from the Sun (instead of 1 A.U.), would the gravity force between the Earth and the Sun be less or more than it is now? By how many times?

4. If Mercury was 0.2 A.U. from the Sun (instead of 0.4 A.U.), would the gravity force between Mercury and the Sun be less or more than it is now? By how many times?

5.5 Gravitational Acceleration

Galileo found that the acceleration due to gravity (called "g") depends only on the mass of the gravitating object and the distance from it. It does not depend on the mass of the object being pulled. In the absence of air drag, a huge boulder will fall at the same rate as a small marble dropped from the same height as the boulder. A tiny satellite at the same distance from the Sun as Jupiter's orbit from the Sun feels the same acceleration from the Sun as the large planet Jupiter does from the Sun. (The satellite and Jupiter will also, therefore, have the *same* orbital period around the Sun—see section 5.7.3.) How is this possible? Most people would agree with Aristotle that the bigger object should fall faster than the smaller object, but experiments show they would be wrong.

things fall with same acceleration

equal distance means equal orbit period

A boulder falling toward the Earth is pulled by a stronger gravity *force* than the marble, since the boulder's mass is greater than the marble, but the boulder also has greater resistance to a change in its motion because of its larger mass. The effects cancel each other out, so the boulder *accelerates* at the *same rate* as the marble. The same line of reasoning explains the equal acceleration experienced by Jupiter and the satellite.

You can use Newton's second law of motion $F = m \times a$ (which relates the acceleration, a, felt by a object with mass m when acted on by a force F) to derive the acceleration due to the gravity (here replace a with g) from a massive object with mass M:

$$\text{The force of gravity} = \frac{GMm}{d^2} = mg$$

so

$$g = \frac{GM}{d^2}.$$

The gravitational acceleration g depends on only the mass of massive object M and the distance d from it. Notice that the mass of the falling object m has been cancelled out. This is why astronauts orbiting the Earth feel "weightless". In orbit they are continually "falling" toward the Earth because of gravity (the Earth's surface curves away from them at the same rate they are moving forward). If Jane Astronaut drops a pen in the space shuttle, it accelerates toward the Earth, but she accelerates by the same amount so the pen remains at the same position *relative to her*. In fact the entire shuttle and its contents are accelerating toward the Earth at the same rate, so Jane and her companions "float" around inside! This is because all of them are at very nearly the same distance from the Earth.

weightlessness explained

zero <u>relative</u> motion

Earth's frame of reference

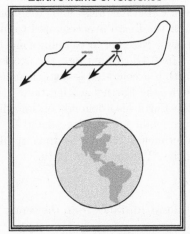

shuttle's frame of reference

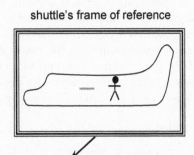

In orbit all objects at the same distance from the Earth accelerate at the same rate and in the same direction. In their own frame of reference, they feel no motion or "weightless", even though gravity is still present.

The acceleration decreases with the SQUARE of the distance (inverse square law). To compare gravity accelerations due to the same object at different distances, you use the gravity acceleration g at distance A = (the gravity acceleration g at distance B) × (distance B / distance A)^2. Notice which distance is in the top of the fraction. An example of using the inverse square law is given in the "How do you do that?" box below.

inverse square law

How do you do that?

Find how many times more gravitational acceleration the Galileo atmosphere probe felt at 100,000 miles from Jupiter's center than the orbiter felt at 300,000 miles. You have

probe's g = orbiter's g × (300,000/100,000)^2 = orbiter's g × (3/1)^2

$\quad\quad$ = orbiter's g × 9.

The probe accelerated by an amount nine times greater than the orbiter.

5.5.1 Measuring the Mass of the Earth

Measuring the acceleration of an object dropped to the ground enables you to find the mass of the Earth. You can rearrange the gravity acceleration relation *check that units match*

math review: appendix B

to solve for the mass M to find $M = gd^2/G$. Close to the Earth's surface at a distance of 6.4×10^6 meters from the center, $g = 9.8$ meters/second^2. The distance is given in meters to match the units of the gravity acceleration—when you do a calculation, you must be sure you check that your units match up or you will get nonsense answers. The big G is the universal gravitational constant, approximately $6.7 \times 10^{-11} \text{m}^3/(\text{kg sec}^2)$. Plugging in the values, you will find the Earth's mass = $9.8 \times (6.4 \times 10^6)^2/(6.7 \times 10^{-11})$ kilograms = 6.0×10^{24} kilograms. If you are unsure of how to work with scientific notation, read the scientific notation section B.6 (pay close attention to the part describing how to enter scientific notation on your calculator!).

You can determine masses of stars and planets in a similar way: by measuring the acceleration of objects orbiting them and the distance between the star or planet and the object. A small object falling to the Earth has mass and, therefore, has a gravitational acceleration associated with it: the Earth is accelerated toward the falling object (an example of Newton's third law)! However, if you plug some typical masses of terrestrial objects (less than, say, 1000 kilograms) into the acceleration formula, you will see that the amount the Earth is accelerated is vastly smaller than the falling object's acceleration. You can ignore the Earth's acceleration.

A side note: determining the mass of the Earth also depends on knowing the value of the gravitational constant G. The constant was first measured by Henry Cavendish in 1798. After discussing his experimental results, he then applied his measurement to the subject of his paper's title: "Weighing the Earth."

Formulae

1. Gravitational acceleration: $g = (\text{G} \times \text{Mass})/(\text{distance from the center})^2$.

2. Comparing gravitational accelerations: acceleration at position A = acceleration at position B $\times$ (distance B/ distance A)^2.

3. Calculating mass: Mass = $(g \times \text{distance}^2)/G$.

Review Questions

1. What did Galileo discover about how objects of different masses fall to the Earth?

2. If you dropped a hammer and feather from the same height above the Earth's surface, which would actually hit the ground first? Why would it be different than what Galileo said about falling objects? Explain why if you let the feather fall quill end first, the result is closer to what Galileo said.

3. If you dropped a hammer and feather from the same height above the airless Moon's surface, which would actually hit the ground first? Explain why your answer is different than for the previous question.

4. How many times less/more gravity acceleration due to the Sun does the Ulysses spacecraft feel at 2.3 A.U. above the Sun than the *solar* gravity acceleration it felt at Jupiter (5.2 A.U. from the Sun)? Is it accelerated more or less at 2.3 A.U. than when it was at 5.2 A.U.?

5. Why do astronauts in orbit around the Earth feel "weightless" even though the Earth's gravity is still very much present?

6. Put the following in order of their acceleration around the Earth: a 200-ton space station 6580 kilometers from the center, a 60-kilogram astronaut 6580 kilometers from the center, a 1-ton satellite 418,000 kilometers from the center, and the 7.4×10^{19}-ton Moon 384,000 kilometers from the center. Explain your answer.

7. How can you find the mass of the Earth using ordinary objects in your house?

5.6 A Closer Look at Newton's Gravity

Newton found that his gravity law is obeyed everywhere in the universe and could explain Kepler's three laws of orbital motion. Newton's development of the unifying law of gravity was also the culmination of a process of Occam's Razor in action. From Ptolemy to Newton, the theories of how the planets move got simpler and more powerful as time went on. Ptolemy's model had become extremely complicated by the time of the Renaissance and Copernicus reduced the number of circular motions to around 50 so it was simpler to use. Kepler vastly simplified the theory of planet motion by reducing the number of essential parts to just three laws. Newton unifed all of those laws to the ONE unifying law of gravity. This law was so simple and elegant that it could also explain motions on the Earth.

Occam's Razor and the laws of motion

But what is gravity? Newton understood how the gravity force affected the motion of objects but not why gravity worked the way it did. Recognizing the limits of his knowledge, he adopted an instrumentalist view: the scientist's job is to capture observations in precise mathematical equations; explain the "how" not the "why". Only things verified by our experience of the world are admissible into science. Though the "why" question is intriguing and a few scientists will spend years trying to answer it, most scientists share Newton's instrumentalist view.

With Newton, there was no longer a hierarchical-teleological universe (one designed by God for some purpose with man playing a crucial role in the plan). The universe was now a perfect machine, based on mathematics, set in motion by God long ago. God is the reference point for absolute space and time. Newtonian mechanics requires an absolute coordinate system to keep things sensible (according to Newton this also gave God something to do).

With the success of Newton's ideas, a major change occurred in how people viewed the world around them. Reality was completely reduced to material objects. Ideas, thought, feelings, and values were secondary. *What is real does NOT depend on us*—this is probably the actual completion of the Copernican revolution and was soon so widely accepted that it became "common sense" (how about that for a paradigm shift!). Newtonism seemed to undercut the role of God and religion and the validity of science: science became just a subjective perspective of the machine universe.

Copernican principle

Decades before Newton, Descartes saw the need to rescue thoughts, ideas and values. Descartes developed a mind-body dualism: a world of thought and spirit exists independent of, but parallel to, the material world. There is a correspondence between the God-inaugurated, mathematical thoughts of scientists and the motions in the physical world. Descartes said that mathematical ideas work so well because there is a pre-established parallelism between the physical world and our mind.

Newton's machine universe with God establishing the reference system of absolute space and time gave Newton and those that followed the conviction that we could eventually understand the universe. In fact, some (such as as Spinoza) saw our attempt to understand that universe through the tools of science and mathematics as a way of studying God. Whether or not a scientist sees science as a religious endeavor, the emphasis is on an external material world that is independent of us. There is an objective reality and our thoughts and values do not affect this reality.

Review Questions

1. What important discoveries and ideas did Newton make?

2. How does Occam's Razor relate to the progress of planet motion theory from Ptolemy to Newton?

3. How can Newton's work be considered the completion of the process started by Copernicus almost 120 years earlier?

5.7   Orbits

Now I will apply Newton's laws of motion and gravity to topics more astronomical: objects moving around other objects. What kinds of things can you find out about celestial objects from just observing their motions?

5.7.1   Centripetal Force

Newton's first law of motion says that an object's inertia will keep it from changing its speed and/or direction unless some force acts on it. This means that satellites orbiting the Earth must be feeling some force that constantly deflects them toward the center of the Earth. If there was no force, they would travel in a straight line at a constant speed.

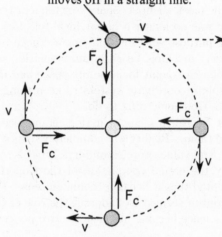

$$F_c = m\,v^2\,/\,r$$

Just enough centripetal force F_c to balance the speed; just enough speed to balance the centripetal force.

centripetal force

If you whirl a ball attached to string around your head, it moves in a circular path around you because the string is always pulling the ball directly toward the hand grabbing the string. The ball wants to move in a straight line and the string is pulling it directly inward. The resulting deflection is a compromise: a circular path. The string is applying a **centripetal force** to the ball: an inward force. If you let go of the string, there is no centripetal force and the ball will fly off in a *straight line* because of its inertia. If you do not whirl the ball fast enough it will move inward to a smaller non-circular path around you. If you whirl the ball too fast, you may not be able to give it enough centripetal force to keep it in a circular path around you. The amount of centripetal force needed to balance an object's inertia and keep it in a circular path of radius r is found from Newton's second law: the centripetal force $= mv^2/r$, where v and m are the object's speed and mass, respectively. The radius of the orbit r is the same as the distance between the moving object and the central body.

5.7.2 Measuring Planet and Star Masses

Now for orbits! Satellites are not being deflected by strings but by gravity. Gravity provides the centripetal force needed to keep the satellites in orbit. If you focus on the simple case of circular orbits, you can use the centripetal force formula above with the law of gravity to determine the mass of a planet or star. Simply set the force of gravity equal to the centripetal force and solve for the mass of the planet or star, M.

$$\frac{GMm}{r^2} = \frac{mv^2}{r}.$$

The satellite mass m cancels out from both sides and if you put M on one side and the rest on the other side of the equation, you get

$$M = \frac{r^2}{G} \times \frac{v^2}{r}$$
$$M = \frac{v^2 r}{G}.$$

This assumes that the satellite's mass, m, is much less than the central object's mass, so you can ignore the acceleration of the central object toward the satellite!

How do you do that?

Let's use the mass relation to get an estimate of the mass of the Sun. You need to use something orbiting with a known radius and speed. The Earth's orbit is roughly circular with radius of 1.5×10^{11} meters and the Earth moves with a speed of 30,000 meters/second (= 30 km/s) in its orbit. The distance is given in meters to match the units of the speed. The distance unit of a meter is used because you will be using the gravitational constant G in your calculation and it uses the meter unit. When you do a calculation, you must be sure you check that your units match up or you will get nonsense answers.

Plug the values into the mass relation:

the Sun's mass = $(30{,}000)^2 \times (1.5 \times 10^{11}) / (6.7 \times 10^{-11}) = 2 \times 10^{30}$ kilograms. This is much larger than the Earth's mass so it was okay to ignore the Sun's movement toward the Earth. Using no approximations (ie., not assuming a circular orbit and including the Sun's motion toward the Earth) gives a value for the Sun's mass that is very close to this. Your answer does not depend on which planet you choose to use (here you used the Earth's orbit). You would get the same value for the mass of the Sun if you had used any of the other planets orbital speeds and sizes.

This relation tells you what you need to know in order to measure a planet's or star's mass: the orbital speed of a satellite and the distance it is from the center of the planet or star. Because the velocity is on top of the fraction, satellites are made to move faster if the mass of the central object is greater. At the same distance, a massive planet will exert more gravity force than a low-mass planet, so the massive planet will produce greater inward accelerations on satellites orbiting it. The satellites will, therefore, orbit at faster speeds.

what you need to measure the mass

Sometimes the orbital period P is measured instead of the orbital velocity. The orbital period is the time it takes the object to travel the circumference of its orbit (for a circle, the circumference = $2\pi r$, where π is approximately 3.1416). Recall that speed = (distance travelled)/time, so the speed v = the circumference of the orbit/orbital period. When you substitute this for the speed in the mass relation above, you get

$$M = \frac{4\pi^2}{G} \times \frac{r^3}{P^2}.$$

Newton's form of Kepler's 3rd law

This may look familiar to you—it is Kepler's third law! There is a distance cubed, an orbital period squared, and some other constant factors. Newton found that when Kepler used the motions of the planets to formulate his third law, Kepler was actually measuring the mass of the Sun. If you use the convenient set of units of an astronomical unit for the distance, a year for the time, and a "solar mass" (mass relative to the Sun) for the mass, the complicated term $4\pi^2/G$ becomes the simple value of 1. For the planets orbiting the Sun, the mass relation becomes $1 = r^3/P^2$, or $r^3 = P^2$, just what Kepler found.

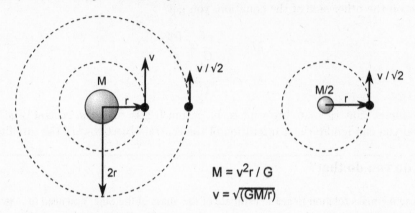

$$M = v^2 r\,/\,G$$
$$v = \sqrt{(GM/r)}$$

5.7.3 Orbital Speed

The mass formula above tells you that satellites orbiting massive planets must move faster than satellites orbiting low-mass planets at the same distance. Massive planets have stronger gravity than low-mass planets so a satellite orbiting a massive planet is accelerated by a greater amount than one going around a lesser mass planet at the same distance. To balance the stronger inward gravitational pull of the massive planet, the satellite must move faster in its orbit than if it was orbiting a lesser mass planet. Of course, this also applies to planets orbiting stars, stars orbiting other stars, etc.

If you solve for the orbit speed, v, in the mass formula, you can find how fast something needs to move to balance the inward pull of gravity:

$$v^2 = \frac{GM}{r}.$$

Taking the square root of both sides (you want just v not v^2), you get

$$v = \sqrt{\frac{GM}{r}}.$$

why acceleration is SAME but force is different

Notice that the orbital speed v (and therefore, the orbital period P) does not depend on the mass of the satellite! The mass M in the formula above is the mass of the central object. If we consider the Sun-Jupiter-Trojan asteroid example in the "How do you do that?" box at the top of the next page (and recall the discussion in section 5.5), the Sun-Jupiter gravity force is MUCH greater than the Sun-Trojan asteroid gravity force but Jupiter has much greater inertia (resistance to change = mass). The greater gravity force between the Sun and Jupiter is compensated for by the greater inertia of Jupiter so the *acceleration* of Jupiter will be the same as the *acceleration* of the Trojan asteroid—Jupiter and the Trojan asteroid will have the same orbital velocity and same orbital period.

How do you do that?

Find the orbital speed of Jupiter around the Sun. Jupiter's distance from
the Sun is 5.2 A.U., or 7.8×10^{11} meters and the Sun's mass is 2×10^{30} kilograms.
The orbital speed of Jupiter around the Sun is $\sqrt{6.7 \times 10^{-11} \times (2 \times 10^{30})/(7.8 \times 10^{11})}$
$= \sqrt{1.718 \times 10^{8}} = 1.3 \times 10^{4}$ meters/second, or 13 kilometers/second. What do you
think you would find if you used one of the Trojan asteroids, millions of times
less massive than Jupiter, that orbits the Sun at 5.2 A.U.?

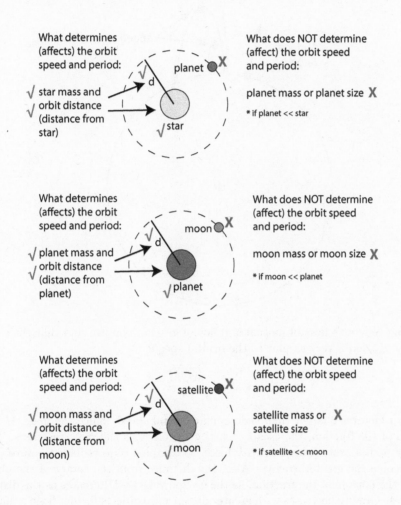

5.7.4 Escape Velocity

If an object moves fast enough it can escape a massive object's gravity and not
be drawn back toward the massive object. The critical speed needed to do this is
the **escape velocity.** More specifically, this is the *initial* speed something needs
to escape the object's gravity and assumes that there is no other force acting on
the object besides gravity after the initial boost. Rockets leaving the Earth do
not have the escape velocity at the beginning but the engines provide thrust for
an extended period of time, so the rockets can eventually escape. The concept of
escape velocity applies to anything gravitationally attracted to anything else (gas
particles in planet atmospheres, comets orbiting the Sun, light trying to escape from

escape velocity

black holes, galaxies orbiting each other, etc.).

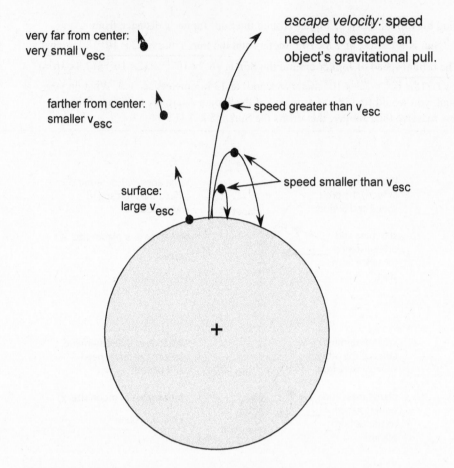

Using Newton's laws of motion and law of gravity, you can find that the escape velocity v_{esc} looks very similar to the orbital speed:

$$v_{esc} = \sqrt{\frac{2GM}{r}}.$$

This is a factor $\sqrt{2}$ larger than the circular orbital speed. Since the mass M is on the top of the fraction, the escape velocity increases as the mass increases. More massive bodies exert greater gravity force, so escaping objects have to move faster to overcome the greater gravity. Also, the distance from the center of the object, r, is in the bottom of the fraction, so the escape velocity DEcreases as the distance increases. Gravity decreases with greater distance, so objects farther from a massive body do not need to move as quickly to escape it than objects closer to it.

Vocabulary

centripetal force   escape velocity

Formulae

1. Mass of central object = [(orbital speed)^2× distance)/G.

2. Mass of central object (Kepler's 3rd law) = $(4\pi^2)/G\times$ [(distance)^3/(orbital period)^2].

3. *Orbital speed* = $\sqrt{G \times \text{Mass/distance}}$.

4. **Escape velocity** = $\sqrt{2G \times \text{Mass/distance}}$.

How do you do that?

Find the escape velocity from the surface of the Earth. Using the acceleration of gravity, you can find that the Earth has a mass of 6.0×10^{24} kilograms. The Earth's radius is 6.4×10^6 meters. Since the mass and distance from the center are in the standard units, you just need to plug their values into the escape velocity relation.

The Earth's surface escape velocity is $\sqrt{2 \times (6.7 \times 10^{-11}) \times (6 \times 10^{24})/(6.4 \times 10^6)} = \sqrt{1.256 \times 10^8} = 1.1 \times 10^4$ meters/second ($= 11$ km/s). Here are some other surface escape velocities: Moon $= 2.4$ km/s, Jupiter $= 59.6$ km/s, Sun $= 618$ km/s.

Review Questions

1. What keeps satellites orbiting the Earth moving along their curved paths?

2. What two things must be determined first in order to calculate the mass of a planet or a star?

3. Jupiter's moon Io has about the same mass as the Moon and orbits Jupiter at about the same distance that the Moon orbits the Earth (center to center). Then why does Io take only 1.8 days to orbit Jupiter but our Moon takes 27.3 days to orbit the Earth?

4. Astronomers were able to accurately measure the orbital periods of the moons of Jupiter since the time of Galileo, so why was an accurate value for Jupiter's mass not found for over 300 years until the astronomical unit was measured accurately?

5. Which would have a shorter orbital period, a planet orbiting a massive star at 3 A.U. or a planet orbiting a low-mass star at 3 A.U.? Explain your answer.

6. If a planet orbiting a massive star has the same orbital period as a planet orbiting a low-mass star, which of the planets orbits at a greater distance from its star? Explain your answer.

7. What two things does the *escape velocity* depend on?

8. Why does the planet Saturn with over 95 times the Earth's mass have a smaller *escape velocity* at its cloudtops than the Earth has at its cloudtops?

9. Why is Jupiter's *escape velocity* at its cloudtops over two times higher than the Earth's surface *escape velocity*, even though Jupiter has a much larger diameter than the Earth?

5.8   Kepler's Third Law

Kepler's third law of planetary motion says that the average distance of a planet from the Sun *cubed* is directly proportional to the orbital period *squared*. Newton found that his gravity force law could explain Kepler's laws. Since Newton's law of gravity applies to any object with mass, Kepler's laws can be used for any object orbiting another object. Let's look at satellites orbiting a planet.

If you have two satellites (#1 and #2) orbiting a planet, Kepler's third law says:

$$\left(\frac{\text{period } \#1}{\text{period } \#2} \right)^2 = \left(\frac{\text{distance } \#1}{\text{distance } \#2} \right)^3,$$

where the distance is the average distance of the satellite from the planet—the orbit's semimajor axis. The satellites must be orbiting the same body in order to use Kepler's third law! Kepler found this law worked for the planets because they all orbit the same star (the Sun).

If you have measured the orbital period of one satellite around a planet, you can then easily find how long it would take any other satellite to orbit the planet in any size oribt. Kepler's third law can be simplified down to

$$\text{period} \#1 \quad = \quad \text{period} \#2 \times \sqrt{\left(\frac{\text{distance} \#1}{\text{distance} \#2}\right)^3}$$

OR

$$\text{period} \#1 \quad = \quad \text{period} \#2 \times \left(\frac{\text{distance} \#1}{\text{distance} \#2}\right)^{3/2}.$$

Those of you with a scientific calculator (one that does powers, trig functions, scientific notation, etc.) will want to use the formula on the last line (remember that $3/2 = 1.5$). Those with a calculator that just has a square root button will want to use the formula on the second-to-last line.

If the satellite is orbiting the Sun, then the relation can be greatly simplified with an appropriate choice of units: the unit of *years* for the orbit period and the distance unit of *astronomical units*. In this case, the reference "satellite" is the Earth and Kepler's third law becomes period = distance$^{3/2}$. Let's use this to find out how long it takes to explore the solar system.

5.8.1   Interplanetary Trips

The simplest way to travel between the planets is to let the Sun's gravity do the work and take advantage of Kepler's laws of orbital motion. A fuel efficient way to travel is to put the spacecraft in orbit around the Sun with the Earth at one end of the orbit at launch and the other planet at the opposite end at arrival. These orbits are called "Hohmann orbits" after Walter Hohmann who developed the theory for transfer orbits. The spacecraft requires only an acceleration at the beginning of the trip and a deceleration at the end of the trip to put it in orbit around the other planet.

Let's go to Mars! The relative positions of Earth and Mars must be just right at launch so that Mars will be at the right position to greet the spacecraft when it arrives several months later. These good positionings happen once every 780 days (the synodic period of Mars). The spacecraft must be launched within a time interval called the "launch window" that is just few of weeks long to use a Hohmann orbit for the spacecraft's path. The Earth is at the **perihelion** (point closest to the Sun) of the spacecraft orbit (here, 1.0 A.U.) and Mars is at the **aphelion** (point farthest from the Sun—here, 1.52 A.U.).

perihelion
aphelion

Kepler's third law relates the semi-major axis of the orbit to its sidereal period. The major axis is the total length of the long axis of the elliptical orbit (from perihelion to aphelion). For the Mars journey, the major axis = 1.52 + 1.0 A.U. = 2.52 A.U. *The semi-major axis is one-half of the major axis*, so divide the major axis by two: 2.52/2 = 1.26 A.U. Now apply Kepler's third law to find the orbital period of the spacecraft = 1.26$^{3/2}$ = 1.41 years. This is the period for a full orbit (Earth to Mars and back to Earth), but you want to go only half-way (just Earth to Mars). traveling from Earth to Mars along this path will take 1.41/2 years = 0.71 years or about 8.5 months.

When the craft is launched, it already has the Earth's orbital velocity of about 30 kilometers/second. Since this is the speed for a circular orbit around the Sun at 1.0 A.U., a reduction in the spacecraft's speed would make it fall closer to the Sun and the Hohmann orbit would be *inside* the Earth's orbit. Since you want it to go beyond the Earth's orbit, the spacecraft needs an increase in its speed to put it in

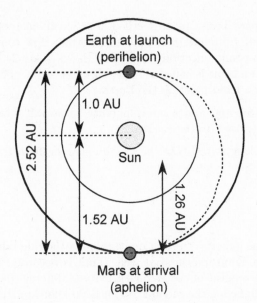

an orbit that is *outside* the Earth's orbit. It will slow down gradually as it nears aphelion.

At aphelion the spacecraft will not be traveling fast enough to be in a circular orbit at Mars' distance (1.52 A.U.) so it will need to arrive at aphelion *slightly* before Mars does. Mars will then catch up to it. But the spacecraft will be moving much too fast to be in a circular orbit *around Mars*, so it will need to slow down to go in orbit around Mars.

On its journey to Mars, the spacecraft's distance from the Sun is continuously monitored to be sure the craft is on the correct orbit. Though the spacecraft responds mostly to the Sun's gravity, the nine planets' gravitational pulls on the spacecraft can affect the spacecraft's path as it travels to Mars, so occasional minor firings of on-board thrusters may be required to keep the craft exactly on track.

Vocabulary

aphelion   perihelion

Formulae

1. Kepler's third law: period #1 = period #2 $\times \sqrt{(\text{distance } \#1/\text{distance } \#2)^3}$

2. Kepler's third law: period #1 = period #2 $\times (\text{distance } \#1/\text{distance } \#2)^{3/2}$

3. If considering objects orbiting the Sun, measure the orbit period in *years* and the distance in *A.U.* With these units, Kepler's third is simply: period = distance$^{3/2}$.

Review Questions

1. How can you predict the orbital period of Jupiter's satellite Europa from observations of the other jovian moon Io?

2. If Io takes 1.8 days to orbit Jupiter at a distance of 422,000 kilometers from its center, find out how long it would take Europa to orbit Jupiter at 671,000 kilometers from its center.

3. If the Moon were twice as far from the Earth as it is now, how long could a solar eclipse last? (Solar eclipses currently last up to about two hours from the start of the cover-up to when the Moon no longer blocks the Sun at all.)

4. The Hubble Space Telescope orbits the Earth 220 kilometers above the surface and takes about 1.5 hours to complete one orbit. How can you find out how far up to put a communication satellite, so that it takes 24 hours to circle the Earth? (Such an orbit is called a "geosychronous orbit" because the satellite remains above a fixed point on the Earth.)

5. Why does NASA not launch interplanetary spacecraft when the planets are at opposition (closest to the Earth)?

6. Find out how long it will take the Cassini spacecraft to travel to Saturn 9.5 A.U. from the Sun.

5.9   Tides

When you look in the paper at the section containing the tide tables, you will often see the phase of the moon indicated as well. That is because the ocean tides are caused by different strengths of the Moon's gravity at different points on the Earth. The side of the Earth facing the Moon is about 6400 kilometers closer to the Moon than the center of the Earth is, and the Moon's gravity pulls on the near side of the Earth more strongly than on the Earth's center. This produces a tidal bulge on the side of the Earth facing the Moon. The Earth rock is not perfectly rigid; the side facing the Moon responds by rising toward the Moon by a few centimeters on the near side. The more fluid seawater responds by flowing into a bulge on the side of the Earth facing the Moon. That bulge is the high tide.

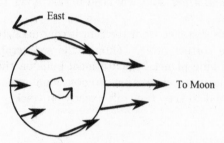

Moon's gravity pulls unequally on Earth. The arrows indicate the strength of Moon's gravity.

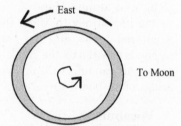

The net effect of Moon's gravity on Earth is to create tidal bulge that always points toward Moon as Earth rotates. The water bulge (color) is greater than the Earth rock bulge.

At the same time the Moon exerts an attractive force on the Earth's center that is stronger than that exerted on the side away from the Moon. The Moon pulls the Earth away from the oceans on the far side, which flow into a bulge on the far side, producing a *second* high tide on the *far* side.

two *tidal bulges*

These tidal bulges are always along the Earth-Moon line and the Earth rotates beneath the tidal bulge. When the part of the Earth where you are located sweeps under the bulges, you will experience a high tide; when it passes under one of the depressions, you experience a low tide. An ideal coast should experience the rise and fall of the tides twice a day. In reality, the tidal cycle also depends on the latitude of the site, the shape of the shore, winds, etc.

The Sun's gravity also produces tides that are about half as strong as the Moon's and produces its own pair of tidal bulges. They combine with the lunar tides. At new and full moon, the Sun and Moon produce tidal bulges that add together to

spring tides   produce extreme tides. These are called **spring tides** (the waters really spring up!).

When the Moon and Sun are at right angles to each other (1st & 3rd quarter), the solar tides reduce the lunar tides and you have **neap tides**.

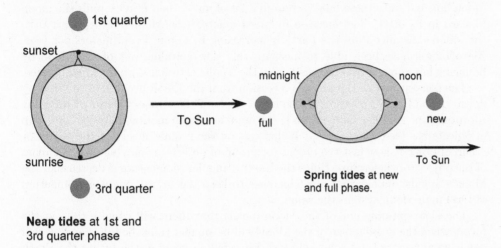

Neap tides at 1st and 3rd quarter phase

Spring tides at new and full phase.

5.9.1 Tides Slow Earth Rotation

As the Earth rotates beneath the tidal bulges, it attempts to drag the bulges along with it. A large amount of friction is produced which slows down the Earth's spin. The day has been getting longer and longer by about 0.0016 seconds each century.

Over the course of time this friction can have a noticeable effect. Astronomers trying to compare ancient solar eclipse records with their predictions found that they were off by a significant amount. But when they took the slowing down of the Earth's rotation into account, their predictions agreed with the solar eclipse records. Also, growth rings in ancient corals about 400 hundred million years old show that the day was only 22 hours long so that there were over 400 days in a year. In July 1996 a research study reported evidence, from several sedimentary rock records providing an indicator of tidal periods, that the day was only 18 hours long 900 million years ago.

Eventually the Earth's rotation will slow down to where it keeps only one face toward the Moon. Gravity acts both ways so the Earth has been creating tidal bulges on the Moon and has slowed it's rotation down so much that it rotates once every orbital period. The Moon keeps one face always toward the Earth.

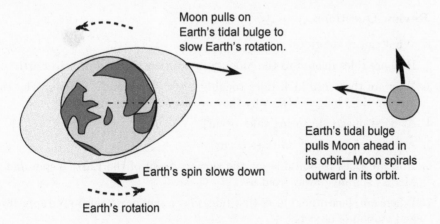

Moon pulls on Earth's tidal bulge to slow Earth's rotation.

Earth's tidal bulge pulls Moon ahead in its orbit—Moon spirals outward in its orbit.

Earth's spin slows down

Earth's rotation

5.9.2   Tides Enlarge Moon Orbit

Friction with the ocean beds drags the tidal bulges eastward out of a direct Earth-Moon line and since these bulges contain a lot of mass, their gravity pulls the moon forward in its orbit. The increase in speed *enlarges* the Moon's orbit. Currently, the Moon's distance from the Earth is increasing by about 3 centimeters per year. Astronomers have been able to measure this slow spiraling out of the Moon by bouncing laser beams off reflectors left by the Apollo astronauts on the lunar surface.

conservation of angular momentum

The consequence of the Moon's recession from the Earth because of the slowing down of the Earth's rotation is also an example of the **conservation of angular momentum**. Angular momentum is the amount of spin motion an object or group of objects has (see appendix A). It depends on the geometric size of the object or group of objects, how fast the object (or group of objects) is moving, and the mass of the object (or the group). Since the Earth's angular momentum is decreasing, the Moon's angular momentum must increase to keep the *overall* angular momentum of the Earth-Moon system the same.

The slow spiraling out of the Moon means that there will come a time in the future when the angular size of the Moon will be smaller than the Sun's and we will not have any more total solar eclipses! Fifty billion years in the future the Earth day will equal 47 of our current days and the Moon will take 47 of our current days to orbit the Earth. Both will be locked with only one side facing the other—people on one side of the Earth will always see the Moon while people on the other side will only have legends about the Moon that left their pleasant sky.

5.9.3   Tidal Effects Elsewhere

Mercury 3-2 spin orbit resonance

Io's volcanism from tidal flexing

galaxy collisions

Tidal effects are larger for more massive objects and at closer distances. The Sun produces a tidal bulge on the planet Mercury (the planet closest to the Sun) and has slowed that planet's rotation period so it rotates three times for every two times it orbits the Sun (a "3–2 spin-orbit resonance"). Jupiter's moon, Io, orbits at about the same distance from Jupiter's center as the Earth's moon. Jupiter is much more massive than the Earth, so Jupiter's tidal effect on Io is much greater than the Earth's tidal effect on the Moon. Io is stretched by varying amounts as it orbits Jupiter in its elliptical orbit. This tidal flexing of the rock material creates huge amounts of heat from friction in Io's interior which in turn is released in many volcanic eruptions seen on Io. Galaxies passing close to each other can be severely stretched and sometimes pulled apart by mutual tidal effects.

Vocabulary

conservation of angular momentum   neap tide   spring tide

Review Questions

1. What causes the tides?

2. How are tides related to the Moon-Sun positions with respect to Earth?

3. Why are there *two* high tides roughly every 12.5 hours? Explain why there are two tidal bulges AND why they are over 12 hours apart.

4. At what phases do spring tides occur?

5. At what phases do neap tides occur?

6. How are tides responsible for the slowing down of the Earth's spin and the Moon's spiraling away from us?

7. Where are some other places that tides play a significant role in the appearance and motion of objects?

Chapter 6

Einstein's Relativity

Newton's laws of motion work very well for anything moving at much less than the speed of light. His law of gravity works very well for any place of weak gravity such as in the solar system. Spacecraft sent to the distant planets in the solar system arrive at their intended destinations (barring mechanical problems) within a few minutes of the expected time even after traveling for billions of kilometers over several years time. The scientists use Newton's laws to guide the spacecraft to its destination. In this chapter you will see what happens when you look at things moving very fast (at a significant fraction of the speed of light) and you will see that space and time can be radically changed in a very strong gravitational field. In fact, you will find that gravity is not really a force!

Albert Einstein (lived 1879–1955)
Image courtesy of The Albert Einstein Archives,
The Jewish National & University Library,
The Hebrew University of Jerusalem, Israel

This revolutionary leap in our understanding of gravity and the nature of space and time was made by *Albert Einstein.* In the first two decades of the 20th century, Einstein laid out a new paradigm of gravity and motion in space and time. In this chapter you will explore his **Special Relativity** and **General Relativity** theories that are this new paradigm. The vocabulary terms are in boldface.

6.1   Spacetime

Time is not completely separate from and independent of space as you would ordinarily assume. In his **Special Relativity** theory, Einstein assumed that the fundamental laws of physics do not depend on your location or motion. Two people, one in a stationary laboratory and another in a laboratory aboard a train or rocket moving in a straight line at uniform speed, should get the same results in any experiment they conduct. In fact, if the laboratory in the train or rocket is soundproof and has no windows, there is no experiment a person could conduct that would show he/she is moving.

The laws of physics include the laws of electromagnetism developed by James Maxwell (see section 7.1) and Maxwell found that electromagnetic waves should travel at a speed given by the combination of two universal constants of nature. Since the laws of physics do not depend on your location or motion, Einstein reasoned that the *speed* of light will be measured to be the *same* by any two observers regardless of their velocity relative to each other. For example, if one observer is in a rocket moving toward another person at half the speed of light and both observers measure the speed of a beam of light emitted by the rocket, the person at rest will get the *same* value the person in the rocket ship measures (about 300,000 kilometers/second) instead of 1.5 times the speed of light (=rocket speed + speed of beam of light). This assumption has now been shown to be correct in many experiments. To get the same value of the *speed* (= distance/time) of light, the two observers moving with respect to each other would not only disagree on the *distance* the light travelled as Newton said, they would also disagree on the *time* it took.

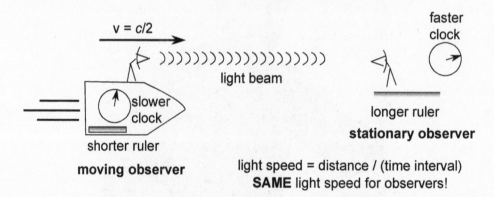

Einstein found that what you measure for length, time, and mass depends on your motion relative to a chosen frame of reference. Everything is in motion. As you sit in your seat, you are actually in motion around the center of the Earth because of the rapid rotation of the Earth on its axis. The Earth is in motion around the Sun, the Sun is in orbit around the center of our Galaxy, the Galaxy is moving toward a large group of galaxies, etc. When you say something has a *velocity*, you are measuring its change of position relative to some reference point which may itself be in motion. All motion is *relative* to a chosen frame of reference. That is what the word "relativity" means in Einstein's Relativity theories. The only way observers in motion relative to each other can *measure* a single light ray to travel the same distance in the same amount of time *relative to their own reference frames*

is if their "meters" are different and their "seconds" are different! Seconds and meters are *relative* quantities.

Two consequences of Special Relativity are a stationary observer will find (1) the length of a fast-moving object is *less* than if the object was at rest, and (2) the passage of time on the fast-moving object is slower than if the object was at rest. However, an observer *inside* the fast-moving object sees everything inside as their normal length and time passes normally, but all of the lengths in the world outside are shrunk and the outside world's clocks are running slow.

One example of the slowing of time at high speeds that is observed all of the time is what happens when *cosmic rays* (extremely high-energy particles, mostly protons) strike the Earth's atmosphere. A shower of very fast-moving muon particles are created very high up in the atmosphere. Muons have very short lifetimes—only a couple of *millionths* of a second. Their short lifetime should allow them to travel at most 600 meters. However they reach the surface after travelling more than 100 kilometers! Because they are moving close to the speed of light, the muons' internal clocks are running much slower than stationary muons. But in their own reference frame, the fast-moving muons's clocks run forward "normally" and the muons live only a couple of millionths of a second.

Time and space are relative to the motion of an observer and they are not independent of each other. Time and space are connected to make four-dimensional **spacetime** (three dimensions for space and one dimension for time). This is not that strange—we often define *distances* by the *time* it takes light to travel between two points. For example, one light year is the *distance* light will travel in a *year*. To talk about an *event*, you will usually tell where (in space) and when (in time) it happened. The event happened in spacetime. *4D* **spacetime**

Another consequence of Special Relativity is that *nothing* can travel faster than the speed of light. Any object with mass moving near the speed of light would experience an increase in its mass. That mass would approach infinity as it reached light speed and would, therefore, require an infinite amount of energy to accelerate it to light speed. The fastest possible speed any form of information or force (including gravity) can operate is at the speed of light. Newton's law of gravity seemed to imply that the force of gravity would *instantly* change between two objects if one was moved—Newton's gravity had infinite speed (a violation of Special Relativity). The three strange effects of Special Relativity (shrinking lengths, slowing time, increasing mass) are only noticeable at speeds that are greater than about ten percent of the speed of light. Numerous experiments using very high-speed objects have shown that Special Relativity is correct. *speed of light is the ultimate speed limit*

why Newton's gravity is incorrect

Special Relativity also predicts that matter can be converted into energy and energy in to matter. By applying Newton's second law of motion to the energy of motion for something moving at high speed (its "kinetic energy"), you will find that energy = mass × (speed of light)^2. More concisely, this is Einstein's famous equation, $E = mc^2$. This result also applies to an object at rest in which case, you will refer to its "rest mass" and its "rest energy", the energy equivalent of mass. The amount of rest energy in something as small as your astronomy textbook, for example, is tremendous. If all of the matter in your textbook was converted to energy, it would be enough energy to send a million *tons* to the Moon! *matter-energy*

$E = mc^2$

6.1.1 Curved Spacetime

Einstein extended his Special Relativity theory to include gravitation and non-uniform motion. Einstein was intrigued by the fact that the two ways of measuring mass come up with the same value. In Newton's second law of motion (section 5.1), an object's mass is measured by seeing how much it resists a change in motion (its *inertia*). In Newton's law of gravity (section 5.2), an object's mass is determined by measuring how much gravity force it feels. The fact that the two masses are the same is why Galileo found that all things will fall with the same acceleration (section 5.5).

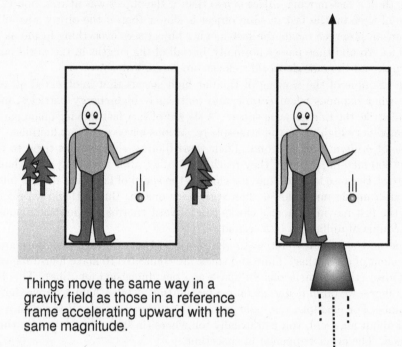

Things move the same way in a gravity field as those in a reference frame accelerating upward with the same magnitude.

Part of Einstein's genius was his ability to look at ordinary things from a whole new perspective and logically follow through on the consequence of the insights he gained from his new perspective. He proposed an experiment involving two elevators: one at rest on the ground on the Earth and another, far out in space away from any planet, moon, or star, accelerating upward with an acceleration equal to that of one Earth gravity (9.8 meters/second^2). (Modern readers can substitute "rocket ship" for Einstein's elevator.) If a ball is dropped in the elevator at rest on the Earth, it will accelerate toward the floor with an acceleration of 9.8 meters/second^2. A ball released in the upward accelerating elevator far out in space will also accelerate toward the floor at 9.8 meters/second^2. The two elevator experiments get the same result!

equivalence principle Einstein used this to formulate the **equivalence principle** that would be the foundation of General Relativity. It states that "there is no experiment a person could conduct in a small volume of space that would distinguish between a gravitational field and an equivalent uniform acceleration". A consequence of this is that if an elevator is falling freely toward the ground because of gravity, an occupant inside will feel weightless just as if the elevator was far away from any planet, moon, or star. No experiment would help you distinguish between being weightless far out in space and being in free-fall in a gravitational field.

Now suppose someone "at rest" outside your elevator way out in space shines a flashlight horizontally across the elevator you occupy toward the far wall of the elevator. If your elevator is at rest, then you will see the beam of light travel in a straight horizontal line. If your elevator is moving at a constant velocity upward relative to the person outside, you will see the beam of light travel in a straight-line path angled downward. The person outside still sees the beam travelling in a horizontal direction. If your elevator is *accelerating* upward, then the beam will follow a *curved* path downward relative to you. But if the beam of light curves in the accelerating elevator, then the equivalence principle says that the beam of light

Things falling freely in a gravity field all accelerate by the same amount, so they move the same way as if they were in a region of zero gravity — ``weightlessness''!

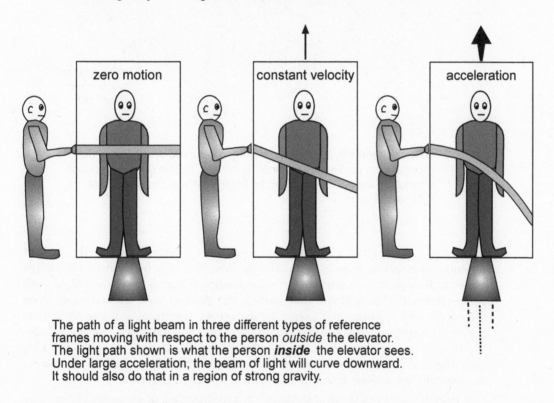

The path of a light beam in three different types of reference frames moving with respect to the person *outside* the elevator. The light path shown is what the person **inside** the elevator sees. Under large acceleration, the beam of light will curve downward. It should also do that in a region of strong gravity.

should also follow a curved path in a gravitational field.

Light travels along the shortest path between two points in spacetime (a *geodesic*). If the geodesic is curved, then the path of light is curved. Einstein proposed in his **General Relativity** theory that what is called gravity is really the result of curved spacetime. The Earth does not orbit the Sun because the Sun is pulling on it. The Earth is simply following the shortest path in four-dimensional spacetime.

General Relativity

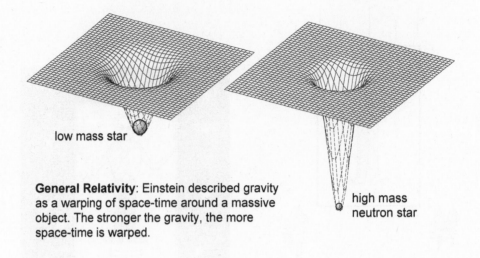

low mass star

General Relativity: Einstein described gravity as a warping of space-time around a massive object. The stronger the gravity, the more space-time is warped.

high mass neutron star

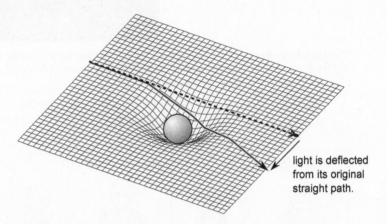

light is deflected from its original straight path.

General Relativity: Light travels along the curved space taking the shortest path between two points. Therefore, light is deflected toward a massive object! The stronger the local gravity is, the greater the light path is bent.

shortest path can be curved

If you have ever taken a long flight, you probably already know that the shortest distance between two cities is not a straight line. Non-stop flights from the United States to Europe fly over parts of Greenland. On a flat map the plane's flight path looks curved, but on a globe, that path is the shortest one! Light travels along a *geodesic* path between two points in spacetime. Far from any gravity source, the shortest distance is a straight line in three-dimensional space. Near a massive object, the shortest distance is curved in three-dimensional space. Stephen Hawking gives the nice analogy that what we see is like the curved motion of a shadow on the ground from a plane flying in a straight line over hilly terrain.

Newton vs. Einstein

Einstein's theory of General Relativity is a continuation or extension of Newton's law of gravity. Einstein's theory is not perfect (no scientific theory is absolutely perfect), but it does give a better understanding of the universe. In weak gravity conditions, they will give essentially the same results or predictions. Newton's law of gravity assumes that the geometry of spacetime is flat while Einstein's General Relativity allows any geometry to apply to spacetime. In weak gravity conditions, the curvature of spacetime is so small that Newton's law of gravity works just fine. Since the mathematics of Newton's laws of motion and gravity are simpler than for Einstein's relativity theories, scientists prefer to use Newton's law of gravity for understanding interactions of slow-moving objects in any weak gravity field. As mentioned at the beginning of the chapter, scientists use Newton's laws of motion and gravity to very accurately guide spacecraft in our solar system. For very strong gravitational fields, Newton's description of gravity becomes inadequate. Einstein's theory of General Relativity must be used to describe the gravitational effects.

6.2 Evidence of Warped Spacetime

If Einstein's theory of General Relativity is an accurate description of gravity, then there are some bizarre consequences. In this section the implications of General Relativity's claim that gravity is the warping of **spacetime** will be explored in a prediction-observation format. A scientific theory must make testable predictions which are tested through observations and experiments.

1. *Prediction:* light passing close to a massive object should be noticeably bent. The amount of bending increases as the mass increases.

   Observation: During a solar eclipse you see that the stars along the same line of sight as the Sun are shifted "outward". This is because the light from the star behind the Sun is bent toward the Sun and toward the Earth. The light comes from a direction that is different from where the star really is. But wouldn't Newton's law of gravity and the result from Einstein's *Special Relativity* theory that $E = mc^2$ predict light deflection too? Yes, but *only half as much*. General Relativity says that *time* is also stretched so the deflection is twice as great.

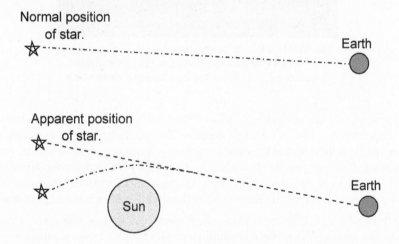

   Observation: The light from quasars is observed to be bent by **gravitational lenses** produced by galaxies between the Earth and the quasars. It is possible to see two or more identical images of the same background quasar (see the figure on the next page). In some cases the light from background quasars or galaxies can be warped to form rings. Since the amount of warping depends on the mass of the foreground galaxy, you can estimate the total mass of the foreground galaxy. The observations of gravitational lensing are now so commonplace, that we use it to map out the distribution of dark matter, to examine extremely distant objects that have been magnified enough for us to study and would have otherwise been undetectable, and to look for exoplanets.

gravitational lens

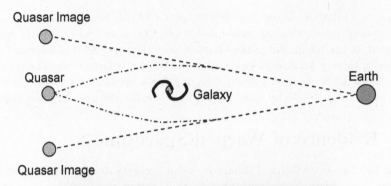

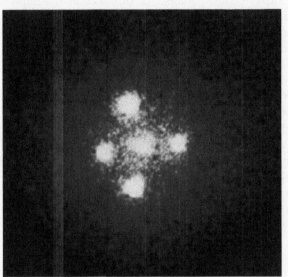

The Einstein Cross: gravitational lensing of a quasar
by a foreground galaxy (at center) into four images.
Image courtesy of the Space Telescope Science Institute/AURA

time dilation

2. *Prediction:* time should run "slower" near a large mass. This effect is called
   time dilation. For example, if someone on a massive object (call her person
   A) sends a light signal to someone far away from any gravity source (call him
   person B) every second according to her clock on the massive object, person
   B will receive the signals in time intervals further apart than one second.
   According to person B, the clock on the massive object is running slow.

   Observation: a) Clocks on planes high above the ground run *faster* than those
   on the ground. The effect is small since the Earth's mass is small, so atomic
   clocks must be used to detect the difference. For objects with greater surface
   gravity, this effect is more noticeable. b) The Global Positioning System
   (GPS) must compensate for General Relativity effects or the positions it gives
   for locations would be significantly off.

3. *Prediction:* light escaping from a large mass should lose energy—the wavelength must increase since the speed of light is constant. Stronger surface
   gravity produces a greater increase in the wavelength.

   This is a consequence of time dilation. Suppose person A on the massive object
   decides to send light of a specific frequency f to person B all of the time. So
   every second, f wave crests leave person A. The same wave crests are received
   by person B in an interval of time interval of $(1 + z)$ seconds. He receives
   the waves at a frequency of $f/(1 + z)$. Remember that the speed of light $c =$

(the frequency f)$\times$ (the wavelength λ). If the frequency is reduced by $(1+z)$ times, the wavelength must INcrease by $(1+z)$ times: $\lambda_{at\,B} = (1+z) \times \lambda_{at\,A}$. In the doppler effect, this lengthening of the wavelength is called a *redshift*. For gravity, the effect is called a **gravitational redshift**.

gravitational redshift

Observation: spectral lines from the top layer of white dwarfs are significantly shifted by an amount predicted for compact solar-mass objects. The white dwarf must be in a binary system with a main sequence companion so how much of the shift is from the doppler effect and how much is from the **gravitational redshift** can be determined. Inside a black hole's event horizon, light is red-shifted to an infinitely long wavelength.

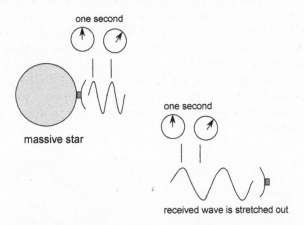

massive star

received wave is stretched out

Since gravity stretches time, we have to wait longer to see the next wave crest pass by us than observers in the strong gravity field: the frequency is smaller. All forms of light travel at the same speed, so the wavelength is longer: *gravitational redshift*.

4. *Prediction:* objects with mass should create ripples in the surrounding spacetime as they move, called *gravitational waves*. These waves do not travel through spacetime, but are the oscillations of spacetime itself! The spacetime ripples move at the speed of light. However, the waves are very small and extremely hard to detect. Since the objects that make significant waves are RARE, they will be on average very far apart in the universe which means they will be very far from the Earth. Therefore, the waves are very small and extremely hard to detect by the time they reach Earth.

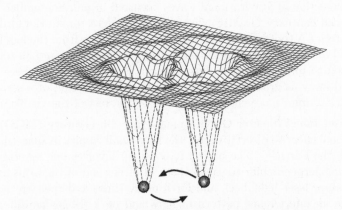

A binary system of compact massive objects rapidly orbiting each other produces ripples in spacetime.

Observation: Before September 14, 2015, the most sensitive detectors had not directly detected the tiny stretching-shrinking of spacetime caused by a massive object moving. On that date the twin LIGO detectors (described below) detected the "chirp" of two merging stellar-mass black holes. Until then, the best evidence we had for gravitational waves came from the observations of the decaying orbits of a binary pulsar system discovered in 1974 by Russell Hulse and Joseph Taylor. The spiraling inward of the binary pulsar system can only be explained by gravity waves carrying away energy from the pulsars as they orbit each other. This observation provides a very strong gravity field test of General Relativity.

The two pulsars in the binary system called PSR1913+16 orbit each other very rapidly with a period of only 7.75 hours in very eccentric and small elliptical orbits that bring them as close as 766,000 kilometers and then move them rapidly to over 3.3 million kilometers apart. Because of their large masses (each greater than the Sun's mass) and rapidly changing small distances, the gravity ripples should be noticeable. Hulse and Taylor discovered that the orbit speed and separation of PSR1913+16 changes exactly in the way predicted by General Relativity. They were awarded the Nobel Prize in physics for this discovery.

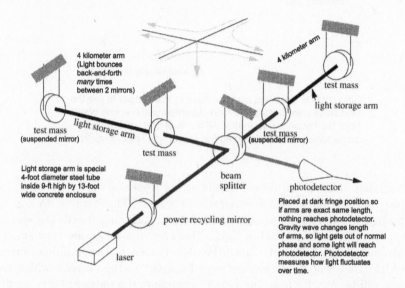

However, this is an *indirect* observation of gravitational waves. The first direct detection of gravitational waves occurred in mid-September 2015 (but announced February 11, 2016) with twin LIGO detectors in Hanford, WA and Livingston, LA (both USA) when ripples of spacetime from the last fraction of a second of the merger of two black holes with masses 29 and 36 solar masses combined to form a 62-solar mass black hole with 3 solar masses of energy radiated away as gravitational waves in that last fraction of a second. That is about 50 times more energy produced by the rest of the visible universe!

LIGO

The Laser Interferometer Gravitational-Wave Observatory (LIGO) is an international effort to directly detect the very small ripples in spacetime passing through the Earth. The basic LIGO set up involves two several-kilometer long arms perpendicular to each other. At either end of the arms are mirrors that bounce laser light back and forth many times and then are recombined to make an interference pattern of light and dark fringes as different parts of a wave's heights and troughs cancel out or combine with another wave's heights and troughs to varying degrees. Without any spacetime ripples, the laser light waves from the two arms will perfectly cancel each other out, so nothing will reach a photodetector. A gravity wave passing through a LIGO site, will stretch one of the arms while squeezing the other arm and then reverse the effect as the gravity waves passes by. This will make the combined light from the two arms get out of phase with each other, resulting in some of the laser light reaching the photodetector. The photodetector then measures how the light fluctuates over time. The technological challenge is to detect minute changes in the length of the arms as small as 10^{-18} meters (many times smaller than a proton!) in the midst of all of the terrestrial "noise" such as seismic events, sloshing ocean waves hitting land, sound waves, random laser fluctuations, and thermal effects of the materials used that can easily overwhelm the very weak gravity wave ripples of spacetime. A schematic for the United States version is shown on the previous page (adapted from a diagram in a slideset from Rainer Weiss).

LIGO sites are located in the United States (at Hanford, WA and Livingston, LA), in Germany (near Hannover), in Italy (near Pisa), in Japan (at the Kamioka mine), and a future site in Australia. Early versions of LIGO did not detect any gravitational waves. These negative results were not surprising, however, as the technology innovations needed in hardware and software are still being developed along with our ability to analyze the weak waves amidst all of the noise. Between late 2010 and early 2015, Advanced LIGO was installed at the two United States sites and began observations in September 2015. Advanced LIGO increases increase the sensitivity of gravity wave detection by a factor of ten times. Being able to detect gravity waves from sources ten times farther away means an increase of a thousand times the volume of space or a thousand times the number of possible sources. This increased sensitivity made it possible to detect the gravitational waves from the merging black holes near the end of the first observing run in September 2015.

A lot of information about the system is encoded in the gravitational waveform. For example with merging binary systems: the amplitude of the gravitational wave depends on the masses of the merging objects and the distance of the source from us; the frequency depends on the mass and orbital period of the objects; how the frequency changes depends on the ratio of the masses; and the maximum frequency before the objects merge tells us the diameter of the objects. Because many of the parameters of the system (e.g., mass, separation distance, distance to the system, etc.) are intertwined in how they shape the gravitational waveform, scientists compare the observed waveform against a database of computed waveforms with different combinations of parameters to find the best fit as well as to sift out the gravitational wave signal from all the other terrestrial sources of noise. With the differences in time the gravitational waves hit different detectors, we can determine the direction from where the waves came.

The gravitational waves were detected by the Livingston detector 7 milliseconds before the Hanford detector as the gravitational waves traveled at the speed of light from the direction of the southern hemisphere sky, roughly in the same direction as the Large Magellanic Cloud. The source was much further away than the LMC as the gravitational waves had traveled between 700 million years to 1.6 billion years. (The detection by just two detectors makes a more precise direction and distance measurement impossible.) LIGO was able to see all three phases of the collision—inward spiral, merger, and ringing as the merged object settled down—happen in the just the way predicted by General Relativity. The increasing amplitude and frequency of the waves during the merger if converted to audio sound waves would make a sound like a chirp of a bird, so the LIGO scientists refer to it as the chirp of a black hole merger. Several other detections were made in the fall 2015 observing run and many more are expected in future observing runs as the sensitivity of Advanced LIGO is increased even further. Hopefully, with that catalog of detections, we will begin to see discrepancies from the predictions of Theory of General Relativity that will lead us to an even deeper understanding of gravity, particularly at the quantum realm.

The fifth gravitational wave event (GW170817), detected in mid-August 2017, was probably even more important than the first detection because it was the first one whose source also produced electromagnetic radiation we could observe with ground and space-based telescopes. Unlike the first four gravitational wave events that involved mergers of black holes, the fifth event involved the merger of neutron stars. The neutron stars collided into each other to create a type of explosion called a "kilonova" that is a thousand times more energetic than a normal nova (see chapter 13). The use of the telescopes enabled us to pinpoint its location to within an elliptical galaxy called NGC 4993, 130 million light years away. Besides confirming theories about the source of some short- duration gamma-ray bursts and the formation mechanism of many of the heavy elements including platinum, lead, gold, and rare earth elements, the gravitational waves enabled us to get a distance to the galaxy independent of the usual step-by-step procedure called the "distance scale ladder" (discussed at the end chapter 15). Coupling that direct distance measurement with the redshift measurements of NGC 4993 enabled astronomers to determine the Hubble Constant which is the expansion rate of the universe. Quite a lot of information from just one event! The LIGO detectors are analogous to microphones that enable us to "hear" the universe. Before we were able to detect gravitational waves, it was like we were watching silent movies about the universe (and not close- captioned either). Putting gravitational wave data together with electromagnetic radiation data gives us a richer, multi-sensory viewing of the universe.

Another laser interferometry system will be the evolving Laser Interferometer Space Antenna (eLISA) scheduled to launch in the mid-2030s. Using three satellites in an equilateral triangle formation with each side a million kilometers long, eLISA will be sensitive to a frequency range about 10 thousand times smaller than what LIGO can observe (10^{-4} to 10^{-1} for eLISA vs. 10 to 10^3 for LIGO). eLISA will be able to detect the gravitational waves from smaller supermassive black holes (those in the tens of thousands to few million solar mass range) and from compact binary stars. LIGO can detect gravitational waves from neutron star mergers and supernovae.

Physicists tested some other predictions of the General Relativity Theory with the Gravity Probe B spacecraft mission. The spacecraft was in a polar orbit (pole to pole) 400 miles above the Earth's surface. Four gyroscopes with *extremely* precise, perfect quartz spheres kept the spacecraft aligned with a particular guide star. Because the Earth warps spacetime around it and the Earth should also "drag" the spacetime around it as it rotates, there should be a twisting of the local spacetime. This twisting and stretching of the local spacetime should cause the gyroscopes in Gravity Probe B to get out of alignment as it orbited the Earth. The twisting and stretching of spacetime by the Earth should be very small because of the Earth's tiny mass, so the drifting of the gyroscopes on Gravity Probe B were very small and the instruments on the spacecraft had to be exquisitely precise to detect the slight twisting and stretching of the spacetime near the Earth. The spacecraft finished data collection in October 2005 and intensive analysis of the data began. In April

2007, the scientists announced that they detected the predicted shift caused by the stretching of spacetime (the "geodetic effect"). After another two and a half years of data analysis, they announced in September 2009 that they were able to extract out the much smaller effect caused by the twisting of spacetime (the "frame-dragging effect"). See the textbook's website for links to the Gravity Probe B experiment.

The imaging of supermassive black holes at the center of M87 and the Milky Way by the Event Horizon Telescope is another confirmation of General Relativity. Future investigations of the motions of the gas and stars very close to the black holes will provide further tests of the limitations of General Relativity in places of extremely warped spacetime. See chapter 15 for more about that.

Vocabulary

equivalance principle	General Relativity	gravitational lens
gravitational redshift	spacetime	Special Relativity

Review Questions

1. When are the unusual effects predicted by the **Special Relativity** theory particularly noticeable? Has this theory been tested? If yes, how so? If not, why not?

2. What two things change when objects move at *high* speeds?

3. How does the speed of light depend on the observer's location and motion?

4. Why is the speed of light the fastest that *anything* can travel?

5. How does the **equivalance principle** lead to the conclusion that spacetime is warped?

6. What did Einstein predict would happen to a light ray passing close to a massive object?

7. When are the unusual effects predicted by the **General Relativity** theory particularly noticeable? Have astronomers been able to test this theory of Einstein? If yes, how so? If not, why not?

8. How is Einstein's theory of gravity the same as Newton's law of gravity?

Chapter 7

Electromagnetic Radiation (Light)

At least 95% of the celestial information we receive is in the form of light. Because of this fact, astronomers have devised many techniques to decode as much as possible the messages that are encoded in the often extremely faint rays of light. These messages include information about the object's temperature, motion, chemical composition, gas density, surface gravity, shape, structure, and more! Roughly 85% of the information in light is uncovered by using **spectroscopy**—spreading the light out into its different constituent colors or wavelengths and analyzing the spectrum. The first part of this chapter covers the characteristics of all forms of light and the following sections cover spectroscopic analysis. The vocabulary terms are in boldface.

spectroscopy

7.1   Electric and Magnetic Fields

In order to understand light, you first need to have an understanding of *electric fields* and *magnetic fields*. Electrical charges and magnets alter the region of space around them so that they can exert forces on distant objects. This altered space is called a *force field* (or just a *field*). Rather than describing the action of forces by having a distant object somehow reach out across space and push or pull on a body, the body simply responds to its local environment. An electric charge or a magnet responds to the field immediately surrounding it. That field is produced by a distant object. In the same way, a massive object can produce a *gravity field* that distant objects will respond to.

Scientists have known since the early part of the 19th century that electrical fields and magnetic fields are intimately related to each other and applications of this connection are found all around you. Moving electric charge (electric current) creates a magnetic field. Coils of wire can be used to make the large electromagnets used in car junk yards or the tiny electromagnetics in your telephone receiver. Electric motors used to start your car or spin a computer's harddisk around are other applications of this phenomenon. In fact, ordinary magnets are produced from tiny currents at the atomic level.

moving charge makes magnetic field

A changing magnetic field creates electrical current—an electric field. This concept is used by power generators—large coils of wire are made to turn in a magnetic field (by falling water, wind, or by steam from the heating of water by burning coal or oil or the heat from nuclear reactions). The coils of wire experience a changing magnetic field and electricity is produced. Computer disks and audio and video tapes encode information in magnetic patterns of alternating magnetic directions

changing magnetic field makes electric field

and magnetic strengths. When the magnetic disk or tape material passes by small coils of wire, electrical currents (electric fields) are produced.

James Clerk Maxwell (lived 1831–1879) put these ideas together and proposed that if a changing magnetic field can make an electric field, then a changing electric field (from an oscillating electric charge, for example) should make a magnetic field. A consequence of this is that changing electric and magnetic fields should trigger each other and these changing fields should move at a speed equal to the speed of light. To conclude this line of reasoning, Maxwell said that light *is* an electromagnetic wave. Later experiments confirmed Maxwell's theory.

Maxwell

changing electric field makes magnetic field

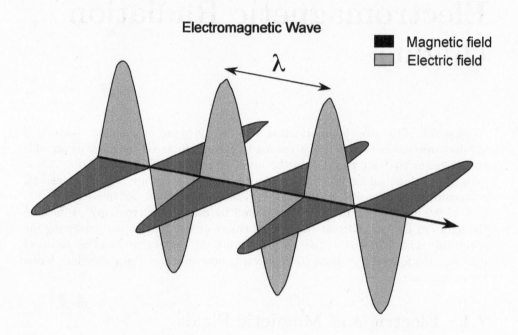

Electromagnetic Wave

λ

■ Magnetic field
▨ Electric field

7.2   Properties of Light

Light, electricity, and magnetism are manifestations of the same thing called **electromagnetic radiation.** The energy you see coming out of the light bulb you are using to read this page is made of fluctuating electric and magnetic energy fields. The electric and magnetic fields oscillate at right angles to each other and the combined wave moves in a direction perpendicular to both of the electric and magnetic field oscillations. This energy also comes in many forms that are not detectable with our eyes such as infrared (IR), radio, X-rays, ultraviolet (UV), and gamma rays.

We feel infrared light as heat and our radios pick up the messages encoded in radio waves emitted by radio stations. Ultraviolet light has high enough energy to damage our skin cells, so our bodies will produce a darker pigment in our skin to prevent exposure of the deeper skin cells to the UV (we tan as a defense mechanism). The special bulbs called "black lights" produce a lot of UV and were used by hospitals to kill bacteria, amoebas, and other micro-organisms. X-rays are produced by very hot things in space. X-rays have more energy than UV, so they can pass through skin, muscles, and organs. They are blocked by bones, so when the doctor takes your X-ray, the picture that results is the shadow image of the X-rays that passed through your body. Because X-rays have such high energy, they can damage or kill cells. A few brief exposures to low-intensity X-rays is okay. The X-ray

electromagnetic radiation

technician would be exposed to thousands of X-ray exposures if s/he did not use some sort of shielding. Gamma rays are the most energetic form of electromagnetic radiation and are produced in nuclear reactions.

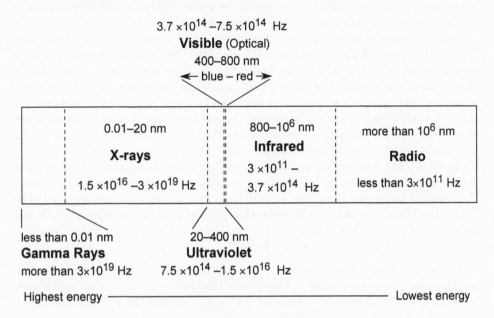

The Electromagnetic Spectrum

The form of electromagnetic radiation your eyes can detect is called "visible" or "optical" light. Astronomers have only recently (within the past few decades) been able to use the other forms of electromagnetic radiation or light. Every time technology has been developed to detect another form of light, a revolution in our understanding of the universe has occurred. The figure above shows all of the forms of electromagnetic radiation in order of INcreasing wavelength (given in nanometers (nm)) and DEcreasing energy. Notice how very narrow is the visible band!

There are some *general properties shared by all forms of electromagnetic radiation:*

1. It can travel through empty space. Other types of waves need some sort of medium to move through: water waves need liquid water and sound waves need some gas, liquid, or solid material to be heard.

2. The speed of light is constant in space. All forms of light have the *same* speed of 299,800 kilometers/second in space (often abbreviated as c). From highest energy to lowest energy the forms of light are Gamma rays, X-rays, Ultraviolet (UV), Visible, Infrared (IR), Radio. (Microwaves are high-energy radio waves.) Light traveling through material slows down and how much it slows down depends on the wavelength or energy of the light.

3. A **wavelength** of light is defined similarly to that of water waves—distance between crests or between troughs. Visible light (what your eye detects) has wavelengths 4000–8000 Ångstroms. 1 Ångstrom = 10^{-10} meter. Visible light is sometimes also measured in nanometers ("nm" in the figure above): 1 nanometer = 10^{-9} meter = 10 Ångstroms, so in nanometers, the visible band is from 400 to 800 nanometers. Radio wavelengths are often measured in centimeters: 1 centimeter = 10^{-2} meter = 0.01 meter. The abbreviation used for wavelength is the greek letter lambda: λ.

wavelength

$\lambda = wavelength$

White light is made of different colors (wavelengths). When white light is passed through a prism or diffraction grating, it is spread out into all of its different colors. You see this happen every time you see a rainbow. In the prism, some colors in the white light travel slower through the prism than other colors, so the different colors are bent by different amounts to make the rainbow.

Not all wavelengths of light from space make it to the surface. Only long-wave UV, Visible, parts of the IR and radio bands make it to surface. More IR reaches elevations above 9,000 feet (2765 meters) elevation. That is one reason why modern observatories are built on top of very high mountains. Fortunately, as far as life is concerned, our atmosphere shields us from the Gamma rays, X-rays, and most of the UV. It also blocks most of the IR and parts of the radio. Astronomers were not able to detect these forms of energy from celestial objects until the space age, when they could put satellite observatories in orbit.

frequency

hertz

Besides using wavelength to describe the form of light, you can also use the **frequency**—the number of crests of the wave that pass by a point every second. Frequency is measured in units of **hertz** (Hz): 1 hertz = 1 wave crest/second. For light there is a simple relation between the speed of light (c), wavelength (λ), and frequency (f):

$$f = c/\lambda.$$

Since the wavelength λ is in the bottom of the fraction, the frequency is inversely proportional to the wavelength. This means that light with a smaller wavelength has a *higher* (larger) frequency. Light with a longer wavelength has a *lower* (smaller) frequency.

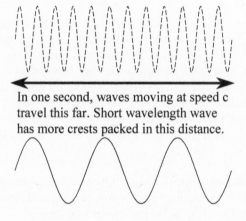

In one second, waves moving at speed c travel this far. Short wavelength wave has more crests packed in this distance.

Joule

Some colors and their approximate wavelength, frequency and energy ranges are given in the table below. The unit of energy is the *Joule* (J). A Joule is how much energy you expend when you lift an object with 1 kilogram of mass (for example, a liter of water) about 10 centimeters above the ground. If you then let it go, the object hits the ground with that much energy. Sometimes light energy is also measured in "ergs", where 1 erg = 10^{-7} Joule.

Note the trends: bluer light has *shorter* λ, *higher* f, and more energy. Redder light has *longer* λ, *lower* f, and less energy.

Planck

At the beginning of the 20th century *Max Planck* suggested that atoms can absorb and emit energy in only discrete chunks (called *quanta)*. This *quantum* behavior of atoms could explain the drop-off of a continuous spectrum's shape at the short wavelength end (this type of spectrum is described in the next section).

Einstein

A few years after Planck's discovery, *Albert Einstein* discovered that the quantum of energy was not due to the atoms but, rather, a property of the energy itself. You

photon

can consider light as packets of energy called **photons**. A **photon** is a particle of

color	λ (nm)	f ($\times 10^{14}$ Hz)	Energy ($\times 10^{-19}$ J)
violet	400 →460	7.5 →6.5	5.0 →4.3
indigo	460 →475	6.5 →6.3	4.3 →4.2
blue	475 →490	6.3 →6.1	4.2 →4.1
green	490 →565	6.1 →5.3	4.1 →3.5
yellow	565 →575	5.3 →5.2	3.5 →3.45
orange	575 →600	5.2 →5.0	3.45 →3.3
red	600 →800	5.0 →3.7	3.3 →2.5

Max Planck (lived 1858–1947)
Image courtesy of The American Institute of Physics

electromagnetic radiation. Bizarre though it may be, light is both a particle and a wave. Whether light behaves like a wave or like a particle depends on how the light is observed (it depends on the experimental setup)! Einstein found a very simple relationship between the energy of a light wave (photon) and its frequency:

$$\text{Energy of light} \; = \; h \times f$$
$$= \; \frac{h \times c}{\lambda},$$

where h is a universal constant of nature called "Planck's constant" $= 6.63 \times 10^{-34}$ Joules·second.

Light can also behave as a particle and a wave at the same time. An example of light acting as both a particle and a wave is the digital camera—the lens refracts (bends and focusses) waves of light that hit a charge-coupled device (CCD). The photons kick electrons out of the silicon in the CCD. The electrons are detected by electronics that interpret the number of electrons released and their position of release from the silicon to create an image.

Another example is when you observe the build-up of the alternating light and dark pattern from diffraction (a wave phenomenon) from light passing through a narrow slit. You see one bright spot (a photon), then another bright spot (another photon), then another... until the diffraction pattern is created from all of the accumulated photons. This happens so quickly that it is undetectable to the human eye.

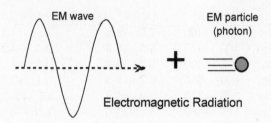

spectrum

To decode the information stored in light, the light is passed through a prism or diffraction grating to create a **spectrum**—any display of the intensity of light (EM radiation) at different wavelengths or frequencies (a picture or a graph of intensity vs. either wavelength or frequency). If white light is examined, then the spectrum will be a rainbow.

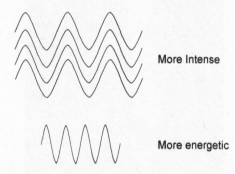

intensity

The term **intensity** has a particular meaning here: it is the number of waves or photons of light reaching your detector; a brighter object is more intense but not necessarily more energetic. Remember that a photon's energy depends on the wavelength (or frequency) only, not the intensity. The photons in a dim beam of X-ray light are much more energetic than the photons in an intense beam of infrared light.

temperature

The type of light produced by an object will depend on its temperature, so let's digress slightly to investigate what "temperature" is. **Temperature** is a measure of the random motion (or energy) of a group of particles. Higher temperature means more random motion (or energy). A natural scale would have zero motion at zero degrees (absolute zero). This scale is the **Kelvin** scale. It scales exactly like the Celsius system, but it is offset by 273 degrees. Here is a comparison of the Kelvin, Celsius, and Fahrenheit temperature scales:

Kelvin *scale*

K	C	F	
0	−273	−459	absolute zero
100	−173	−279.4	
273	0	32	water freezes
310	37	98.6	human temperature
373	100	212	water boils (STP)
755	482	900	oven on "clean" setting
5840	5567	10078	Sun's temperature

Vocabulary

electromagnetic radiation	frequency	hertz
intensity	Kelvin	photon
spectroscopy	spectrum	temperature
wavelength		

Formulae

1. Frequency and wavelength relation: $f = c/\lambda$.

2. Energy of a photon: $E = h \times f$, where h is a constant of nature.

3. Energy of a photon: $E = (h \times c)/\lambda$.

Review Questions

1. Why is light so very important to astronomy? What kinds of information can you get from it?

2. Why is light called **electromagnetic radiation**? Is radio a form of light?

3. Put the following forms of light in order of *increasing* frequency (lowest frequency first): ultraviolet, infrared, gamma rays, visible, radio, X-rays. Put them in order of *increasing* wavelength (shortest wavelength first). Put them in order of *increasing* energy (lowest energy first).

4. Do all forms of light travel at the same speed in a vacuum (empty space)? Why is it important that light can travel through empty space?

5. What forms of light can be observed from the ground (including high mountains)? What forms can be observed at high altitudes in our atmosphere? What forms must be observed in space?

6. Is electromagnetic radiation a wave or a particle? What determines if you will see light as a wave or a **photon**?

7. Which of these are a **spectrum**: plot of intensity vs. wavelength, plot of intensity vs. brightness, plot of frequency vs. wavelength, rainbow, plot of acceleration vs. time, plot of energy vs. frequency.

8. What is the difference between **intensity** and energy? If a particular CCD chip requires light energies of 4.2×10^{-19} J to release electrons from the silicon, which will produce more electrons (and hence, a brighter computer image): an intense beam of yellow light or a dim beam of UV light? Explain your answer!

9. Why is the **Kelvin** scale preferred over the Celsius or the Fahrenheit scales?

10. Where is absolute zero on the three temperature scales? Where is the Sun's temperature on the three temperature scales?

7.3   Production of Light

When light is passed through a prism or a diffraction grating to produce a spectrum, the type of spectrum you will see depends on what kind of object is producing the light: is it a thick or thin gas, is it hot or cool, is it a gas or a solid? There are two basic types of spectra: **continuous spectrum** (energy at all wavelengths) and **discrete spectrum** (energy at only certain wavelengths).   Astronomers usually refer to the two types of discrete spectra: **emission lines** (bright lines) and   **absorption lines** (the dark lines in an otherwise continuous spectrum) as different types of spectra.

continuous spectrum
discrete spectrum
emission lines
absorption lines

7.3.1   Continuous Spectrum

A rainbow is an example of a **continuous spectrum**. Most continuous spectra are from hot, dense objects like stars, planets, or moons. The continuous spectrum from these kinds of objects is also called a **thermal spectrum**, because hot, dense

thermal spectrum

*only depends on temper-
ature*

objects will emit electromagnetic radiation at all wavelengths or colors. Any solid,
liquid and dense (thick) gas at a temperature above absolute zero will produce a
thermal spectrum. A thermal spectrum is the simplest type of spectrum because
its shape depends on only the temperature. A discrete spectrum is more complex
because it depends on temperature and other things like the chemical composition
of the object, the gas density, surface gravity, speed, etc. Exotic objects like neutron stars and black holes can produce another type of continuous spectrum called
"synchrotron spectrum" from charged particles swirling around magnetic fields, but
I will discuss them in another chapter later on. For now, let's look at a thermal
spectrum.

Sometimes astronomers use the term "blackbody" spectrum for a thermal spectrum. A "blackbody" is an object that absorbs all the light falling on it, reflecting
none of it, hence, it appears black. When the "blackbody" object is heated, it
emits light very efficiently without any gaps or breaks in the brightness. Though
no object is a perfect "blackbody", most stars, planets, moons and asteroids are
near enough to being "blackbodies", that they will produce spectra very similar to
a perfect thermal spectrum.

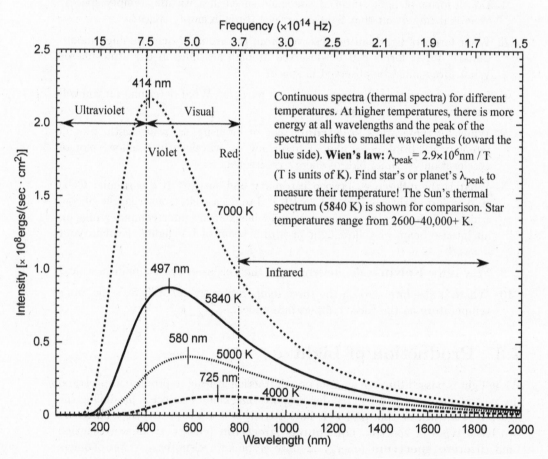

Continuous spectra (thermal spectra) for different temperatures. At higher temperatures, there is more energy at all wavelengths and the peak of the spectrum shifts to smaller wavelengths (toward the blue side). **Wien's law:** $\lambda_{peak} = 2.9 \times 10^6 \text{nm} / T$ (T is units of K). Find star's or planet's λ_{peak} to measure their temperature! The Sun's thermal spectrum (5840 K) is shown for comparison. Star temperatures range from 2600–40,000+ K.

Some key features of a thermal (continuous) spectrum are as follows:

1. There is light from a dense object at *all* possible wavelengths *IF* the object is
   above 0 K (absolute zero). Since everything in the universe is above 0 K, all
   dense objects (solids, liquids, thick gases) will produce a thermal spectrum.

2. The shape of a continuous spectrum depends on only the temperature of
   the object *NOT* its chemical composition. This allows you to determine the
   temperature of an object from a great distance away.

3. As the temperature of an object increases, more light is produced at all wavelengths than when it was cooler. You can see this effect with a light bulb wired to a dimmer switch. As you raise the current going to the bulb, the bulb's filament gets hotter and brighter.

4. As the temperature of an object increases, the peak of thermal spectrum curve shifts to *smaller* wavelengths (higher frequencies)—cool things appear red or orange, hotter things appear yellow or white, and very hot things blue or purple. This is opposite to what artists use for "cool" colors (blues) or "hot" colors (reds)! You can also see this effect with a light bulb wired to a dimmer switch. The dim bulb will have an orange color and as you make it brighter, the bulb will turn yellow and even white.

Wilhelm Wien (lived 1864–1928) discovered that the peak of the thermal spectrum curve, λ_{peak} in nanometers, is related to the temperature by $\lambda_{\text{peak}} = 2.9 \times 10^6/$temperature (in K). This simple relation is now known as **Wien's law**. Using this you will find that cool objects like cars, plants, and people radiate most of their energy in the infrared. Very cold objects radiate mostly in the radio band.

Wien

Wien's law

5. A small change in the temperature produces a HUGE change in the amount of energy emitted by every unit area of the object. If you add up all of the energy emitted every second by an area of one square meter on the object's surface, you find it equals $\sigma \times$temperature^4, where σ is another universal constant of nature $[= 5.67 \times 10^{-8}$ J/(m^2 K^4 s)$]$. This relation is called the **Stefan-Boltzmann law**. Because the temperature is raised to the fourth power, a small rise in the temperature of an object will produce a HUGE increase in the amount of energy it emits.

Stefan-Boltzmann law

Luminosity is proportional to the *fourth* power of temperature.

Sun

6000 K
L = 1

12,000 K
L = 16
$\left(\frac{12,000}{6000}\right)^4 = 2^4$

2000 K
L = $\frac{1}{81}$
$\left(\frac{2000}{6000}\right)^4 = (1/3)^4$

When you add up all of the energy of all of the square meters on the object's surface, you get the **luminosity**—the total amount of energy emitted every second by the object. The luminosity = (total surface area) $\times(\sigma \times$temperature^4). If our Sun were just twice as hot as it is now, it would produce $2^4 = 16$ times more energy than it does now!

luminosity

7.3.2 Discrete Spectrum

Close examination of the spectra from the Sun and other stars reveals that the rainbow of colors has many dark lines in it, called **absorption lines.** They are produced when cooler thin gas absorbs certain colors of light produced by hotter dense objects, so for stars, the cooler, low-density upper layers absorb certain colors

absorption lines

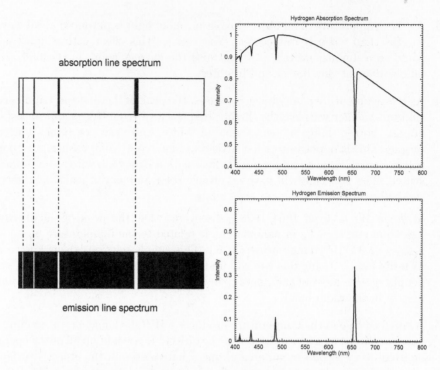

Two ways of showing the same spectra: on the **left** are pictures of the dispersed light and on the **right** are plots of the intensity vs. wavelength. Notice that the pattern of spectral lines in the absorption and emission line spectra are the **same** since the gas is the same.

produced by the deeper, denser layers. The cool thin gas is thin enough that most of the light can pass right through it without hitting any atoms or molecules (e.g., as thin as the upper layers of the Earth's atmosphere many *tens of kilometers above the Earth's surface*). You can also see them in the reflected light spectrum from planets. Some of the colors in the sunlight reflecting off the planets are absorbed by the molecules on the planet's surface or in its atmosphere.

The process in making absorption lines is analogous to putting a filter in a narrow stream of dirty water that is collecting in a bucket (see figure next page). Without the filter, all of the dirty water and dirt chunks collect in the bucket. With the filter, some of the dirty water and the dirt chunks get deflected away from the bucket, so not as much of the dirty water and dirt chunks make it into the bucket. In the analogy, the source of the continuous spectrum light is like the faucet spewing out the dirty water, the cool thin gas is like the filter, and the bucket is like the camera or light detector. What is not in the analogy is the spectrometer that takes the collected light and spreads it out into its constituent colors.

emission lines

The spectra of hot, thin (low density) gas clouds are a series of bright lines called **emission lines.** In both of these types of spectra you see spectral features at certain, discrete wavelengths (or colors) and no where else.

temperature of gas relative to what's in the background

The type of spectrum you see depends on the temperature of the thin gas. If the thin gas is *cooler* than the thermal source in the background, you see absorption lines. Since the spectra of stars show absorption lines, it tells you that the density and temperature of the upper layers of a star is lower than the deeper layers. In a few cases you can see emission lines on top of the thermal spectrum. This is produced by thin gas that is *hotter* than the thermal source in the background. Unlike the case for absorption lines, though, the production of emission lines does NOT require a thermal source be in the background. The spectrum of a hydrogen-

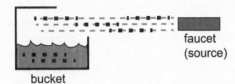

Dirty water stream with filter analogy
for absorption lines

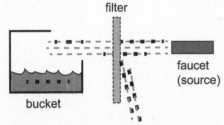

With filter, some dirty water still goes through
but some dirty water with large dirt chunks
gets deflected away.
Faucet => hot dense object, source of
                continuous spectrum
Filter => cool, thin gas absorbing some
           of the light
Bucket => light collector (camera)

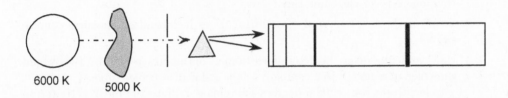

Type of spectrum seen depends on the temperature of the thin gas **relative to**
the background. TOP: thin gas is *cooler* so **absorption lines** are seen.
BOTTOM: thin gas is *hotter* so **emission lines** are seen.

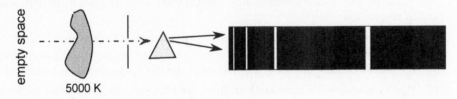

emission nebula ("nebula" = gas or dust cloud) is just a series of emission lines
without any thermal spectrum because there are no stars visible behind the hot
nebula. Some objects produce spectra that is a combination of a thermal spectrum,
emission lines, and absorption lines simultaneously!

What is very useful about discrete spectra is that the pattern of lines you see
depends on the chemical composition of the thin gas. Each element or molecule
produces a distinct *pattern* of lines—each element or molecule has a "fingerprint"
you can use to identify it (like a UPC barcode or QR code). This allows you to
remotely determine what stars, planets, nebulae, etc. are made of!

The composition canNOT be found from just one line because one element may

ID from the *pattern* only

have one spectral line at the same wavelength as another element's spectral line. However, an element's *pattern* of lines is unique. Using a single line to identify a gas would be like identifying the name of someone using just one letter of their name—many people will have that same letter in their name, but the *pattern* of letters (which letters and how they are arranged) is unique to that one person. Of course, stars, planets, nebulae, etc. are made of more than one type of material, so you see the discrete spectra of many elements and molecules superimposed on each other—all of the spectral lines add together. An experienced astronomer can disentangle all the different patterns and sort out the elements and molecules (but it does take time!).

complicated spectrum: all the spectral lines added together

Vocabulary

absorption line spectrum	continuous spectrum	discrete spectrum
emission line spectrum	luminosity	Stefan-Boltzmann law
thermal spectrum	Wien's law	

Formulae

1. **Wien's law:** $\lambda_{\text{peak}} = 2.9 \times 10^6/\text{temperature}$. The units of the peak wavelength are nanometers and the temperature is in Kelvin.

2. **Stefan-Boltzmann law:** Energy emitted by a square meter on an object's surface $= \sigma \times \text{temperature}^4$, where σ is a constant of nature.

Review Questions

1. What are the three basic kinds of spectrum? Can an object produce more than one type at the same time?

2. What produces a **thermal spectrum**? Does it depend on chemical composition?

3. How can temperature be determined from a continuous spectrum? How would the color of a hot object compare to the color of a cooler object? At what wavelength do you at 98.6 degrees Fahrenheit radiate the most? (Hint: use the temperature scales table.)

4. How will the **thermal spectrum** produced by a chunk of lead compare to the thermal spectrum produced by a chunk of iron of the same size and temperature?

5. What produces an **emission line spectrum**? Do you need a thermal source in the background?

6. Can you see emission lines if a thermal source is in the background? What does their visibility depend on? (Think about the temperature of the gas producing the emission lines and the temperature of the the the background thermal source.)

7. What produces an **absorption line spectrum**? Do you need a thermal source? Would you see absorption lines if the gas in front of a thermal source was *hotter* than the thermal source? Explain why!

8. Why must you use a *pattern* of lines to find the composition? Why is one line not sufficient?

9. What kind of spectrum and what pattern of lines would you see if you heated up a tube filled with hydrogen, helium and neon gas?

7.4   Bohr atom

Scientists have had the technology to observe discrete spectra since the beginning of the 19th century. They had to wait over a hundred years, though, for an explanation of how the discrete spectra were produced. They knew that it was produced by atoms and that atoms had negative and positive charges in them. Some models of the atom were similar to our current one: the positive charges are concentrated in a central nucleus with the negative charges swarming around it, but the atoms should be unstable. As the negative charges (called **electrons**) move around the nucleus, they should radiate light and spiral into the nucleus in about 10^{-16} second. This is obviously contradicted by common experience!

electron

Niels Bohr (lived 1885–1962)
Image courtesy of The American Institute of Physics

Niels Bohr provided the explanation in the early 20th century. He said that the electron can be only found in energy orbits of a certain size and as long as the electron is in one of those special orbits, it would radiate no energy. If the electron changed orbits, it would radiate or absorb energy. This model sounds outlandish, but numerous experiments have shown it to be true.

In Bohr's model of the atom, the massive but small positively-charged **protons** and massive but small neutral **neutrons** are found in the tiny nucleus. The small, light negatively-charged **electrons** move around the nucleus in certain specific orbits (energies). In a neutral atom the number of electrons = the number of protons. The arrangement of an atom's energy orbits depends on the number of protons and neutrons in the nucleus and the number of electrons orbiting the nucleus. Because every type of atom has a unique arrangement of their energy orbits, they produce a unique pattern of absorption or emission lines.

proton
neutron
electron

All atoms with the same number of protons in the nucleus are grouped together into something called an **element.** Because the atoms of an element have the same number of protons, they also have the same number of electrons and, therefore, the same chemical properties. For example, all atoms with one proton in the nucleus have the same chemical properties and are called Hydrogen. All atoms with two protons in the nucleus will not chemically react with any other atoms and are known as Helium. The atoms called Carbon form the basis of life and have six protons in the nucleus. In the figure on the next page, atom (a) is Hydrogen, atom (b) is Helium, atoms (c), (d), and (e) are Lithium.

element

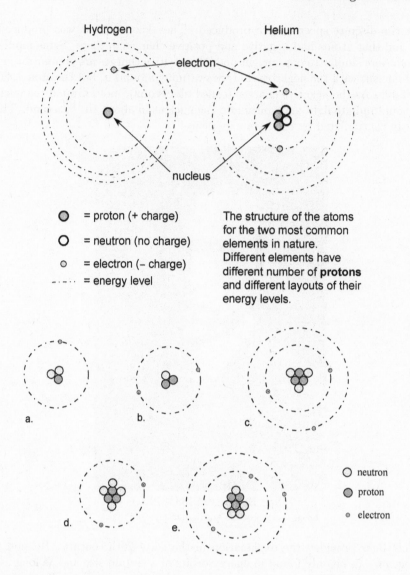

The structure of the atoms for the two most common elements in nature. Different elements have different number of **protons** and different layouts of their energy levels.

isotope

Elements are sub-divided into sub-groups called **isotopes** based on the number of protons AND neutrons in the nucleus. All atoms of an element with the same number of neutrons in the nucleus are of the same type of **isotope.** An element's isotopes will have very nearly the same chemical properties but they can behave very differently in *nuclear* reactions. For example, all of the isotopes of the element Hydrogen have one electron orbiting the nucleus and behave the same way in chemistry reactions. The ordinary Hydrogen isotope has 0 neutrons + 1 proton while another Hydrogen isotope called *Deuterium* has 1 neutron + 1 proton and another Hydrogen isotope called *Tritium* has 2 neutrons + 1 proton in the nucleus. Tritium is *radioactive*—its nucleus spontaneouly changes into another type of nucleus. In the figure above, atoms (c), (d), and (e) are different *isotopes* of the same *element* called Lithium.

Most atoms in nature are neutral, the negative charges exactly cancel the positive charges. But sometimes an atom has a hard collision with another atom or absorbs an energetic photon so that one or more electrons are knocked out of the atom. In some rare cases, an atom may temporarily hold onto an extra electron. In either case, the atom has an extra positive or negative charge and is called an

ion

ion. For example, the carbon ion C^+ has 6 protons and 5 electrons and the iron ion Fe^{2+} has 26 protons and 24 electrons. Because the number of electrons are different, an ion of an element will behave differently in chemical reactions than its neutral cousins. In the figure on the previous page, atom (d) is a Li^+ ion [compare it with atom (c) or (e)].

In order to explain discrete spectra, Bohr found that atoms obey three basic rules:

1. Electrons have only certain energies corresponding to particular distances from nucleus. As long as the electron is in one of those energy orbits, it will not lose or absorb any energy. The energy orbits are analogous to rungs on a ladder: electrons can be only on rungs of the ladder and not in between rungs.

2. The orbits closer to the nucleus have lower energy.

3. Atoms want to be in the lowest possible energy state, called the **ground state** (all electrons as close to the nucleus as possible).

ground state

7.5   How Atoms Produce the Spectra

Let's see how Bohr's model of the atom explains the three types of spectra. An **emission line** is produced by an atom in an "excited" energy state—the electron is *not* in as low an energy orbit as possible. Remember rule #3! In order to go to a *lower* energy orbit, the electron *must* lose energy of a certain *specific* amount. The atom releases the energy is the form of a photon with that particular energy. The energy of photon = the difference in energy of the energy orbits (energy ladder rungs).

how to make an emission line

Example: An atom with an electron at the E_2 orbit wants to get to the lower E_1 energy orbit. It gives off a photon with energy $E_{photon} = h \times f = E_2 - E_1$ (figure next page). The electron may reach the ground state in one jump or it may temporarily stop at one or more energy levels on the way, but it cannot stop somewhere *between* the energy levels. Different jumps produce photons of different energies. *A larger jump to a lower energy level, will produce a photon with greater energy (smaller wavelength).*

larger jump means smaller wavelength

The atom produces light of certain wavelengths. (Remember that light is both a photon and a wave!) The more atoms undergoing a particular transition, the more intense the emission line will be. The intensity depends on the density and temperature of the gas.

Emission line

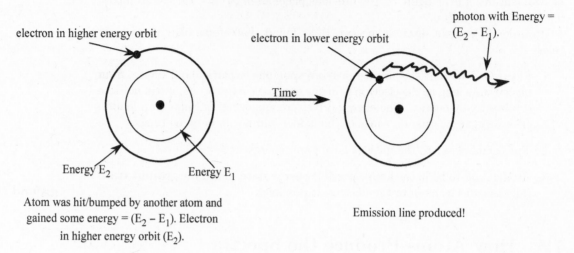

electron in higher energy orbit

electron in lower energy orbit

photon with Energy = $(E_2 - E_1)$.

Time

Energy E_2 Energy E_1

Atom was hit/bumped by another atom and
gained some energy = $(E_2 - E_1)$. Electron
in higher energy orbit (E_2).

Emission line produced!

how to make an absorption line

An **absorption line** is produced when a photon of just the right energy is absorbed by an atom, kicking an electron to a higher energy orbit. The photon had energy = the difference in energy of the energy orbits. Because the energy levels in an element's atoms are fixed, the size of the outward jumps made by the electrons are the same as the inward jumps. Therefore, the pattern of absorption lines is the same as the pattern of emission lines. Other photons moving through the gas with the wrong energy will pass right on by the atoms in the thin gas. They make up the rest of the continous spectrum you see.

Example: An atom with electron in the E_1 orbit sees a photon with energy $E_{photon} = E_2 - E_1$. The photon is absorbed and the electron moves outward to E_2. The photon is later re-emitted but in a *random* direction—not necessarily in the same direction as the original photon! An observer will see less photons from the direction of the continuous source at that specific frequency (color) than other frequencies (colors). Photons of other energies pass right on by without being absorbed (see figure next page). The atom can absorb photons of just the right energy to move an electron from one energy level to another level. (See the "How do you do that?" box two pages over for a more detailed example of the absorption

"How do you do that?" box two pages over

how to make a thermal spectrum

lines for hydrogen.) The more atoms undergoing a particular absorption transition (the more photons being absorbed), the darker (or "stronger") the absorption line. The strength of the absorption line depends on the density and temperature.

A thermal spectrum is produced by atoms that are closely packed together. The energy levels of the atoms are distorted by their neighboring atom's electrons. This smears out the normally sharp spectral lines (they become fatter).

Example: An orange line is fattened so that one edge is in the yellow wavelengths and the other edge is in the red wavelengths. The amount of smearing, or broadening, depends on the density. Eventually, the density gets high enough to where the smeared lines all merge together to produce the rainbow of colors of a continuous spectrum.

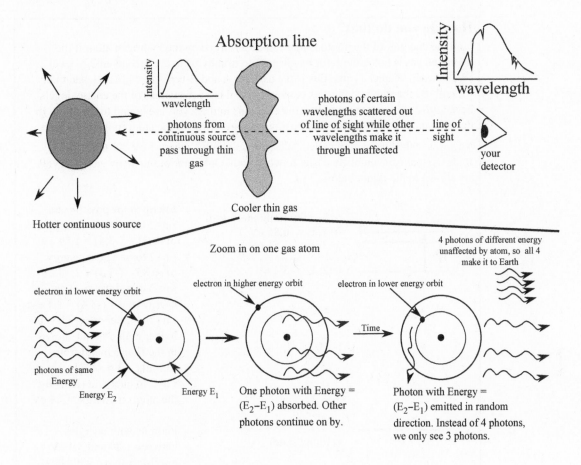

Absorption line

7.6 Universality of Physical Laws in Space and Time

The pattern of spectral lines and particular wavelengths produced by an atom depend very sensitively on the masses and charges of the sub-atomic particles and the interactions between them (forces and rules they follow). If different parts of the universe had even slight differences in the rules of quantum mechanics that govern the interactions of the protons, electrons, and neutrons or differences in the strengths of the fundamental forces of nature from that observed on the Earth, we would see noticable changes in the spacing and strength of the spectral lines. If the subatomic particles had different amount of charge or mass, the pattern of lines would be different than what you see on the Earth. We observe that all hydrogen atoms produce the *same* pattern of lines everywhere in the universe, whether they are in the Sun, other stars, distant galaxies, or intergalactic space. (Hydrogen is not special in this regard—all of the other types of atoms produce the same pattern that is unique to that type of atom.) ***The fact that we see the same pattern of lines for a given element (type of atom) everywhere in the universe tells us that the same laws of physics used in the structure of atoms work everywhere in the universe.***

Recall from the first chapter that astronomy gives us a sort of time machine: when we look at very distant objects we see them *as they were* a long time ago because light, traveling at a fast but finite speed, has taken a long time to travel the vast distances between us and the distant objects. The light from those distant objects tells us about the physical laws operating in that part of the universe when

How do you do that?

Find the energies of the photons that can be absorbed by the hydrogen atom if the hydrogen gas is hot enough for its electron to usually be in the second energy level. (We'll see in chapter 11 that this is the case for A and B-type stars.) In this example, we will use the standard physics convention and have the values of the energy levels be *negative* numbers to mean that the electrons in the levels are bound to the atom. In this convention, an electron with positive energy is free of the atom (unbound). Also, we will use the energy unit called "electron volt" (eV), where 1 eV = 1.602 x 10^{-19} Joules to make the numbers easier to work with. Only four of the many energy levels are shown in the figure below.

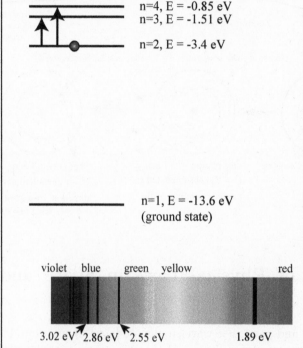

n=infinity (unbound), E = 0
n=4, E = -0.85 eV
n=3, E = -1.51 eV

n=2, E = -3.4 eV

n=1, E = -13.6 eV
(ground state)

Energy hops possible are:
• n=2 to n=3 at an energy of -1.51 – (-3.4) = 1.89 eV;
• n=2 to n=4 at an energy of -0.85 – (-3.4) = 2.55 eV;
• n=2 to n=infinity at an energy of 0 – (-3.4) = 3.4 eV;
• n=2 to other energy levels higher than n=4 not shown in the figure found from formula: 13.6 x $(1/4 - 1/n^2)$;
• n=2 to unbound (ionizing the atom) if energy > 3.4 eV.

Photons with energies between 1.89 and 3.4 eV not listed above will NOT be absorbed by the atom.

violet   blue   green   yellow   red

3.02 eV   2.86 eV   2.55 eV   1.89 eV

Hydrogen absorption line energies. The line at 2.86 eV is for n=2 to n=5 and line at 3.02 eV is for n=2 to n=6.

the light was emitted long ago. *The fact that we see the same pattern of lines for a given element in light emitted by objects at any time in the universe tells us that the laws of physics are the same throughout time—they do not change.*

You will also see in the following chapters that the same kind of conclusions can be reached by looking at the gravitational interactions of objects at any position and distance from us. We see the same laws of nature operating at all places and times in the universe. If you reflect a bit on that fact, it is pretty darn amazing!

Vocabulary

electron	element	ground state
ion	isotope	neutron
proton		

Review Questions

1. Where are electrons, protons, and neutrons located in the atom? Can the

electron be found at any position or energy in the atom?

2. How does the Bohr atom model explain emission line spectra?

3. Which produces a *shorter* wavelength of light: an electron jumping from the 6th to 2nd energy level, or one jumping from 3rd to 2nd energy level? Explain your answer.

4. How does the Bohr atom model explain absorption line spectra?

5. Which would produce an absorption line at a *longer* wavelength: an electron jumping from the 1st to 5th energy level, or one jumping from 1st to 3rd energy level? Explain your answer.

6. Which will produce a stronger absorption line: a 10,000 K cloud with 100 particles in front of a hot star or a 10,000 K cloud with 1,000,000 particles in front of a hot star? Why is that?

7. If the atom absorbs a photon and later emits it, why do we see any absorption lines at all?

8. How does the Bohr atom model explain thermal spectra?

9. How will the spectra from atoms of the hydrogen isotopes deuterium and tritium compare to the spectra of ordinary hydrogen atoms?

10. Why would you not expect the absorption lines of the calcium ion Ca^+ to be the same as the ones of neutral calcium Ca?

11. Will the hydrogen ion H^+ produce any absorption lines or emission lines? Explain your answer.

12. How do we know that the laws of physics (nature) are the same everywhere in the universe and that they are the same throughout time?

7.7   Doppler Effect

The wave nature of light means there will be a shift in the spectral lines of an object if it is moving. This effect is known as the **doppler effect.** You have probably heard the doppler effect in the change of the pitch of the sound coming from something moving toward you or away from you (eg., a train whistle, a police siren, an ice cream truck's music, a mosquito buzzing). Sounds from objects moving *toward* you are at a *higher* pitch because the sound waves are compressed together, shortening the wavelength of the sound waves. Sounds from objects moving *away* from you are at a *lower* pitch because the sound waves are stretched apart, lengthening the wavelength. Light behaves in the same way.

doppler effect

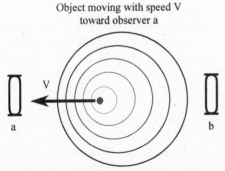

Object moving with speed V
toward observer a

Observer a sees compressed waves (blue-shifted)
Observer b sees stretched waves (red-shifted)

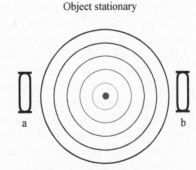

Object stationary

Both observer a and b see same
wavelengths.

faster   speed—greater shift

Motion of the light source causes the spectral lines to shift positions. An object's motion causes a wavelength shift $\Delta\lambda = \lambda_{new} - \lambda_{rest}$ that depends on the speed and direction the object is moving. The amount of the shift depends on the object's speed: $\Delta\lambda = \lambda_{rest} \times (V_{radial}/c)$, where c is the speed of light, λ_{rest} is the wavelength you would measure if the object was at rest and V_{radial} is the speed along the line of sight.

There is a lot of information stored in that little formula! First, it says that the *faster* the object moves, the *greater* the doppler shift $\Delta\lambda$. For example, a particular emission line of hydrogen from nearby galaxies is shifted by a smaller amount than the same line from faraway galaxies. This means that the faraway galaxies are moving faster than the nearby galaxies.

radar reflection   radar transmission

Radar guns use the doppler effect to tell how fast cars are moving. The faster the car is moving toward the radar gun, the more scrunched the reflected waves will be. Which car is going to get the ticket?

The "radar guns" used by police officers operate on this principle too. They send out a radio wave of a set wavelength (or frequency) that reflects off a car back to the radar gun. The device determines the car's speed from the difference in the wavelength (or frequency) of the transmitted beam and reflected beam.

motion toward or away only

Second, the term V_{radial} means that only the object's motion *along the line of sight* is important. If object moves at an angle with respect to the line of sight, then the doppler shift ($\Delta\lambda$) tells you only about the part of its motion along the line of sight. You must use other techniques to determine how much of an object's total velocity is perpendicular to the line of sight.

Finally, which way the spectral lines are shifted tells you if the object is moving toward or away from you. If the object is moving *toward* you, the waves are compressed, so their wavelength is *shorter*. The lines are shifted to shorter (bluer) wavelengths—this is called a **blueshift**. If the object is moving *away* from you, the waves are stretched out, so their wavelength is *longer*. The lines are shifted to longer (redder) wavelengths—this is called a **redshift**.

blueshift: *motion toward you*
redshift: *motion away from you*

This explanation also works if you are moving and the object is stationary or if both you and the object are moving. The doppler effect will tell you about the *relative* motion of the object with respect to you. The spectral lines of nearly all of the galaxies in the universe are shifted to the red end of the spectrum. This means that the galaxies are moving away from the Milky Way galaxy and is evidence for the expansion of the universe.

why not use color to measure speed

The doppler effect will not affect overall color of an object unless it is moving at a significant fraction of the speed of light (VERY fast!). For an object moving toward us, the red colors will be shifted to the orange and the near-infrared will be shifted to the red, etc. All of the colors shift. The overall color of the object depends on the combined intensities of all of the wavelengths (colors). The first figure on the next page shows the continuous spectra for the Sun at three speeds (zero, a fast

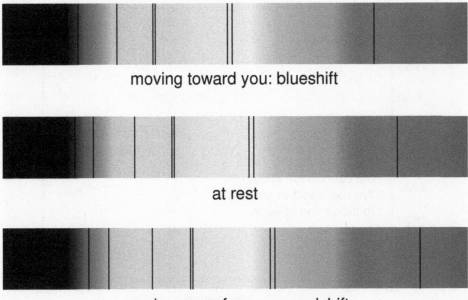

moving toward you: blueshift

at rest

moving away from you: redshift

0.01*c*, a VERY fast 0.1*c*). The Hydrogen-α line (at 656.3nm) is shown too. Objects in our galaxy will be moving at speeds much less than 0.01*c*. The doppler shifted continuous spectrum for the Sun moving at 0.01*c* is almost indistinguishable from the Sun at rest even when you zoom in to just the optical wavelengths (figure next page). However, the doppler shift of the spectral line is easy to spot for the slow speed. By zooming in even further, you can detect spectral line doppler shifts for speeds as small as 1 km/sec or lower (less than $3.334 \times 10^{-6}c$!).

use spectral lines to measure speed

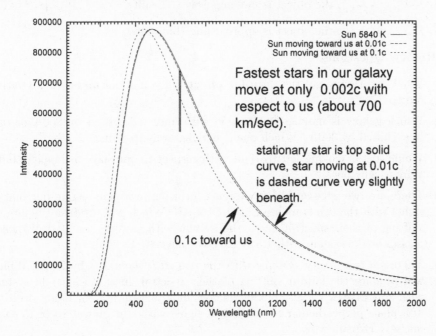

Fastest stars in our galaxy move at only 0.002c with respect to us (about 700 km/sec).

stationary star is top solid curve, star moving at 0.01c is dashed curve very slightly beneath.

0.1c toward us

Vocabulary

blueshift   doppler effect   redshift

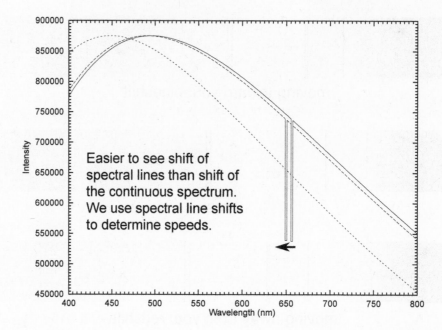

Formulae

1. Wavelength shift: $\Delta\lambda = \lambda_{new} - \lambda_{rest}$. λ_{rest} is the wavelength measured if the object is at rest and λ_{new} is the wavelength measured for the moving object.

2. **Doppler effect:** $\Delta\lambda = \lambda_{rest} \times (V_{radial}/c)$, where V_{radial} is the object's speed along the line of sight and c is the speed of light. Greater speeds produce greater wavelength shifts.

3. If $\lambda_{new} > \lambda_{rest}$, the object is moving away (redshift).

4. If $\lambda_{new} < \lambda_{rest}$, the object is approaching (blueshift).

Review Questions

1. What two things can the **doppler effect** tell you about an object's relative motion?

2. Which galaxy is moving faster: one with lines red-shifted by 200Å or one blue-shifted by 300Å? Which one is moving away from us?

3. Would a star moving left to right with respect to you have a doppler shift? Why or why not?

4. There are two edge-on binary systems (orbiting in a plane along our line of sight) with the two stars separated by 2 AU. Which will produce the largest shifting of their spectral lines: the system with star masses 10 & 15 solar masses or the system with 1.5 & 2.0 solar masses? Explain why.

5. There are two binary systems with the two stars separated by 2 AU. Which will produce the largest shifting of their spectral lines: an edge-on system with star masses 1.5 & 2.0 solar masses or a face-on system (stars orbiting in a plane perpendicular to our line of sight) with star masses 10 & 15 solar masses? Explain why.

6. Why should you use spectral lines to measure velocities rather than the change in color of an object?

Chapter 8

Telescopes

Men and women have looked up at the sky and wondered about the things they see up there for as long as humans have lived on our Earth. Long ago, the Sun and Moon were mysterious objects that could be seen in the day and night. But the planets and stars were even more mysterious probably because they are so far away that we could only see them as points of light. Unlike the things on the Earth that we can study up close, handle, listen to, smell, and taste, the only way ancient watchers of the sky had to learn about things in space was to use their eyes and imaginations. Only very recently in the history of humanity have astronomers been able to extend the reach of our eyes (and our imaginations!).

Galileo pioneered modern explorations in the early 1600's by using a device originally invented for naval operations to explore the heavens. The device he used, of course, was the **telescope**, an instrument used to gather and focus light. Our atmosphere prevents most of the electromagnetic radiation from reaching the ground, allowing just the visible band, parts of the radio band, and small fractions of the infrared and ultraviolet through. Our eyes can detect the visible (optical) band, so the early telescopes were all built to observe in that part of the electromagnetic spectrum. It wasn't until the 1930's that astronomers began observing with another part of the electromagnetic spectrum—the radio band. The development of space technology has enabled astronomers to put telescopes above the atmosphere and explore all of those places out there using the full range of the electromagnetic spectrum. This chapter covers the basics of telescopes and the effects of the atmosphere on images. Vocabulary terms are in boldface.

telescope

8.1 Types of Telescopes

There are two basic types of telescopes, refractors and reflectors. The part of the telescope that gathers the light, called the **objective**, determines the type of telescope. A **refractor** telescope uses a glass lens as its objective. The glass lens is at the front of the telescope and light is bent (refracted) as it passes through the lens. A **reflector** telescope uses a mirror as its objective. The mirror is close to the rear of the telescope and light is bounced off (reflected) as it strikes the mirror.

objective
refractor

reflector

8.1.1 Refractor Telescopes

The refractor telescope uses a lens to gather and focus light. The first telescopes built were refractors. The long thin telescopes sold in department stores are refractors, as well as, those used for rifle scopes.

Advantages

1. Refractor telescopes are rugged. After the initial alignment, their optical system is more resistant to misalignment than the reflector telescopes.

2. The glass surface inside the tube is sealed from the atmosphere so it rarely needs cleaning.

3. Since the tube is closed off from the outside, air currents and effects due to changing temperatures are eliminated. This means that the images are steadier and sharper than those from a reflector telescope of the same size.

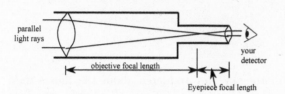 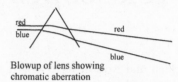

Though excellent refractors are still made, the disadvantages of the refractor telescope have blocked the construction of very large refractors for use in astronomical research.

Disadvantages

chromatic aberration

1. All refractors suffer from an effect called **chromatic aberration** ("color deviation or distortion") that produces a rainbow of colors around the image. Because of the wave nature of light, the longer wavelength light (redder colors) is bent less than the shorter wavelength light (bluer colors) as it passes through the lens. This is used in prisms to produce pretty rainbows, but it can ruin an image! There are a couple of ways to reduce chromatic aberration. One way uses multiple compensating lenses to counteract chromatic aberration. The other way uses a very long objective *focal length* (distance between the focus and the objective) to minimize the effect. This is why the early refractor telescopes were made very long.

2. How well the light passes through the lens varies with the wavelength of the light. Ultraviolet light does not pass through the lens at all.

3. How well the light passes through decreases as the thickness of the lens increases.

4. It is difficult to make a glass lens with no imperfections inside the lens and with a perfect curvature on *both* sides of the lens.

5. The objective lens can be supported only at the ends. The glass lens will sag under its own weight.

Because of these disadvantages, the largest refractor telescope built is the one at Yerkes Observatory. It has an objective 1.02 meters (40 inches) across at one end of a 19.2-meter (63 feet) tube. The text's website has pictures of this telescope and the 0.9-meter (36-inch) at Lick Observatory outside of San Jose, CA. You will also find web links to the observatories and more information about these refractors.

8.1.2   Reflector Telescopes

The reflector telescope uses a mirror to gather and focus light. All celestial objects (including those in our solar system) are so far away that all of the light rays coming from them reach the Earth as parallel rays. Because the light rays are parallel to each other, the reflector telescope's mirror has a parabolic shape. The parabolic-shaped mirror focusses the parallel lights rays to a single point. All modern research

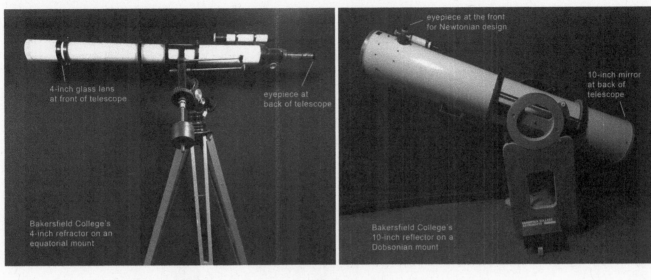

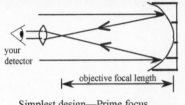

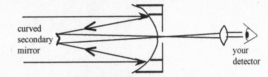

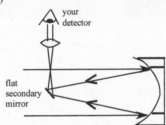

Simplest design—Prime focus
(Why isn't there a shadow cast
by the observer on the image?)

More common (and more convenient!)
Cassegrain design. Hole in
mirror—why doesn't that affect image?

Popular Newtonian design found
in many amateur telescopes

telescopes and large amateur ones are of the reflector type because of its advantages over the refractor telescope.

Advantages

1. Reflector telescopes do not suffer from chromatic aberration because all wavelengths will reflect off the mirror in the same way.

2. Support for the objective mirror is all along the back side so they can be made very BIG!

3. Reflector telescopes are cheaper to make than refractors of the same size.

4. Because light is reflecting off the objective, rather than passing through it, only one side of the reflector telescope's objective needs to be perfect.

Alas! Despite the advantages of the reflector telescope, astronomers must contend with some minor annoyances.

Disadvantages

1. It is easy to get their optics out of alignment.

2. A reflector telescope's tube is open to the outside and the optics need frequent cleaning.

3. Often a secondary mirror is used to redirect the light into a more convenient viewing spot. The secondary mirror and its supports can produce diffraction effects: bright objects have spikes (the "christmas star effect").

The Gemini North Telescope on Hawaii's Mauna Kea has a mirror 8.1 meters across. Notice the person next to the mirror for scale.
Image courtesy of Gemini Observatory/AURA.

The text's website has links to more pictures and information about the Gemini Telescope and also the 10-meter Keck Telescope.

In both the reflector and refractor telescopes, the focus is before the eyepiece, so the image in astronomical telescopes is upside down. Telescopes used to look at things on the Earth's surface use another lens to re-invert the image right-side up. Most reflector telescopes will use a smaller secondary mirror in front of the large primary mirror to reflect the light to a more convenient viewing spot. Isaac Newton used a flat secondary mirror at a 45° angle to reflect the light to an eyepiece at the side of the telescope tube near the top. Such an arrangement, called a *newtonian* design, is used by many amateur telescopes.

Many reflector telescope use another light path design called the *cassegrain* design to reflect the light back through a hole in the primary mirror, so that detectors or the eyepiece can be conveniently placed behind the telescope. Most of the large telescopes used for research, including the Hubble Space Telescope, are of this design. Some of the largest telescopes like the Hale Telescope and the Keck Telescope have places to put detectors at the prime focus, where the light from the primary mirror first comes to a focus. The images in reflector telescopes do not have holes or shadows in them because the light rays from the unblocked parts of the primary mirror are all added together when they are focused together. Even though part of the primary mirror is blocked or missing, there is still plenty of usable primary mirror space to gather the light.

spherical aberration

Both types of telescope can suffer from a defect called **spherical aberration** so that not all of the light is focused to the same point. This can happen if the mirror is not curved enough (shaped like part of a sphere instead of a paraboloid)

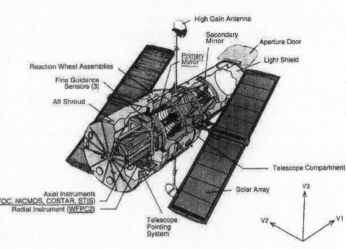

The Hubble Space Telescope. A shematic of the telescope is shown at right.
Images courtesy of the Space Telescope Science Institute/AURA

or the glass lens is not shaped correctly. The Hubble Space Telescope objective suffers from this (it is too flat by 2 microns, about 1/50 the width of a human hair), so it uses corrective optics to compensate. The corrective optics intercept the light beams from the secondary mirror before they reach the cameras and spectrographs. Fortunately, the Hubble Space Telescope's spherical aberration is so perfect, that

Hubble Space Telescope fix

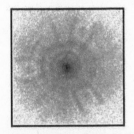

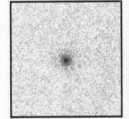

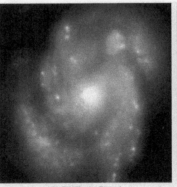

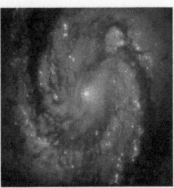

BEFORE COSTAR   **AFTER COSTAR**

Images before and after corrective optics were installed on the Hubble Space Telescope to correct for **spherical aberration**. The left two images are of a single star and the right two images are of a spiral galaxy.
Images courtesy of the Space Telescope Science Institute/AURA

it is easy to correct for!

Even before the 1993 servicing mission that installed the corrective optics 2.5 years after the Hubble Space Telescope was put in orbit (in April 1990), astronomers were able to get significant results from the telescope. The images were computer-enhanced to correct for the spherical aberration to produce sharper images than from any ground-based telescope. Also, astronomers were able to observe ultraviolet light from celestial objects and fainter objects than could be seen from the ground. However, the computer processing took a long time and the aberration prevented the focusing of most of the light. This meant that astronomers could not see the very faint (and distant) objects they were looking for. Astronomers and the public were very pleased after the corrective optics were installed. Ground-based telescopes larger than Keck that will outperform even the Hubble Space Telescope (in the optical and infrared bands using adaptive optics, section 8.3.1) are being built now. See the textbook website for links to these huge telescopes.

8.1.3   Radio Telescopes

Radio astronomy has its roots back in the 1930's when Karl Jansky accidentally detected radio emission from the center of the Milky Way as part of his research on the interference on transatlantic phone lines. The British advanced radio antenna technology in their development of radar technology to fight the German warplanes in World War II. After the war, astronomers adapted the technology to detect radio waves coming from space.

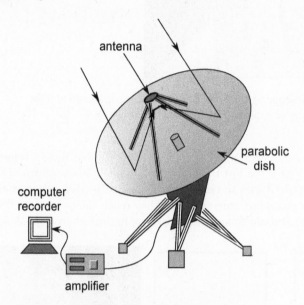

A radio telescope reflects radio waves to a focus at the antenna. Because radio wavelengths are very large, the radio dish must be very large.

A radio telescope uses a large metal dish or wire mesh, usually parabolic-shaped, to reflect the radio waves to an antenna above the dish. Looking from underneath some radio telescopes, a person can see the clouds in the sky overhead but to the much longer wavelength radio waves, the metal mesh is an excellent reflector. Radio telescopes designed to also receive smaller wavelengths, such as the Green Bank Telescope (GBT; see the textbook's website for a picture and tour of the GBT and the NRAO site at Green Bank, WV), have solid metal dishes. The GBT's metal surface is made up of 2004 panels, each roughly the size of a queen-sized bed, mounted on actuators to fine-tune the shape as the telescope is tilted and wind speed and direction changes.

The signal is then sent to an amplifier to magnify the very faint signals. At the last step, the amplified signal is processed by a computer to turn the radio signals into an image that follows the shape of the radio emission. False colors are used to indicate the intensity of the radio emission at different locations (see the text's website for examples).

Radio telescopes are much larger than optical telescopes because radio wavelengths are much longer than optical wavelengths. The longer wavelengths means that the radio waves have lower energy than optical light waves. In order to collect enough radio photons to detect a signal, the radio dishes must be very large. Both optical and radio telescope reflectors use a parabolic shape to perfectly focus the light to a point. Increasing the size of the radio dish is also necessary in order to improve the clarity of the radio images. I will discuss the issue of image clarity further in the next two sections.

Radio telescopes detect the emission from cool clouds of hydrogen in the space between the stars. Hydrogen atoms are the most common type of atoms in the universe and much of the hydrogen gas is too far away from any star to produce emission in the optical wavelength band. Therefore, radio telescopes are a vital tool in understanding the universe. I will discuss further the use of radio waves to explore the material between the stars and the structure of our galaxy in chapter 14.

Vocabulary

chromatic aberration	objective	reflector
refractor	spherical aberration	telescope

Review Questions

1. What are the two basic types of telescopes? What are their advantages and disadvantages?

2. Why are the large modern telescopes reflector telescopes?

3. How is the rainbow of colors produced around the images in refractor telescopes?

4. How will **spherical aberration** affect an image?

5. How does the size and shape of a radio telescope compare to an optical telescope? Why is there such a difference in their sizes?

6. What are the parts of a radio telescope?

7. What kinds of things can be seen with a radio telescope that cannot be detected by an optical telescope?

8.2 Powers of a Telescope

There are three features of a telescope that enable them to extend the power of our vision: a telescope's superior light-gathering ability enables us to see faint objects, a telescope's superior resolving power enables us to see even the tiniest of details, and the magnification power enables us to enlarge tiny images. Department stores and camera shops which do not know anything about telescopes, loudly proclaim their telescope's magnifying power. Magnification is the least important power of a telescope. Amateur and professional astronomers know that the light-gathering power and resolving power are the most important. These two abilities depend critically on the objective, so they make sure the optics of the objective are excellent.

8.2.1 Light-Gathering Power

The ability of a telescope to collect a lot more light than the human eye, its **light-gathering power,** is probably its most important feature. The telescope acts as a "light bucket", collecting all of the photons that come down on it from a far away object. Just as a bigger bucket catches more rain water, a bigger objective collects more light in a given time interval. This makes faint images brighter. This is why the pupils of your eyes enlarge at night so that more light reaches the retinas. Very far away, faint objects can be seen only with BIG objective telescopes. Making faint images brighter is critical if the light is going to be dispersed to make a spectrum.

light-gathering power

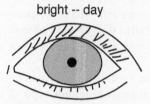
bright -- day

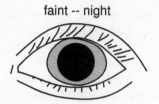
faint -- night

small light-gathering power   large light-gathering power

Your eye improves its light-gathering power in low-light conditions by making your pupil larger.

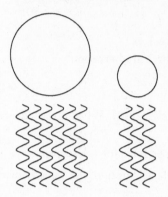

Bigger objective gathers more light: brighter images! Depends on **area** of objective = $(\pi D^2)/4$.

comparing   light-gathering powers

The area of the objective is the determining factor. Since most telescope objectives are circular, the area = $\pi \times$(diameter of objective)$^2/4$, where the value of π is approximately 3.1416. *To compare light-gathering powers of two telescopes, you divide the area of one telescope by the area of the other telescope.* For example: a 40-centimeter mirror has *four* times the light-gathering power of a 20-centimeter mirror: $[(\pi 40^2/4)/(\pi 20^2/4) = (40/20)^2 = 4]$.

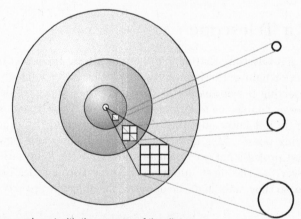

If 1-meter telescope has area = 1 and if it can see an object at 1 AU

THEN:
2-meter telescope has area = 4; can see same object at 2 AU

3-meter telescope has area = 9; can see same object at 3 AU

Light spreads out with the **square** of the distance. Through a sphere twice as large, the energy covers an area **four** times larger. Through a sphere three times as large, the energy covers an area **nine** times larger.

The light from a glowing object becomes more dilute as it spreads out from the object in a predictable way. The light covers larger and larger concentric spheres centered on the object, so that the object appears dimmer with the square of the distance. An object will appear four times dimmer when it is twice as far away, it will appear nine times dimmer when it is three times as far away, etc. Since the light-gathering power depends on the square of the diameter of the objective, the *distance* that an object can be detected increases as just the diameter of the objective (no square). *To compare how much farther one telescope can detect an object than another telescope, you divide the diameter of one telescope by the diameter of the other telescope.* Some examples are given in the figure on the next page. Consider another example of how much farther one could see with the 10-meter Keck telescope than with the human eye. The largest the pupil of the eye can dilate is 9 mm (for a young eye—older eyes do not dilate as much). So the Keck telescope at 10 meters × 1000 mm/meter = 10,000 mm across can see an object at least 10,000/9 = 1111 times farther away than with the unaided, dark-adapted eye for the same exposure time. For the human eye, the exposure time is about one-tenth of a second: that is the refresh rate of an image on the retina. Longer exposures enable a telescope to detect objects at even greater distances.

comparing how far out you can see

See farther with greater exposure time

8.2.2   Resolving Power

Another important power of a telescope is its ability to make us see really small details and see sharp images. This is its **resolving power.** Objects that are so close together in the sky that they blur together into a single blob are easily seen as separate objects with a good telescope. The resolving power is measured in the absolute smallest angle that can be resolved. The absolute minimum resolvable angle in arc seconds $\theta_R = 252,000 \times$ (observation wavelength) / (objective diameter). The wavelength and diameter must be measured in the same length units (i.e., both wavelength and objective diameter given in meters or both in nanometers). A telescope with one arc second resolution would be able to see a dime from about 3.7 kilometers (2.3 miles) away. Modern telescopes are able to count the number of lines in President Roosevelt's hair on a dime at that distance.

resolving power

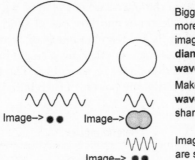

Bigger objective samples more of the light: sharper images! Depends on **diameter** of objective and **wavelength**: $\theta_R \sim (\lambda/D)$.

Make **diameter** *bigger* or **wavelength** *smaller* for sharper images.

Images for same two stars are shown.

The desire is to make θ_R as small as possible. This can be done by making the observation wavelength small (e.g., use UV instead of visible light) or by making the objective diameter large. Another way to understand it is the more waves that can be packed on the objective, the more information the telescope detects and, therefore, the more detailed the image is. A 40-centimeter telescope has *two* times the resolution of a 20-centimeter telescope at the same observing wavelength (θ_R for the 40-centimeter telescope is one-half the θ_R for the 10-inch telescope). However, fluctuations in the atmosphere will usually smear images into a fuzzy blob about one arc second or more across so the resolution is usually limited to the resolution from a 12.5-centimeter telescope on the ground. I will discuss the atmosphere's effect on images further in section 8.3 and ways you can compensate for it.

smaller θ_R is better

The desire for greater resolving power is a major reason why radio telescopes are so enormous compared to their optical counterparts. Radio wavelengths are LARGE so the radio telescope must be LARGE to get decent resolving power (and also to increase the signal strength of the low-energy radio waves—light-gathering power!). The Keck 10-meter telescope is considered a very large optical telescope. However, it is easily dwarfed by the HUGE 305-meter Arecibo Radio Telescope. This telescope was built in a natural bowl-shaped valley in Puerto Rico. China built an even larger radio telescope within a natural basin in the southwester Guizhou province: the Five-hundred-meter Aperture Spherical Telescope (FAST). It began operation in September 2016. The text's website has links to more pictures and information about the Arecibo telescope and FAST.

The 305-meter radio telescope of the Arecibo Observatory.
Image courtesy of the NAIC - Arecibo Observatory, a facility of the NSF
Photo by David Parker, Science Photo Library

interferometer

Another way to increase the resolution is to connect telescopes together to make an **interferometer**. Radio waves from an object reach each telescope in the interferometer at slightly different times, so the waves are out of sync with one another. Knowing the distances between the telescopes and how out of sync the waves are, the signals can be combined electronically to create an image of exceptional resolution. The image has the same sharpness as one taken by a single instrument that would extend from one end of the interferometer to the other. The light-gathering power is equal to the sum of the light-gathering powers of each individual telescope.

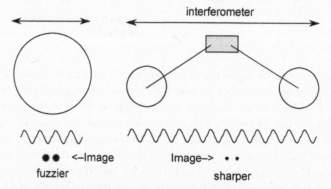

Telescopes connected together to make an *interferometer* can make even sharper images than a single large telescope if the *interferometer* is bigger than the large telescope. Images for same two stars are shown.

VLA

A spectacular example of such a system is the Very Large Array. This telescope is made of 27 radio dishes, each 25 meters in diameter, on a Y-shaped track. Fully extended, the Very Large Array is 36 *kilometers* across and has a resolution of around one arc second (depending on the radio wavelength). It has the light-gathering power of a 130-meter telescope. See the textbook's website for more pictures and links to more information.

Image courtesy of the National Radio Astronomy Observatory and Associated Universities, Inc.

An aerial view of the Very Large Array in its closest arrangement of the 27 dishes (left) and the author in front of and on the dish of one of telescopes (right).

The Very Long Baseline Array is a huge interferometer that uses ten telescopes placed in sites from Hawaii to the Virgin Islands (see the map on the next page). This telescope is 8,600 kilometers across and has a resolution as good as 0.0002 arc second! With a resolution about 50 times better than the Hubble Space Telescope, it is able to detect features as small as the inner solar system at the center of our galaxy, about 27,000 light years away. A similarly-sized array of radio telescopes, called the Event Horizon Telescope, is being used to image the supermassive black holes at the centers of galaxies. Astronomers are constructing radio telescopes out in space that work in conjunction with ground-based radio telescopes to make interferometers much larger than the Earth. Other huge radio telescope arrays include Australian Square Kilometre Array Pathfinder (ASKAP) made of 36 identical antennae, each 12 meters in diameter, in western Australia; and the Atacama Large Millimeter/submillimeter Array (ALMA) at over 16,500 foot (5000 meters) elevation in the Atacama Desert in Chile. ALMA is made of 66 total antennae with 54 of them 12 meters in diameter and 12 of them 7 meters in diameter in an array 16 kilometers across. Both ALMA and ASKAP are large international projects. Astronomers are also connecting optical telescopes to increase their resolving power. Two nice examples are the Large Binocular Telescope Interferometer on Mt Graham in Arizona, Hawaii and the Very Large Telescope Interferometer of Paranal Observatory on Cerro Paranal in the Atacama Desert, northern Chile. See the textbook's website for further details on all of these arrays.

VLBA

Event Horizon Telescope

ASKAP

ALMA

8.2.3 Magnifying Power

The ability of a telescope to enlarge images is the best-known feature of a telescope. Though it is so well-known, the **magnifying power** is the *least important* power of a telescope because it enlarges any distortions due to the telescope and atmosphere. A small, fuzzy faint blob becomes only a big, fuzzy blob. Also, the light becomes

magnifying power

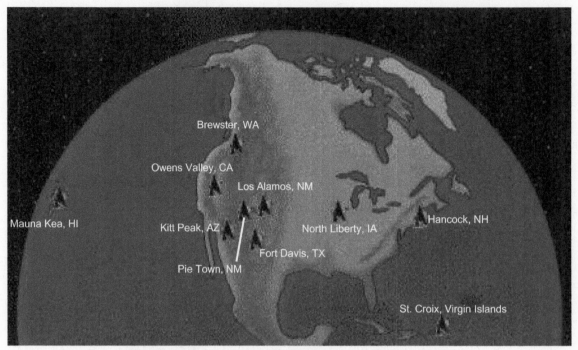

The ten sites of the 8,600-kilometer Very Long Baseline Array
Map courtesy of the National Radio Astronomy Observatory and Associated Universities, Inc.

more spread out under higher magnification so the image appears fainter! The magnifying power = (focal length of objective) / (focal length of eyepiece); both focal lengths must be in the same length units. A rough rule for the maximum magnification to use on your telescope is $20 \times D$ to $24 \times D$, where the objective diameter D is measured in *centimeters*. So an observer with a 15-centimeter telescope should not use magnification higher than about $24 \times 15 = 360$-power.

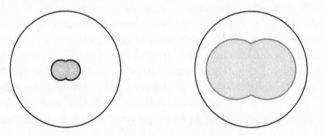

Magnification increases the size of an image in the
field of view, but a small fuzzy blob just becomes
a large fuzzier blob and the contrast is less.

The set of four figures on the next page shows the effect of a larger objective size. They have the same magnification. These are ideal images of two stars separated by 0.5 arc seconds which would be the angular separation for two objects separated by a distance equal to the distance between Jupiter and the Sun if the two objects were 33 light years from us. The frames are 1.5 arc seconds square and are at the observation wavelength of 500 nanometers. The resolving power is given by θ_R and they all have the *same brightness*—the light in the bottom images from the large telescopes is just much more concentrated than for the small telescopes. The image from the 0.1524-meter telescope (image A) would take 30 minutes to make, but the image from the 5.08-meter telescope (image D) would take only 1.6 *seconds*! The exposure times for the other telescopes are given.

The pictures clearly show the increase in sharpness as the objective size is increased. The size of each of the blobs is the size of the *smallest* detail that can be seen with that telescope under ideal conditions. Atmospheric distortion effects (smearing of the binary star images to a blob the size of the entire frame) and obscuration and diffraction by the secondary and its supports are NOT shown here.

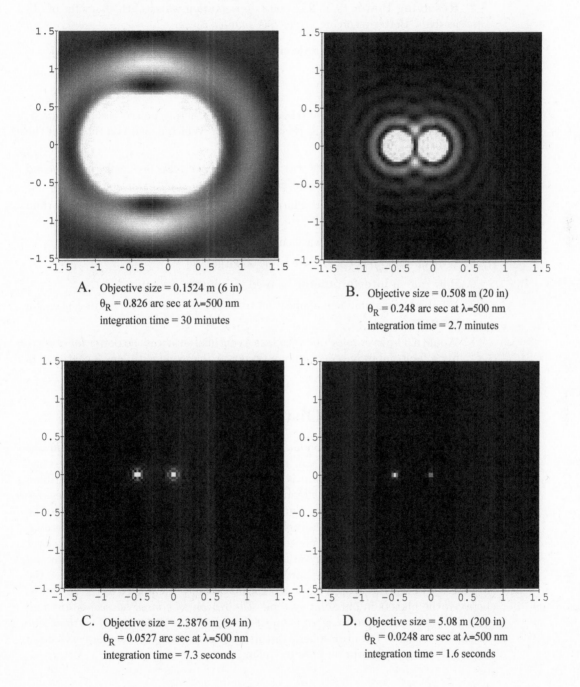

A. Objective size = 0.1524 m (6 in)
θ_R = 0.826 arc sec at λ=500 nm
integration time = 30 minutes

B. Objective size = 0.508 m (20 in)
θ_R = 0.248 arc sec at λ=500 nm
integration time = 2.7 minutes

C. Objective size = 2.3876 m (94 in)
θ_R = 0.0527 arc sec at λ=500 nm
integration time = 7.3 seconds

D. Objective size = 5.08 m (200 in)
θ_R = 0.0248 arc sec at λ=500 nm
integration time = 1.6 seconds

Vocabulary

interferometer   light-gathering power   magnifying power
resolving power

Formulae

1. **Light-Gathering Power** $= \pi \times$ (diameter of objective)$^2/4$.

2. **Resolving Power** $\theta_R = 252,000 \times$ (observation wavelength/diameter of objective). Better resolving power has *smaller* θ_R.

3. **Magnifying Power** $=$ (objective focal length) / (eyepiece focal length).

Review Questions

1. Of the three powers of the telescope (light-gathering power, resolving power, magnifying power) which is least important? Which depend on the size of the objective mirror or lens?

2. How many times brighter will a 60-centimeter telescope make a 10-second exposure image than a 12-centimeter telescope?

3. How many times better resolution does a 48-centimeter telescope have than a 12-centimeter telescope?

4. Will a shorter or longer wavelength enable us to see smaller details?

5. Why do radio telescopes have to be so large?

6. How can an **interferometer** be used to improve resolution?

7. What is the maximum magnification that should be used with an 20-centimeter telescope?

8. Would a 30-power telescope with lens 4 centimeters across be better for observing a faint, faraway object than a 60-power telescope with lens 3 centimeters across? Why or why not?

8.3 Atmospheric Distortion

Many people believe that astronomers want to build telescopes on tall mountains or put them in space, so they can be "closer" to the objects they are observing. This is *incorrect!* The nearest star is over 41,500,000,000,000 kilometers (26 trillion miles) away. If you ignore the 300-million kilometer variation in the distances due to the Earth's motion around the Sun and the 12,756-kilometer variation due to the Earth's rotation, being 4 kilometers closer on a tall mountain amounts to a difference of at most 1×10^{-11} *percent*. Telescopes in space get up to 1×10^{-9} percent closer (again ignoring the much larger variations of the Earth's orbit around the Sun and the telescope's orbit around the Earth). These are extremely small differences—the distances to even the nearby stars are 100,000's times greater than the distances between the planets in our solar system. *The reason why large telescopes are built on tall mountains or put in space is to get away from the distortion of starlight due to the atmosphere.* The atmospheric distortion is poor seeing, reddening, extinction and the adding of absorption lines to stellar spectra.

why high elevation observing is better

8.3.1   Seeing

The air is in turbulent motion and light from celestial objects is bent randomly in many ways over time periods of tens of milliseconds. Images dance about (twinkle) and images are blurred. The atmospheric blurring distorts the view of astronomical objects much as ripples in water distort the objects below the surface. This atmospheric effect is called **seeing.** Light from a star is refracted in random directions by rapidly-moving pockets of air of varying densities and temperatures. The light reaches different parts of the telescope's objective from slightly different directions and different times. A highly magnified view (see figure below) shows multiple images of the star that dance about in the field of view many times a second, so a second or longer exposure picture will show a fuzzy blob (called the "seeing disk") the size of the entire distribution of dancing images. See the textbook's website for an animation of this and a link to a movie of an actual observation of a star under high magnification.

Good seeing is when the air is stable (little turbulence) and the twinkling is small. Details as small as 0.5 arc seconds can be seen when the seeing is good (still much poorer than the theoretical resolving power of large research telescopes). Poor seeing happens when the air is turbulent so the images dance about and details smaller than 2–3 arc seconds cannot be seen. The more atmosphere there is above a telescope, the greater is the turbulent motion and the poorer is the seeing. This is one reason why research telescopes are located on very high mountains.

seeing

stars become very blurred and fuzzy

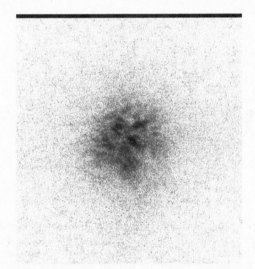

A highly-magnified, short exposure negative image of the double star WDS 01017+2518 under typical seeing conditions. The rapid motion of the seeing disk is frozen. The frame is six arc seconds across.

Image courtesy of Keith T Knox, Air Force Research Laboratory

Speckle interferometry can get rid of atmospheric distortion by taking many fast exposures of an object. Each fraction-of-a-second exposure freezes the motion of the object. Extensive computer processing then shifts the images to a common center and removes other noise and distortions caused by the atmosphere, telescope, and electronics to build up a distortion-free image. Another technique called **adaptive optics** makes quick changes in the light path of the optics to compensate for the atmospheric turbulence. Before the focused light from the objective reaches the camera, it bounces off a thin deformable mirror that can be adjusted thousands of times a second to reposition the multiple images back to the center. A site to explore this topic further is the *Center for Adaptive Optics* website (see the textbook's website for the link).

speckle interferometry

adaptive optics

Telescopes in orbit like the Hubble Space Telescope are above the turbulent effect of the atmosphere and can achieve their theoretical resolving power. The Hubble Space Telescope has a 2.4-meter objective, making it the largest telescope ever put in orbit (so far). One major drawback to satellite observatories is the large cost to build and maintain them. Adaptive optics on ground-based telescopes now can remove the seeing effects on small patches of the sky at a time and enable the huge research telescopes to take even sharper pictures than those from the Hubble Space Telescope.

8.3.2   Reddening and Extinction

reddening

The air also absorbs and scatters electromagnetic radiation by an amount that varies with the wavelength. Redder (longer wavelength) light is scattered less by atmosphere molecules and dust than bluer (shorter wavelength) light. This effect is known as **reddening.** This effect explains why the Sun appears orange or red when it is close to the horizon. The other colors of sunlight are scattered out of your line of sight so that only the orange and red colors make it through the atmosphere to your eyes. This effect also explains why the sky is blue. Since blue light is scattered more, you will see more blue light scattered back to your eyes when you look in a direction away from the Sun.

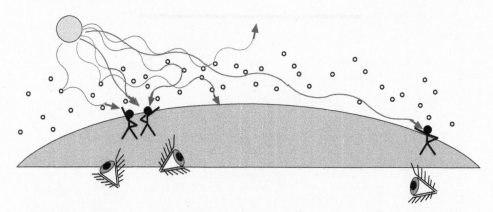

Blue light scatters more than red light. When the Sun is high in the sky you will see all of the colors if you look right at the Sun. But looking in other directions, you will see just the blue colors because some of the blue sunlight will be scattered back to you. When the Sun is near the horizon, the blue sunlight is scattered away leaving only the red and orange sunlight---the Sun appears red.

extinction

get above water vapor that absorbs infrared light

All wavelengths of light are scattered or absorbed by some amount. This effect is called **extinction.** Some wavelength bands suffer more extinction than others. Some of the infrared band can be observed from mountains above 2750 meters elevation, because telescopes are above most of the water vapor in the air that absorbs much of the infrared energy from space. Carbon dioxide also absorbs a lesser amount of the infrared energy. Gamma-rays and X-rays are absorbed by oxygen and nitrogen molecules very high above the surface, so none of this very short wavelength radiation makes it to within 100 kilometers of the surface. The ultraviolet light is absorbed by the oxygen and ozone molecules at altitudes of about 60 kilometers. The longest wavelengths of the radio band are blocked by electrons at altitudes around 200 kilometers.

The atmosphere also scatters light coming from the ground to wash out a lot of the fainter stars and planets in what is called *light pollution.* As more people move to the cities and the cities get larger, an increasing percentage of people are missing out on the beauty of a star-filled night sky. The increasing light pollution is also threatening the amount and quality of research that can be done at many of the major astronomical observatories. The image at the top of the next page shows how much of the world is now cut off from the night sky. See the textbook website for the link to the International Dark-Sky Association, an organization dedicated to bringing back the night sky to even our cities.

The Hubble Space Telescope (HST) is able to observe in the ultraviolet, something that ground-based research telescopes cannot do. This is one advantage that HST will always have over ground-based telescopes, even those with adaptive optics. Even though HST has a smaller objective than many ground-based telescopes, its ability to observe in shorter wavelengths will keep its resolving power very competitive with the largest ground-based telescopes with the best adaptive optics. The Hubble Space Telescope can also observe in a broader swath of the infrared than can be done from the ground. Furthermore, HST has no sky glow background (the sky background random noise contamination is less in space) so it is able to easily detect very faint objects against a truly black background—HST can see fainter things than can the ground-based telescopes.

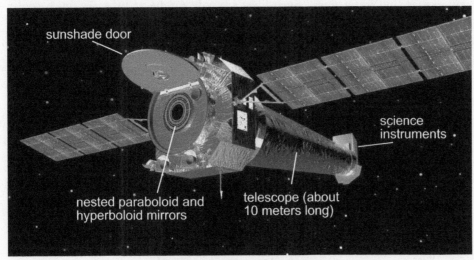

The Chandra X-ray Observatory
Spacecraft image courtesy of NASA/CXC/SAO and TRW, Inc.

Telescopes used to observe in the high-energy end of the electromagnetic spectrum must be put above the atmosphere and require special arrangements of their reflecting surfaces. The extreme ultraviolet and X-rays cannot be focused using an ordinary mirror because the high-energy photons would bury themselves into the mirror. But if they hit the reflecting surface at a very shallow angle, they will bounce off. Using a series of concentric cone-shaped metal plates, high energy ultraviolet and X-ray photons can be focused to make an image (see figure below). Gamma rays have too high an energy to be focused with even the shallow angle reflecting technique, so gamma ray telescopes simply point in a desired direction and count the number of photons coming from that direction.

On the long wavelength end are the infrared space telescopes. They are cooled to very low temperatures (just a few degrees above absolute zero) and they observe from behind a sun shield so that the sun and the telescope's own internal heat will not interfere with the observations. Infrared observations are especially good for studying objects hidden behind thick dust clouds such as forming stars and planets, cool objects such as asteroids, dim stars, and exoplanets, and very distant galaxies, including the first galaxies that formed in the universe. See the textbook's website for examples of space telescopes and links to more information.

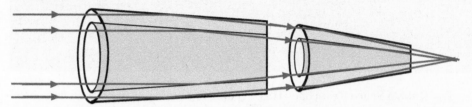

High-energy photons reflect off a metal surface at shallow angles (``grazing incidence''). A nested series of 2 or more cone-shaped reflectors focus the extreme-ultraviolet and X-ray light to make an image.

8.3.3   Atmospheric Lines

Gases in the Earth's atmosphere can introduce extra absorption lines into the spectra of celestial objects. The atmospheric spectral lines must be removed from the spectroscopy data, otherwise astronomers will find a hot star with molecular nitrogen, oxygen and water lines! Such lines are only produced by gases much cooler than that in stars.

Vocabulary

adaptive optics	extinction	reddening
seeing	speckle interferometry	

Review Questions

1. The distance to the *nearest* star is 4.3 light years = 4.3×9.7 trillion kilometers = 41,800,000,000,000 kilometers. Does Mauna Kea's elevation of 4177 meters (=2.6 miles) put it significantly closer to even the nearest star than something at sea level? Explain your answer. (1 kilometer = 1000 meters.)

2. What causes stars to twinkle? What would make good **seeing**?

3. Even with perfectly clear skies free of human-made pollution, the seeing on Mauna Kea (4177 meters elevation) is much better than at sea level. Why is that?

4. What absorbs infrared light in our atmosphere and up to what height above sea level is most of this infrared absorber found?

5. Even with perfectly clear skies free of human-made pollution, infrared observations can be made at Mauna Kea but not at Kitt Peak (2070 meters elevation). Why is that?

6. Why are all ultraviolet, X-ray, and gamma ray telescopes put up in orbit?

Chapter 9

Planetary Science

The star we call the Sun has a number of small objects circling around it. Many other stars in our Galaxy have objects orbiting them too and astronomers have recently discovered over four hundred of these other systems already. The largest members of the Sun's family are called planets, and one of these we call home. That planet, Earth, has many unique characteristics that enable life to exist on it. What are the other planets like? What we call a "planet" has been the subject of much debate recently with the latest definition creating a "dwarf planet" class of which Pluto is a member. A "planet" in our solar system is a celestial body that "(a) orbits the Sun; (b) has sufficient mass for its self-gravity to overcome rigid-body forces so that it assumes a hydrostatic equilibrium (nearly round) shape; and (c) has cleared the neighborhood around its orbit." See section 10.6.2 in the next chapter for more on this.

We have learned more about our solar system in the past few decades than probably any other field of astronomy. The planets are no longer just objects up in our sky, but *places* we have been to and explored—worlds in their own right. To give an adequate coverage of each of the planets would fill up a whole book (or more)! Since this textbook is an introduction to all of astronomy, I will not explore each planet individually. Instead, I will focus on the common characteristics of the planets such as their atmospheres, magnetic fields and interiors.

Special attention will be given to the planets Venus and Mars because their orbits are similar to the Earth's orbit. Venus, Earth, and Mars were made from the same material at about the same distance from the Sun, so they should to be similar to one another. However, they are radically different from one another! Venus is extremely hot with a very thick, carbon dioxide atmosphere, Mars is cold with a very thin carbon dioxide atmosphere, and the Earth has moderate surface temperatures and a moderately-thick nitrogen atmosphere that has a large amount of very reactive molecules of oxygen. At the end of the chapter I include a section about the large moons of the planets and the rings found around each of the jovian planets.

The next chapter covers the objects that give clues of our origins: comets, meteorites, and asteroids. These objects are much smaller than planets and are made of left-over material that did not get incorporated into the planets. I will also give a brief description of what we know about how our solar system was formed in the next chapter.

This chapter covers aspects shared by all of the planets. There is a lot of high-quality information about each of the planets available on the web. Several people and organizations have put together very nice tours of the solar system with actual photos from space missions. Starting points for the best of these tours are given at the textbook's website. The vocabulary terms in this chapter are in boldface. Many references to the textbook's website are made for supplementary material. Choose the Planetary Science chapter link and then select the links embedded in the text.

9.1   Determining Planet Properties

How can you find out what the other planets are like by just observing them carefully from the Earth? Most of the information comes in the form of electromagnetic radiation but we also have little chunks of rock, called meteorites, that give other clues. Before you can do any sort of comparison of the planets, you need to know how far away they are. Once you know their distances, you can determine basic properties of the planets such as mass, size, and density.

9.1.1   Distances

Several hundred years ago Copernicus was able to determine approximate distances between the planets through trigonometry. The distances were all found relative to the distance between the Earth and the Sun, the *astronomical unit* (often abbreviated as "A.U."). Kepler refined these measurements to take into account the elliptical orbits. However, they did not know how large an astronomical unit was.

how long is an A.U.?

To establish an absolute distance scale, the actual distance to one of the planets had to be measured. Distances to Venus and Mars were measured from the parallax effect by observers at different parts of the Earth when the planets were closest to the Earth.

use parallax effect

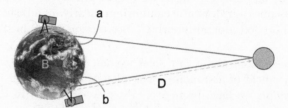

Triangulation gives the distance: measure angles (a & b) and distance (B) between the observation points. Derive the distance (D) to the nearby object.

Knowing how far apart the observers were from each other and coordinating the observation times, astronomers could determine the distance to a planet. The slight difference in its position on the sky due to observing the planet from different positions gave the planet's distance from trigonometry. The state-of-the-art measurements still had a large margin of uncertainty. The last major effort using these techniques was in the 1930's. Parallax observations of an asteroid, called Eros, passing close to Earth were used to fix the value of the astronomical unit at 150 million kilometers.

use radar to measure the A.U.

With the invention of radar, the distance to Venus could be determined very precisely. By timing how long it takes the radar beam travelling at the speed of light to travel the distance to an object and back, the distance to the object can be found from distance = (speed of light) × (total time)/2. The total time is halved to get just the distance from the Earth to the object. Using trigonometry, astronomers now know that the *astronomical unit* =149,597,871 kilometers. This incredible degree of accuracy is possible because the speed of light is known very precisely and very accurate clocks are used. You cannot use radar to determine the distance to the Sun directly because the Sun has no solid surface to reflect the radar efficiently.

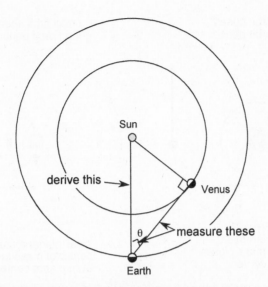

Measuring the angle θ between Venus and the Sun and
the distance between Earth and Venus enables us to find the
distance between the Earth and the Sun using trigonometry.

9.1.2 Masses

Once you know how far away a planet is, you can use the orbital periods (P) of
moons circling a planet and how far the moons are from the planet (d) to measure
the planet's mass. You measure the angular separation between the moon and
the planet and use basic trigonometry to convert the angular separation into the
distance between the planet and moon. That conversion, though, first requires that
the distance *to* the planet and moon be known.

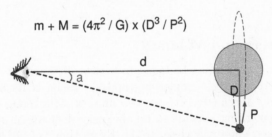

$$m + M = (4\pi^2 / G) \times (D^3 / P^2)$$

Measure: angular distance (a) and orbital period (P).
Derive: orbit size (D) from known distance (d) and
angle (a), *then* the planet mass from Kepler's 3rd law.

Isaac Newton used his laws of motion and gravity to generalize Kepler's third law of planet orbits to cover any case where one object orbits another. He found for any two objects orbiting each other, the sum of their masses, planet mass + moon mass = $(4\pi^2/G) \times$ [(their distance apart)^3/(their orbital period around each other)^2]. Newton's form of Kepler's third law can, therefore, be used to find the combined mass of the planet and the moon from measurements of the moon's orbital period and its distance from the planet.

Newton's form of Kepler's 3rd law

planet mass found from motions of its satellites

You can usually ignore the mass of the moon compared to the mass of the planet because the moon is so much smaller than the planet, so Kepler's third law gives you the planet's mass directly. Examples are given in section 5.7.2 of the gravity chapter. The one noticeable exception is Pluto and its moon, Charon. Charon is massive enough compared to Pluto that its mass cannot be ignored. The two bodies

see ch. 5

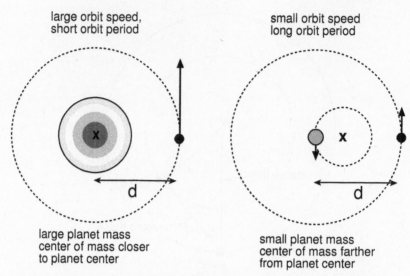

large orbit speed,
short orbit period

small orbit speed
long orbit period

large planet mass
center of mass closer
to planet center

small planet mass
center of mass farther
from planet center

Planet + moon mass found from Kepler's 3rd law (use separation
distance and orbit period). Individual masses found from planet and
moon center distances from center of mass ("x" in the picture).

center of mass

orbit around a common point that is proportionally closer to the more massive
Pluto. The common point, called the **center of mass**, is 7.3 times closer to Pluto,
so Pluto is 7.3 times more massive than Charon. Before the discovery of Charon in
1978, estimates for Pluto's mass ranged from 10% the Earth's mass to much greater
than the Earth's mass. After Charon's discovery, astronomers found that Pluto is
only 0.216% the Earth's mass—less massive than the Earth's Moon! For planets
without moons (Mercury and Venus), you can measure their gravitational pull on
other nearby planets to derive an approximate mass or, for more accurate results,
measure how quickly spacecraft are accelerated when they pass close to the planets.

9.1.3   Diameters and Volumes

The physical size of a planet can be found from measurements of its **angular size**
and its *distance*. How large   something appears to be is its **angular size** or
angular diameter—the angle between two lines of sight along each side of the
object. How big something appears to be obviously depends on its distance from
us—it appears bigger when it is closer to us. Every time you drive a car or ride a
bicycle, you use another car's or bicycle's angular size to judge how far away it is
from you. You assume that you are not looking at some toy model. The planets
are close enough to the Earth that you can see a round disk and, therefore, they
have a measurable angular size. All of the stars (except the Sun) are so far away
that they appear as mere points in even the largest telescopes, even though they
are actually much larger than the planets.

**angular size, angular
diameter**

If you know how how far away a planet is from you, you can determine its linear
diameter D. The diameter of a planet $= 2\pi \times$ (distance to the planet) $\times$ (the planet's
angular size in degrees)$/360°$, where the symbol π is a number approximately
equal to 3.14 (your calculator may say 3.141592653...). The figure on the next page
explains where this formula comes from. This technique is used to find the actual
diameters of other objects as well, like moons, star clusters, and even entire galaxies.

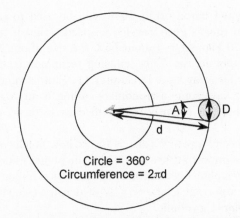

Circle = 360°
Circumference = 2πd

Angular diameter A is same fractional amount of 360° as
object's linear diameter D is of circumference, so

$$\frac{D}{2\pi d} = \frac{A}{360}$$

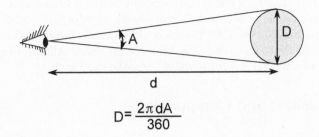

$$D = \frac{2\pi dA}{360}$$

How do you do that?

As the planets orbit the Sun, their distance from us changes. At "opposition" (when they are in the direct opposite direction from the Sun in our sky) a planet gets closest to us. These are the best times to study a planet in detail. The planet Mars reaches opposition every 780 days. Because of their elliptical orbits around the Sun, some oppositions are more favorable than others. Every 15--17 years Mars is at a favorable opposition and approaches within 55 million kilometers to the Earth. At that time its angular size across its equator is 25.5 arc seconds. In degrees this is

25.5 arc seconds $\times$ (1 degree/3600 arc seconds) = 0.00708 degrees, cancelling out arc seconds top and bottom.

Its actual diameter = $(2 \times \pi \times 55,000,000 \text{ km} \times 0.00708°)/360° = 6800$ kilometers. Notice that you need to convert arc seconds to degrees to use the angular size formula.

Little Pluto is so small and far away that its angular diameter is very hard to measure. Only a large telescope above the Earth's atmosphere (like the Hubble Space Telescope) can resolve its tiny disk. However, the discovery of its moon, Charon, gave another way of measuring Pluto's diameter. Every 124 years the orientation of Charon's orbit as seen from the Earth is almost edge-on, so you can see Charon pass in front of Pluto and then behind Pluto. This favorable orientation lasts about 5 years and, fortunately for us, it occurred from 1985 to 1990.

When Pluto and Charon pass in front of each other, the total light from the Pluto-Charon system decreases. The length of time it takes for the eclipse to hap-

eclipses give the diameter

pen and the speed that Charon orbits Pluto can be used to calculate their linear diameters. Recall that the distance traveled = speed×(time it takes). Pluto's diameter is only about 2270 kilometers (about 65% the size of our Moon!) and Charon is about 1170 kilometers across. This eclipsing technique is also used to find the diameters of the very far away stars in chapter 11. Pluto's small size and low mass (see previous section) have some astronomers calling it an "overgrown comet" instead of a planet and it was recently re-classified as a "dwarf planet" (see section 10.6.2

volume
Another way to specify a planet's size is to use how much space it occupies, i.e., its *volume*. Volume is important because it and the planet's composition determine how much heat energy a planet retains after its formation billions of years ago. Also, in order to find the important characteristic of density (see the next subsection), you must know the planet's volume.

Planets are nearly perfect spheres. Gravity compresses the planets to the most compact shape possible, a sphere, but the rapidly-spinning ones bulge slightly at the equator. This is because the inertia of a planet's material moves it away from the planet's rotation axis and this effect is strongest at the equator where the rotation is fastest (Jupiter and Saturn have easily noticeable equatorial bulges). Since planets are nearly perfect spheres, a planet's volume can be found from = ($\pi \times$ diameter^3/6). Notice that the diameter is cubed. Even though Jupiter has "only" 11 times the diameter of the Earth, over 1300 Earths could fit inside Jupiter! On the other end of the scale, little Pluto has a diameter of just a little more than 1/6th the diameter of the Earth, so almost 176 Plutos could fit inside the Earth.

9.1.4   Densities and Compositions

Density depends on the composition of the material

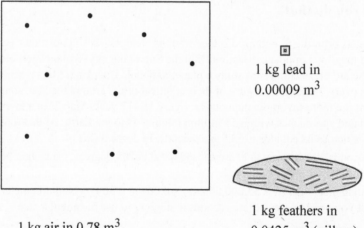

1 kg lead in
0.00009 m^3

1 kg feathers in
0.0425 m^3 (pillow)

1 kg air in 0.78 m^3

density
An important property of a planet that tells what a planet is made of is its **density**. A planet's **density** is how much material it has in the space the planet occupies: *density = mass/volume*. Planets can have a wide range of sizes and masses but planets made of the *same material* will have the *same density* regardless of their size and mass. For example, a huge, massive planet can have the same density as a small, low-mass planet if they are both made of the same material. I will specify the density relative to the density of pure water because it has an easy density to remember: 1 gram/centimeter^3 or 1000 kilograms/meter^3.

terrestrial planets
The four planets closest to the Sun (Mercury, Venus, Earth, Mars) are called the *terrestrial planets*   because they are like the Earth: small rocky worlds with

terrestrial planets all to same scale counter-clockwise from top left: Earth, Venus, Mercury, Mars

Images courtesy of NASA and JPL

relatively thin atmospheres. Terrestrial (Earth-like) planets have overall densities = 4–5 (relative to the density of water) with silicate rocks on the surface. Silicate rock has density = 3 (less than the average density of a terrestrial planet) and iron has a density = 7.8 (more than the average density of a terrestrial planet). Since terrestrial planets have average densities greater than that for the silicate rocks on their surface, they must have denser material under the surface to make the overall average density what it is. Iron and nickel are present in meteorites (chunks of rock left over from the formation of the solar system) and the presence of magnetic fields in some of the terrestrial planets shows that they have cores of iron and nickel. Magnetic fields can be produced by the motion of liquid iron and nickel. Putting these facts together leads to the conclusion that the terrestrial planets are made of silicate rock surrounding a iron-nickel core.

The four giant planets beyond Mars (Jupiter, Saturn, Uranus, Neptune) are called the *jovian planets* because they are like Jupiter: large, mostly liquid worlds with thick atmospheres (see the figure on the next page and notice how tiny the Earth is compared to them!). Jovian (Jupiter-like) planets have overall densities = 0.7–1.7 (relative to the density of water) with light gases visible on top. Gases and light liquids (like hydrogen and helium) have densities less than water. Using reasoning similar to before you conclude that the jovian planets are made of gaseous and liquid hydrogen, helium and water surrounding a possible relatively small rocky core. Spectroscopy says the jovian planets have hydrogen, helium, methane, ammonia, and water gas in their thick atmospheres so the predictions are not too far off track.

jovian planets

The properties determined for each planet are given in the planet tables in the appendix. Links to further information about each planet are given on the textbook's website.

Vocabulary

angular diameter   angular size   center of mass
density

Formulae

1. *Planet mass* $= (4\pi^2/G) \times [\text{distance}^3/(\text{moon's orbital period})^2]$ – moon's mass. The moon's mass can usually be ignored.

2. *Planet diameter* $= 2\pi \times (\text{distance to the planet}) \times (\text{planet's angular size in degrees})/360°$.

3. *Planet volume* $= (\pi/6) \times (\text{planet diameter})^3$.

4. **Density** $= \text{mass/volume}$.

Review Questions

1. How does angular size depend on distance? (As its distance increases, does an object's angular size increase or decrease?)

2. How large is the Moon if its angular size is about 30 arc minutes and it is 384,000 kilometers away from us?

3. How many times bigger is the Sun than the Moon if the Sun is about 390 times farther away than the Moon but has the same angular size? What is the Sun's diameter in kilometers? (Hint: use the Moon data in the previous question.)

4. If two objects at the same distance from you have different angular sizes with one 22 times smaller than the other, how many times larger in linear diameter is one than the other? If the large object is 141,000 kilometers across, how large is the other object?

5. A planet 140,000 kilometers across is 780 million kilometers from the Sun and rotates every 9.8 hours on its axis. It has a moon that orbits 380,000 kilometers from the planet's center in 1.8 days. Explain what information you would use to find the mass of the planet and how the mass could be determined.

6. The Earth has a radius of 6400 kilometers and a mass of 6.0×10^{24} kilograms. What is its density?

7. A planet has a rocky surface of material with density 3 (relative to the density of water) and an interior of material with density 2.5. Will its overall average density be greater or less than 3? If the planet's interior is made of material with density 9, will the overall average density be greater or less than 3?

9.2 Atmospheres

A planet's atmosphere helps shield a planet's surface from harsh radiation from the Sun and it moderates the amount of energy lost to space from the planet's interior. An atmosphere also makes it possible for liquid to exist on a planet's surface by supplying the pressure needed to keep the liquid from boiling away to space—life on the surface of a planet or moon requires an atmosphere. All of the planets started out with atmospheres of hydrogen and helium. The inner four planets (Mercury, Venus, Earth, and Mars) lost their original atmospheres. The atmospheres they have now are from gases released from their interiors, but Mercury and Mars have even lost most of their secondary atmospheres. The outer four planets (Jupiter, Saturn, Uranus, and Neptune) were able to keep their original atmospheres. They have very thick atmospheres with proportionally small solid cores while the the inner four planets have thin atmospheres with proportionally large solid parts.

The properties of each planet's atmosphere are summarized in the planet atmospheres table in the appendix. Two key determinants in how thick a planet's atmosphere will be are the planet's **escape velocity** and the **temperature** of the atmosphere.

9.2.1 Escape of an Atmosphere

The thickness of a planet's atmosphere depends on the planet's gravity and the temperature of the atmosphere. A planet with weaker gravity does not have as strong a hold on the molecules that make up its atmosphere as a planet with stronger gravity. The gas molecules will be more likely to escape the planet's gravity. If the atmosphere is cool enough, then the gas molecules will not be moving fast enough to escape the planet's gravity. But how strong is "strong enough" and how cool is "cool enough" to hold onto an atmosphere? To answer that you need to consider a planet's **escape velocity** and how the molecule speeds depend on the **temperature**.

Escape Velocity

If you throw a rock up, it will rise up and then fall back down because of gravity. If you throw it up with a faster speed, it will rise higher before gravity brings it back down. If you throw it up fast enough it just escapes the gravity of the planet—the rock initially had a velocity equal to the **escape velocity**. The **escape velocity** is the initial velocity needed to escape a massive body's gravitational influence. In chapter 5 the escape velocity is found to $= \sqrt{(2G \times (\text{planet or moon mass})/\text{distance})}$. The distance is measured from the planet or moon's center.

escape velocity

Since the mass is in the top of the fraction, the escape velocity increases as the mass increases. A more massive planet will have stronger gravity and, therefore, a higher escape velocity. Also, because the distance is in the bottom of the fraction, the escape velocity *decreases* as the distance increases. The escape velocity is lower at greater heights above the planet's surface. The planet's gravity has a weaker hold on the molecules at the top of the atmosphere than those close to the surface, so those high up molecules will be the first to "evaporate away."

Do not confuse the distance from the planet's center with the planet's distance from the Sun. The escape velocity does NOT depend on how far the planet is from the Sun. You would use the Sun's distance only if you wanted to calculate the escape velocity *from the Sun.* In the same way, a moon's escape velocity does NOT depend on how far it is from the planet it orbits.

Temperature

temperature

The **temperature** of a material is a measure of the average kinetic (motion) energy of the particles in the material. As the temperature increases, a solid turns into a gas when the particles are moving fast enough to break free of the chemical bonds that held them together. The particles in a hotter gas are moving quicker

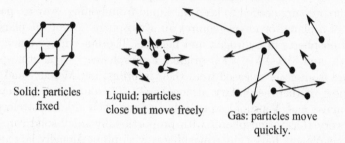

Solid: particles fixed

Liquid: particles close but move freely

Gas: particles move quickly.

than those in a cooler gas of the same type. Using Newton's laws of motion, the relation between the speeds of the molecules and their temperature is found to be temperature = (gas molecule mass) × (*average* gas molecule speed)^2/(3k), where k is a universal constant of nature called the "Boltzmann constant". Gas molecules of the same type at the same temperature will have a spread of speeds—some moving quickly, some moving slower—so use the *average* speed.

If you switch the temperature and velocity, you can derive the average gas molecule velocity = $\sqrt{(3k \times \text{temperature}/(\text{molecule mass}))}$. Remember that the mass here is the tiny mass of the gas molecule, not the planet's mass. Since the gas molecule mass is in the bottom of the fraction, the more massive gas molecules will move slower on average than the lighter gas molecules. For example, carbon dioxide molecules move slower on average than hydrogen molecules at the same temperature. Because massive gas molecules move slower, planets with weaker gravity

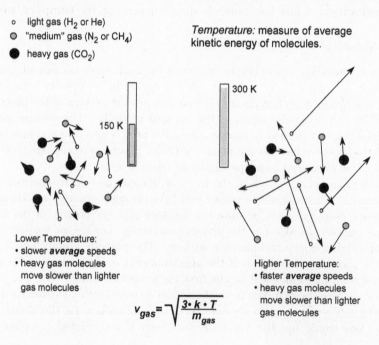

o light gas (H$_2$ or He)

◉ "medium" gas (N$_2$ or CH$_4$)

● heavy gas (CO$_2$)

Temperature: measure of average kinetic energy of molecules.

150 K

300 K

Lower Temperature:
• slower *average* speeds
• heavy gas molecules
  move slower than lighter
  gas molecules

Higher Temperature:
• faster *average* speeds
• heavy gas molecules
  move slower than lighter
  gas molecules

$$v_{gas} = \sqrt{\frac{3 \cdot k \cdot T}{m_{gas}}}$$

(e.g., the terrestrial planets) will tend to have atmospheres made of just massive molecules. The lighter molecules like hydrogen and helium will have escaped.

The dependence of the average speed of the gas molecules on their mass also explains the compositional structure observed in planet atmospheres. Since the distance a gas molecule can move away from the surface of a planet depends only on how fast it is moving and the planet's gravity, the lighter gas molecules can be found both close to the surface and far above it where the gravity is weaker. The gas molecules high up in the atmosphere are most likely to escape. The massive gas molecules will stay close to the planet surface. For example, the Earth's atmosphere is made of nitrogen, oxygen, and water molecules and argon atoms near the surface but at the upper-most heights, hydrogen and helium predominate.

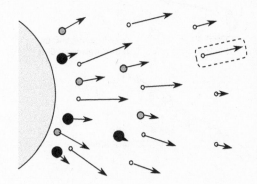

lighter molecules move faster on average so can get higher on average than heavier molecules. Lighter molecules high up more likely to escape planet or moon.

Does Gravity Win or Temperature?

Gravity   Temperature

The effects of gravity and temperature work opposite to each other. A higher temperature tries to dissipate an atmosphere while higher gravity tries to retain an atmosphere. If the particle's average speed is close to the escape velocity, then those type of gas particles will not remain for billions of years. The general rule is: if the average gas molecule speed for a type of gas is *less than* $0.2\times$(the escape velocity), then more than 1/2 of that type of gas will be left after one billion years. If the average speed is greater than that critical value, then more than 1/2 of that type of gas will be gone after one billion years. A flowchart of this is given on the escaping atmosphere page at the end of the chapter.

how quickly atmosphere leaks away: $0.2\times v_{esc}$ critical value

Because the jovian planets are massive and cold, they have THICK atmospheres of hydrogen and helium. The terrestrial planets are small in mass and warm, so they have thin atmospheres made of heavier molecules like carbon dioxide or nitrogen.

9.2.2   Atmosphere Escape via Non-Thermal Processes

The processes described above occur from the heating of the atoms and molecules in an atmosphere to the point where they can escape the planet's gravity. They are called *thermal* processes. Other ways involve the presence or lack of a magnetic field and asteroid or comet impacts. Ions are atoms that have an extra charge (usually by losing an electron). Ions will spiral around magnetic field lines so a planet's magnetic field (discussed more in a later section) will have a lot of ions trapped in

solar wind

it. When a fast-moving hydrogen ion (a proton) bumps into a neutral atom it can steal an electron to become a neutral atom that is not trapped by the magnetic field and it escapes the planet's gravity. This is called *charge-exchange*. Some of the magnetic field lines are so wide that they get stretched out by the high-speed stream of ions from the Sun called **solar wind**. The stretched out lines do not loop back and just open out into interplanetary space. Ions spiraling around these open magnetic field lines can escape along those lines in what is called a *polar wind*.

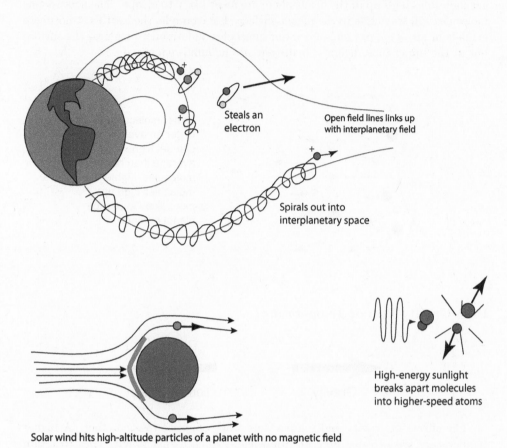

Steals an electron

Open field lines links up with interplanetary field

Spirals out into interplanetary space

Solar wind hits high-altitude particles of a planet with no magnetic field

High-energy sunlight breaks apart molecules into higher-speed atoms

If a planet does not have a magnetic field (for reasons described later), the solar wind can strip an atmosphere through a process called *sputtering*. Without a magnetic field, the solar wind is able to hit the planet's atmosphere directly. The high-energy solar wind ions can accelerate atmosphere particles at high altitudes to great enough speeds to escape. An additional way of atmosphere escape called *photodissociation* occurs when high-energy sunlight (e.g., ultraviolet or x-rays) hits high-altitude molecules in the planet's atmosphere and breaks them apart into individual atoms or smaller molecules. These smaller particles have the same temperature as the larger molecules and, therefore, as described above, will move at faster speeds, possibly fast enough to escape.

The processes described so far in this section work particle to particle over long time periods as the atmosphere leaks away particle by particle. In contrast, impacts by comets or asteroids can inject a huge amount of energy very quickly when the projectile vaporizes upon impact. The expanding plume of hot gas drives off the air above the impact site, with the larger the impact energy, the wider is the cone of air that is removed above the impact site. The impact removal process was probably particularly effective for Mars (proximity to the asteroid belt) and the large moons of Jupiter (Jupiter's strong gravity attracted numerous comets and asteroids).

9.2.3 Gas Behavior

Now that we have seen what determines if a planet has an atmosphere or not, let's look at how atmospheres behave and how they affect the conditions on the surface of a planet. Only three things are needed to describe how a gas will behave: temperature, pressure, and density. Temperature and density have already been discussed, although for gases it is usually easier to use "number density" as in "number of particles per volume" instead of the usual mass density. Let's take a closer look at pressure.

Pressure

Pressure is the amount of force exerted on a surface per unit area such as a number of newtons per square meter (or pounds of force per square inch). In the metric system, the unit of pressure is the *pascal (Pa)*. This pressure is supplied by all of the particles in an atmosphere colliding into each other. At the Earth's surface there are approximately 25 million trillion (2.5×10^{19}) molecules in every cubic centimeter moving about at speeds of hundreds of meters per second, so yes, they are going to bump into each other!

At the Earth's surface at sea level there is about 100 kilopascals of pressure exerted all over your body. For planet atmospheres, scientists will usually use a unit called a *"bar"* equal to 100 kilopascals, so the Earth's surface pressure at sea level is about 1 bar. That pressure is equivalent to about 1 kilogram pressing down in one Earth gravity on every square centimeter. If an adult pinky is about 1 centimeter in width (more or less), your body has quite a lot of square centimeters of surface area. So why do you not feel all that weight pushing you down at the Earth's surface? As described in the figure below, the air pressure pushes in all directions equally and the pressure of the fluid in your body pushing outward balances the air pressure.

pressure

pascal

bar

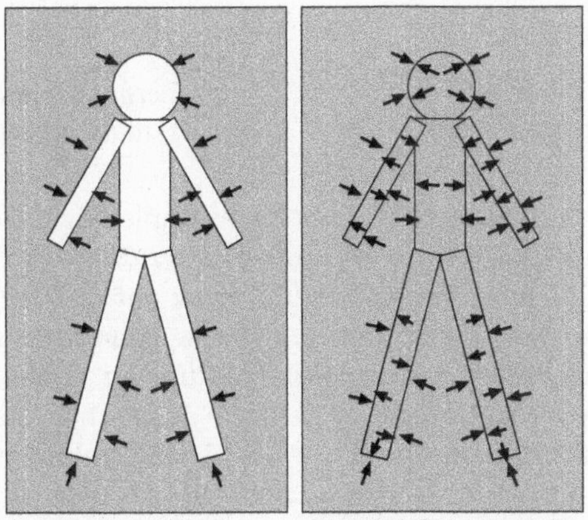

Pressure pushes in all directions equally: up, down, sideways so no net downward force.

Internal body fluid pressure pushes outward in all directions to balance inward air pressure, so you feel no net pressure.

Ideal Gas Law

Given the three parameters of temperature, density, and pressure, how the gas behaves is described by the *equation of state*. Most gases will obey a simple equation of state called the **ideal gas law** in which a doubling of the temperature or a doubling of the (number) density leads to a doubling of the pressure. For example, if you blow twice as much air into a balloon, the gas inside the balloon will push outward with twice as much pressure and the elastic material will expand

equation of state
ideal gas law

until a new pressure balance is reached with the outside air pressure. Heating the air inside a hot air balloon increases the pressure inside the fabric enclosure so the balloon fabric that started out laid out all flat on the ground is now puffed into a round shape. (This also explains why your car's manual will tell you to measure the air pressure of your tires when they are cold, so you if you have been driving for a while, you will need to wait several minutes at least for the air inside the tire to cool off to get an accurate tire pressure reading.)

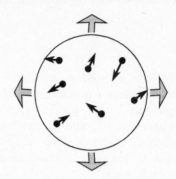

Pressure = constant x number density x temperature

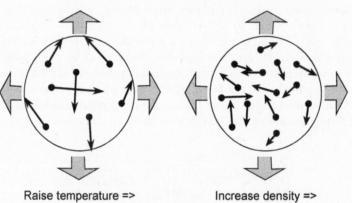

Raise temperature =>   Increase density =>
more pressure   more pressure

Let's continue with the hot air balloon example to make another important point. Once the balloon fabric is all puffed up, raising the temperature further inside the balloon will cause the air inside to flow out of the hole in the bottom of the balloon and density inside will drop. At the same pressure, less dense things will float upward (*Archimedes' principle*)—the hot air balloon will rise up off the ground. At a given pressure, cooler air is more dense than hotter air so the cooler air will sink. In an atmosphere, rising warmer air and sinking cooler air can transfer heat energy from a hotter surface to a cooler upper layer of the atmosphere in a process called **convection** that will be covered in more detail later.

warm air rises, cool air sinks

9.2.4   Hydrostatic Equilibrium

Gravity pulls downward/inward on the molecules in an atmosphere but atmospheres remain "puffy" because of the moving gas particles supply pressure upward/outward. An atmosphere will not get puffier or shrink if the outward thermal pressure of the gases is balances by the inward gravity compression. This balance between pressure and gravity is called **hydrostatic equilibrium**. In the interior of planets, the resistance of the solid or liquid material supplies the pressure. In an atmosphere, the moving gases supply the pressure. If the Earth was at the distance of Pluto from the Sun, the nitrogen, oxygen, water, etc. in our air would freeze

hydrostatic equilibrium
pressure balances gravity

out and gravity would cause it all to collect on the surface about 12 meters thick. At our warmer position, these materials are in a gaseous state and make a layer 100 kilometers thick. [More accurately, our atmosphere extends out even further, beyond where the Space Shuttle can reach and where the International Space Station is but the air pressure is extremely small so 100 kilometers has been set as the "boundary" (fuzzy though it is) where space begins. Objects in low Earth orbit do feel a slight drag though and therefore need to be periodically boosted back up to their original orbit or they will spiral downward and burn up in our atmosphere.]

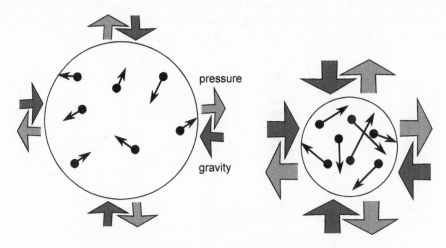

Hydrostatic equilibrium: gravity compression balanced by pressure outward. Greater gravity compresses gas making it denser and hotter, so the outward pressure increases.

Lower layers of the atmosphere feel greater gravity compression from all of the material in the layers above pushing down on them. Therefore, they exert greater pressure to keep the balance.

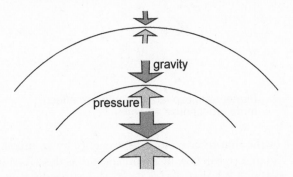

Deeper layers have more gravity compression, so they have greater outward pressure to compensate.

9.2.5 Surface Temperature

What temperature is and how it relates to a particle's speed and mass and how a gas' temperature affects the pressure has been discussed above but what will raise or lower the temperature of the air, particularly the air at the surface of a terrestrial world or the upper layers of a jovian planet's atmosphere? The *surface* temperature of a terrestrial planet is determined by how much energy the planet receives from the Sun and how quickly it radiates that solar energy back to space. As described in a later section, a terrestrial planet's *interior* temperature is determined by its size. The crust is a very poor conductor of any heat from the interior so the surface heat is all from the Sun. Jupiter, Saturn, and Neptune have extra heat energy coming from their interiors. Recall from section 3.6.5 that in order to keep the temperature the same, there must be a balance between the solar energy flowing onto the planet and the energy radiated back out to space.

On global scales, three things can affect this energy flow and therefore, the average global surface temperature. As shown in the figure below, they are the planet's distance from the Sun, the planet's surface reflectivity (**albedo**), and the planet's atmosphere (through a process called the **greenhouse effect**).

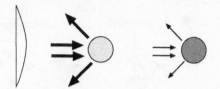

Distance from the Sun: closer => hotter

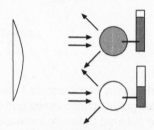

Surface reflectivity (albedo): greater reflectivity (albedo closer to 1) => cooler

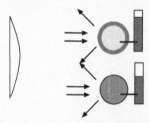

Planet's atmosphere (greenhouse effect): more greenhouse => hotter

Planets closer to the Sun receive more solar energy by an amount that depends on their distance squared (recall how light spreads out as described in section 8.2.1). Also recall from section 7.3.1 that hotter dense things produce more energy (they are brighter). With more solar energy flowing to the closer planets, they must be hotter to re-radiate that energy back out to space. The amount of solar energy reflected immediately out to space is determined by the material on the planet's surface or clouds in the atmosphere. The fraction of sunlight that is reflected from an object is the **albedo**. If the albedo is closer to 1 (100% reflectivity), the planet does not need to be as hot to have its outflow of energy balance the inflow of solar energy. Darker objects absorb more solar energy and, therefore, they need to heat up more to re-radiate that energy back out to balance the inflow of solar energy. For example, you probably notice the difference between wearing a white T-shirt vs. wearing a black T-shirt outside on a sunny, summer day. Another example is the liquid water in our oceans absorb more solar energy than the ice areas at our

albedo

poles.

Let's pause here and find out what the surface temperature should be for some of the planets. The rate of energy absorbed by the planet equals (the absorbing area of the planet) x (brightness of sunlight at the planet's distance from the Sun) x (fraction of sunlight absorbed). The rate of energy radiated by the planet using the discussion in section 7.3.1 (see item 5 in the list) equals (the surface area of the planet) × (energy radiated by each square meter every second, which changes as temperature to the fourth power). Setting the rate of solar energy absorbed equal to the rate of energy radiated by the planet, you find using the values for the distances and albedo given in the planet tables appendix C, that Mercury should have an average temperature of 160 deg C, Venus should be −42 deg C, Earth should be −19 deg C, and Mars should be −63 deg C. Their actual temperatures are: Mercury = 425 deg C (day)/ -175 deg C (night) = midway value of 125 deg C; Venus = 464 deg C; Earth = 15 deg C; and Mars = −31 deg C (day)/−89 deg C (night) = midway value of −60 deg C. Mercury has such a large variation between day and night as well as a large variation between the daytime polar temperature of 317 deg C and daytime equatorial temperature of 452 deg C that the rather arbitrarily chosen midway value of 125 deg is close enough to the calculated value of 160 deg C.

How do you do that?

To find the expected temperature of a planet, you need to set the rate of energy radiated by the planet equal to the rate of energy absorbed by the planet. So:

$$\left(\begin{matrix}\text{surface area}\\\text{of the planet}\end{matrix}\right) \times \left(\begin{matrix}\text{energy radiated by}\\\text{each square meter}\\\text{every second}\end{matrix}\right) = \left(\begin{matrix}\text{absorbing area}\\\text{of the planet}\end{matrix}\right) \times \left(\begin{matrix}\text{brightness of}\\\text{sunlight at the}\\\text{planet's distance}\\\text{from the Sun}\end{matrix}\right) \times \left(\begin{matrix}\text{fraction of}\\\text{sunlight absorbed}\end{matrix}\right)$$

$$4\pi R^2 \ \times \ \sigma T^4 = \pi R^2 \times \frac{L_\odot}{4\pi d^2} \times (1-a),$$

where R is the radius of the planet, d is the distance from the Sun, a is the albedo, $L_\odot$ is the luminosity of the Sun (how much energy it emits every second), T is the temperature of the planet, and σ is the Stefan-Boltzmann constant (see the astronomical constants table in appendix C for its value). Using algebra to solve for just the temperature:

$$T = \left[\frac{L_\odot (1-a)}{16\sigma\pi}\right]^{1/4} \times 1/\sqrt{d}$$

Plugging in the values for the constants from the astronomical constants table in appendix C, you find

$$T = 279 \times (1-a)^{1/4} \times 1/\sqrt{d} \quad \text{Kelvin}$$

if the distance is measured in astronomical units. Finally, to convert to degrees Celsius, subtract 273 from the Kelvin value.

For example, for the Earth, the albedo is 0.306 and the distance is 1.000 AU, so the expected temperature is 254 K or −19°C — significantly below the freezing point of water!

The difference between actual temperature values and the calculated values for the other three planets are a bit more interesting because of the effect of their atmospheres. A planet's atmosphere can hinder the rate that energy flows outward to space from the warm ground so the ground must heat up to increase the energy leaking out enough to balance the inflow of solar energy. This blanket effect of the atmosphere is called the **greenhouse effect** and is described in detail below. A planet's atmosphere can also hinder the rate that energy flows inward from space to the ground. The Moon and the Earth are at the same distance from the Sun but the Moon has a very large change in temperature from day to night due to the Moon's lack of an atmosphere. The Moon's surface temperature at its equator ranges from about 100 K (-173 deg C) at night to almost 400 K (127 deg C) during the day!

Greenhouse Effect

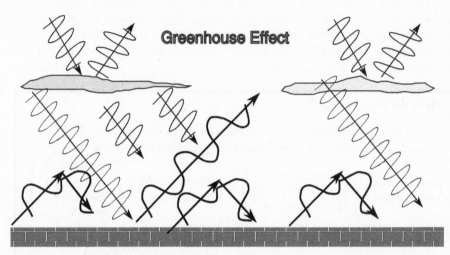

Incoming *visible* light from the Sun (short wavelength) is either reflected back to space by clouds of liquid droplets or solid particles or makes it to the ground to heat it up. Visible light passes easily through H_2O and CO_2 gases. Since the ground is much cooler than the hot Sun's surface, it reradiates the energy in the form of *infrared* light (long wavelength) instead of visible light. Greenhouse gases (like H_2O and CO_2) and clouds reflect some of the infrared light back to the ground trapping the heat close to the surface. Some infrared light does escape back to space—otherwise the surface would continually get hotter and hotter.

The greenhouse effect is named after the glass houses used to keep plants warm during cold weather. Energy in the form of visible light from the Sun passes through the glass walls and glass roofs of a greenhouse and heats up the plants and soil inside the greenhouse. The air in contact with the plants and soil gets warmed up. The glass walls and roofs prevent the hot air from escaping to the outside. The same sort of thing happens to the interior of your car when you leave it out in the Sun with the windows rolled up.

On a planet, certain gases like carbon dioxide or water vapor in the atmosphere prevent heat energy in the form of infrared light from leaking out to space. These so-called "greenhouse gases" allow *visible* light from the Sun to pass through and heat up the surface. A planet's surface is warm enough to emit *infrared* light. Some of the infrared light is absorbed by the greenhouse gases and radiated back toward the surface, warming the surface even more. Some of the energy is radiated back toward space. The surface warms enough so that the amount that *does* leak back out to space balances the solar energy flow inward. Note that if the greenhouse

input: visible light
output: infrared

was a *perfect* blanket, then the surface would continue to get hotter and hotter.

The primary greenhouse gases found in the atmospheres of our solar system's planets are given in the figure below. Not shown are chlorofluorocarbons (CFC's) and hydrofluorocarbons (HFC's) that are synthesized by humans. On the Earth the relative amounts these molecules contribute to the total greenhouse effect occurring are approximately: 60% for water, 26% for carbon dioxide, 5% for methane, 4% for ozone, 4% for the CFC's/HFC's, and 2% for nitrous oxide (rounding of the numbers to integer values means they will not add up to exactly 100%).

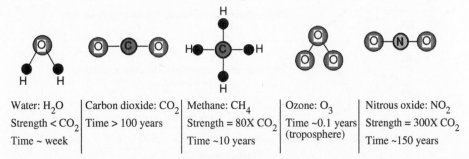

Water: H_2O	Carbon dioxide: CO_2	Methane: CH_4	Ozone: O_3	Nitrous oxide: NO_2
Strength $< CO_2$	Time > 100 years	Strength $= 80X\ CO_2$	Time ~0.1 years (troposphere)	Strength $= 300X\ CO_2$
Time ~ week		Time ~10 years		Time ~150 years

Some greenhouse gases. Molecules containing different elements can vibrate in a variety of directions and are, therefore, able to absorb infrared energy (and then re-radiate it). The Strength is the amount of infrared energy the molecule can absorb compared to a molecule of carbon dioxide. The Time is how long a molecule produced by human activity will remain in the Earth s atmosphere. Just the ozone in the troposphere is considered here (not the stratospheric ozone that blocks the UV).

Now back to our three planets. Venus' actual temperature is over three times more than if there was no greenhouse effect at work. Earth has a natural greenhouse effect mostly caused by water vapor to raise the temperature by about 34 deg C so the oceans do not freeze. Mars has only a very slight warming because of its thin atmosphere.

9.2.6 Atmosphere Structure

Planet atmospheres have a layered structure based on how the temperature changes with increasing altitude. The greenhouse effect plays a major role for the lowest layer of a terrestrial planet's atmosphere and other heating agents can raise the temperature of the upper layers. In this section we will take a look at the Earth's atmosphere layers, then compare it to the other terrestrial planet atmospheres, and finally finish with the structures of the jovian planets atmospheres.

The figure on the next page shows the bottom four layers of the Earth's atmosphere. Here are short descriptions of each layer.

- **Troposphere:** lowest layer (closest to the ground). The greenhouse effect is present in some amount. The temperature drops with increasing altitude because of more greenhouse heating lower down. Convection is important. In fact, without convection the temperature difference between the mountain tops and sea level would be even greater. The churning of the air by convection makes our storms. Ultimately, solar energy is what powers our storms. Clouds of water droplets and ice crystals are found in here. Other planets will have clouds made of other molecules in here.

  troposphere

- **Stratosphere:** where the temperature begins rising with increasing altitude above the troposphere. Ultraviolet light is absorbed by the **ozone** molecules in this layer. Ozone is the molecule made up of three oxygen atoms you came across in the greenhouse section above. It is beneficial to life when it is up in the stratosphere. Upon absorbing the ultraviolet light the fragile

  stratosphere
  ozone

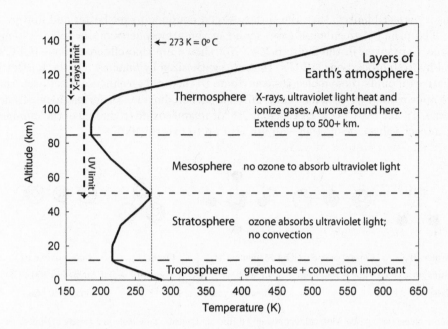

ozone molecules break apart. They re-form later when an oxygen atom combines with an oxygen molecule to complete the cycle. The absorption of the ultraviolet light is why the temperature increases. Ozone in the stratosphere is considered "good ozone" because of its shielding effect. Ozone in the troposphere is considered "bad ozone" because it causes respiratory problems and other negative health effects as well as being destructive to organic materials such as plastics.

good ozone vs. bad ozone

mesosphere

- **Mesosphere:**   where the temperature begins falling again with increasing altitude above the stratosphere because there is no ozone to absorb the ultraviolet light.

thermosphere

- **Thermosphere:**   where the temperature begins rising again with increasing altitude as the gases absorb X-rays and some ultraviolet light and heat up. No X-rays reach below the thermosphere. The X-rays have enough energy to knock electrons out of atoms making the atoms charged, a process called *ionization*. Where the ionization happens the most is called the *ionosphere*, a layer important for radio communication because the radio waves reflect off this layer and enable them to travel beyond the line-of-sight horizon. Aurorae occur in this layer (described in section 9.3.1).

exosphere

- **Exosphere:**   the uppermost layer where the gases escape to space at about 500 kilometers or so from the Earth's surface. Very low density gases heated by X-rays and ultraviolet light. Mercury and the Moon technically also have exospheres but their exospheres begin right at their surfaces.

Both Mars and Venus have tropospheres of greater extent than the Earth, though for different reasons (see figure next page). Mars' atmosphere is much thinner than Earth's and there is less compression because of Mars' weaker gravity. Although Venus has weaker gravity than Earth, it has over ninety times the amount of atmosphere because of a runaway greenhouse effect that occurred *at least* hundreds of millions of years ago. That is described in section 9.6.1 but it does provide a warning to us that drastic global climate change is possible. Because their tropospheres extend over a greater distance than the Earth's troposphere, Mars' and Venus' clouds are found at higher altitudes. Mars and Venus also have thermospheres. What is

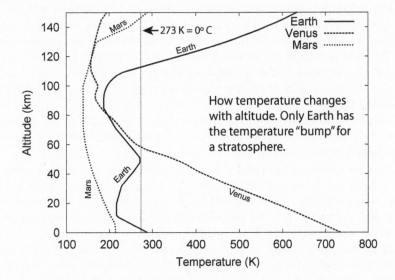

missing is the temperature bump of a stratosphere (and mesophere) because they do not have an ozone layer to absorb the ultraviolet light. (Planet models courtesy of Jere Justus at NASA/MSFC.)

The jovian planets have the same atmosphere layers as the Earth, though, their compositions, of course, are very different. Jupiter's atmosphere structure is described in the figure below.

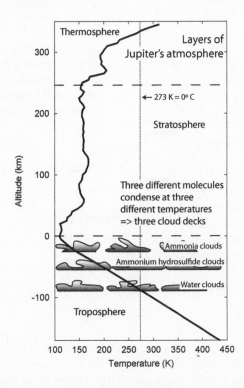

Jupiter's troposphere extends much further down merging smoothly into its interior. Mixed in with the abundant molecular hydrogen and helium are trace amounts of ammonia, water, and methane. Even smaller amounts of hydrogen sulfide (the stinky stuff of rotten eggs), other hydrogen polysulfides, and phosphorus are also present. Ammonia and hydrogen sulfide will mix together in water to make

condensation

three cloud decks

ammonium sulfide. Molecules of ammonia, ammonium hydrosulfide, and water will form droplets (*condense*) when the temperature is low enough. They will condense (and freeze) at different temperatures, though, so clouds of these molecules will form at different depths in the troposphere. There are three main clouds decks on Jupiter. Water condenses at a higher temperature than the other two, so water clouds are thought to exist at the deepest cloud layer. Higher up the temperature is low enough for the ammonium hydrosulfide to condense. Finally, just below the upper bound of the troposphere, the temperature is cold enough for ammonia to condense. Note that the cloud layers mark the upper bound of that type of molecule in the hydrogen/helium atmosphere.

The Galileo spacecraft dropped a probe into Jupiter's atmosphere when it arrived at Jupiter in December 1995. The probe got down to a depth of 161 km below the cloud tops before the probe stopped functioning because of high pressures and temperatures. At that depth the pressure was 22 bars and the temperature about 425 K. From the atmosphere structure figure on the previous page, the Galileo probe should have penetrated to where the water vapor is but it did not find the water. Unfortunately, the probe entered one of the clear, dry areas produced by downdrafts. Although, the probe got over 160 km below the cloud tops, it was still in the troposphere and its deepest point represents just 0.3% of Jupiter's radius. Ultraviolet heating makes a stratosphere but other molecules instead of ozone absorb the ultraviolet light. At the highest levels are the thermosphere and the exosphere.

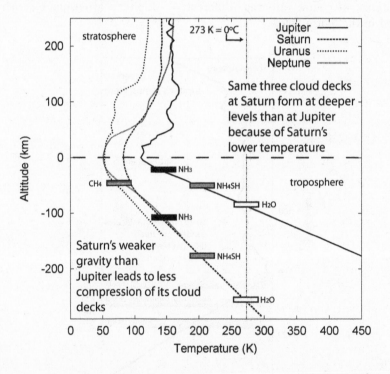

Saturn has the same three main cloud decks, though they are found at lower altitudes than on Jupiter because of Saturn's lower temperature (it is further from the Sun). Also, Saturn's cloud decks are further apart from each other because of Saturn's lower gravity—there is less compression of the gases. Because Saturn's clouds form at deeper positions in its troposphere, its cloud patterns appear more muted than on Jupiter. It is thought that the three cloud decks (of ammonia, ammonium hydrosulfide, and water) would be found much too deep in the tropospheres of Uranus and Neptune for us to see. Instead, Uranus and Neptune being even further from the Sun have cold enough tropospheres for methane to condense and freeze to form clouds (Jupiter and Saturn are too warm for methane clouds). Neptune has extra heat energy from its interior so its atmosphere temperature is warmer than Uranus.

In the next section we will take a look at how the gases move about and distribute energy.

9.2.7 Energy Transport

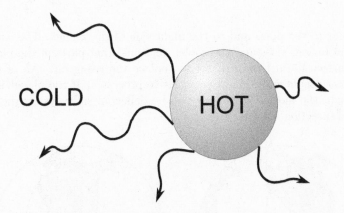

Planet atmospheres slow down the rate that heat escapes from a planet's surface or interior, as well as, distribute heat over a planet's surface. Because there is a temperature difference between the surface or interior of a planet and space, heat energy will flow from the warmer surface to the cold space. How well an atmosphere transfers heat and the methods it uses will have a profound effect on the surface temperature and weather. There are three ways gases can transfer energy:

1. *radiation*—photons (energy packets) leak outward by scattering off gas particles. Nature prefers this way.

2. *conduction*—fast-moving atoms collide with other atoms imparting some of their motion to them. This is used by metals like copper or aluminum to transfer heat (e.g., from your stove element to the food), but it is not used by a gas since the gas molecules are so far apart from one another. The process of conduction is too inefficient in a gas to worry about. (This is why you can stick your hand into your oven while something is baking and not immediately burn your hand if it does not touch anything, especially the metal sides and rack.)

3. **convection**—big pieces of the atmosphere cycle between cold regions and warm regions. Hot air below expands and its density decreases so it rises. Cooler, denser air falls and displaces the hot air. As a hot bubble rises, it cools by giving up its heat energy to the cool surroundings. The gas will then fall and heat up when it comes into contact with the warm surface or interior. It is a sort of "energy conveyor belt" motion of gas. Nature will use convection only if there is a large change in temperature over a small distance (a "steep temperature gradient"). Such conditions are found in planet atmospheres (compared to size of a planet, atmospheres are very thin!) and the interiors of stars.

convection

In addition to transporting energy outward to space, convection also distributes the heat *across* the planet, from the warm daylit equatorial regions to the cooler

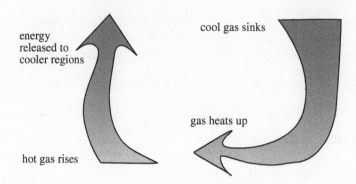

latitudes closer to the poles and to the night side of the planet. The warm air at the equatorial regions rises and the cooler air from other parts of the planet flows across the surface toward the equator to replace the rising air. All of the winds in a planet's atmosphere are due to convective processes. If the planet is rotating quickly enough, the motion of the air can be deflected sideways by the **Coriolis effect** (see also section 4.4.1).

Coriolis effect

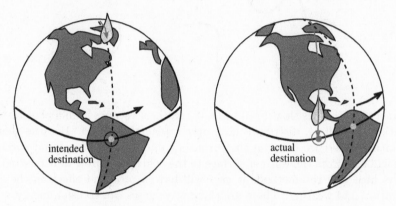

Coriolis effect: Original path of air is deflected westward
by the rotation of the planet.

    If a pocket of air from the pole moves toward the equator without changing direction, the planet will rotate beneath it. The packet of air has a sideways motion equal to the rotation speed at the pole, but the parts of the planet's surface closer to the equator have a greater rotational speed because they are farther from the rotation axis. To an observer on the ground, the path appears deflected to the west. The Coriolis effect on a spherical body is actually a bit more complicated than just the east or west deflection described above but a more complete treatment of the Coriolis effect requires higher level physics beyond the scope of this textbook. For our purposes, it is sufficient to say that objects will be deflected to the right in the northern hemisphere and to the left in the southern hemisphere, even for objects traveling due east or due west. The Coriolis deflections produce the spiral patterns of cyclonic storms (winds spiraling inward counter-clockwise in the northern hemisphere and clockwise in the southern hemisphere) and air flow away from high-pressure regions (winds rotate clockwise in the northern hemisphere and counter-clockwise in the southern hemisphere).

why storms spiral on the Earth

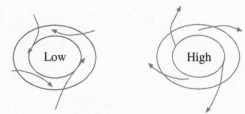

Air flows *into* a low-pressure region but the coriolis effect creates a spiralling pattern. Air spirals *out of* a high-pressure in the opposite direction.

The rapid rotation of a planet will also complicate the convective flow of energy from the warm equator to the cool poles. On a planet with little or no rotation (Venus, for example), the air circulation is very simple: warm air rises along the equator, flows at high altitudes toward the poles, and near the surface returns to the equator. On a planet with rapid rotation (Earth or the jovian planets, for example), the surface winds from the poles are deflected into large-scale eddies with belts of wind and calm (figure next page). At high altitudes narrow bands of high-speed winds called *jet streams* are formed and they play an important role on the surface weather. Land masses sticking up into the air flow disrupt the spiraling circulation and provide a place for storms to expend their energy.

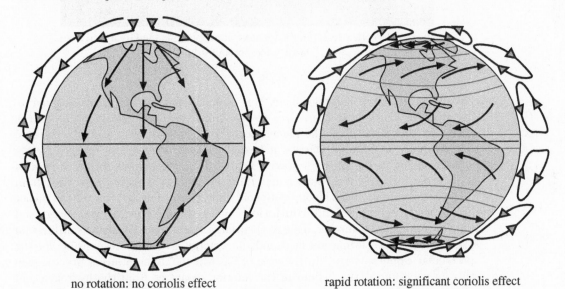

no rotation: no coriolis effect   rapid rotation: significant coriolis effect

On a planet with little or no rotation, the global air circulation pattern is very simple. On a planet with rapid rotation, the coriolis effect creates large-scale eddies with belts of wind and belts of calm.

The rapidly rotating jovian planets have much greater Coriolis effects. The powerful, narrow jet streams deflect the clouds into belts moving parallel to the planet equators. The winds in a belt move in the opposite direction of the belt next to it. Large vortices can form from the interplay of the belts. A large vortex can last for decades, even centuries or longer because the jovian planets do not have a solid surface for storms to expend their energy. Jupiter's Great Red Spot is an example of a large vortex. Twice the size of the Earth, it is at least 400 years old.

why jovian planets have belts of clouds

Jupiter's Great Red Spot

For most of the planets, the Sun provides the energy to maintain the atmosphere temperature (and surface temperature for the terrestrial planets) and to drive the

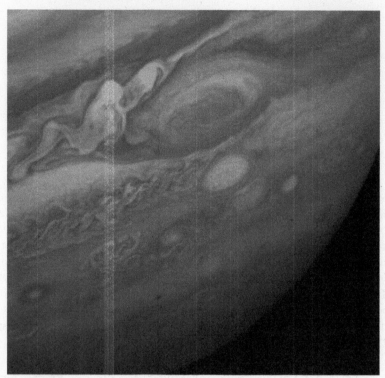

The largest vortex in Jupiter's dynamic atmosphere is the Great Red Spot.
Image courtesy of NASA/JPL

jovians have extra heat

convective motions of the atmosphere. But   Jupiter, Saturn, and Neptune generate over twice as much heat than they receive from the Sun. Most of this energy is leftover heat from when the planets formed 4.6 billion years ago. As material collected onto the forming planets, it heated up when energy was released by the material falling in the planet's gravity field. All of the planets were hot enough to be liquid. The heavier, denser materials (like iron and nickel) separated from the lighter materials (like silicon, hydrogen, and helium) and fell toward the planet cores. This process called **differentiation**   released more gravitational energy and heated up the planets further. Due to their large size, the jovian planets still retain a lot of their initial formation heat and that energy is what is responsible for the spectacular cloud patterns. In the case of Saturn, the differentiation process may still be going on as the helium in the interior separates from the hydrogen and sinks toward the core, a "helium rain". The helium rain is probably why there is a smaller percentage of helium in Saturn's atmosphere than in Jupiter's atmosphere.

differentiation

The much blander atmosphere of Uranus is a result of its lower heat emission. Most of the heat inside the much smaller Earth and Venus is produced from radioactivity (see section 10.3) in the rocky material (in fact, the higher radioactive heating long ago may have been necessary for the terrestrial planets to undergo differentiation). However, the heat of Venus' and Earth's interior has little to zero effect on their atmospheres because the crust is such a poor conductor of heat (though convection in their interiors is responsible for the geologic processes seen on their surfaces). Sunlight energy is what determines their surface temperatures and drives their weather.

atmosphere makes a blanket
cosmic rays

Atmospheres moderate the heat lost to space at night and shield the planet surface from energetic radiation like solar ultraviolet and X-rays and the high-speed charged particles in solar wind and most **cosmic rays** (extremely high-energy particles from space, mostly protons). The planet Mercury has almost no atmosphere and so there is a difference of several hundred degrees between places in the shade and sunlit areas! The planet Mars has a very thin atmosphere, so it experiences a temperature drop of over a 100 degrees when night comes. Humans landing on the martian surface will need to contend with the extreme cold of the night and will need to protect themselves from the harmful solar radiation during the day. The Earth's atmosphere is thick enough that the temperature difference between night and day is at most a few tens of degrees. Our atmosphere also blocks high-energy light like UV and X-rays and solar wind particles. Some cosmic ray particles have high enough energy to penetrate the atmosphere and even several meters of rock! If a cosmic ray strikes the DNA in the cells, the DNA structure can be altered. Cosmic rays are responsible for some of the genetic mutations in life.

atmosphere makes a shield

9.2.8   Clouds and Air Circulation

Clouds form when the temperature is cool enough for certain molecules in a planet's atmosphere to form droplets (condense). Clouds are usually made from minor ingredients in a planet's atmosphere (for example, Earth's clouds are made of water droplets that makes up less than 1% of our air globally while the majority of Earth's atmosphere is nitrogen and oxygen).

Clouds are important because (1) they block input energy from the Sun (a cooling effect); and (2) they trap energy from the surface (a heating effect). It is difficult to figure out which effect has greater long-term significance in how the temperature will change over time periods of years. Clouds are also extremely hard to model because they are so variable and changeable. The formation of clouds is also part of an energy transfer process because of an energy called *latent heat*. When a liquid turns into a gas such as liquid water evaporating, it absorbs energy while the temperature remains constant. The absorbed energy is the latent heat. (This is why we sweat—as the droplets of sweat produced by our bodies evaporate, they absorb energy from our overheated body taking away the excess energy we produce during exercise.) That latent heat is released when the gas condenses into droplets (clouds form). On the Earth, water evaporation and condensation provide a major source of energy transfer to drive the winds and they are key parts of the water cycle (*hydrological cycle*) shown in the figure below.

latent heat

water cycle

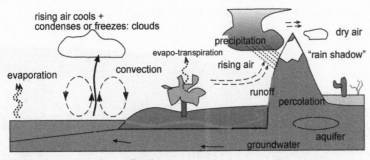

Hydrological cycle on Earth:

1) Water evaporates into atmosphere (also transpiration from plants, respiration from animals).
2) Convection carries warm moist air upward. Mountains also direct warm moist air upward.
3) Water vapor condenses or freezes to make clouds.
4) Droplets or flakes grow to point where air cannot hold them anymore and they precipitate out (rain or snow). Air on other side of mountains is dry: "rain shadow" area.
5) Surface water runs downhill toward oceans. Water also percolates through soil into ground. Some groundwater collects into aquifers and other groundwater flows out to the oceans.

Water from the oceans, rivers, and lakes evaporates to become water vapor. Warm air is able to hold more water vapor than cool air so as convection in the troposphere moves air upward, the water vapor will condense at the cooler altitudes. The cloud droplets (or crystals) will grow as they pick up more water vapor. Eventually, the cloud droplets grow so large that the cooler air cannot hold them anymore and they fall to the surface. The rainwater (or snowmelt during warm days) runs downhill starting out as streams that flow into small rivers that in turn flow into large river down to the oceans. Water also percolates into the soil to become part of the groundwater that totals approximately 10% of the mass of the oceans. Some of the groundwater collects in reservoirs underground called *aquifers*. Groundwater can remain in aquifers for a million years or more. Some aquifer water can reach the surface and flow out to the oceans. Water that falls as snow can also store water for long periods of time as ice sheets and glaciers near the poles or at high elevations.

aquifers

A similar sort of evaporation-condensation-precipitation cycle is found on other planets but the molecule may be something other than water. The situation closest to what happens on the Earth is what is found on Titan, a moon of Saturn. There, methane is the key player, instead of water. In fact, Titan is so cold that water is in deep freeze, so water ice there plays the same role that rock plays here.

Mountains

The water cycle figure also shows the effect of mountains. The mountains on the Earth are high in comparison to the thickness of our troposphere so they can provide a significant barrier to the circulation of air or change the circulation patterns. They can also "speed up" the condensation-precipitation process by forcing sideways moving air to rise upward leading to storms on the mountainsides that face the prevailing winds. Air on the other side of the mountains is much drier so the land on the other side has little rainfall—a "rain shadow". Some example rain shadows include the southern part of the San Joaquin valley in California (formed by the Diablo Range and the Tehachapi Mountains), the eastern half of Oregon and Washington (formed by the Cascade Range), and the Atacama Desert (the driest place on Earth formed by the Chilean Coast Range).

Ocean Currents

Our oceans also affect atmospheric circulation by transporting heat energy and water, heating or cooling the land and air. For example, the California Current is a current in the Pacific Ocean that moves southward along the western coast of North America, from British Columbia to southern Baja California. The movement of the cooler northern waters southward makes the coastal waters cooler than the coastal areas of the eastern United States at the same latitudes. The Gulf Stream is a warm surface ocean current born in the Gulf of Mexico that flows up the eastern United States seaboard and then veers northeastward toward Europe at about 6 km/hour (4 mph). The North Atlantic Drift (aka North Atlantic Current) continues carrying the warm water north of the British Isles to Scandinavia. This warm water makes western Europe have climate more like the United States instead of Canada of which it shares the same latitude range. Northern Norway is near the Arctic Circle but most of its coast remains snow/ice-free, even during the winter.

Tropical storms form over warm waters and can gather enough energy and moisture from the warm waters to turn in hurricanes (or typhoons). Sea surface temperatures must be 27.8 deg C or warmer to create and sustain a tropical cyclone. The ocean currents play a key role in why the southeastern United States experiences hurricanes in the summer and fall. The oceans store a lot of heat energy and release it more slowly than land or the atmosphere, so they provide a moderating influence on local climates and even global climate changes. Air circulation also affects the surface ocean currents so the air and ocean circulation are constantly playing off each other, though the ocean moves much more slowly than the air so the oceans lag behind the atmosphere. This complex interplay between ocean circulation and air circulation is a key piece of the Earth's climate puzzle that still needs a lot of research! See the textbook website for links to more about the roles of the oceans in Earth's climate.

9.2.9 Weather vs. Climate

The preceding sections have talked about weather and climate and what affects them. Weather is often confused with climate, so this section will explain the difference between them as well as what can produce changes in a planet's global climate. The figure below illustrates the difference between weather and climate.

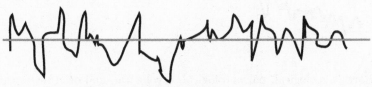

Weather => wiggles // Climate => green line

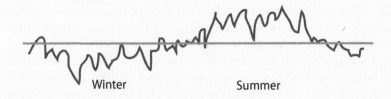

Winter   Summer

Weather is the ever-changing combination of winds, clouds, temperature, and pressure at a particular location and time. **Climate** is the long-term average of

weather
climate

weather (usually 30 years or longer for Earth climate), which means it can change only on much longer time scales. The long-term averaging removes the chaotic wiggles making it possible to make long-term predictions of future climate. Weather predictions vs. climate predictions is analogous to not being able to predict if a particular coin toss will be heads or if it will be tails but you can easily predict the statistical results of a large number of coin tosses.

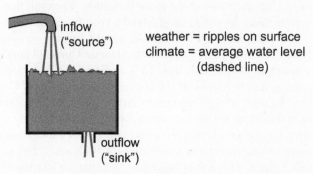

System with energy or material coming in balanced by
energy or material going out ("sources and sinks")

climate system

Another analogy David Archer uses in his book *The Long Thaw* involves water in a sink with water flowing into it via a faucet and water flowing out via a drain: weather is like the ripples on the surface of the water while the average water level in the sink would be climate. Predicting the average water level in the sink is much easier than predicting all of the features of the ripples on the surface. (For more on climate vs. weather, see the FAQ 1.2 of the Climate Change 2007: Working Group I report of the IPCC.) The hydrological (water) cycle, mountain ranges (rain shadows), and ocean currents all play key roles in determining climate on the Earth.

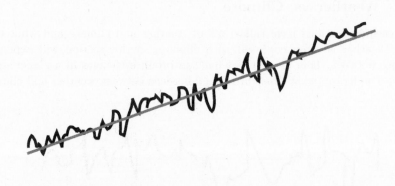

The Earth's geological, paleontological, cryological, and even historical records show that climates can change but, by definition, these changes take place over decades at least on up to millennia. Careful study of the polar ice caps on Mars and other surface features show that Mars has also undergone climate changes, some drastic. Venus was once a more comfortable place but it underwent a drastic global climate change as well to become a hellishly hot and very dry place.

ice cores give us climate history

One of the records we have for reconstructing the temperature of the Earth to times more than 800,000 years ago are ice cores drilled into the ice sheets in Antarctica and Greenland (a cryological record). On the next page are temperature reconstructions from deuterium isotope abundance measurements in ice cores drilled by the EPICA group at Dome C in Antarctica (data courtesy of Jouzel, J., et al).

interglacials
ice ages

The records show a cyclic pattern of brief warm spells called *interglacials* (the peaks in the graph) separated by long cold spells, the ice ages. The pattern repeats

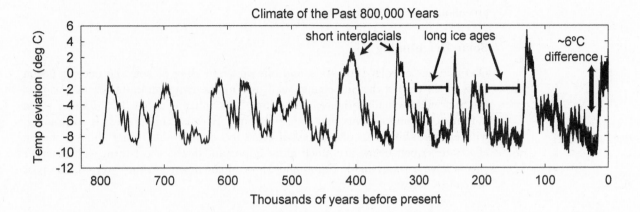

with a period of approximately 100,000 years. Because there were no thermometers way back then, temperature *reconstructions* must use *measurements of isotope abundances* such as deuterium (hydrogen-2) or oxygen-18 to create temperature data. The isotope measurement methods use the fact that water made of oxygen-18 and/or deuterium will evaporate and condense (then precipitate) differently than ordinary water (made of hydrogen-1 and oxygen-16) because of differences in the masses of the isotopes. Water made of the *lighter* isotopes *evaporates* more easily and water made from the *heavier* isotopes *condenses and precipitates* out more readily. When the climate near the poles is colder than usual, the separation of the isotopes from the water vapor in the air is more pronounced. The result is that ice sheets are isotopically light and the oceans are isotopically heavy.

isotope ratios as temperature proxies

Oxygen in the oceans can get incorporated in the calcium carbonate in marine shells. Measuring the amount of oxygen-18 in fossil marine shells of different ages can give us a record of the global climate throughout time because the oceans are well-mixed over very short timescales, geologically speaking. The deuterium in ice cores and oxygen-18 in fossil marine shells give very similar results. That tells us that the data and conclusions derived from them are reliable since the very different data come from totally different places.

Another thing the plot shows is that the temperature climbs very quickly and then falls back down more gradually. The pattern is the result of subtle changes in the Earth's orbit and tilt (described more fully below), along with complex feedback loops involving water, carbon dioxide, and other trace molecules in the climate system.

Going much further back in time, the geological records show that between 580 million and 750 million years ago, the Earth experienced some particularly severe ice ages with glaciers going all the way to the equator. A time of such extreme ice age is called *Snowball Earth*. Earth was able to get out of the snowball Earth phases via climate change agents described below. Evidence for the Snowball Earth episodes comes from glacial sediments that were embedded within icebergs. The sediments of material from the middle of continents were deposited on the ocean floor far from where the glaciers would have met the oceans. Also glaciers grind up surface rock and the glaciers carry the debris along with them and deposit them in rubble piles called moraines. Rocks moving with the glaciers can scratch the surface rock layer to create long, parallel scratches. These glacier-formed features are found in places that would have been near the equator when they were created. Another piece of evidence for the Snowball Earth episodes is described in section 9.6.3.

Snowball Earth

Recalling what affects the surface temperature of a terrestrial planet (section 9.2.5), we can make a brief list of what can cause long-term climate changes: solar brightening, changes in the orbit and axis tilt, change in reflectivity, and changes in greenhouse gas abundance.

Solar Brightening

Observations of solar-type stars and our understanding of how the nuclear fusion rates in the core of the Sun change as it uses up its hydrogen in its core tell us that the Sun will gradually brighten with time. The Sun was about 30% dimmer when it formed 4.6 billion years ago than it is now. Because this process is so gradual, *very long-term effect* with effects taking tens of millions of years to be noticeable, other climate change effects described below are much more important in the short-term. These other effects have actually made Earth and Mars *cooler* now than they were in the past instead of hotter.

Solar Brightening will increase the amount of
energy reaching the planet => planet warms

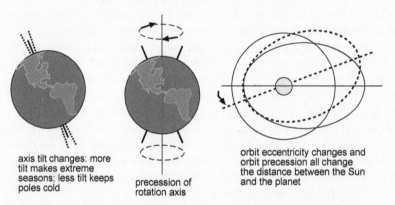

axis tilt changes: more
tilt makes extreme
seasons; less tilt keeps
poles cold

precession of
rotation axis

orbit eccentricity changes and
orbit precession all change
the distance between the Sun
and the planet

Axis tilt and orbit changes affect the angle of sunlight hitting a
given point on the planet's surface and the distance from the Sun

Reflectivity changes: increase
reflectivity cools planet, decrease
reflectivity warms planet

**Greenhouse gas abundance
changes**: more gas warms
planet, less gas cools planet

Reflectivity (Albedo) Changes

Increases in the albedo of a planet will mean less solar energy absorbed and therefore cooling of the planet. Natural ways to increase a planet's albedo are through volcanic eruptions—the dust particles reflect the sunlight (the smaller they are, the more they reflect), increased ice coverage, and increased cloud cover. On the Earth, if the volcanic dust can reach the stratosphere, it can spread around the globe and stay aloft for several years. A natural way to decrease a planet's albedo is through melting of ice. On the Earth, human activity has led to increases and decreases in the Earth's reflectivity of which we are still trying to determine the net effect. Smog acts like the volcanic dust particles to increase the albedo. Deforestation also increases the albedo by removing the sunlight absorbing plants. However, building of cities and roads tend to make the surface darker, the so-called "urban heat island" effect.

Greenhouse Gas Abundance Changes

More greenhouse gases in the atmosphere usually mean more infrared energy is trapped close to the planet's surface. A warmer surface can lead to increased evaporation or sublimation (ice directly to vapor) and therefore increase the surface air pressure. On the Earth, the increased amount of water vapor would further amplify the greenhouse effect from carbon dioxide and methane. Decreased greenhouse gases usually mean cooler temperatures and if the cooling is great enough (as found on Mars, for example), a drop in atmospheric pressure as gases freeze. Note that I inserted the word "usually" in the expected trends as a warming planet from increased greenhouse gas abundance could have increased cloud cover which may dampen or delay the warming because of the increased albedo. Clouds and dust (*aerosols*) create the largest uncertainties in our current climate models. Aerosols are very small droplets of material or particles suspended in the atmosphere like dust and sulfuric acid droplets but are not water droplets or ice. However, they can serve as the nuclei around which water can accumulate to make clouds, so they can have a direct effect of reflecting sunlight or an indirect effect of creating clouds that reflect sunlight.

clouds and aerosols

Because of water's short residency time in our atmosphere (a water molecule will be in the atmosphere for about a week) and the amount of water vapor present depends very sensitively on the temperature, water vapor is considered just an *enhancer* of climate change by the greenhouse effect rather than an agent of change. If another gas starts to warm a planet, the increased amount of water vapor from evaporation will approximately double the greenhouse effect of the other gas. Similarly, if a decrease in another gas cools the planet, the amount of water vapor will drop too to further weaken the greenhouse effect. In this way water vapor creates a *positive feedback*. A positive feedback enhances whatever initial change is made in a system. A *negative feedback* dampens any initial change in a system to return it back to its original state. An example in another area of experience: if you put a microphone next to a speaker, a positive feedback creates the high-pitched, very loud squeal. When you move the microphone away from the speaker to minimize the squeal, that's a negative feedback.

water vapor just enhances change, not cause change

positive feedback

Other gases like carbon dioxide have much longer residency times (decades to centuries). Their presence does not depend so sensitively on the temperature so they can be agents of change moving a climate system out of balance. In the climate change research, the long-lived gases are called *radiative forcing* agents while water vapor is just a feedback actor.

Axis Tilt and Orbit Changes

Gravitational interactions of a planet, its moons, and the other planets of the solar system cause the tilt of the planet's rotation axis to change and the planet's orbit to change shape and orientation in a periodic way. In addition, the rotation axis precesses. Put all of these agents together, all with different periods, and they can create dramatic changes in a planet's climate by changing the *insolation*: the angle of sunlight hitting a given point on the planet's surface and the amount of solar radiation reaching the planet's surface. Adding in the other agents of climate

insolation

change above can make the effects from even subtle changes in the axis or orbit much more significant.

The angle of the tilt of the Earth's rotation axis varies about its current value of 23.44° from between about 22° and 25° with a period of approximately 41,000 years. Larger tilt creates more extreme seasons—warmer summers and colder winters. A decreasing tilt is thought to bring about ice ages because the milder summers allow ice and snow to last throughout the year in the higher latitudes (closer to the poles). This increased ice coverage increases the reflectivity of a planet compounding the effect of the milder summers. It also appears that the amount of carbon dioxide falls as ice sheets grow, leading to further cooling. The amount of the tilt of the Earth's rotation axis is prevented from changing too much because of the stabilizing influence of the Moon's gravity. Mars' rotation axis is now about 25.2°, close to the Earth's tilt, so it experiences seasons similar to ours (though roughly twice as long because of its larger orbit). Mars does not have any massive moons so it has experienced much wilder fluctuations in its rotation axis tilt throughout its history— between 13° and 40° and maybe up to 60° over a 100,000-year cycle. Mars is also closer to Jupiter so Jupiter's gravity has a greater influence in perturbing Mars' rotation axis than Jupiter has with the Earth. Recent evidence of these climate cycles on Mars can be seen in the Mars Reconnaissance Orbiter's observations of rock layering and of layering of the polar ice caps.

Mars has larger climate swings than Earth

Recall from section 3.6.5 that the Earth's orbit is elliptical and that it gets closest in early January. With an orbit eccentricity of 0.0167, Earth receives about 7% more solar energy in early January than at its aphelion point in early July. The Earth's orbit changes eccentricity on cycles of about 100,000 and about 400,000 years. At greatest eccentricity, the Earth can receive over 20% more solar energy at perihelion than at aphelion. Mars has a more elliptical orbit than the Earth and as a result, its southern hemisphere winters are long and extreme while its northern hemisphere winters are short and milder.

Section 3.5 discusses the precession of the Earth's rotation axis that is caused by the Sun's gravity and the Moon's gravity pulling on the non-perfectly round Earth. The Earth bulges a bit at the equator and is flattened at the poles primarily because of its rapid spin. The Sun's and Moon's gravities cause the rotation axis to slowly wobble with a period of 26,000 years. Another precession is with the orbit of the Earth. The slight influences of the other planets in the solar system, primarily Jupiter and Saturn, cause the perihelion direction to shift. This reduces the cycle of when perihelion would occur from 26,000 years to about 21,600 years.

Milankovitch cycles

For the Earth we have an approximately 41,000-year axis tilt period plus the 100,000-year and 400,000-year cycles of variation in the Earth's orbit shape. Add in the 21,600-year cycle of precession of the Earth's perihelion date, you will find the net effect to be quite complex to predict. James Croll in the mid-1800s suspected that these orbit variations might cause the rise and fall of the ice ages. Later, in the early 1900s, Milutin Milankovitch quantified the changes and developed the mathematical theory behind the orbit/tilt variations and so these cycles are called *Milankovitch cycles*   in his honor. Milankovitch's calculations have been refined since his time but the basic idea of his theory is still valid. Past ice ages correlate well to the summer insolation at 65° N latitude. The northern hemisphere is more important because of the greater amount of land area in the northern hemisphere compared to the southern hemisphere—the oceans have a larger heat capacity than land and so they tend to dampen changes in the temperature.

changes in reflectivity and greenhouse gases enhance Milankovich

However, the axis tilt and orbit variations cannot by themselves, explain the magnitude and quickness of the temperature changes between the ice ages and the interglacials. One has to include the effects of reflectivity changes and greenhouse gas abundance changes—the positive and negative feedback effects of them—to explain the magnitude and quickness of the temperature changes fully. Use the links on the textbook's website for this section to find out more about the Milankovitch cycles.

9.2.10 Appearance and Colors of the Atmospheres

Most of the planet atmospheres reflect enough of the visible sunlight that only the upper layers of their atmospheres can be seen. Only the Earth and Mars have atmospheres transparent to most of the visible light so that we can see what lies below their atmospheres. I acknowledge that I have a visible light bias in this section—the other planet atmospheres are more transparent at other wavelengths outside of the visible band. If humans had eyes sensitive to certain parts of the infrared, we would probably say that Earth's atmosphere was a thick haze that prevented photography of the surface from space.

In visible light, Venus is a bland, yellow-white planet. Venus' atmosphere is 96 percent carbon dioxide but it is the thick cloud layer of sulfuric acid droplets that reflects back about 70 percent of the sunlight and make Venus brighter than any other object in our sky besides the Moon and the Sun (in fact Venus can be seen in broad daylight if the Earth's atmosphere above you is very clear). Venus' cloud layer extends from 30 kilometers to 60 kilometers above the surface. Below 30 kilometers Venus' atmosphere is clear because the high temperature near the surface evaporates any cloud droplets that drop too far. What sunlight that makes it through the clouds, has an orange tinge to it because the blue colors are absorbed by the clouds. The sulfuric acid may be from sulfur compounds, possibly from volcanoes, that chemically react with the trace amounts of water vapor left in the atmosphere.

Venus' clouds

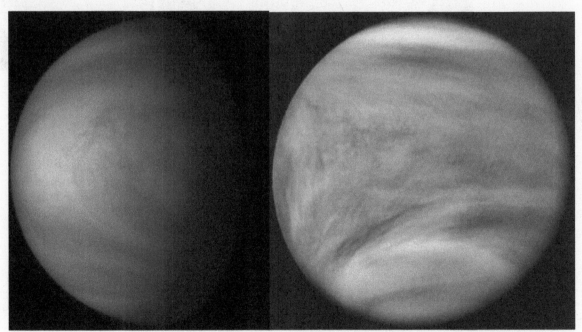

Galileo spacecraft optical band image of Venus.   Pioneer spacecraft ultraviolet image of Venus. The ultraviolet band highlights the cloud structure.
Images courtesy of NASA/JPL

The structure of the clouds are revealed in ultraviolet light. It is the ultraviolet images that most astronomy books will use to show what Venus looks like. To see what lies below the surface, astronomers use the long wavelengths of radio. The rocky surface of Venus has been mapped using imaging radar by spacecraft orbiting

Venus, such as the spectacular Magellan spacecraft that surveyed Venus in the early 1990's.

Earth

Earth's atmosphere is mostly transparent to visible light with a blue tint caused by the preferential scattering of blue sunlight by the nitrogen and oxygen molecules. Clouds of water droplets and ice crystals form up to about 10 kilometers above the surface. The droplets and crystals are large enough to reflect all wavelengths of visible equally, so the clouds have a white color. Because of the Coriolis effect (recall the previous section), the clouds form spiral patterns.

Earth and Mars to the same scale. Transparent atmospheres allow us to see their surfaces.
Images courtesy of NASA and USGS

Mars

Mars' carbon dioxide atmosphere is also mostly transparent to visible light. Its thin white clouds are mostly water ice crystals. Near the poles the temperature is cold enough that carbon dioxide can freeze to form white clouds of carbon dioxide ice crystals. Some clouds have a yellow color because they are composed of fine dust particles a few micrometers across. Astronomers expected Mars' sky to have a deep blue color as seen from the surface because the atmosphere is only one percent the thickness of the Earth's atmosphere. However, pictures from the Mars surface landers show the martian sky to be pink from sunlight bouncing off dust particles blown off Mars' red surface.

Jupiter and Saturn

Jupiter's atmosphere is very dynamic and colorful and Saturn's atmosphere is a muted version of Jupiter's. Even though their atmospheres are primarily hydrogen and helium, the clouds of ammonia ice crystals in their upper atmospheres give the planets their appearance. The strong Coriolis effect from their rapid rotation deflect the clouds into bands parallel to their equators. The bright zones on Jupiter are regions of upwelling convection cells in the upper atmosphere with more ammonia clouds than the darker bands. The dark bands are where we see to the warmer clouds made of ammonium hydrosulfide ice crystals about 20 to 30 kilometers below the ammonia cloud deck. Clouds of water ice crystals are thought to exist about 100 kilometers below the ammonia cloud deck, but the Galileo probe that plunged through Jupiter's clouds in early December of 1995 found no water layer. However, this may because the Galileo probe descended through an unusually dry and cloud-

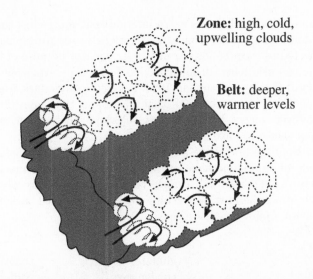

Zone: high, cold, upwelling clouds

Belt: deeper, warmer levels

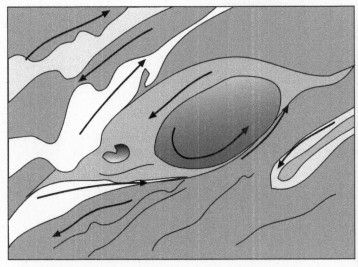

Strong, alternating eastward, westward jet streams cause shearing of the clouds and make turbulent eddies such as the Great Red Spot on Jupiter.

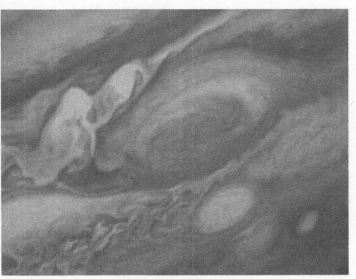

Jupiter's Great Red Spot.
Image courtesy of NASA/JPL

free part of the atmosphere.

Saturn's layer of clouds is about twice as thick as Jupiter's because of the colder temperatures and lower gravity compression on Saturn. The strong jet streams in their atmospheres create turbulent eddies of swirling clouds, some several thousands of kilometers across. One spectacular example is the Great Red Spot on Jupiter—a hurricane twice the size of the Earth that has lasted for over 400 years. Such storms and the belted patterns on the jovian planets can last so long because there is no solid surface for the storms to expend their energy.

large storms

What is puzzling about the clouds is their color. The ammonia ice clouds should be white, yet they have a variety or red, orange, yellow, and brown colors. Sunlight striking the clouds causes photochemical reactions with the molecules in the clouds. The resulting organic compounds, or trace amounts of sulfur and phosphorus may be responsible for the colors in the clouds.

the color of the clouds

Uranus and Neptune also have thick cloud decks but Uranus' atmosphere does not have the prominent bands and storms seen on the other jovian planets. This

Uranus and Neptune

is because Uranus does not have an extra internal heat source like the other jovian planets, so it does not have the convective motions in its atmosphere. Neptune's clouds are deflected to form bands parallel to its equator because of its rapid rotation. Neptune can also have turbulent eddies form in its atmosphere. When the Voyager spacecraft flew by Neptune in 1989, it found a large dark storm, called the Great Dark Spot (very original, yes?), that was about the size of Jupiter's Great Red Spot. However, recent Hubble Space Telescope photographs show that the Great Dark Spot seems to have dissipated.

cause of blue color

Uranus and Neptune both have a blue color. Instead of ammonia clouds, their clouds are made of frozen methane crystals because they are much colder than Jupiter and Saturn. The red and orange colors of sunlight are absorbed by the methane in their atmospheres while the blue colors are scattered back out, producing the blue color with a faint greenish tinge.

Vocabulary

albedo	climate	convection
Coriolis effect	cosmic rays	differentiation
escape velocity	exosphere	greenhouse effect
hydrostatic equilibrium	ideal gas law	mesosphere
ozone	pressure	solar wind
stratosphere	temperature	thermosphere
troposphere	weather	

Formulae

1. *escape velocity* $= \sqrt{(2 \times G \times \text{mass/distance})}$, where the mass is that of the planet or moon, the distance is measured from the center of the planet or moon, and G is the universal gravitational constant.

2. *average gas speed* $= \sqrt{(3 \times k \times \text{temperature/gas molecule mass})}$, where k is the universal Boltzmann constant.

3. general rule of atmophere escape: if the *average* gas molecule speed is less than $0.2 \times$ (the escape velocity), then more than 1/2 of that type of gas will remain after 1 billion years.

Review Questions

1. In what ways are *jovian* planets different from *terrestrial* planets?

2. Why are jovian and terrestrial planets different from one another?

3. What two things determine the thickness of a planet's atmosphere?

4. Which will have a large escape velocity: something with small surface gravity or something with large surface gravity?

5. Does a moon's escape velocity depend on the gravity of the planet it orbits? If yes, explain how; if not, why not?

6. At a given temperature, which molecule travels fastest: a massive one or a light one? Which of the two would most likely escape from a planet's atmosphere? Which of the two would most likely remain?

7. Which of the following things would tend to make a thick atmosphere: cold temperature, high gas particle mass, weak gravity, outgassing from the interior (volcanic eruptions)?

8. In what way does a magnetic field protect a planet's atmosphere? In what ways is it involved with atmosphere loss?

9. Why don't we feel a downward force on our bodies from the miles of air above us or why don't our bodies implode from the air pressure?

10. What are two ways to increase the pressure of a gas?

11. If a gas is compressed, what is expected to happen to the temperature of the gas?

12. Explain why the pressure in your automobile tires is slightly less when they are cold than right after a long drive.

13. Why do hot air balloons float upward?

14. Why must deeper layers of an atmosphere exert more pressure?

15. How would the depth of an atmosphere change if a planet warms up or cools off?

16. What are three ways to make a planet's average temperature greater?

17. On a planet with a thin atmosphere, what would you expect for the temperature difference between night and day to be (small, moderate, large)? Explain why.

18. What would be the expected average surface temperature of Venus, Earth, and Mars if they did not have an atmosphere?

19. Why are their actual average surface temperatures greater than the no-atmosphere temperature?

20. If the clouds of Venus were perfect reflectors of visible light from the Sun so that no visible light reached Venus' surface, what would happen to the surface temperature? Explain your answer.

21. If the atmosphere of Venus trapped all of the infrared light from the surface, what would happen to the surface temperature? Explain your answer.

22. What are the primary greenhouse gases in the Earth's atmosphere? Which ones can remain in the atmosphere for decades or more?

23. What are the layers of the Earth's atmosphere? What layers are not found on Mars and Venus and why is that? In what layer of an atmosphere do clouds form?

24. Why does the temperature in our stratosphere increase with altitude and how is it beneficial to life on the surface?

25. What heats the thermosphere of a planet?

26. How are the three clouds on Jupiter and Saturn formed and what are they made of?

27. Is there expected to be any water vapor at the same elevation as the ammonia clouds on Jupiter and Saturn? Why or why not?

28. Is there expected to be any ammonia vapor at the same elevation as the water clouds on Jupiter and Saturn? Why or why not?

29. Why are the cloud decks of Saturn found at greater depths than on Jupiter?

30. Why is there so much convective motion in many planet atmospheres and some planet interiors?

31. Why do low-pressure storm systems develop cyclonic spirals, and why are the patterns in the two hemispheres mirror images of each other?

32. Suppose the atmosphere circulation on the Earth were stopped. What would be the effect on the temperature of the atmosphere near the equator, at the mid-latitudes, and near the poles?

33. If the Earth rotated faster, would the Coriolis effect be greater or less than what it is now? Explain your answer by comparing what would happen to a rock thrown from the north pole and landing on the equator on a rapidly spinning Earth with that thrown on a slowly spinning Earth.

34. How do clouds affect the surface temperature of a planet?

35. On Earth a molecule of water leaves the ocean. Describe the possible paths the molecule could take to return to the ocean.

36. How do mountains affect a location's climate, particularly its annual amount of precipitation?

37. How do ocean current affect a location's climate?

38. How do the ocean currents affect air circulation and how do the winds affect ocean currents?

39. What is the difference between weather and climate?

40. If we cannot accurately predict the weather two weeks from now, how can we possibly predict the climate 50 years from now?

41. How has the temperature of the Earth changed over the past million or so years and how do we know?

42. What five things can cause long-term climate changes?

43. How has the Sun's brightness changed since it formed?

44. If water vapor is the dominant greenhouse gas on Earth, why is there such a concern about other greenhouse gases such as carbon dioxide or methane?

45. What is a "positive feedback"? What is a "negative feedback"?

46. What is responsible for triggering the ice ages on Earth?

47. Is it possible for a planet's rotation axis and orbit shape to change? What affect would those changes have on a planet's average global temperature?

48. In what ways are the atmospheres of the terrestrial planets like each other? In what ways are they different from each other?

49. How are the atmospheres of Jupiter and Saturn different than the atmospheres of Uranus and Neptune?

50. What are visible clouds of the jovian planets made of and why are they different from each other?

9.3   Magnetic Fields

Some planets have a magnetic field that acts like there is a giant bar magnet in the center of a planet (there isn't really a giant bar magnet, though). The magnetic field can be aligned differently than the rotational axis. For example, the Earth's magnetic field is tilted by about 18° with respect to our rotation axis, so compasses point to a magnetic pole that is just off the coast of northern Canada.

A planet's magnetic field forms a shield protecting the planet's surface from energetic, charged particles coming from the Sun and other places. The Sun is constantly sending out charged particles, called the **solar wind**, into the solar system. When solar wind particles run into a magnetic field, they are deflected and spiral around the magnetic field lines. Magnetic "field lines" are imaginary lines used to describe the direction charged or magnetic particles will move when responding to a magnetic field. In the same way, gravity "field lines" point to the center of an object producing the gravity. You can see the direction of an ordinary

solar wind

household magnet's field lines by sprinkling tiny iron filings around a magnetic—they will tend to bunch up along particular magnetic field lines.

Most of the solar wind gets deflected around the planet but a few particles manage to leak into the magnetic field and become trapped in the planet's magnetic field to created radiation belts or "charged particle belts".

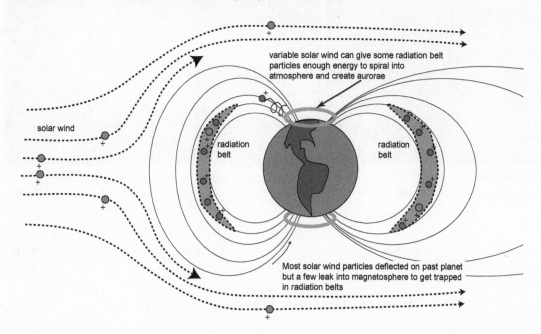

9.3.1   Aurorae

One glorious effect seen when the solar wind interacts with a planet's magnetic field is **aurorae**. Aurorae are shimmering light displays produced by molecules in the upper atmosphere. Fluctuations in the solar wind can give energy to the trapped charged particles in the belts. Particles with enough energy can leave the belts and spiral down to the atmosphere to collide with molecules and atoms in the thermosphere of a planet. These collisions excite the atmosphere molecules (bumping their electrons to higher energy levels). The electrons then release the excess energy as they hop downward back toward the atomic nuclei. The glow of the aurorae is the emission line spectra produced by the electrons in the rarefied gas dropping back down to lower atomic energy levels.

Aurorae in the Earth's atmosphere occur many tens of kilometers above the surface (in the thermosphere) and pose no threat to life on the surface below. They make some spectacular displays that look like shimmering curtains or spikes of different colors of light. The magenta colors are produced by nitrogen molecules at the lower end of the aurorae (up to 100 kilometers above the surface), between 100 and 200 kilometers above the surface excited oxygen atoms produce the green colors and ionized nitrogen atoms produce the blue colors, and greater than 200 kilometers above the surface oxygen atoms produce the deep red colors. In the northern hemisphere, the aurorae are called *aurora borealis* or "the northern lights" and in the southern hemisphere, they are called *aurora australis* or "the southern lights." Occasionally the aurorae seem to erupt with a burst of activity of multi-color shimmering of reds, whites, and purples. This happens when stressed or flexing magnetic field lines about a third of the way to the Moon squeeze together and reconnect. That sends a massive burst toward the Earth that hits the upper atmosphere to make the aurora eruption. The textbook's website gives links to

aurorae
solar wind interacting with planet's magnetic field

emission line spectra
altitude of aurorae

Curtain aurorae near Fairbanks, Alaska in September 2007 when solar wind energy was "only 3" on scale of 1 to 10.

Aurorae seen from above by the Shuttle astronauts. Notice the large gap between the aurorae and the surface.
Image courtesy of NASA

several resources on the interaction of the Earth's magnetic field with the solar wind called *Space Weather*.

9.3.2   Magnetic Dynamo Theory

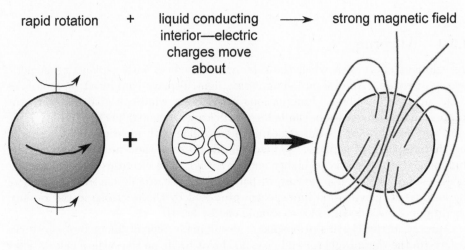

rapid rotation   +   liquid conducting interior—electric charges move about   →   strong magnetic field

magnetic "field lines" show in which direction charged particles will be deflected.

Planets do not have giant bar magnets in their cores, so what produces the magnetic field? Recall from the beginning of chapter 7, that a magnetic field can be produced by circulating electrical charges. A theory called the **magnetic dynamo** theory says that the magnetic fields in planets are produced by swirling motions of liquid conducting material in the planet interiors. Materials that can conduct electricity have some electrical charge that is free to move about. Such materials are called *metallic* and are not necessarily shiny solids like copper, aluminum, or iron. Jupiter and Saturn have a large amount   of hydrogen that is compressed so much it forms a liquid. Some of that liquid hydrogen is in a state where some of

magnetic dynamo

liquid metallic hydrogen

the electrons are squeezed out of the atoms and are free to move around.

A moving charge will produce a magnetic field (see chapter 7). The liquid conducting material in a planet's interior can be made to swirl about if the planet is rotating quickly enough. The faster a planet rotates, the more the material gets stirred up and, therefore, the stronger the generated magnetic field. If the liquid interior becomes solid or if the rotation slows down, the magnetic field will weaken. So in summary what a planet needs in order to produce a strong magnetic field are *(1) a liquid conducting (metallic) interior* and *(2) rapid rotation* to get the conducting material moving about. For the *terrestrial planets* plate tectonics may also play a role. Plate tectonics (described in sections 9.4 and 9.5.5) cools the planet's mantle creating a large enough temperature difference between the core and mantle to produce convection in the metallic core needed to make a magnetic field. Let's see how this theory explains the presence or lack of a magnetic field around some of the planets:

1. Venus has no magnetic field (or one so weak, it hasn't been detected yet). It   *Venus*
   probably has a liquid conducting interior for a couple of reasons:

   (a) Since it is almost the size of the Earth, its interior should still be very
       warm. Larger planets lose their heat from formation and radioactive
       decay more slowly than small planets. A planet with a larger volume   *why large planets have*
       than another planet of the same composition will start off with a larger   *warm interiors*
       supply of heat energy. In addition, the heat in a large planet's interior
       has a great distance to travel to reach the planet's surface and the cold
       outer space.

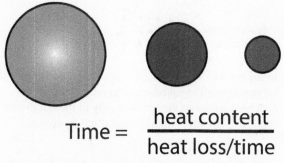

$$\text{Time} = \frac{\text{heat content}}{\text{heat loss/time}}$$

heat content ~ volume (diameter^3)
heat loss/time ~ surface area (diameter^2)

   The *rate* of heat loss increases with the surface area. A planet with a
   larger surface area than another planet with the same internal temperature will have a larger rate of heat loss. The time it takes for a planet
   to cool off depends on the total amount of heat stored/rate of heat loss
   or (its volume)/(its surface area). Recall from section 9.1.3 that the volume increases as the diameter^3. The surface area increases as only the
   diameter^2, so the planet's cooling time increases as diameter^3/diameter^2 *cooling time*
   = diameter. Even though its heat loss rate is greater, a larger planet has
   a much larger amount of energy stored in it and, thus, it will take longer
   to cool off than a smaller planet. Venus should have a iron-nickel core
   that is still liquid like the Earth's.

   (b) High resolution radar imaging of Venus' surface by the Magellan space-
       craft shows several places where volcanos have erupted recently and pro-
       duced large lava flows. Recent infrared imaging of Venus' surface by the
       Venus Express spacecraft shows material that has just come out of some
       shield volcanoes, so Venus is still active.

The reasons why Venus does not have a magnetic field are that it spins very s-l-o-w-l-y (about once every 243 days!) and the absence of convection in the liquid core (probably because of the lack of plate tectonics for the past half billion years).

Mars

2. Mars has an extremely weak magnetic field but for a different reason than Venus. Mars is about half the diameter of the Earth and has about 1/10th the Earth's mass, so its internal heat should have disappeared to space long ago. So even though Mars spins quickly (once every 24.6 hours), its metallic core is mostly solid—the charges are not able to swirl about. A recent gravity field map shows that Mars has a liquid outer core of molten rock. Mars' crust is also probably too thick for plate tectonics to occur even if the core had not cooled.

Earth

3. Earth has a strong magnetic field because it spins fast (once every 23.93 hours), it has a liquid conducting core made of liquid iron-nickel, and it has plate tectonics.

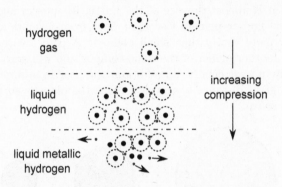

In Jupiter and Saturn the gravitational compression is great enough to squeeze electrons out of the hydrogen atoms so they move easily in the liquid and conduct electricity—liquid "metallic" hydrogen.

Jupiter

4. Jupiter has a HUGE magnetic field. Jupiter has a large of amount of hydrogen that is super-compressed to form the strange liquid called liquid metallic hydrogen. This material cannot be produced on the Earth because the super-high pressures needed to squeeze some of the electrons out of the atoms in the liquid hydrogen cannot be produced. Jupiter also spins very quickly—one rotation in under 10 hours!

Jupiter's magnetic field is so large that from the Earth it has an angular size over four times the size of our Moon. One of the first radio sources detected from space was Jupiter. Charged particles in Jupiter's radiation belts that are energized by the solar wind spiral around magnetic field lines to produce electromagnetic radiation in many different frequency bands. For Jupiter a lot of this energy is in the form of radio. In addition, there is a flux tube of electrical current of millions of amps flowing between Jupiter and its very geologically-active moon, Io. As described in section 9.7.2, Io has a number of volcanoes erupting all of the time. Particles in Jupiter's radiation belts collide with the volcanic dust particles and charge them, further adding to the radiation belts. Charged particles flowing back and forth produce aurorae larger than the entire Earth. Spacecraft sent to Jupiter have to be specially "radiation-harded" to protect their electronics from the charged particles in Jupiter's radiation belts.

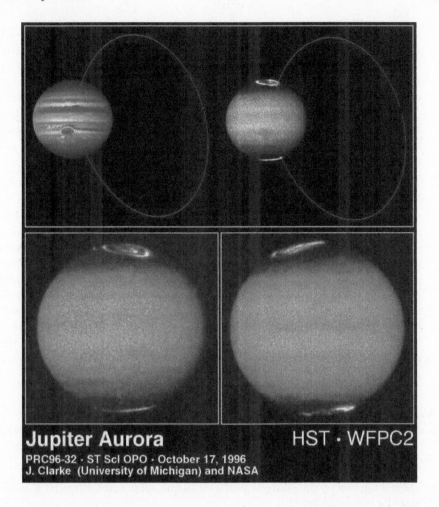

Jupiter Aurora HST · WFPC2
PRC96-32 · ST ScI OPO · October 17, 1996
J. Clarke (University of Michigan) and NASA

5. Mercury is a bit surprising because it has a global magnetic field. Mercury is the smallest of the terrestrial planets, so its interior should have cooled off long ago. Also, Mercury spins slowly—once every 58.8 days. Mercury's high density tells us that it has a proportionally large iron-nickel core. Its magnetic field implies that Mercury's interior is probably partially molten. In mid-2007 astronomers announced independent evidence in favor of a molten core for Mercury. Using very careful observations of Mercury's rotation, they found that Mercury's core could not be solid (see section 9.4 for more on this technique). *Mercury*

Mercury's situation was a major challenge to the magnetic dynamo theory. In true scientific fashion, the theory made a testable prediction: Mercury should have no magnetic field or one even less than Mars' one because its core should be solid. Observation, the final judge of scientific truth, contradicted the prediction. Should we have thrown out the magnetic dynamo theory then? Astronomers were reluctant to totally disregard the theory because of its success in explaining the situation on the other planets and the lack of any other plausible theory.

So most take a more conservative route: either modifying the magnetic dynamo theory or investigating Mercury more closely to find out what is so unusual about its interior to produce a magnetic field despite our expectations. Is their reluctance a violation of the objectivity required in science? Perhaps, but past experience has taught us that when you are confronted with such a contradiction, nature is telling you that you forgot to take some- *incremental progress in science* thing into account or you overlooked a crucial process. The MESSENGER mission confirmed the existence of Mercury's liquid core through careful tracking of the spacecraft's motion in Mercury's gravity field. The Mercury spin data and gravity field measurements have solved part of the problem (part of the core is molten), but how has the core remain molten and convecting (even partially) despite Mercury's small size? MESSENGER also found that the magnetic field is offset toward the north pole by about 20% of Mercury's radius. This offset suggests that Mercury's dynamo is created near the core-mantle boundary.

Another example of this conservative route is the discovery of the planet Neptune. When its near twin planet, Uranus, was discovered, astronomers were very confident in Newton's gravity theory because of its over a hundred-year success rate in explaining the motions of many different types of objects. So they applied Newton's gravity theory to Uranus' orbit. However, after several decades of further observation of Uranus, the predicted orbit was significantly different from the observed orbit. Rather than throwing out Newton's gravity theory, astronomers used the contradiction to predict the presence of another planet beyond Uranus. Within a couple of years Neptune was discovered at the position predicted! Might the same sort of thing be happening with the magnetic dynamo theory and Mercury's magnetic field? Perhaps. One thing is for sure, scientists love a good puzzle and will work hard at trying to solve it!

Vocabulary

aurorae   magnetic dynamo   solar wind

Review Questions

1. What happens to the charged particles in the solar wind when they reach a planet's magnetic field?

2. What happens to some of the solar wind particles that are deflected toward a planet's magnetic poles?

3. What does the fact that **aurorae** are from emission lines tell you about the density of the gas where they are produced?

4. What two basic things are needed to create a magnetic field? For a terrestrial planet, what might be a third thing needed?

5. Why does the Earth have a magnetic field but its companion, the Moon, has no detectable magnetic field?

9.4   Planet Interiors

Terrestrial planet interiors are composed of three basic parts: a dense, metallic *core*, a lower density solid *mantle* surrounding the core, and a solid outer shell called the *crust*. Jovian planets have a core and a fluid mantle that merges smoothly into their atmospheres.

I have already discussed several observations and techniques you can use to get initial clues of what a planet's interior is like. I will summarize them and then discuss ways to increase the accuracy of those rough initial models. Methods and observations already mentioned are:

1. The planets have flattened spherical shapes from the action of gravity and the centrifugal effect of their rotation. In table C.4 (in appendix C) the amount

of the rotational flattening is the *oblateness*. The amount of flattening also depends on the fluidity or elasticity of the interior's material.

2. Compute the overall average density of the planet.

3. Compare the surface material density with the overall density to find out how much differentiation has occurred.

4. Determine the composition of surface and atmosphere material from landers or remotely with spectroscopy.

5. The presence of a magnetic field requires the interior to have a liquid metallic component.

Astronomers have several other tools to probe the interiors of planets. By carefully observing the rotation of a planet, you can detect the *precession* (wobbling) of its rotation axis (the precession of the Earth's rotation axis is discussed in chapter 3). The *rate* of precession depends on a parameter called the *moment of inertia* which tells you how much the mass is concentrated toward the center. The Earth's core is considerably denser than its surface. The jovian planets have even greater concentration of their mass at their cores than the Earth does. Tiny twists in a terrestrial planet's spin can be used to determine if the core is solid or liquid. For example, the tiny twists in Mercury's spin rate are too great to be caused by a completely solid core, so its core (or parts of it) must be liquid. You can illustrate this by comparing the spin of a raw egg and the spin of a hard-boiled egg—you will notice that the raw egg's spin slows down because of the fluid inside sloshing about. The Mars InSight lander includes this technique in its suite of methods to probe Mars' interior beginning in November 2018.

precession rate gives mass concentration

The mass distribution of a planet can be probed by observing the motions of satellites (moons or spacecraft) in the planet's gravitational field. Mass lumps in the surface layer can be detected, as well as, asymmetries in the overall mass distribution. For example, the center of the Moon's mass is 2 kilometers closer to the Earth than the center of its overall shape (the geometric center). The Moon's crust on the Earth-facing side is several kilometers thinner than the crust on the far side. This is probably a remnant of the Earth's gravity acting on the early Moon's molten interior billions of years ago. Mars' center of mass is north of the geometric center. This is associated with the fact that Mars' southern cratered highlands stand about four kilometers higher than the northern volcanic plains. The GRAIL mission that orbited the Moon and the GRACE mission that orbited the Earth (now replaced by the GRACE-FO mission in 2018) measured their respective object's gravity field by very precise measurements of the distance between two spacecraft in the same orbit around the body, one trailing the other. With this technique, lumps in the gravity field cause the distance between the two spacecraft to change slightly as each leading spacecraft experiences slightly different acceleration than that felt by the trailing spacecraft. The GRACE spacecraft orbited long enough (over fifteen years) to even map decreases in the amount of land ice near the poles and decreases in the amount of water in aquifers through the pumping of the water for agriculture. The gravity field of Mercury was mapped by the single MESSENGER spacecraft. Measurements of changes in the speeds of the three NASA spacecraft orbiting Mars have been used to make gravity field maps of Mars. The Juno spacecraft started mapping Jupiter's gravity field when it began orbiting Jupiter in July 2016. See the textbook's website for links to all of these space missions.

small deflections of satellites map gravity field

GRAIL and GRACE

MESSENGER and Juno

Planet interiors are warmer than outer space, so energy will flow outward from the interior toward the surface. There are three possible sources of heat in a planet's interior. One is the heat of accretion during its formation—dust, pebbles, and rocks stuck together as they were gravitationally attracted together in the planet's formation, releasing gravitational potential energy. A second source is during differentiation—loss of gravitational potential energy as the denser material sunk to the core. Both of those sources occur early in a planet's history. The primary source today, billions of years later, is the heat from radioactive decay (section 10.3) of unstable atomic nuclei: uranium-238, uranium-235, thorium-232, and potassium-40. The heat in a terrestrial planet's rock/metal interior is *not* from the great pressures as happens in a gas because the rock/metal are compressed only slightly—a chunk of granite from the surface would be compressed to half its size at the base of the mantle. Rock in the deep interior will eventually become cold at the same high pressure as before.

energy flow in the planet interior

Energy flows from hot to cold places through radiation (glowing), convection (bulk motions of the fluid), and conduction. Radiative energy transfer is not used in rock because light cannot pass through it, convection occurs in the core and mantle, and conduction occurs very slowly in the crust and the top of the mantle below the crust and is much faster in the metallic core. Radiative energy transfer happens at the surface where the infrared energy photons can travel with much greater ease through the atmosphere to space.

heat loss rate

The rate of heat loss from the warm interior and the rate at which the temperature increases at greater depths closer to the core are important parameters for determining the interior structure. On the Earth, scientists can drill several kilometers into the crust and measure the temperature difference between the bottom of the hole and near the top. The Mars InSight will bore a temperature probe almost 5 meters into Mars' surface to measure the temperature profile down to that depth. For the jovian planets, infrared telescopes are able to detect their large heat flows.

seismology

For the terrestrial planets, the most useful data comes from **seismology**—the study of the interior   from observations of how *seismic waves* ("planetquake" waves) travel through the interior. Seismic waves slightly compress rock or cause it to vibrate up and down. They are produced when parts of a planet's crust suddenly shift and can be felt on the surface as a quake. These quakes have been studied extensively on the Earth, so I will focus on the use of earthquakes in what follows but remember that the same principles can be applied on any solid surface where instruments, called *seismometers*, are placed to study the jolts. Seismometers were left on the Moon by the Apollo astronauts (see section 9.7.1) and the Viking 2 lander on Mars had a working seismometer but persistent buffeting by the martian winds prevented it from being able to definitely detect any marsquakes (the seismometer on Viking 1 did not work). No seismometers have been placed on Venus or Mercury. The Mars InSight lander has a seismometer.

how seismic waves move depends on the material they pass through

The speed, amplitude, and direction the seismic waves move depend on the particular type of wave and the material they pass through. Just as a physician can use an ultrasound to get a picture of your anatomy or of a fetus, you can use seismic waves to get a picture of the Earth's interior (though it is a bit cruder than the physician's ultrasound). Earthquakes will produce two main types of waves: P (pressure) waves and S (shear) waves (see figure next page).

P waves

P waves are like sound waves—matter in one place pushes against adjacent matter compressing it. The result is a series of alternating stretched and compressed rock propagating in the same direction as the compression. It is like what happens when you stretch out a Slinky horizontally on a long table and give one end a sudden horizontal shove. You will see a wave of compressed metal coil move across the length of the Slinky to the other end. P waves can travel through solid *and* liquid material and move faster than S waves.

S waves

S waves are like waves in a jerked rope—matter moves up and down or side to side. Liquid matter prevents S waves from spreading. Timing of the arrival of seismic waves from at least three stations in a triangular array allows the earthquake center to be located. Seismometers on the opposite side of the Earth from the earthquake detect only P waves so there must be liquid material in the Earth's core.

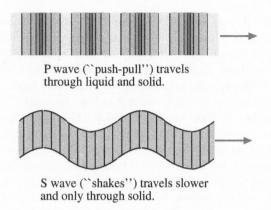

P wave (``push-pull'') travels
through liquid and solid.

S wave (``shakes'') travels slower
and only through solid.

The size of the liquid core can be constrained from how far away a seismometer can
be and still detect both S and P waves.

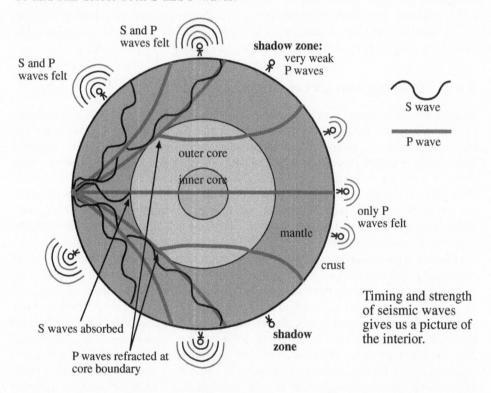

S and P
waves felt

shadow zone:
very weak
P waves

S and P
waves felt

S wave

P wave

outer core

inner core

only P
waves felt

mantle

crust

Timing and strength
of seismic waves
gives us a picture of
the interior.

S waves absorbed

P waves refracted at
core boundary

shadow
zone

Seismic waves *refract* (bend) inside the Earth because of the change in speed
of the waves as they move through material of variable density, composition, and
temperature. Abrupt changes in direction occur at the boundary between two
different layers. P waves entering the core are bent toward the Earth's center so
they only reach the part of the Earth's surface opposite the earthquake. There is
a *shadow zone* between the P waves that pass through the mantle only and those
that pass through the mantle *and* the core. The shadow zone location also puts
constraints on the size of the liquid core. It has a radius of about 3500 kilometers
and is made of an iron-nickel alloy with a small percentage of sulfur, cobalt, and
other minerals and has a density of around 12 (water = 1). Very weak P waves are
felt in the shadow zone, indicating that a smaller solid component resides at the
very center with a radius of about 1300 kilometers and a density around 14. Even
though the temperature of the interior increases toward the center (it is about 6300
K at the center), the high pressures in the inner solid core (up to 3.64 million bars

*refraction and absorption
of seismic waves*

at the center) make it solid while the outer metallic core remains liquid.

The Earth's mantle is made of hot but not quite molten iron-rich silicate and magnesium minerals like olivine, pyroxene, modified spinel, spinel, perovskite (primarily crystals of a dense form of magnesium silicate), and postperovskite (even denser magnesium silicate) and is around 2900 kilometers thick. Geologists further sub-divide the mantle into an upper mantle below the crust about 625 kilometers thick and a lower mantle 2300 kilometers thick. The upper mantle is made of in order of increasing depth olivine and pyroxene, modified spinel, and spinel layers. The lower mantle is made of a perovskite layer 2000 kilometers thick on top of a thinner 300-kilometer thick postperovskite layer just above the core. The density increases from about 3.5 below the crust to over 5 at the core boundary. The temperature at the top of the mantle below the crust is about 1700 K to about 3100 K at the base of the mantle—*not* hot enough to liquify the rock at the pressures inside the mantle (about 1.36 million bars at the base of the mantle next to the core). Even though the mantle is not liquid, it can deform and slowly flow when stressed. Convective motions in the mantle rub on the crust to produce earthquakes and volcanoes. This convective motion is very slow compared to a human lifetime, it can take several tens of millions of years for a chunk of rock to move from the inner boundary of the mantle to just below the crust.

9.4.1   Putting the Pieces Together

From these observations and knowledge of the physical laws of nature, astronomers can construct and refine computer models of the planet interiors. The three parameters of pressure, density, and temperature determine the state of the material and a relation called the **equation of state** relates the three parameters to each other. It tells what the density is for a given pressure and temperature. For rock, the equation of state is complex and somewhat uncertain. Rocky materials of different compositions *and* phase or state of the material (solid, liquid, gas) all will have different equations of states. (In contrast, the equation of state for stellar interiors is fortunately much simpler—see chapter 12 for a discussion of stellar structure.)

Planets exist in a balance between the compression of gravity and the pressure of the liquid and solid. Deeper layers experience more compression from the overlying material so the balancing outward pressure must increase. (This principle can also be applied to the gas of atmospheres to show why the atmosphere is thicker closer to the surface.) The computer model calculates the density in each layer from the equation of state with appropriate values of the temperature at that depth. The computer program starts off with the observed surface conditions and layer-by-layer, works its way toward the center. If the model does not arrive at a value of the total planet mass by the time it reaches the center, it must be revised. The models are checked against the other observables described above (moment of inertia, oblateness, gravity field measurements, heat flow, etc.) and refined further.

What follows is a brief description of the other planet interiors found from putting all of the observations and theory together (see figures next page). Mercury has a very large iron core that is about 85% of its radius surrounded by a thin silicate layer (crust and mantle) only 260 kilometers thick. Its metallic core is unusual in that it has a liquid layer sandwiched between two solid layers. Its core must also contain some lighter element such as sulfur to lower the melting temperature. The thin, solid iron-sulfide outer core layer is probably responsible for damping Mercury's magnetic field from that expected from the amount of the liquid metallic part of the core.

Venus's interior is very much like the Earth's except its iron-nickel core probably makes up a smaller percentage of its interior. Mars has a solid iron and/or iron-sulfide core 2600 to 4000 kilometers in diameter, surrounded by a silicate mantle

equation of state

terrestrial planet interiors

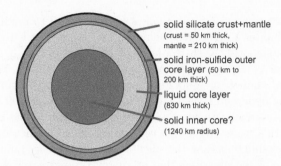

Mercury's new interior revealed by MESSENGER.
Core is larger than previously thought: 85% radius.

and rocky crust that is probably several hundred kilometers thick. Recent gravity field maps of Mars show that the outer core is liquid but the extent of the liquid part is not known. We will find out much more about Mars' interior with the InSight mission that landed on Mars in November 2018.

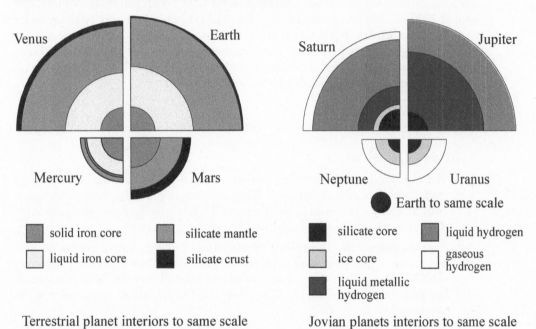

Terrestrial planet interiors to same scale   Jovian planets interiors to same scale

The crust and the outermost part of the mantle make up a layer of hard rock called the **lithosphere**. The rigid, brittle lithosphere gradually turns into the softer, more pliable (and hotter) *asthenosphere*. Small planets have very thick lithospheres that extend from the surface to almost the core or all the way to the core. Large planets will have thin lithospheres because they still retain a lot of heat. Earth's lithosphere is thin enough to be cracked into chunks called "plates" that will discussed in detail in the next section. The Earth's lithosphere is on average about 100 kilometers thick, with the oceans plates being thinner than the continental plates. Venus' lithosphere is a little thicker than the Earth's. Mars' lithosphere extends hundreds of kilometers almost all the way to its core. Mercury's lithosphere may be up to 260 kilometers thick but it may be thinner than that due to the presence of an asthenosphere below it.

lithosphere

The jovian planets are made of lighter materials that exist under much higher pressures than can occur anywhere on the Earth. Direct observations of their structure are still limited to the top several hundred kilometers of their atmospheres.

jovian planet interiors

Using those observations, computer models are calculated to predict what their interiors are like. Jupiter's hydrogen, helium atmosphere is at least 1000 kilometers thick and merges smoothly with the layer of liquid molecular hydrogen. The liquid hydrogen layer is about 20,000 to 21,000 kilometers thick. The pressure near the center is great enough to squeeze electrons from the hydrogen atoms to make the liquid metallic hydrogen layer that is around 37,000 to 38,000 kilometers thick. Jupiter probably has a silicate/ice core twice the diameter of the Earth with about 14 times the Earth's mass. Although the core is made of silicates and ices, those materials are much different than the silicates and ices you are familiar with here on the Earth because of the pressures that are many times greater than the pressures at the Earth's core and temperatures in the 20,000 to 30,000 K range. Saturn is a smaller scale version of Jupiter: silicate core 26,000 kilometers in diameter, ice layer (solid methane, ammonia, water, etc.) about 3500 kilometers thick beneath a 12,000-kilometer thick layer of liquid metallic hydrogen, liquid molecular hydrogen layer around 28,000 kilometers thick, and atmosphere about 2000 kilometers thick.

The compression on Uranus and Neptune is probably not enough to liquify the hydrogen. Uranus and Neptune have silicate cores 8000 to 8500 kilometers in diameter surrounded by a slushy mantle of water mixed with ammonia and methane around 7000 to 8000 kilometers thick. This mantle layer is probably responsible for their strange magnetic fields which are not centered on the planet centers and are tipped by large degrees from their rotation axes. At the top is the 9000 to 10,000-kilometer thick atmosphere of hydrogen and helium. Tiny Pluto probably has a rocky core half its size surrounded by an ice mantle/crust.

Vocabulary

equation of state   lithosphere   seismology

Review Questions

1. What methods of determining the structure of planet interiors can be done from Earth-bound observations? What methods require observations by spacecraft flying by a planet or in orbit around it? What methods require spacecraft to land on the surface or travel into the planet's interior?

2. Suppose spacecraft are orbiting two identical-looking planets having no natural moons. The spacecraft orbiting the first planet has a perfectly elliptical orbit and the spacecraft orbiting the second planet has a nearly elliptical orbit but with small accelerations. What does this tell you about the interior of the two planets?

3. Where does the heat inside a planet come from and how does it eventually leak out to space?

4. Why is the placement of seismometers on a planet's surface so beneficial for understanding the planet's interior?

5. Why will seismology never be possible on the jovian planets?

6. Compare and contrast the structure of Jupiter with that of the Earth.

7. Compare the thicknesses of Saturn's various layers to the corresponding layers in Jupiter.

8. How are the interiors of Uranus and Neptune different from the interiors of Jupiter and Saturn?

9.5 Planet Surfaces

Terrestrial planets have hard surfaces that can be re-shaped by several different processes: impact cratering, volcanism, erosion, and tectonics.

9.5.1 Impact Cratering

There are still small chunks of rock orbiting the Sun left over from the formation of the solar system. Some of them have orbits that cross the orbits of the planets and moons. When they get close enough to a planet or moon, they will be pulled in by the large body's gravity and strike the surface at a speed of at least the escape velocity of the planet or moon, i.e., faster than a bullet. At such speeds, the projectile explodes on impact and carves out a round bowl-shaped depression on the surface. This process is **impact cratering**. How can you distinguish an impact crater from a volcanic crater?

impact cratering

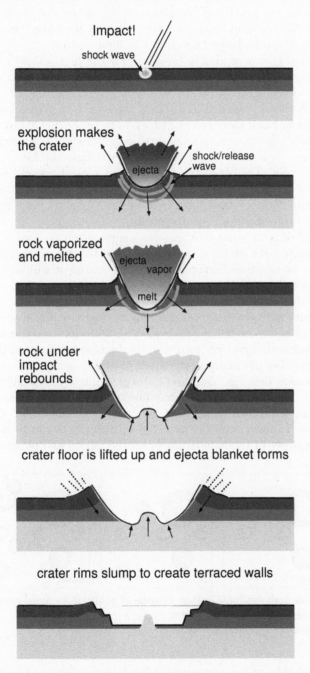

Volcano craters are above the surrounding area on mountaintops while the craters from impacts are below the surrounding area with raised rims. The craters on all of the moons except Io, Mercury, and most of the ones on Mars are from impacts. The kinetic energy of the impacting meteorite or asteroid is converted into heat, sound, and mechanical energy—the projectile explodes on impact. The explosion is what carves out the crater so almost all craters are round (otherwise they would be oblong in shape).

explosion makes the crater

The rock on the surface of the planet or moon is bent backward, upward, and outward so the amount of material ejected is much larger than the projectile. Large craters will have a central peak formed by the rock beneath the impact point rebounding upward and they may also have terracing of the inner walls of the crater from the collapsing of the crater rim inward. The size of the craters having central peaks depends on the gravity of the planet or moon: on the Moon craters larger than about 60 kilometers in diameter have central peaks while the crater diameter on the Earth needs to be larger than just 1 to 3 kilometers.

late heavy bombardment

Impact cratering was especially prevalent for the first several hundred million years after the planets formed as the planets swept up left-over material. The last stage of that "sweeping up", called the *late heavy bombardment,* occurred from about 4.1 to 3.8 billion years ago. Impacts as large as the one that led to the demise of the dinosaurs in much more recent history were happening about once a month. Most of the impact basins—craters measured in hundreds of kilometers—were made during this time. It is noteworthy that about the time the heavy bombardment ended, life took hold. The oldest fossil evidence of ancient organisms dates back to 3.5 billion years ago and evidence for biological activity based on isotopic ratios of carbon *may* date back to about 3.85, even up to 4.2 billion years ago, though the carbon isotope ratio evidence is controversial.

crater age dating

The number of craters per unit area on a surface can be used to determine an approximate age for the planet or moon surface if there is no erosion. The longer the surface has been exposed to space, the more craters it will have. If you know how frequently craters of a given size are created on a planet or moon, you can just count up the number of craters per unit area. This assumes, of course, that the cratering rate has been fairly constant for the last few billion years. The heavy bombardment of about 3.8 billion years must be taken into account when using the crater age dating technique. For example, the highland regions on the Moon have ten times the number of craters as the maria, but radioactive dating (explained in section 10.3) shows that the highlands are approximately 500 million years older than the maria, not ten times older. At a minimum, crater-age dating can tell you the relative ages of surfaces (which surface is older than another). Careful studies of how the craters overlap other craters and other features can be used to develop a history or sequence of the bombardment on the moons and planets.

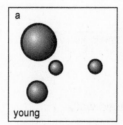 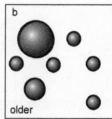 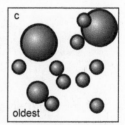

Older surfaces have greater chance of being hit => more impact craters. In the top right corner of pane (c), which of the overlapping craters formed first?

Another technique developed recently for dating craters on the Moon uses the fact that younger craters have more large rocks on their surface than older craters (micrometeorite impacts grind down rocks over long periods of time) and larger rocks take more time to cool off during the night. Therefore, younger craters will take longer to cool off at night than older rocks. This technique works for craters that are up to about a billion years old. A study announced in 2019 using this new technique found that the rate of asteroid impacts on the Moon increased by about 2.6 times starting about 290 million years ago and a careful analysis of craters on specially-chosen places on Earth with little erosion in the past 650 million years showed the same increase. We don't know yet what caused the increase in the impact rate.

All bodies with hard surfaces have impact craters. Worlds with less volcanism or erosion or tectonic activity in their history will retain more impact craters since the planet formed. Worlds with more geological or erosional activity will have newer surfaces or craters that have been so worn away as to be unrecognizable. Earth has over 170 impact craters on its continents with the 1.2-km diameter Meteor Crater in northern Arizona being one great, well-preserved example. Even Venus with its thick atmosphere has impact craters, though they all have diameters measured in kilometers because smaller projectiles burn up in its atmosphere.

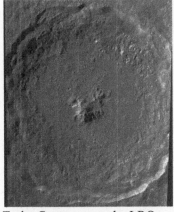

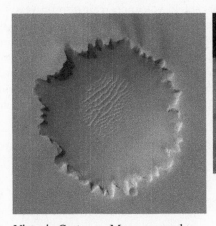

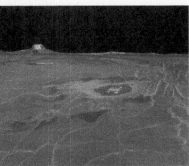

Tycho Crater as seen by LRO. Tycho is 85 km wide. It displays the classic terraced crater walls and central peak of a complex crater. See the textbook's website for a link to a flyover of the crater.
Image courtesy of NASA/Goddard/ Arizona State University

Victoria Crater on Mars as seen by the Mars Reconnaissance Orbiter. Victoria is 800 m in diameter. It is a simple crater that has been partially filled in with sand—note the sand dunes on its floor.
Image courtesy of NASA/JPL-Caltech/ Univ AZ/Cornell/Ohio St Univ

Cunitz Crater is the 48.5-km diameter crater in the foreground of this 3D perspective view of Eistla Regio on Venus as seen by Magellan. In the distance is the 3-km high volcano Gula Mons.
Image courtesy of NASA/JPL

9.5.2 Volcanism

Volcanism is any eruption of molten lava onto the surface. The molten rock has a lower density than solid rock so it rises. Also the pressure from the surrounding solid rock squeezes the molten rock upward. Molten rock contains trapped gases that expand as it rises causing it to rise even faster. The structures that result from erupting lava depend on the thickness and density of the lava.

Very thick, low-density lava can make steep-sided *stratovolcanoes* like the Cascade volcanoes in Oregon and Washington and Mt Fuji in Japan. The lava does not flow as far as the other two types, so their diameters are not as great as the other types. They are common on the Earth. The "pancake domes" on Venus may be considered a type of stratovolcano but their shapes are much more cylindrical without a peak.

stratovolcanoes

Thickest lava:
stratovolcano

Thinner lava:
shield volcano

Thinnest lava:
volcanic plain

tall and wide

low and very wide

tall and skinny
Common on Earth

Earth and other
planets + moons

Earth and other
planets + moons

basalt
shield volcano

If the lava is made of thinner, higher density material called *basalt*, the volcanoes will be much wider in diameter. Thicker basalt will make *shield* volcanoes like the Hawaiian volcanoes, Sif Mons on Venus, and Olympus Mons on Mars. These types of volcanoes are found throughout the solar system. Besides being very wide in diameter, shield volcanoes can also be very tall—from its base below the ocean surface to its peak, Mauna Kea and Mauna Loa are taller than Mt Everest. Olympus Mons is about three times taller than Mt Everest (24 km above the surrounding plains) and would cover up most of Texas (about 600 km in diameter). Although the stratovolcanoes in the Cascade volcanic arc get most of the attention because of their vertical height and spectacular appearance, shield volcanoes make up the great majority of the volume of the Cascade volcanic arc.

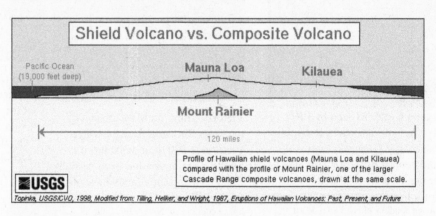

Shield Volcano vs. Composite Volcano

Pacific Ocean
(19,000 feet deep)

Mauna Loa

Kilauea

Mount Rainier

120 miles

Profile of Hawaiian shield volcanoes (Mauna Loa and Kilauea)
compared with the profile of Mount Rainier, one of the larger
Cascade Range composite volcanoes, drawn at the same scale.

USGS

Topinka, USGS/CVO, 1998, Modified from: Tilling, Heliker, and Wright, 1987, Eruptions of Hawaiian Volcanoes: Past, Present, and Future

volcanic plains

The thinnest, runniest basalt will make lava plains that can re-shape the surface by covering up things. Lava plains are found here and elsewhere in the solar system. For example, large lava flows covered up most of modern-day eastern Washington and northeastern Oregon with a layer more than 1.5 kilometers thick (see figure next page). The dark mare on the Moon are basalt lava plains that filled in giant impact basins approximately 3.5 billion years ago. Mercury has lava plains that formed after the late heavy bombardment when it was still geologically active. Much of Venus is covered in lava plains.

outgassing

Volcanism also adds gases to a planet's atmosphere either explosively during a volcanic eruption such as Mt St Helens in Washington or Mt Pinatubo in the Philippines, or more quietly as in the volcanic vents in Hawaii and Yellowstone in Wyoming. This *outgassing* is what created the terrestrial planets current atmospheres (Earth's has undergone further significant processing through the action of life).

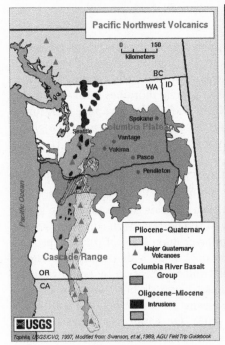

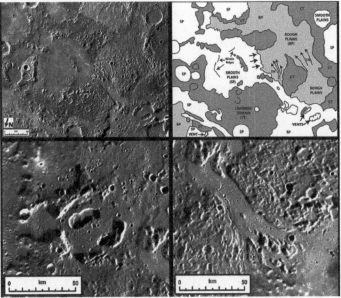

Top left: context image of Mercury. **Top right:** feature diagram.
Bottom left: detail of bottom right corner of context image (and flipped).
Pits interpreted as source vents on Mercury.
Bottom right: detail of center right part of context image (and flipped).
Teardrop-shaped hills and channel interpreted to be formed by
lava erosion on Mercury. Courtesy AAAS/Science

Mount Saint Helens eruption of May 18, 1980 sent volcanic ash,
steam, water, and debris to a height of 18.3 km (into the stratosphere).
The mountain lost 396 m of altitude. Image courtesy of USGS/Austin Post

9.5.3   Erosion

Erosion is the breaking down or building up of geological structures and transporting of material (rock for our purposes here) by ice, liquid, or wind. Water ice in the form of glaciers carves out bowl-shaped valleys such as Yosemite in California and those in Glacier National Park in Montana. Glacial moraines form from gravel transported by glaciers. The gravel comes from the glacier scraping rock and it gathers along the side and front of the glacier. The gravel comes from the glacier scraping rock and it gathers along the side (*lateral moraine*) and front (*terminal moraine*) of the glacier. When these rivers of ice merge with other glaciers, one individual glacier's lateral moraine can merge with another glacier's lateral moraine to make a *medial moraine*. From the air one can see curvy striped patterns.

When the glacier recedes the gravel piles from the side and front of the glacier remain. One classic example is Wallowa Lake in the northeastern corner of Oregon. Liquid water on the Earth has carved through layer upon layer of rocks to produce such spectacular things as the Grand Canyon on Earth. Valleys carved by liquid water have much sharper V-shapes than glacial valleys. Erosion by liquid water on Mars in the past is responsible for river drainage channels but the sublimation of carbon dioxide on the walls of impact craters seems to cause rock and soil to flow downhill to make the gullies seen on crater walls. On Titan, the largest moon of Saturn, liquid methane has carved features into the ground made of frozen water that are quite reminiscent of features on Earth. All of the tributaries suggest that methane rainfall is effectively eroding the surface. Liquid rock (lava) can also cause erosion—see the Mercury image in the volcanism section above for one nice example.

Canyon systems that have been carved by rivers of liquid methane on Titan. Fluids flowed from high plateaus on the right to lowland areas on the left. All of the tributaries suggest that methane rainfall is effectively eroding the surface.

Gullies etched into the walls of Newton Crater by carbon dioxide on Mars sometime in its past. The crater rim is on the right and the crater floor is on the left. The area shown is about 3 kilometers wide. It was taken by the Mars Global Surveyor during southern winter when the atmosphere was especially clear.
Image courtesy of NASA/JPL/Malin Space Science Systems

This is a radar image taken by the Cassini synthetic aperture radar. It covers an area 335 x 239 kilometers.
Image courtesy of NASA/JPL

Wind picks up small sand particles on a planet's surface and strikes it against a hard surface to chip pieces of it away (to make more sand!). The winds can also shape hills of sand into sand dunes as seen on the Earth, Mars, and Titan.

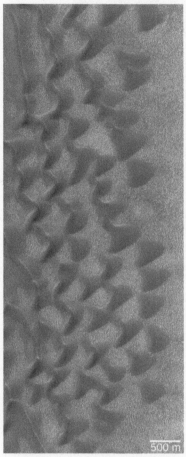

Sand dunes in Proctor Crater on Mars created by winds blowing largely from the east/northeast. Sunlight illuminates them from the upper left.
Image courtesy of NASA/JPL/MSSS

Dunes near the equatorial band of Titan shaped by winds coming from the west and northwest and generally blowing toward the east. The image covers an area of 220 x 170 kilometers with north toward the top of the image. Synthetic aperture radar image from Cassini. (Vertical stripe is a data artifact.)
Image courtesy of NASA/JPL/Space Science Institute

The agents of erosion can, of course, work together. Water expands when it freezes so when it trickles into cracks in rocks and freezes during the winter, it can enlarge the cracks enough to separate the minerals from each other. (Plant roots do the same thing as well.) Liquid water from rainfall and snowmelt takes those minerals down to the oceans—a process which also helps to remove carbon dioxide from the atmosphere. Wind whittles away the exposed rock left behind and the result can be beautiful formations like Bryce Canyon in Utah.

Besides chipping away at mountains and other rises in the land bit by bit, erosion can also add to formations by depositing sediments when liquid slows down enough for the suspended sediments to sink to the stream or river bed such as the Mississippi River Delta and the Lena River Delta in Russia (shown in the figure on the next page). Fossilized river deltas are seen on Mars.

Lena River delta in Russia. Image courtesy of NASA/GSFC

9.5.4   Tectonics

Tectonics is any stretching or compression of the lithosphere. Usually tectonic activity is due to convection in the mantle below the lithosphere but it can occur when an especially massive landform such as a volcano makes the lithosphere under it buckle from its weight or a rising plume of extra hot material in the mantle pushes on the lithosphere overhead to make a bulge such as coronae features on Venus and possibly the Tharsis Bulge on Mars (though that one may be due to mantle convection long ago—see figure next page).

Mercury has high cliffs (as tall as 3 km) called "lobate scarps" that run for hundreds of kilometers that are probably the result of the shrinking of Mercury as it cooled from its formation. Recall that Mercury has the proportionally largest metallic core of the planets. As the metallic core cooled, it shrank and the mantle and brittle crust would have had to shrink too, crinkling in the process. The image on the next page from MESSENGER's first flyby of Mercury indicates that the volcanic flows in Mercury's early history occurred while the crinkling was going on. The two smaller white top arrows point to a scarp that formed after the lava plain flow had filled in a number of the craters. The bottom three larger white arrows point to a possible older scarp against which the lava plain flow stopped. The black arrow points to a small crater that formed after the top lobate scarp. The filled in impact crater at center left (with the second small white arrow and black arrow) is about 100 km across.

A special type of tectonic activity unique to Earth in our solar system is called "plate tectonics". It is the major agent of changing the Earth's surface and plays a key role in keeping the Earth habitable. It warrants its own section of discussion.

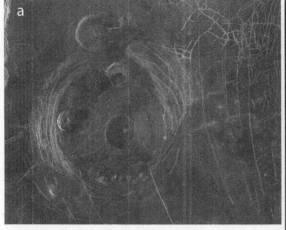

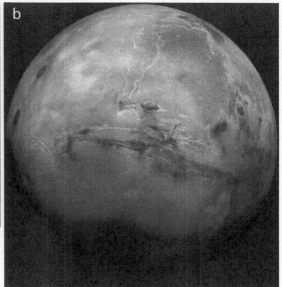

Image a (left): Aine Corona on Venus as seen by Magellan. Aine Corona is approximately 200 kilometers across. Just north of Aine is a 35-km diameter "pancake" dome feature made from extremely viscous (thick) lava. Another pancake dome is inside the western ring of the corona's fractures. Pancake domes are a type of volcanic structure seen only on Venus. Image courtesy of NASA/JPL

Image b (right): Tharsis Bulge side of Mars as seen by the Viking 1 orbiter shows the true "Grand Canyon" of the solar system, Valles Marineris, a huge fracture that probably formed as that side of Mars was raised up. Valles Marineris would stretch across the entire United States with a bit left over. To the west (left) are large shield volcanoes on Tharsis each about 25 kilometers high. See the textbook website for a link to a flyover of Valles Marineris. Image courtesy of NASA/USGS

Scarps form as Mercury cooled and contracted slightly. Surface rock fractured causing blocks of crust to thrust over others along great faults. The eroded crater on the far left appears to have formed before the scarp while other more distinct craters formed after Mercury cooled. Image courtesy of NASA/Johns Hopkins University Applied Physics Laboratory/Carnegie Institution of Washington

9.5.5 Plate Tectonics

The Earth's lithosphere is broken up into chunks called *plates* with densities around 3 (see the Earth plate boundary map below). Oceanic plates are made of basalts (cooled volcanic rock made of silicon, oxygen, iron, aluminum, and magnesium). Oceanic *crust* is only about 6 kilometers thick. The continental plates are around 20 to 70 kilometers thick and are made of another volcanic type of silicates called granite. Continental *crust* is much thicker than oceanic crust—up to 35 kilometers thick. Continental plates are less dense than the oceanic plates. The mantle convection causes the crustal plates to slide next to or under each other, collide against each other, or separate from one another in a process called **plate tectonics**. **Plate tectonics** is the scientific theory that describes this process and how it explains the Earth's surface geology. The Earth is the only planet among the terrestrial planets that has this tectonic activity. This is because plate tectonics probably requires liquid water to solidify the oceanic plates at the mid-ocean ridges where seafloor spreading is happening (see below) and more importantly, the liquid water lubricates the asthenosphere and softens the lithosphere enough so that the plates can slide past or under one another. Venus has enough interior heat to have convection in its mantle like the Earth, but through processes described in section 9.6.1, Venus lost its water, so its plates are poorly lubricated at best.

Earth's unique plate tectonics
plate tectonics

plate tectonics may need liquid water

Plate Tectonics Theory Evidence

Plate tectonics is a relatively recent theory having been proposed in the late 1960s and finally being verified enough so that it could be put in the introductory geology textbooks in the 1980s (remember all of the peer review, error-correction process that happens before something is fit to print in a textbook). What finally made scientists accept the theory? Today we can easily measure plate motion using GPS sensors on either side of plates. As in any robust scientific theory there are multiple lines of evidence supporting the theory. For plate tectonics, the evidence is continental motion, seafloor spreading, earthquake and volcano locations, and the difference between the seafloor crust and continental crust. I will give just a brief outline of the evidence for plate tectonics here. See the textbook's website for links to more detailed explanation of the evidence.

- **Continental motion:** The locations of rock-types and certain fossil plants and animals on present-day, widely separated continents would form definite patterns if the continents were once joined. For example the eastern side of South America fits nicely next to the western edge of Africa and several fossil areas match up nicely at those points of intersection.

- **Seafloor spreading:** An immense submarine mountain chain zig-zags between the continents and winds its way around the globe. At or near the crest of the ridge, the rocks are very young, and become progressively older away from the ridge crest. The youngest rocks at the ridge crest always have present-day (normal) polarity. Stripes of rock parallel to the ridge crest alternate in magnetic polarity (normal-reversed-normal, etc.)

Alternating stripes of magnetically different rock are laid out in rows on either side of the mid-ocean ridges: one stripe with normal polarity and the adjoining stripe with reversed polarity. This happens when magnetite in molten rock at the ridge aligns itself with the Earth's magnetic field. When the molten rock with the magnetite hardens, it "freezes" in the orientation of the Earth's magnetic field at that time. The Earth's magnetic field has changed polarity numerous times in its history with a 300,000 year *average* time interval between reversals (some reversals were just tens of thousands of years apart and others millions of years apart). When the Earth's magnetic field changes polarity, newly rising molten rock at the ridges will have its magnetite aligned accordingly. New oceanic crust is forming continuously at the crest of the mid-ocean ridge and cools to become solid crust. The oceanic crust becomes increasingly older at increasing distance from the ridge crest with seafloor spreading. The result will be a zebra-like striping of the magnetic polarity in the rock that parallels the mid-ocean ridge. Further evidence for seafloor spreading comes from determining ages of the seafloor at various distances from the mid-ocean ridges.

- **Earthquake and volcano locations:** The locations of earthquakes and active volcanoes are not random but, instead, they are concentrated along areas thought to be plate boundaries—the oceanic trenches and spreading ridges.

- **Seafloor crust vs. continental crust:** From radioactive dating and crater-age dating, we know that the seafloor crust is less than 200 million years old while continental crust has a wide range of ages up to 4 *billion* years old. Also, the seafloor crust is thinner and denser than the continental crust. Earth is the only place in our solar system with two different types of crust.

This figure shows the boundaries of the major plates on top of a map of the Earth. The arrows show the direction of the plates with respect to each other. The white areas are elevations greater than 2400 meters (7900 feet). Adapted from a plate boundary map from Dietmar Mueller, Univ. of Sydney and plate motion data from the United States Geological Survey.

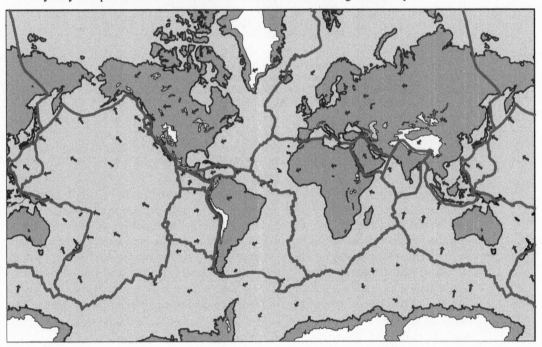

Plate Tectonics Process

Places where molten rock from the asthenosphere rises along weak points in the lithosphere can push apart the lithosphere on both sides (see the "When plates separate" figure on the next page). These places are at the mid-ocean ridges (such as the Mid-Atlantic Ridge that bisects the Atlantic Ocean) and continental rift zones (such as the East Africa Rift Zone). Sea-floor spreading caused the Atlantic Ocean to grow from a thin sliver 100 to 200 million years ago to its present size and now continues at a rate of about 25 kilometers per million years.

This pushing apart of some plates from each other means that others will collide. When oceanic crust runs into oceanic crust or into continental crust, the

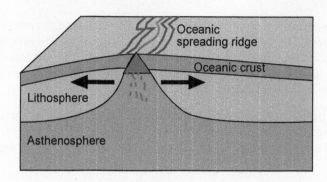

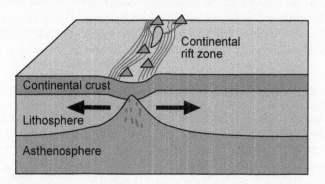

When plates separate: *(top)* new oceanic crust is created as parts of the lithosphere are pushed apart by rising molten rock at a midoceanic ridge. *(bottom)* new continental crust is created at a continental rift zone.

subduction zone

denser lithosphere material slides under the less dense lithosphere material, eventually melting in the deepest layers of the mantle. The region where the lithosphere pieces contact each other is called a *subduction zone* and a trench is formed there. At the subduction zone, the right combination of temperature, pressure and rock composition can create small pockets or fissures of molten rock in the solid asthenosphere that then rise up through cracks in the crust to create a range of volcanoes (see the "When plates collide" figure on the next page). In section 9.6.3 you will see that this has a profound effect on regulating the climate of the Earth.

When two continental pieces bump into each other, they are too light relative to the asthenosphere and too thick for one to be forced under the other. The plates are pushed together and buckle to form a mountain range. It also possible for two

transform fault

plates to slide past each other at what is called a *transform fault* such as the San Andreas Fault in California and the Anatolian Fault in Turkey.

Examples of ocean-continental plate subduction include the Juan de Fuca plate off the coast of northwestern United States subducting under the North American continental plate to create the Cascade Volcano range, the Nazca plate subducting under the western edge of the South American plate to create the Andes range of volcanic mountains. An example of the ocean-ocean plate subduction are the chains of islands on the Asia side of the Pacific: the Aleutians, Japan, Philippines, Indonesia, and Marianas. An example of continent-continent plate collision is the Indian plate running into the Eurasian plate to create the Himalayas.

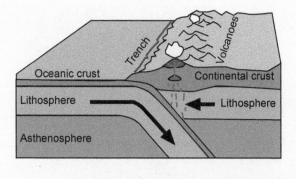

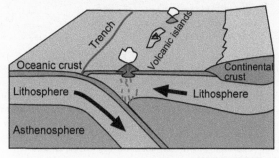

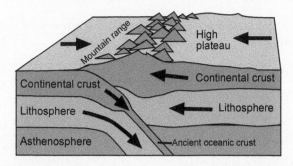

When plates collide: *(top)* Denser oceanic plate slides under a continental plate at a subduction zone. Crust melts in the asthenosphere and molten rock rises through cracks in the continental plate to create a volcanic mountain range. *(middle)* One oceanic plate slides under another. Volcanoes reaching the surface appear as island arcs. *(bottom)* Continental plates push together and buckle forming a mountain range. Adapted from diagrams in *This Dynamic Earth* of the United States Geological Survey.

9.5.6 Conclusions

To end the Planet Interiors section, here is a summary of the terrestrial planet surface shaping agents at work today.

Looking at table 9.1 (next page), we can draw some conclusions as to what planet properties will determine the type of planet surfacing that can occur. Impact cratering can occur on any object with a solid surface at any time. If a planet has an atmosphere and is still geologically active, then the effects of impact cratering will be erased. Volcanism and Tectonics require the *planet to be of sufficient size* to still have heat in its interior. Erosion requires an atmosphere with winds to work efficiently. Even better is if liquid can be present to add to the weathering by the atmosphere. Erosion works best on Earth. Earth is of *sufficient size* to hang on to its atmosphere (unlike the Moon). Earth is at a *good distance from the Sun* so it is not too hot for its atmosphere to either evaporate away or become excessively thick that winds will not blow on the surface (as is the situation with Venus). Also, its

This section of California from the Shuttle Radar Topography Mission clearly shows the intersection of the Garlock Fault and the San Andreas Fault. Notice the bend of the San Andreas near the intersection. Color coding is directly related to topographic height, with blue and green at the lower elevations, rising through yellow and brown to white at the highest elevations.
Image courtesy of NASA/JPL/NIMA

Table 9.1: Planet Surface Shapers of the Terrestrial Planets

Surface Shaper Agent	Mercury	Venus	Earth	Moon	Mars
Impact Cratering	Yes	Minor	Minor	Yes	Yes
Volcanism (needs internal heat)	No (only long ago)	Yes	Yes	No (only long ago)	No (only in the past)
Tectonics (needs internal heat)	No (only long ago)	Yes	Yes	No	No (only in the past)
Erosion	No (no liquid or atmosphere)	No (no surface winds)	Yes (ice, water, air)	No (no liquid or atmosphere)	Yes (air today + water in past)

good distance from the Sun enables the surface temperatures to be warm enough for liquid water to flow (unlike Mars) and so its atmosphere does not freeze out on its surface as happens with Mars. Earth's *rotation is fast for its size* (unlike Venus), so it can create complicated air circulation (wind) patterns as well as ocean currents. Also, rapid rotation enables the creation of the magnetic field shield to protect a planet's atmosphere from the solar wind.

Vocabulary

erosion   impact cratering   plate tectonics
tectonics   volcanism

Review Questions

1. Why are almost all impact craters round?

2. How can you use the number of craters to determine the age of a planet's or moon's surface?

3. The lunar highlands have about ten times more craters on a given area than

do the maria. Does this mean that the highlands are ten times older? Explain your reasoning.

4. What determines if volcanism will make a steep-sided mountain or something with a gentler slope?

5. How do shield volcanoes compare in size to stratovolcanoes in diameter and height?

6. How do volcanic eruptions affect a planet's atmosphere?

7. What does volcanism require as far as interior conditions?

8. How does erosion change the surface of a planet (or moon)?

9. What is the difference of a valley carved by glaciers vs. one carved by flowing water?

10. Besides wearing away geological features, what does the process of erosion do?

11. How is tectonics different than plate tectonics?

12. What does tectonics require as far as interior conditions?

13. How does the plate tectonics theory explain such things as the widening of the Atlantic Ocean, the Andes of South America and the Cascades of the northwestern U.S, and the high mountain ranges such as the Himalayas and the Rocky Mountains?

14. What is the evidence for plate tectonics?

15. What properties of a planet will determine what type of planet shaping can occur on it?

16. What type of planet shaping occurs on Mercury, on Venus, on Mars, and on the Earth and the Moon?

9.6   Earth-Venus-Mars

Venus, Earth, and Mars are at approximately the same distance from the Sun. This means they formed out of the same material and had approximately the same initial temperatures 4.5 billion years ago. Long ago, these three planets probably had moderate enough temperatures suitable for life. However, Venus is now much too hot for life and Mars is too cold for life. What happened to these two planets and why are they so different from the comparative paradise here on Earth? This section explores these three planets in more detail in order to answer this important question and what it might say for the future of the Earth.

9.6.1   Venus

Venus is about 95% the size of the Earth and has 82% of the Earth's mass. Like the Earth, Venus has a rocky crust and iron-nickel core. But the similarities stop there. Venus has a thick atmosphere made of 96% carbon dioxide (CO_2), 3.5% nitrogen (N_2), and 0.5% other gases. Venus' ever-present clouds are made of sulfuric acid droplets between 45 and 66 km above the surface. It is those clouds that continually block our view of Venus' surface, so we must use radar imaging (bouncing radio waves off its hard surface) to "see through" the clouds. Between the equator and about 55 degrees latitude the lower clouds in Venus' atmosphere move at about 210 km/h and the uppermost clouds move much faster at 370 km/h. Near the poles, the winds are weaker and do not change with height because of the huge hurricane-like vortex that exists there. At the center of the vortex, there are no winds. Close to the surface, the winds are also essentially non-existent.

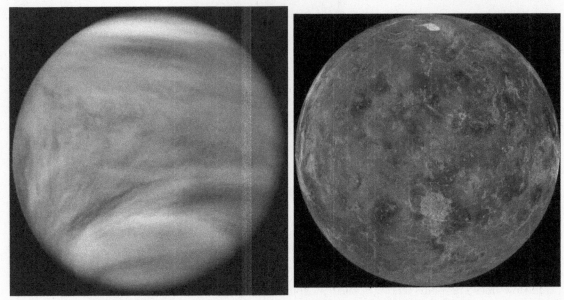

Venus cloudtops in ultraviolet (left) the surface imaged with radar (right).
Images courtesy of NASA/JPL

very thick carbon dioxide-rich atmosphere

At Venus' surface, the air pressure is 92 times the Earth's surface atmospheric pressure. Venus' surface atmospheric pressure is the same as what you would feel if you were 1 *kilometer* below the ocean surface on the Earth. The deepest free-divers can get down to around 160 meters (and divers breathing special mixtures of gases can get down to 730 meters). If you want to send someone to Venus, that person would need to be in something like a diving bell.

Surface of Venus from the Venera 13 lander on March 3, 1982. Note the flat basaltic rocks that are still sharp and un-eroded. The spacecraft edge is at the bottom right corner of the image. The view extends out to the horizon at the top left corner of the image. The shiny piece on the middle right is the camera cover. Venera 13 lasted for 127 minutes before the extreme heat overcame the electronics. Image courtesy of NASA

greenhouse effect from CO_2

Besides being in a diving bell, the Venus explorer would also need a very powerful cooling system: the surface temperature is 737 K (= 477° C)! This is hot enough to melt lead and is over twice as hot as it would be if Venus did not have an atmosphere. Why does Venus have such a thick atmosphere and why is it so hot on its surface? Venus is so hot because of a huge greenhouse effect (section 9.2.5) that prevents heat from escaping to space. On Venus, the super-abundance of CO_2 in its atmosphere is responsible for the huge greenhouse effect. Why is Venus' CO_2 all in its atmosphere while most of the Earth's CO_2 is locked up in its sediments? Earth has some 35 to 50 entire Earth atmospheres worth of carbon dioxide in the form of carbonates. Venus' greenhouse effect probably started from the presence of a lot of water vapor, but Venus is now a very dry place.

Runaway Greenhouse

Venus was originally cooler than what it is now and it had a greater abundance of water several billion years ago. Also, most of its carbon dioxide was locked up in the rocks. Through a process called a **runaway greenhouse**, Venus heated up to its present blistering hot level. Because Venus was slightly closer to the Sun than the Earth, its water never liquified and remained in the atmosphere to start the greenhouse heating. As Venus heated up, some of the carbon dioxide in the rocks was "baked out." The increase of atmospheric carbon dioxide enhanced the greenhouse heating. That baked more carbon dioxide out of the rocks (as well as any water) and a runaway *positive* feedback loop process occurred. This positive feedback loop occurred several hundred million to a few billion years ago so Venus has been very hot for that length of time.

runaway greenhouse

positive *feedback loop magnifies itself*

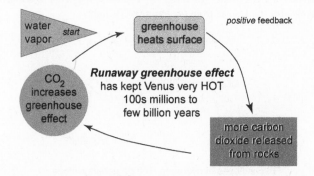

The loss of water from the rocks means that Venus' rocks are harder than the rocks of Earth and its lithosphere is now probably too thick and hard and its asthenosphere is too poorly lubricated for plate tectonics to occur. The water Venus originally had is now gone because of a process called **dissociation**.

Ultraviolet Dissociation of Water

Venus' water was always in the gaseous form and could reach high enough in the atmosphere for ultraviolet light from the Sun to hit it. Ultraviolet light is energetic enough to break apart, or **dissociate,** water molecules into hydrogen and oxygen. The very light hydrogen atoms were able to escape into space and the heavier oxygen atoms combined with other atoms. Venus' water was eventually zapped away. The Earth's ozone layer prevents the same thing from happening to the water here.

dissociation

Hydrogen/Deuterium Ratio

How is it known that Venus originally had more water? Clues come from comparing the relative abundances of hydrogen isotopes on Venus and Earth. An **isotope** of a given element will have the same number of protons in the atomic nucleus as another isotope of that element but not the same number of neutrons (see section 7.4). An isotope with more particles in the atomic nucleus will be more massive (heavier) than one with less particles in the nucleus. Ordinary hydrogen has only one proton in the nucleus, while the isotope *deuterium* has one proton + one neutron. Therefore, deuterium is about twice as heavy as ordinary hydrogen and will stay closer to the

isotope

Dissociation of Water

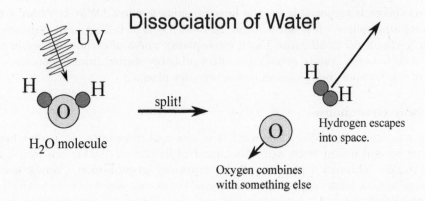

Venus' early water was hot enough to remain in a gaseous form and high enough to be dissociated by *ultraviolet* light (very short wavelength) from the Sun. The low-mass hydrogen molecule resulting from the dissociation moved fast enough to escape Venus and the higher-mass (and slower moving) oxygen atom combined with other atoms. Eventually the water disappeared. The Earth created an ozone shield above the "cold trap" (height where the temperature is cold enough for water to freeze and fall back to the ground). The UV light cannot reach the water because the ozone absorbs the UV light. The ozone also shields life from the harmful UV light.

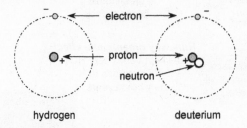

Two isotopes of hydrogen. The deuterium isotope
has an extra neutron in the nucleus.

surface on average. Gases higher up in the atmosphere are more likely to escape to space than those close to the surface (recall section 9.2.1).

On Earth the ratio of ordinary hydrogen to deuterium (H/D) is 1000 to 1, while on Venus the proportion of deuterium is about ten times greater—the H/D ratio is 100 to 1. The H/D ratio on Venus and Earth are assumed to have been originally the same, so something caused the very light hydrogen isotopes on Venus to preferentially disappear. An easy explanation for it is the ultraviolet dissociation of water.

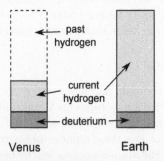

Proportions of hydrogen to deuterium on Venus
and Earth are very different—ordinary hydrogen
isotope was preferentially removed on Venus.

A summary flowchart of what happened on Venus is given on the Earth-Venus-Mars summary page at the end of the chapter. Water vapor started the greenhouse heating. Carbon dioxide was baked out of the rocks, further aggravating the greenhouse effect. A runaway greenhouse started. The end result was all of the carbon dioxide in the atmosphere and the water dissociated away. The flowchart on the Earth-Venus-Mars summary page up to the last arrow occurred several hundred million to a few billion years ago. The diamond at the end describes the current state: CO_2 maintains the extremely hot temperature.

Magellan radar image of three large craters in the northwestern portion of Lavinia Planitia that is in the southern hemisphere of Venus. Howe Crater in the foreground is 37.3 km in diameter. Danilova Crater to the upper left of Howe is 47.6 km in diameter. Aglaonice at the right is 62.7 km in diameter. Image courtesy of NASA/JPL

Gula Mons stands 3 kilometers above the rest of Eistla Regio. Lava flows extend for hundreds of kilometers across the fractured plains. The Venus Express spacecraft has seen evidence that some volcanoes at least were active very recently and perhaps still are. Image courtesy of NASA/JPL

There is a bit of uncertainty in how long ago the runaway process happened because of what happened to Venus' entire surface about 750 million years ago. Venus has the same number of craters/area all over its surface and when you compare the number of large craters/area on Venus with other places in our solar system, you derive an age of 750 million years (give or take a few tens of millions of years) for all of the surface of Venus. It appears that Venus underwent a global repaving event involving a large amount of tectonics or volcanism or combination thereof. That activity would have vaporized any carbonates locked up in the rocks adding to any greenhouse effect already going on. The global repaving event would have also removed whatever water might have been in the mineral matrix of the rocks making the rocks much harder than before. This is one reason why the rocks around craters are much more jagged and sharp than they would be if they were Earth rocks (lack of erosion is another). The removal of the water from the rocks would prevented any further plate tectonic activity *if* there was any to begin with. Venus is much too hot and dry now for plate tectonics to work. Venus does have volcanism occurring today as a result of hot magma plumes reaching the surface at some of its shield volcanoes.

global repaving event

It may be that the loss of water led to the shutting down of plate tectonics and the steady build-up of heat in the interior because it could not be released like what happens with the Earth through plate tectonics. In this view, the global repaving would happen when the interior heat builds up to a critical point. Could Venus have been a much nicer place before the global repaving event, how much did the global repaving event contribute to the runaway process, and whether or not Venus has had multiple global repaving events are three questions for further research.

9.6.2   Mars

Two views of Mars. The 450-kilometer Schiaparelli crater is prominent at the center of the left image. Valles Marineris, a canyon that would stretch across the entire United States, is seen at the center of the right image.

Images courtesy of NASA/JPL

very thin carbon dioxide-rich atmosphere

Mars is about half the diameter of the Earth and has 1/10th the Earth's mass. Mars' thin atmosphere (just 1/100th the Earth's) does not trap much heat at all even though it is 95% carbon dioxide (CO_2). The other 3% is nitrogen (N_2). Because the atmosphere is so thin, the greenhouse effect is insignificant and Mars has rapid cooling between night and day. When night comes the temperature can drop by over 100 K (180° F)! The large temperature differences create strong winds. The strong winds whip up dust and within a few weeks time, they can make dust storms that cover the entire planet for a few months.

Liquid Water Long Ago

What makes Mars so intriguing is that there is evidence for running liquid water in its past. Some geologic features look very much like the river drainage systems on Earth and other features points to huge floods. The Mars Pathfinder studied martian rocks in the summer of 1997 and found some rocks are conglomerates (rock made of pebbles cemented together in sand) that require flowing water to form. Abundant sand also points to widespread water long ago. The larger and *Mars Exploration Rovers* more advanced Mars Exploration Rovers (one called "Spirit" and the other called "Opportunity") further strengthened the conclusion in 2004 that there was liquid water in the past. Highly magnified images of the rocks examined by Opportunity show a particular type of rippling patterns on the rocks that are formed under a gentle current of water instead of wind (see the textbook's website for the image and explanation). Furthermore, detailed chemical analysis of the compositions of the rocks by Opportunity show that they formed in mineral-rich water when the water got very concentrated with the minerals as the water evaporated. In 2012

Opportunity found veins of the mineral gypsum near the edge of the large crater Endeavour. The gypsum veins show that water flowed through the rocks and they are even stronger evidence for water than mentioned above.

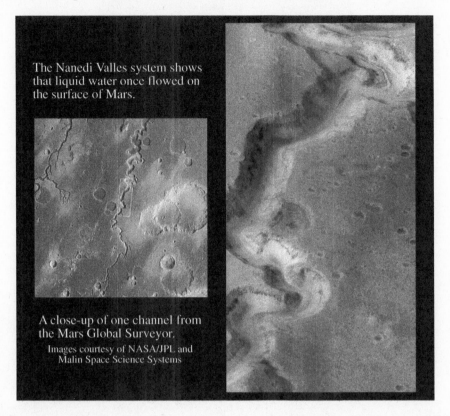

The Nanedi Valles system shows that liquid water once flowed on the surface of Mars.

A close-up of one channel from the Mars Global Surveyor.
Images courtesy of NASA/JPL and Malin Space Science Systems

The Mars Science Laboratory, "Curiosity", landed in Gale Crater near the equator of Mars on August 5, 2012. It has a suite of instruments for identifying organic compounds such as proteins, amino acids, and other acids and bases that attach themselves to carbon backbones and are essential to life as we know it. It is also able to detect gases that *could* be the result of biological activity but it does not have the instruments to determine if there is currently existing biological activity going on. It will identify the best possible sites of biological activity (past or present) for a follow-up mission to more definitively confirm. Gale Crater is 155 kilometers (96 miles) across with a large mountain (Mount Sharp) inside it that is the remnant of an extensive series of deposits. The layers at the base of the mountain contain clays and sulfates that very likely formed in liquid water. Curiosity will also investigate: the geology of the area to figure out how the rocks and soil formed; how the atmosphere has changed through time and the cycling of water and carbon dioxide; and the radiation environment at the surface (photons and particles from the Sun and the rest of the galaxy). In the first couple of months of its exploration, Curiosity found rounded pebbles in conglomerate rocks that are the result of *sustained*, vigorous flow of water, i.e., water-transported gravel. Curiosity landed downstream from an alluvial fan of materials washed down from the crater rim (see the figures on the next page).

Mars Science Laboratory

At locations near where Curiosity landed in Gale Crater, it found deposits of gravel made of well-rounded pebbles eroded off of sedimentary conglomerate outcrops (left image). On Earth (right image of sedimentary conglomerate), rocks that are well-rounded are a common sign of rocks that have been transported by water in a river or stream. If the flow of water is great enough, the pebbles are lifted up in the flow or rolled along the bed and they get pounded against each other so the edges get rounded off. The sizes of the pebbles are too large to have been transported by wind; they must have been transported by a sustained, vigorous flow of water. Image courtesy of NASA/JPL-Caltech/MSSS and PSI.

Landscape features and details in the rocks show that part of Gale Crater was a lake. All images courtesy of NASA/JPL-Caltech/MSSS.
Picture A at top is the Kimberley formation taken by Curiosity on sol 580. The strata in the foreground dip towards the base of Mount Sharp, indicating flow of water toward a basin that existed before the larger bulk of the mountain formed.
Picture B at bottom left shows a network of cracks in a Martian rock slab called "Old Soaker" possibly from drying mud. Image taken by Curiosity on sol 1555 in the Murray formation mudstone area.
Picture C at bottom right is the rock called "Jura" taken by Curiosity on sol 1925. The various crystal-shaped bumps are characteristic of gypsum crystals. This bedrock also exhibits mineral veins with both bright and dark material.

Features such as the gullies in the sides of craters provide a cautionary tale for how we have to be careful in assuming that water must be the cause of sinewy features (and how Mars can fool us if we are too Earth-like in our thinking!). The Mars Global Surveyor found places where gullies are etched into the sides of craters that themselves have very few smaller impacts inside of them. That means the crater walls are geologically young, so the gullies have to be even younger still. The orbiter also found gullies where bright new deposits were seen in images taken just four years apart from each other that seemed to be the result of water carrying sediments down the sides of the craters for a short time. However, the gullies formed mostly on the crater walls facing the poles. Also, the gullies were far more active (forming new features) in the southern hemisphere than in the north. These patterns better match the seasonal changes of carbon dioxide frost (dry ice) formation and then *sublimation* (when a solid turns directly to gas without the intermediate liquid phase). Mars' southern hemisphere winters are longer and colder than those in the north, so more frost forms and piles up in the southern hemisphere. As the dry ice sublimates it causes the rock and soil to flow downhill. Such action by dry ice can happen on Mars but not the Earth because Mars can get extremely cold—colder than Antarctica.

Arrows point to warm season flows ("recurring slope lineae") in Newton Crater. Image courtesy of NASA/JPL-Caltech/Univ. of Arizona

Even with this cautionary tale, there does appear to be evidence for liquid water flowing relatively recently. In 2011 the team of scientists working with the Mars Reconnaissance Orbiter (MRO) released images of seven craters where thin (0.5 to 5 meters wide) dark streaks are seen to flow down steep slopes repeatedly during the summer seasons when temperatures on the surface there can reach -23° to +27°C (-10° to +80°F). In an effort to not bias our interpretation of them, the team has called the features "recurring slope lineae" (="RSL"). One example is shown above.

MRO

recurring slope lineae

Mars' surface air pressure is much too low for pure liquid water to exist now. At very low pressure, water can exist as either frozen ice or as a gas but not in the intermediate liquid phase. If you have ever cooked food at high elevations using boiling water, you know that it takes longer because water boils at a lower temperature than at sea level. That is because the air pressure at high elevations is less. If you were several miles above the Earth's surface, you would find that water would boil (turn into steam) at even room temperature! However, if the liquid is very salty water, then it may be able to exist long enough to flow partway down the crater walls before freezing or evaporating. The dark streaks that grow during the warm summer time could be the result of liquid brines near the surface of Mars breaking through to the surface. Because of the widespread presence of salts on the surface of Mars, even pure water from below would get mixed with the salts. Unfortunately, the spectrometer on board MRO does not have sufficient spatial resolution to analyze the very narrow dark streaks.

testing ideas on making RSL

Research teams tested the argument for these being the result of salty water flowing downhill by simulating the conditions (soil composition, low air pressure, and temperature) in the lab to see what all could create the dark streaks. In 2012 the MRO team increased the number of recurring slope lineae to 15 and strengthened their conclusion that they are caused by briny water melting and seeping downhill through the soil. However, a newer study in August 2016 seems to rule out the briny water idea. Using ground temperature measurements from the Mars Odyssey orbiter, the team found that there are no differences in temperature between slopes with the dark streaks compared to nearby slopes with no streaks, even when the dark streaks were growing. If the dark streaks were seasonal flows of briny water followed by evaporation, annual buildup of crust-forming salt should affect temperature properties.

RSL moisture from deliquescence process

The measurements put an upper limit of just three percent water. That upper limit is as dry as the driest deserts on Earth. The temperature difference study also rules out the streaks being just powdery dust falling downhill after it accumulated too much from dusty air. More likely the salts in the soil become hydrated by pulling water vapor from the air through a process called deliquescence. The RSL features have now been found in more than 50 locations from the equator to about halfway to the poles. A 2017 study of the steepness of the slopes for over 150 RSL found that the dark streaks could be where grains of sand and dust slip downhill. The RSL are restricted to slopes steeper than 27 degrees and end at slopes too shallow for gravity to make a slope of loose material unstable. The seasonal changes in the flows and their coloring may be due to changes in the deliquescence hydration of the sand grains but that raises of the question of why RSL don't appear on all steep slopes.

possible subglacial lake

In July 2018 a team using the MARSIS instrument on the Mars Express spacecraft (that has orbited Mars since 2003) announced the possible presence of a subglacial lake of water underneath the south polar ice cap. The MARSIS instrument sends out low-frequency radio pulses into the planet from a pair of boom antennae that each extend out 20 meters from the spacecraft. The radio waves can penetrate as much as three miles below the surface. Boundaries between layers of different materials can be good radio reflectors. The MARSIS team crunched the numbers from an intense observation campaign that ran from late May 2012 to late December 2015 and after a few years of looking at other possible explanations for an unusually radio reflective feature about one mile below the polar ice surface, the team announced its possible discovery for scrutiny by the larger scientific community.

The twelve-mile across features temperature is probably about −68 deg C. Water could still be liquid at that very low temperature if there is a lot of salt, especially perchlorate salts, mixed in it to make it a very briny lake. Mars has plenty of perchlorates, so a liquid water buried lake is possible. However, another possible explanation is that the feature could be a muddy sludge. TheSHARAD instrumenton theMars Reconnaissance Orbiteris also a ground-penetrating radar and it has not detected radio-bright features below the southern polar ice cap. Although SHARAD operates at a different radio frequency than the MARSIS instrument and cant penetrate as far, it should be able to pick up the radar reflection from a briny lake. SHARAD would have a hard time detecting water-saturated sediments, so perhaps its non-detection means that the MARSIS instrument has found a pocket of muddy sludge instead.

martian life?

Where there is liquid water, there is the possibility for life to arise. Tiny structures in a meteorite that was blasted from Mars in a huge impact of an asteroid look like they were formed by ancient simple lifeforms. However, there is still a lot of debate among scientists on that but strong evidence of contamination by terrestrial organic molecules has probably killed the possibility of conclusive proof of martian life in the meteorite. The dissenters are not wanting to be party poopers. They just want greater certainty that the tiny structures could not be formed by ordinary geologic processes. The great importance of discovering life on another world warrants great skepticism—"extraordinary claims require extraordinary evidence". The search for martian life will need to be done with a sample-return mission or experiments done right on Mars. The intense scrutiny of the RSL features and the subglacial lake described in the previous paragraphs and the effort to find explanations for them that do not require much or any water are other examples of this scientific skepticism. When all other possibilities are exhausted, then we can be more confident in a water-based conclusion (and all the astrobiology possibilities that come with it).

The fact that Mars had liquid water in the past tells us that the early Martian atmosphere was thicker and the surface was warmer from the greenhouse effect a few billion years ago. Some of the topics for follow-up research are: how long was there liquid water present on the surface; when did the liquid water disappear from the surface; how widespread was the liquid water; how much liquid water was there; and were there repeated episodes of liquid water appearing and then disappearing.

Surface of Mars from the Viking 2 Lander.
Image courtesy of NASA/JPL

Surface of Mars from the Pathfinder Lander.
Image courtesy of NASA/JPL

Life *may* have started there so current explorations of Mars are focusing on finding signs of ancient, long-dead life. An important step in that search is to

The Mars Exploration Rover, Opportunity looks back at its landing site.
Image courtesy of NASA/JPL

determine how habitable Mars might have been long ago. Besides liquid water, life would need to have some source of energy to drive its metabolism. In early 2013, the Curiosity rover began drilling into the sedimentary rocks in Gale Crater. Drilling into the rocks may give us information about the conditions on Mars further back in time than what the Mars Exploration Rovers can give us with their wire brush tool.

The rock powder from Curiosity's first drilling was gray with a hint of green, not red, from olivine and magnetite that have less oxygen than the hematite found in rocks studied by the Mars Exploration Rovers. The *range of oxidation* of the materials in the rock could be used as a sort of chemical battery by micro-organisms. In addition, the reduced oxygen minerals would be better at preserving organics than the more oxidized rocks studied by the Mars Exploration Rovers. The rock studied by Curiosity has sulfur (including sulfur dioxide and hydrogen sulfide), nitrogen, oxygen, phosphorus, and carbon (in the form of carbon dioxide)—key ingredients for life. The presence of calcium sulfate and other minerals suggest that the clay minerals were formed from neutral or mildly alkaline water that wasn't too salty instead of the extremely high acidity and saltiness of the water that would have formed the rocks explored by the Mars Exploration Rovers. Examinations of other rocks in the Gale Crater area explored by Curiosity in late 2012-early 2013, show cracks between rocks filled with hydrated minerals that may indicate the Gale Crater floor was soaking wet more than once.

In mid-December 2014 it was announced that organic compounds had been found by the SAM instrument on Curiosity. In June 2018, the research team added to the list of organic compounds to include sulfur-containing thiophenes, the hydrocarbons benzene and toluene, and small carbon chains such as propane or butene. The 2018 samples have a hundred times higher concentration of organic molecules than the 2014 samples. The June 2018 results also included three Martian years of seasonal variations in atmospheric methane. However, the organic materials and varying methane levels can be made by non-biological processes as well as the more exciting biological processes. The best we can say is that all the ingredients for life were present on Mars, Mars was habitable in the past, and biosignatures could be preserved in the rocks on Mars, just waiting for more advanced analysis to uncover them. Curiosity is now climbing up Mt. Sharp to find out how the past habitability changed as it samples younger layers higher up.

Any lifeforms living now would have to be living *below* the surface to prevent exposure from the harsh ultraviolet light of the Sun. Mars has no protective ozone layer, so all of the ultraviolet light reaching Mars can make it to the surface. The Viking landers that landed in 1976 conducted experiments looking for biological activity, past or present, in the soil but found the soil to be sterile with no organic matter (in the top several centimeters at least). The soil is more chemically reactive than terrestrial soil from the action of the harsh ultraviolet light. More recently, the Phoenix mission described below in the "Ice on Mars" section found the reason for the lack of organic matter in the soil: perchlorate in the soil would break down any organic compounds that would have been in the soil when the soil was heated up during the Viking experiments. Curiosity also found perchlorates in the soil of Gale Crater. In any case, Mars appears to have undergone significant global change. What changed Mars into the cold desert of today?

Atmosphere Escape

There are several ways for Mars to have lost its atmosphere:

1. Mars' low gravity let the atmosphere leak away into space;

2. A lot of impacts of asteroids blasted part of the atmosphere away. Such large impacts occurred very frequently in the early solar system several billion years ago. The energy of the impacts could have been enough to push the gas away from a planet with small gravity.

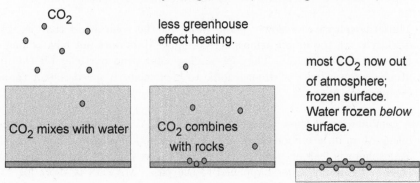

3. Mars had a reverse greenhouse effect, called a **runaway refrigerator**, occur. Since Mars was slightly further from the Sun than the Earth, Mars' initial temperature was lower. This meant that the water vapor condensed to form a liquid water layer on the surface. Gaseous carbon dioxide dissolves in liquid water and can then be chemically combined with rocks. This would have happened on Mars long ago. The removal of some of the carbon dioxide

caused a temperature drop from the reduced greenhouse effect. This caused more water vapor to condense, leading to more removal of atmospheric carbon dioxide and more cooling, etc.

runaway refrigerator

This *positive* feedback process is called a **runaway refrigerator** and is described in the first two panels on the left of the figure on the previous page. This runaway process occurred probably a billion years ago, so Mars has been cold for a long time. Mars' water is now frozen in a permafrost layer below the surface and the atmosphere is very thin. Mars has undergone several dramatic climate swings, so it may have undergone a warming and cooling several times in its past with the latest cooling possibly being more recently than a billion years ago. During the warm periods some water may have flowed across Mars' surface and then froze again when Mars returned to the very cold times. Mars is unfortunately too small to retain enough internal heat to drive something like plate tectonics. As explained in section 9.6.3 below, plate tectonics plays a key role in regulating a planet's climate, so the planet avoids becoming either a hot Venus or a cold Mars.

The runaway refrigerator is also described in a flowchart on the Earth-Venus-Mars summary page at the end of the chapter. The flowchart up to the last dashed arrow occurred a LONG time ago. The box at the end describes the current state: frozen water and carbon dioxide below the surface and a very thin atmosphere.

MRO finds carbonates

The runaway refrigerator theory recently received further support when the Mars Reconnaissance Orbiter found places where deposits of iron and calcium carbonates had been uncovered at large impact sites great distances apart from each other. These types of carbonates form most easily in the presence of large quantities of liquid water and fit the runaway refrigerator idea of atmospheric carbon dioxide dissolving in bodies of liquid water. The carbonate layers are buried under a few miles (about 5 kilometers) of younger rocks, including volcanic flows, similar to what Spirit found when exploring Gusev crater. At Gusev Crater, Spirit had to climb the hills near where it landed to find the older minerals that formed in the presence of liquid water sticking above the surrounding crater floor covered in lava flows. Large impacts are able to uncover the deeper carbonate layers, so MRO will explore other large impact craters closely to see how widespread the buried carbonate layers are.

4. The atmosphere was slowly eaten away by the solar wind that is able to directly reach the upper atmosphere because Mars does not have a magnetic field (see section 9.2.2). The fast-moving solar wind particles hit the upper atmosphere particles with such force to kick them to speeds faster than the escape velocity.

5. A combination of these effects. The NASA MAVEN mission that began orbiting Mars in late September 2014 is investigating how and how fast Mars' atmosphere is leaking away now and hopefully, provide the information we need to figure out what happened in the past. MAVEN is short for "Mars Atmosphere and Volatile Evolution Mission". After a year of study, MAVEN determined that solar wind is the main agent for the loss of Mars's atmosphere today. The solar wind is stripping away Mars's atmosphere at a rate of about 100 grams per second (or over 3 million metric tons per Earth year) with higher rates during solar storms. Billions of years ago, the loss rate would have been higher because the younger Sun was more active than it is now. How long ago Mars lost its magnetic field is somewhat uncertain but due to Mars's small size, it was at least a few billion years ago.

Human explorers will need to use spacesuits on Mars' surface. The low pressure would kill them in a fraction of a second without something to provide an inward pressure on their bodies. Explorers will also need to contend with temperatures that are way below the freezing point of water even during the day and have enough shielding to block the abundant ultraviolet light and particle radiation from the Sun.

Ice on Mars

One of the predictions of the runaway refrigerator is that there should be water ice below the surface. Mars does have polar ice caps made of frozen carbon dioxide ("dry ice") and frozen water, but is there frozen water below the surface away from the polar ice caps? Yes!

Some of the craters on Mars are of a type called a *rampart crater* (or "splash crater") because of the distinctive ridges along the edge of the "fluidized" ejecta. An example is Yuty Crater shown on the next page. This image from the Viking 1 orbiter as well as others it took of craters in the surrounding area show features formed when frozen (or liquid?) water was melted and mixed with the dirt and rocks to flow like mud upon impact. See the textbook's website for links to higher resolution images of this crater from the Mars Global Surveyor spacecraft.

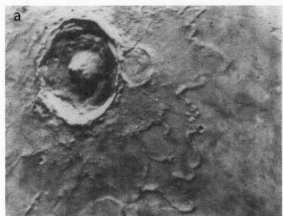

Image a (left): Yuty Crater—a rampart crater. Image from the Viking 1 orbiter courtesy of NASA/JPL

Image b (right): Phoenix Mars Lander uncovered ice in this trench called "Dodo-Goldilocks" that sublimated (from ice directly to water vapor) over the course of four Mars days. The lumps seen in the lower left corner of the trench on day 20 are no longer there on day 24 (inset shows magnified view). If the ice was carbon dioxide, they would have sublimated away in less than a day at the temperatures of Phoenix's location when the trench was dug. Image courtesy of NASA/JPL-Caltech/University of Arizona/Texas A&M University

The Mars Odyssey spacecraft orbiting Mars found that the highest concentrations of the sub-surface ice are near the poles from about latitudes 60 degrees and higher. The Phoenix Mars Lander that landed at the end of May 2008 scooped up ice and soil at its landing spot near the martian north pole south of the north polar cap. It uncovered water ice just a few centimeters below the surface. Phoenix also ran tests to see if the soil and ice could be habitable for microbial life. Phoenix did not have the capability to detect biological activity; it could only determine if

Phoenix Mars Lander

perchlorate

life *could* exist in the soil at its landing spot. The answer: maybe. Phoenix and Curiosity found perchlorate that is toxic to most Earth life but it can be food for some types of microbes. Water vapor from the atmosphere could attach to the perchlorate to form a thin film layer of water for biological activity. In addition perchlorate in water can lower its freezing temperature enough to keep it liquid even in Mars' cold temperatures.

Images from the Mars Reconnaissance Orbiter (see the textbook's website for one) show that frozen water is just below the surface at latitudes closer to the equator than thought possible before. Bright areas in the images are sub-surface water freshly exposed by meteorite impacts. Those areas fade over 15 weeks as the water ice sublimates. The freshly made craters were near the location of the Viking 2 lander and the scientists figured that if Viking 2 had been able to dig just 15 cm (6 in) deeper, it would have found the ice (33 years before Phoenix). Other images from the Mars Reconnaissance Orbiter show ice cliffs and ice mounds at middle latitudes. An improved analysis in 2017 of data collected by the Mars Odyssey orbiter a decade earlier also points to sub-surface ice near the equator.

See the textbook website for movies zooming into the location of the Mars Exploration Rovers and the "Face on Mars".

9.6.3 Earth

Our home planet: the Earth.
Image courtesy of NASA

Our home planet, the Earth, is the largest of the terrestrial planets with a diameter of 12,742 kilometers and a mass of 5.9736×10^{24} kilograms. It has a moderately-thick atmosphere that is 78% nitrogen (N_2) and 21% oxygen (O_2). Although the atmosphere makes up less than 0.0001% of the Earth's mass, it is a very important component. The Earth has the right surface temperature and atmospheric pressure for life and liquid water on the surface to exist. It is the only place that has either of these things. It is the only place that has either of these things. Some water is also in the form of water vapor and ice. The total amount of water on the Earth (in all phases) is about 0.023% of the Earth's mass—the Earth is primarily rock and iron. See the textbook's website for a photo album of some beautiful places on the Earth.

Free Oxygen

Compared to the other planets, the Earth has a bizarre atmosphere! The presence of free oxygen (O_2) is very unusual because oxygen loves to chemically react with other atoms and molecules. The oxygen in our atmosphere would soon disappear (within about 5000 years) if photosynthesizing organisms like plants and cyanobacteria (blue-green algae) did not regenerate the oxygen. In the process of **photosynthesis**, plants take in water, carbon dioxide, and sunlight and convert them to carbohydrates and oxygen. The oxygen is given off as a waste product and the carbohydrates are stored as a source of energy to be used later by the plants. Since life keeps oxygen in the form of O_2 and its fragile cousin, **ozone** (O_3) around, absorption lines of these two molecules in the spectrum of a planet beyond our solar system would be one signature of life on that planet. Ozone has a spectral signature in the infrared—the spectral band where a search for bio-markers would take place (see section 17.4).

photosynthesis makes the oxygen in our air

ozone

Liquid Water

Most of the Earth's water is liquid and some is frozen. The rest that is water vapor works with carbon dioxide in the atmosphere to create a small greenhouse effect, raising the surface temperature about 34° C (see sections 9.2.5 and 9.2.9). This natural greenhouse effect makes it warm enough on the surface for liquid water to exist. Besides making life possible, the liquid water also helps to keep the amount of atmospheric carbon dioxide from getting too high. Carbon dioxide dissolves in liquid water to form "carbonic acid" (soda water). Some of the dissolved carbon dioxide will combine with minerals in the water and settle to the ocean floor to form limestone. A similar process happens with the weathering process. Carbon dioxide dissolved in rainwater (and in snowmelt) combines with minerals eroded away from the mountains to carry carbonates down to the oceans. The amount of atmospheric carbon dioxide is also kept in check by biological processes.

Life's Role in the Carbon Cycle

Plants extract atmospheric carbon dioxide in the photosynthesis process and use it to form organic compounds. Most of the carbon dioxide released by biological processes is released back into the atmosphere when plants decay (or are burned). Some organic material (plants and bacteria) is deposited in marine sediments. The organic material in the marine sediments *may* be converted to oil, natural gas, or coal if the temperature and pressure conditions underground are right. This locks up the carbon dioxide until these fossil fuels are extracted and burned. Burning them releases the carbon dioxide back into the atmosphere.

Aquatic plants extract carbon dioxide dissolved in the water to use in their photosynthesis process. Aquatic animals use the carbon dioxide and calcium in the water to make shells of calcium carbonate ($CaCO_3$). When the animals die, their shells settle to the ocean floor where, after years of compacting and cementing, they form limestone, locking up the carbon dioxide. A great majority of the Earth's carbon dioxide is buried deep below the surface in the form of carbonates. Some of the locked up carbon dioxide is released into the atmosphere via geologic heating processes such as volcanism.

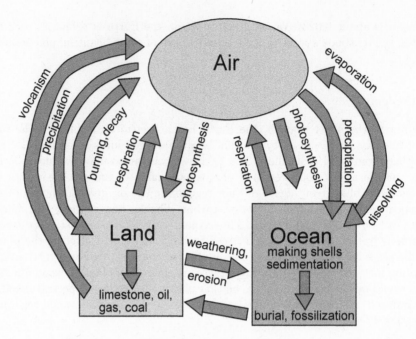

The carbon cycle on Earth

Plate Tectonics's Role in the Carbon Cycle

Earth is unique in that its crust is broken up into chunks called "plates" and these "plates" jostle about because of the convection motion of the mantle below the crust. Among other things plate tectonics does in keeping our planet habitable (see for example, section 9.3.2), plate tectonics play a key role in regulating the amount of carbon dioxide in the Earth's atmosphere. Carbon dioxide in the atmosphere dissolves in rainwater. The slightly acidic rainwater erodes land rocks and the broken down minerals are carried to the oceans via the runoff. Calcium in the broken down minerals combines with the dissolved carbon dioxide in the oceans to create carbonates such as limestone at the ocean floor. Through plate tectonics, mountains are formed when plates collide and weathering of the mountains removes carbon dioxide from the atmosphere and puts it onto the ocean floor. Through plate tectonics, the limestone and other carbonate minerals are carried to subduction zones where they are melted. The melted rock releases carbon dioxide through volcanoes. (Plate tectonics giveth; plate tectonics taketh away.) Volcanoes are the major natural (non-human) way that carbon dioxide is released back into the atmosphere over tens of millions of years of time (in the short term they are just a hundredth of the human annual contribution). The figure on the next page shows some of the plate tectonics events with climate changes over the past 540 million years using the changing ratio of oxygen-18 to oxygen-16 as a proxy for temperature changes as discussed in section 9.2.9. A one part in 1000 change in the oxygen-18 corresponds to a 1.5 to 2 degrees Celsius change in the sea surface temperature.

The formation of the limestone happens most easily in shallow water. On Earth the presence of continents makes it possible for places of shallow water to exist. The continents are created from lower-density material than oceanic plates through the subduction process of plate tectonics. Liquid water plays a key role in helping the subduction process of plate tectonics to work by lowering the melting point of the oceanic crust and keeping the lithosphere pliable enough to bend and descend far enough into the mantle to melt. In turn the temperature regulation of plate tectonics enables liquid water to remain on the Earth's surface.

The temperature regulation happens because of a *negative feedback* process that

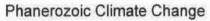

Phanerozoic Climate Change

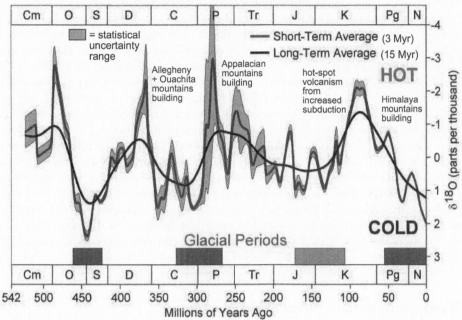

cools the Earth if it gets too hot and warms the Earth if it gets too cool. The rate that carbon dioxide is removed from the atmosphere depends on the temperature such that the higher the temperature, the higher the rate that carbon dioxide is removed. If the Earth warms up, there will be more evaporation and rainfall, resulting in greater removal of atmospheric carbon dioxide. The reduced atmospheric carbon dioxide leads to a weakened greenhouse effect that counteracts the initial warming and cools the Earth back down. If the Earth cools off, the rainfall decreases, resulting in less removal of atmospheric carbon dioxide. The atmospheric carbon dioxide level will build back up because of the outgassing of volcanoes. A strengthened greenhouse effect counteracts the initial cooling and heats the Earth back up.

negative feedback stabilizes climate

The thermostat did not work as well before about 540 million years ago. The Snowball Earth episodes discussed in section 9.2.9 alternated with episodes of ex-

Snowball Earth

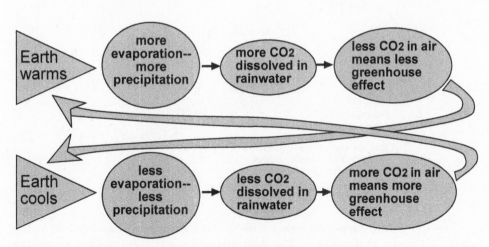

Carbon cycle is the Earth's thermostat

treme warmth ("hothouse Earths") with large amounts of carbon dioxide in the atmosphere. The large amount of carbon dioxide would have been needed to provide the amount of greenhouse warming necessary to melt the ice. Recall that glaciers leave piles of rubble. Several layers of rubble piles are found in dozens of places on the Earth dated between about 800 million to 600 million years ago and these places would have been near the equator at those times. Right above the glacial rubble pile layers are found layers of carbonate deposits ("cap carbonates"). Ordinarily, such a juxtaposition of these two types of layers is not found, nor expected because glacial deposits are usually found in higher (cooler) latitudes while carbonates form easily in lower (warmer) latitudes. The Snowball Earth theory predicts that a hothouse Earth would follow a snowball Earth; just what is seen in the geological record. The carbon cycle would then have worked to bring the temperatures to more moderate levels. Interestingly, it may be the presence of multi-cellular life, particularly worms, that has prevented the large temperature swings from happening again. Worms in the ocean sediments wiggling about prevent the methane and carbon dioxide from getting locked away and bringing on too large a drop in the greenhouse effect. Complex, multi-cellular life did not evolve until around 540 million years ago—after the last Snowball Earth-hothouse Earth swing. See the textbook's website for links to more about the carbon cycle including videos.

Human Role in the Carbon Cycle

carbon cycle

This whole process of the cycling of the carbon dioxide in the water, life, rocks, and air is called the **carbon cycle** or the **carbon dioxide cycle** in geology and oceanography. There is the equivalent of 35–50 atmospheres of CO_2 locked up in the Earth's rocks as carbonates. The contribution of carbon dioxide from the burning of fossil fuels by humans is a new input into this cycle with uncertain consequences. We are inputting carbon dioxide into the atmosphere at about 120 times the natural rate of carbon recycling [from Turco, *Earth Under Siege* (1997) p. 307]. How do we know that the increase in carbon dioxide is due to fossil fuel burning?

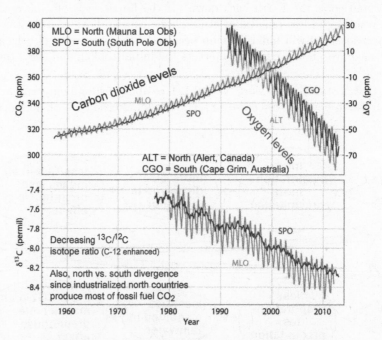

The top graph shows the recent carbon dioxide increase measured from the north and south hemispheres. The light green curve (larger wiggles) shows the data collected by Charles Keeling at the Mauna Loa Observatory Hawaii (data collection started in the late 1950s and now continues after his death in 2005). The dark green is from the South Pole Observatory. The wiggles up and down are due to the increase of photosynthesis in the spring and summer and decrease in the fall and winter. The northern hemisphere has more land—more photosynthesizing plants, so the wiggles are more pronounced. If fossil fuel burning is producing the extra carbon dioxide, we should see a decrease in the amount of oxygen. That is shown in the light blue (for Alert, Canada, larger wiggles) and dark blue (for Cape Grim, Australia) wiggles. Note that the scale for the oxygen plot has been magnified to make it more easily visible.

The bottom graph shows the *reduction* (more negative) of measured carbon-13 to carbon-12 isotope ratio as only happens with fossil fuel burning. This is the chemical signature of fossil fuel burning. Biochemical reactions have a preference for carbon-12, so biologically produced materials will be enriched in carbon-12 (or proportionally reduced in carbon-13) compared to the carbon in inorganic materials. See the IPCC Working Group I report for further details and references to the peer-reviewed research on the use of carbon isotope ratios. The textbook's website includes a link to the RealClimate blog posting for a detailed answer to this question. Both graphs also show that the levels in the north and south hemispheres are slowly diverging, separating from each other, over the decades because the industrialized countries in the north produce most of the fossil fuel carbon dioxide. The IPCC Working Group I report (especially chapter 6) gives other proofs of the human contribution to the atmospheric carbon dioxide levels.

fossil fuel signature

Could this artificial input into the carbon cycle upset the natural balance and create a runaway greenhouse effect like that on Venus? Maybe. How much would it take to tip the balance? We don't know. We are in the midst of a great planetary experiment. Current estimates of the amount of carbon dioxide locked up in fossil fuels say that it is highly unlikely that burning all of the fossil fuels will create a runaway greenhouse effect. As mentioned above, carbon dioxide levels and global temperatures many millions of years ago have sometimes been much higher than what they are today. *HOWEVER*, while life *in general* and the Earth will survive "just fine" regardless of what amount of warming we cause, the particular form of life known as human (Homo Sapiens) requires cooler temperatures to be comfortable (or even survive). Furthermore, it does not take a large change in the global average temperature to create huge stresses that could threaten the survival of human civilization.

Life survives but human civilization may not

To put things into perspective on how much difference just a few degrees change in the global average temperature can make, recall the temperature plots from the ice core data discussed in the Weather vs. Climate section 9.2.9. Approximately 6 degrees Celsius in the global average temperature that separates the pleasant environment today with the last ice age when there were ice sheets over a kilometer thick covering a lot of our land (see figures next page). If you zoom in on the past 120,000 years, you will notice that the global temperature has been remarkably stable for a stretch of time longer than other interglacials—about 11,570 years. The top temperature graph on the next page is from data courtesy of Jouzel, J., et al and the bottom carbon dioxide graph is from data courtesy of Luthi, D., et al.

small   temperature change has big effect

Art and culture are about 30,000 years old *but* agriculture and settlements (societies) did not exist until about 10,000 years ago. Agriculture and complex societies seemed to take about a thousand years of climate stability (and a stabilized sea level) to get organized. Archaeology has shown that *minor* climate changes have resulted in significant social disruption in great civilizations of the past which may have implications for us in how we will deal with climate change in the future.

The pre-historic climate records show that carbon dioxide levels have tracked the temperature changes very closely but there is some controversy about what causes what (did temperature change before carbon dioxide levels or was it the other way

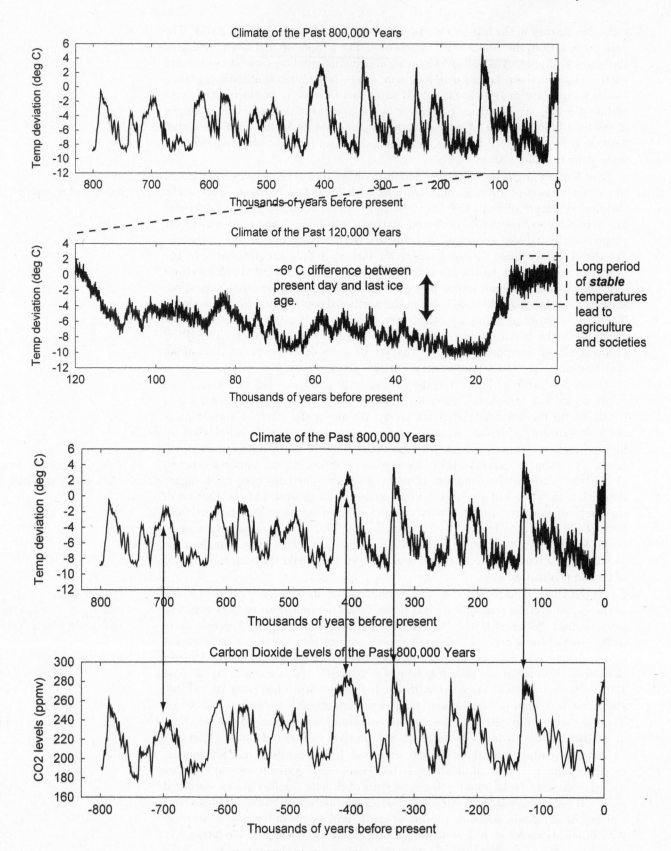

Climate of the Past 800,000 Years

Climate of the Past 120,000 Years

~6° C difference between present day and last ice age.

Long period of *stable* temperatures lead to agriculture and societies

Climate of the Past 800,000 Years

Carbon Dioxide Levels of the Past 800,000 Years

around?) because of the age determinations of the components in the ice core data cannot be made with sufficient resolution to definitively determine what came first. The climate feedback processes discussed in section 9.2.9 can make a cause-effect relationship between carbon dioxide and temperature in the past tricky to establish. Past climate changes such as ice ages/interglacials have been triggered by changes in the Earth's axis tilt and orbit shape. In those cases carbon dioxide/greenhouse effect and albedo changes have acted as feedback agents to enhance the effect of the axis tilt/orbit changes. Although the pre-historic climate records *may* show that greenhouse heating *may* have sometimes lagged behind temperature changes, the physics of the greenhouse effect has been well understood for over a century now, so we do know what an increase in atmospheric carbon dioxide can do. Now we are adding carbon dioxide independently of any *natural* temperature changes and that extra carbon dioxide will be the triggering, forcing agent to a change in the global temperature via the well-understood greenhouse effect.

climate feedback processes

We do know that the amount contributed by human activity has had an effect that is long-lasting because of the *long* time it takes for the extra atmospheric carbon dioxide input to be absorbed back into the Earth. The increase has happened in a very short time scale compared to past natural fluctuations in the carbon dioxide levels. Particular forms of life require much longer timescales to adapt to changes in global climate than what will occur with the rapid increase in the carbon dioxide levels. Therefore, the mix of species of life will undergo drastic changes in the next century or so. Human societies will need to adjust to those changes along with the changes of where food can be grown and changes in levels of available fresh water.

IPCC

IPCC

An excellent summary on the science of climate change is from the Intergovernmental Panel on Climate Change, particularly their WG I: The Physical Science Basis report at www.ipcc.ch. The Intergovernmental Panel on Climate Change (IPCC) is a review organization peopled by several hundred governmental and academic scientists from around the world. It publishes assessment reports every six years based on peer-reviewed literature. The IPCC does not do the climate research itself as an organization—it uses the results from the peer-reviewed research. The conclusions in the reports have to be agreed upon by politicians in all of the countries before they are published (and that includes the U.S.) so they tend to get watered down from the stronger conclusions from the scientists.

In trying to explain the warming *that has already happened*, climate models of different research groups using different inputs have found that the human factor must be included in the climate forcings ("*forcings*" are agents of change that can move a system out of balance). Models that include just natural forcings like the Sun and volcanoes (bottom bands of the plots on the next page) show that the average temperature of the world and individual continents should have been stable (unchanged) since at least 1900—they cannot produce the observed change in global, continental, and ocean temperature. The graphic on the next page shows the temperature (beige panels), ocean heat content (light blue panels), and polar ice (white panels) changes (black lines in each of the panels) over the past decades along with models that try to fit what has happened in the past. The blue bands are results with 95% confidence level uncertainties of multiple climate models with just natural agents of solar activity and volcanoes. The pink bands are results with 95% confidence level uncertainties of multiple climate models that include human-generated agents of change ("anthropogenic forcings"). Only the pink bands fit the observations (black lines).

climate forcings

Climate studies use *hundreds to thousands* of measurements all over the globe to look at averages (remember the difference between weather and climate—section 9.2.9). *Any* data set will have some scatter about the mean (average) so you are bound

Courtesy of IPCC Working Group I Fifth Assessment Report

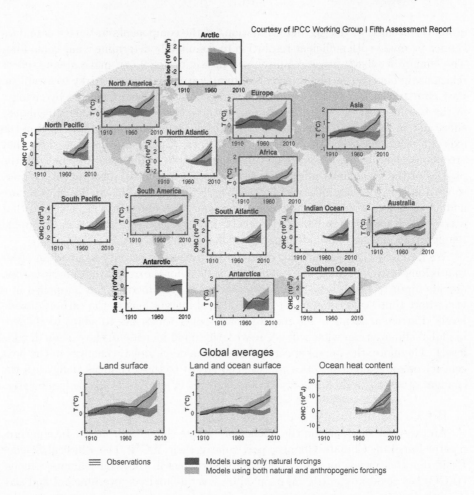

to find some examples that are less than the observed average trend. You cannot cherry pick your data—honest work includes them all. Once a climate simulation model has been validated against the climate conditions in the past, i.e., reproduce the climate conditions we know existed in the past hundred or more years, they are used to make predictions of what will happen in the future assuming various scenarios such as: we either continue at the present rate of carbon dioxide emission, the *rate* of carbon dioxide emitted by humans continues to accelerate at the current observed acceleration, something in between, or we transition to non-fossil fuel energy production.

The discussion above has focused on temperature measurements but if climate change is real, there should be other indicators of changes in the climate. There are, including:

other indicators besides temperature

- Decreases in the Arctic sea ice (it is now declining at a rate of 11.5% per decade and the rate is increasing).

- Decreases in the mass of land ice on Antarctica and Greenland as measured by NASA's GRACE mission.

- Rising sea level and the *rate* of sea level increase itself is increasing. Today it is caused mostly by the expansion of sea water as the water warms and some by melting ice. In the future the sea level rise will be much more dramatic as more of the polar ice melts permanently.

- Other lines of evidence given on NASA's Climate Change site and in the National Research Council's Climate Change: Lines of Evidence booklet. The

National Research Council is the working arm of the National Academy of Sciences established in 1863 by President Abraham Lincoln and whose members serve pro bono as advisors to the nation on science, engineering, and medicine. Links to the data sources for all of these observations are given on the textbook's website.

Unfortunately, it would take many decades, even centuries, for the additional (human-generated) amount of carbon dioxide to be removed via the processes described above even if we stopped all burning of fossil fuels today (see David Archer's book *The Long Thaw* for more on the timescales involved). Also, the climate change effects take decades to build up so people have been unwilling to make the needed changes in energy generation systems today. See the textbook's website for links to further resources on human-induced global warming.

Political Controversy

The controversy over global warming is being fought over in the popular media even though the consensus of the scientific community that actually researches climate change is that humans are having a greater impact on global warming than natural sources. The IPCC WG I report mentioned above has an excellent Frequently Asked Questions section that includes questions raised by the skeptics. The overwhelming consensus of the scientific community who actually do climate research (i.e., those who are actively engaged in climate research, publish their results in peer-reviewed journals, and allow their conclusions to be tested by others) is that the global warming that is happening is mostly human-caused by the burning of fossil fuels. Any increase in solar luminosity has a much smaller effect on the climate. As a measure of the certainty of this, major *insurance companies* are now revising their business projections to take the IPCC's conclusions into account. Even the U.S. Department of Defense recognizes that climate change is happening and that it will bring stresses on food and water supply systems. Finally, while life in general and the Earth will survive "just fine" regardless of what amount of warming we cause, the particular form of life known as human (Homo Sapiens) requires cooler temperatures to be comfortable (or even survive). The predicted effects of global warming (such as sea level rise, increased forest fires, increased frequency of extreme weather events, etc.) will eventually lead to the expenditures of many *trillions* of dollars to mitigate those effects. To keep "business as usual," are we also planning ahead for such large expenditures of money? On a more personal note, we need to address the fairness issue:

- The poorer, developing countries will bear the brunt of the future negative effects resulting from the choices made today by the richer, advanced countries.

- The costs/consequences of the future societal changes our children and grandchildren will have to live with as a result of the current benefits we experience today of our cheap energy production but they do not have a say in the choices made today.

The textbook's website has a section on answers to global warming skeptics for more on this as well as links to the carbon dioxide and climate change data from the Carbon Dioxide Information Analysis Center and pre-historic climate data from the NOAA Paleoclimatology Center. A flowchart of the carbon cycle on the Earth is given on the Earth-Venus-Mars summary page at the end of the chapter. While the flowcharts for Venus and Mars show what happened long ago, the flowchart for the Earth shows the cycle as it currently operates.

Cold Trap

The Earth has a layer of ozone in our stratosphere that prevents most of the

ozone blocks solar UV

ultraviolet from reaching the surface. The blocking of ultraviolet light enables life to exist on the land—the full range of the solar ultraviolet light would kill lifeforms living on the land. The ozone layer also shields the water from being dissociated by the ultraviolet light.

water vapor not dissociated

The temperature of the atmosphere decreases with increasing altitude above the surface up to the ozone layer. The temperature below the ozone layer is below the freezing point of water. If water vapor gets up too high in the atmosphere, it condenses and rains back to the surface. This height is *below* the ozone layer, so the water vapor does not get high enough to be dissociated—there is a "cold trap" below the ozone layer.

CFC's

Within the past couple of decades, the ozone layer has been partially destroyed by some of the chemicals used in modern devices. One class of ozone-destroying chemicals are called *chlorofluorocarbons* (CFC's) that are used in aerosol sprays, the cooling fluid in older refrigerators and air conditioners and in making styrofoam. Most of the industrialized nations have taken steps to reduce the production of CFC's, but the CFC's already in the atmosphere will take some time to disappear and the ozone destruction will continue for a while. You may have heard that some ozone is produced by engines here on the surface. Unfortunately, that ozone does not make it to the ozone layer high up. Also, ozone can damage our respiratory system.

Vocabulary

carbon cycle (carbon dioxide cycle)   dissociation   photosynthesis
runaway greenhouse   runaway refrigerator

Review Questions

1. What distinguishes Venus from the rest of the planets? Why is Venus so hot?

2. What is a **runaway greenhouse**?

3. How does the UV-water interaction explain why Venus is so dry? How is the same process prevented on the Earth?

4. What major geological event occurred on Venus over half a billion years ago? How do we know?

5. If Mars' atmosphere is over 90% carbon dioxide like Venus', why does it have such a small greenhouse effect?

6. What atmospheric phenomenon can quickly wipe out any view of Mars' surface from above? What causes this phenomenon?

7. Why does Mars have such a thin atmosphere? What is the **runaway refrigerator**?

8. How does liquid water remove carbon dioxide gas from an atmosphere?

9. Why does Titan, a moon of Saturn less massive than Mars, have a more extensive atmosphere than Mars and Earth? (Recall the factors that affect atmosphere thickness.)

10. How do we know that liquid water once flowed on the surface of Mars?

11. If life exists on Mars today, where would it be found and why?

12. Where is water ice found today on Mars and how do we know? How deeply is it buried?

13. What distinguishes Earth from the rest of the planets? What is so unusual about its atmosphere and what produces this unusual feature?

14. What are the different ways that life removes carbon dioxide from the Earth's atmosphere?

15. Where do coal, oil, and natural gas come from? What happens when they are burned?

16. What is a natural way (non-human) that most of the carbon dioxide is returned to the atmosphere on Earth?

17. How does plate tectonics regulate the climate of the Earth?

18. What is the interaction of plate tectonics and liquid water?

19. What is a non-natural, human activity that returns a lot of carbon dioxide to the atmosphere?

20. How do we know that the increase in the Earth's atmospheric carbon dioxide is due to fossil fuel burning?

21. How much difference could just a few degrees change in the global average temperature make in our climate? How could that affect our civilization?

22. What have climate scientists found about the effect of humans on global climate?

23. How are climate models tested?

24. What are the benefits of the presence of the ozone layer?

25. Is the greenhouse problem on Earth different from the ozone problem? How so?

9.7 Moons and Rings

This section gives a brief discussion of the large moons in the solar system and the characteristics of the rings found around all of the jovian planets. The best known moon is the only other object that humans have explored directly—the Earth's moon. I will discuss the Moon first and then move to the large moons of the jovian planets. The two moons of Mars and most of the moons of the jovian planets are small, rocky objects about the size of a large city or smaller. Most of them are probably asteroids that wondered too closely to the planet and got trapped by the planet's gravity.

9.7.1 The Earth's Moon

At 3474 kilometers in diameter, the Moon is about one-quarter the diameter of the Earth—if placed on the United States, it would extend from Los Angeles to almost Washington D.C. With that diameter and a mass 1/81 times the Earth's mass, the Moon is proportionally the largest moon in relation to its primary planet of any of the planets in the solar system. The Moon has held a special place in history. This is because it moves quickly among the stars and it changes—it goes through a cycle of phases, like a cycle of birth, death, and rebirth (see section 3.7). The Moon is also primarily responsible for the tides you experience if you spend any time near the coast (see section 5.9). When Galileo looked through his telescope, he discovered a wondrous place. The Moon became a *place* to explore. Galileo discovered impact craters, mountains and valleys. The Moon is rough like the Earth.

The Moon also has large, dark smooth areas covering about 17% of the Moon's surface that people originally thought were seas of liquid water so they are called **mare** (Latin for "seas"—they are what make out the face on the Moon). Now it known that the mare are vast lava flows that spread out over many hundreds of square miles, covering up many craters that were originally there (section 9.5.2). The mare material is basaltic like the dark material on the Earth's ocean crust and that coming out many of our shield volcanoes (e.g., the Hawaiian islands).

mare

The Earth's Moon

Mercury also has maria but they are lighter in color because of the different chemical composition and they do not stand out from its heavily cratered areas.

water on the Moon?

Liquid water cannot exist on the Moon because of the lack of an atmosphere—the Moon has only about 1/6th the Earth's surface gravity. If there is any water to be found on the Moon, it will be in a frozen state in a place of constant shade such as deep craters near the poles. Recent missions have discovered some of those ice blocks near the poles. The ice blocks will be the source of water for any humans that decide to set up bases on the Moon.

Craters

The Moon's surface is almost as old as the Earth. The rough highland regions are 3.8 to 4.2 billion years old and the younger maria are between 3.1 and 3.8 billion years old. All of the planets and moons experienced a period of heavy bombardment about 3.8 billion years ago that lasted for about 500 million years as most of the remaining chunks of rock left over from the formation of the solar system pelted the planet and moon surfaces. The Moon, some of the moons of the giant planets, and Mercury preserve a record of this bombardment. The record of this heavy cratering was erased on the Earth long ago because of erosion and geologic activity that continues to this day. The Moon has no erosion because of the lack of liquid water and an atmosphere and it is small enough that its interior cooled off long ago so geologic activity has essentially ceased (an occasional very small moonquake can still occur). The small size of the Moon meant that not much heat could be stored

why the Moon is geologically dead

from its formation and its small size also means that any remaining heat can easily escape to space (the ratio of its volume to its surface area is smaller than that for the Earth).

Interior and Composition

The average thickness of the Moon's crust is between 34 and 43 kilometers thick. The strong tides from the Earth pulled the early Moon's liquid interior toward the Earth, so the far side's crust is thicker than the near side's crust. The thinness of the near side's crust is also why there are more mare on the near side than the far side. The near side was thin enough to be cracked apart when large asteroids hit the surface and formed the mare but the far side crust was too thick.

Our knowledge about the Moon took a huge leap forward during the Apollo missions. One main science reason for going to the Moon was to return rock samples to find about their ages and composition. Using their knowledge of geology gained from the study of Earth rocks, scientists were able to put together a history for the Moon. The Apollo astronauts also left seismometers on the Moon to detect moonquakes that can be used to probe the interior using seismology.

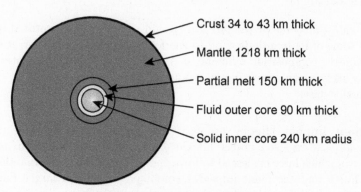

Crust 34 to 43 km thick

Mantle 1218 km thick

Partial melt 150 km thick

Fluid outer core 90 km thick

Solid inner core 240 km radius

The Moon's interior structure

The Moon's density is fairly uniform throughout and is only about 3.3 times the density of water. A recent re-analysis of the Apollo seismic data shows that the Moon has a small iron-rich core made of three parts: a solid inner iron core 480 kilometers in diameter, a fluid iron outer core shell 90 kilometers thick, and a third part unique to the Moon that is a shell of partial melt about 150 kilometers thick. The iron core also contains a small percentage of lighter elements such as sulfur. Further refinements of our view of the Moon's interior will undoubtedly occur as scientists analyze all of the gravity data from the recently-completed GRAIL mission.

The small core is a sharp contrast from planets like Mercury and the Earth that have large iron-nickel cores and overall densities more than 5 times the density of water. The Moon's mantle is made of silicate materials, like the Earth's mantle, and makes up about 90% of the Moon's volume. The temperatures do increase closer to the center and are high enough to partially liquify the material close to the center. Its lack of a large liquid iron-nickel core and slow rotation is why the Moon has no magnetic field.

Moon is mostly pure rock

Lunar samples brought back by the Apollo astronauts show that compared to the Earth, the Moon is deficient in iron and nickel and volatiles (elements and compounds that turn into gas at relatively low temperatures) such as water and lead. The Moon is richer in elements and compounds that vaporize at very high temperatures. The Moon's material is like the Earth's mantle material but was heated to very high temperatures so that the volatiles escaped to space.

Formation

There have been a variety of scenarios proposed to explain the differences between the Moon and Earth. The one that has gained acceptance after much study is the **giant impact theory** developed by Hartmann and Davis in the mid-1970s. Earlier theories came in a variety of flavors.

1. The *capture (pick up) theory* proposed that the Moon formed elsewhere in the solar system and was later captured in a close encounter with the Earth.

The theory cannot explain why the ratio of the oxygen isotopes (Oxygen-16 vs. Oxygen-18) is the same as that on the Earth but every other solar system object has different oxygen isotope ratios. The theory also requires the presence of a third large body in just the right place and time to carry away the extra orbital motion energy.

2. The *double planet (sister) theory* said that the Moon formed in the same place as the Earth but it could not explain the composition differences between the Earth and Moon.

3. The *spin (daughter or fission) theory* said that the Earth rotated so rapidly that some of its mantle flew off to the form the Moon. However, it could not explain the composition differences. Also, the spun-off mantle material would more likely make a ring, not a moon and it is very unlikely that the Earth spun that fast.

giant impact theory

    The **giant impact theory** proposes that 50 million years after the Earth formed, a large Mars-sized object hit the Earth and blew mantle material outward, some of which later coalesced to form the Moon. Most of the mantle material from the Earth and the giant impactor combined to make a larger Earth. The Earth had already differentiated by the time of the giant impact so its mantle was already iron-poor. The impact and exposure to space got rid of the volatiles in the ejecta mantle material. Such an impact was rare so is was not likely to have also occurred on the other terrestrial planets. The just-formed Moon was only about 64,000 kilometers (40,000 miles) from the Earth and it has been spiraling away from us ever since (though, at an ever-decreasing rate). The tides the Earth experienced from the Moon at that early time was enough to raise solid ground 60 *meters* during high tide and the Earth was spinning much faster back then—one day was about five hours long (section 5.9).

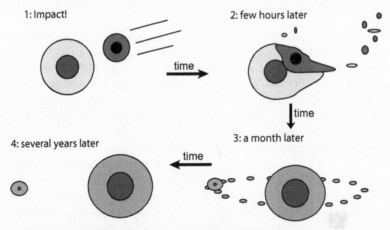

A long time ago in a planet system close to home...
A giant impact made the Moon. The Moon is mantle material from the
Earth and impactor. Earth today is mantle+core from early Earth + impactor.

    The one "drawback" of the theory is that it has a lot of parameters (impactor size, speed, angle, composition, etc.) that can be tweaked to get the right result. A complex model can usually be adjusted to fit the data even if it is not the correct one (recall Ptolemy's numerous epicycles). But the giant impact theory is the only one proposed that can explain the compositional and structural characteristics of the Moon.

The Galilean satellites (Jupiter's four largest moons) to the same scale. Our Moon is also shown for reference.

Images courtesy of NASA/JPL and UCO/Lick Observatory

9.7.2 Jupiter's Large Moons

Jupiter holds a special place in history because of the discovery by Galileo in 1610 of four large moons orbiting it. This observation gave Galileo strong evidence against the popular Earth-centered universe of his day. Like the Earth, Jupiter was a planet with moons orbiting it. Galileo took the Jupiter system to be like a miniature solar system. These four satellites are called the *Galilean satellites* in honor of their discoverer. In order of increasing distance from Jupiter they are Io, Europa, Ganymede and Callisto. Since then, fifty-nine other moons have been discovered orbiting Jupiter. The Galilean satellites are of particular interest here.

Io

The Galilean moon closest to Jupiter is Io. Io has no impact craters even though it has a rocky, solid surface. The surface must be very young because something has erased the impact craters. Even though Io has nearly the same size (3643 km across) and density (3.53× water) as the Moon, Io is the most geologically active world in the solar system. Io has many volcanoes and all of its craters are volcanic in origin. It is so active despite its small size because of the enormous stresses it experiences from Jupiter.

Even though Io is about the same distance from Jupiter as the Moon is from the Earth, Io experiences much stronger tidal stretching because Jupiter is over 300

Visible band (left + top right) and infrared views of
the volcanoes of Io with the New Horizons spacecraft.
Note the infrared glow from at least ten fainter volcanoes.
Courtesy of NASA/John Hopkins Univ Applied Physics Laboratory./Southwest Research Institute

tidal heating of Io's interior

times more massive than the Earth—Io's rock surface bulges up and down by as much as 100 meters! Io also takes 1.77 days to orbit Jupiter—compare that with the 27.3 days that the Moon takes to orbit the Earth. Io's orbit is kept from being exactly circular by the gravity of its Galilean neighbor Europa and the more distant Ganymede. Io, Europa, and Ganymede have a 4:2:1 orbital resonance that keeps their orbits elliptical. For every four orbits of Io, Europa orbits twice and Ganymede orbits once. Io cannot keep one side exactly facing Jupiter and with the varying strengths of the tides because of its elliptical orbit, Io is stretched and twisted over short time periods. The tidal flexing heats Io's interior to the melting point just as kneading dough warms it up.

many powerful volcanoes

The heat escapes through powerful eruptions spewing sulfur compounds in giant umbrella-shaped plumes up to almost 300 kilometers above the surface. The tidal heating from Jupiter has driven away much of the volatile materials like water, carbon dioxide, etc. Io's surface is a splotchy mixture of orange, yellow, black, red, and white. The colors are created by sulfur and sulfur dioxide at various temperatures in liquid and solid states.

why small icy moons can still be geologically active

A note of caution before proceeding further: although heating of the interior by tidal effects is a significant reason why some of the moons of the jovian planets exhibit geologic activity, it is not the only reason. Tidal heating cannot explain all or any of the activity seen on some of the icy moons. Other mechanisms such as rotational shearing from a wobbly rotation axis can play a role. Ultimately, it is the composition of the icy moons that makes the difference. The ices are able to deform and melt at lower temperatures than the silicate and metal rocks found in the inner terrestrial planets and their moons.

Europa

The next moon out from Jupiter is the smooth, white moon called Europa. It is smaller than Io (3122 km across) and has a density of 3.01× water. Europa is of particular interest to astronomers because of what is below its ice crust. Europa

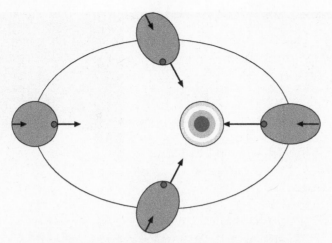

A moon experiences variable amounts of tides because of its elliptical orbit. The closer the moon is to the planet, the larger is tidal bulge. The changing amount of the tides produces frictional heating inside the moon.
The arrows indicate the strength of gravity from the planet on the near and far sides of the moon. Tides are due to differences in the strength of gravity acting *on* an object. The small red circle shows how the tidal bulge shifts with a particular location on the moon.

has a rocky core surrounded by a deep ocean of liquid water that is frozen on the surface. The Galileo spacecraft provided high-resolution images of its surface and showed giant blocks of ice that appear to have been broken off and floated away into new positions (see figure next page).

liquid water ocean below the surface?

Europa has no impact craters which means the surface is very young. Depending on the assumptions of whether it is asteroids or comets pelting the surface, Europa's surface might be as young as 100 million years old if asteroids make the craters or still have activity today if comets make the craters. The Galileo spacecraft found that Jupiter's magnetic field at Europa changes in strength as Jupiter spins. A changing magnetic field can produce electrical currents in a salty ocean that will in turn produce a magnetic field to counter Jupiter's magnetic field (something called *Lenz's Law*). The presence of an *induced* magnetic field at Europa is a strong argument for the presence of a salty global ocean.

induced magnetic field means Europa ocean

Europa is farther from Jupiter than Io, so the tides it feels from Jupiter's enormous gravity is less. It takes about 3.5 days to go around Jupiter in its elliptical orbit. Weaker tides over a longer time period mean the tidal flexing is less than what Io experiences, but the calculated amount of tidal heating at Europa could be enough to maintain liquid water. Europa is too small for radioactive decay in its rocky core to provide enough heating. Geological activity on the moons of the jovian planets, even those smaller than Europa, is possible not only because of tidal heating but also because of their composition. Ice melts and flexes at lower temperatures than rock. The flexing of the ice from changes in the tides, as it moves around Jupiter in its elliptical orbit, creates an impressive system of cracks on the surface. The cause of the dark colors of the cracks is unknown, but it may be due to organic materials or salts (see figure next page).

small moons can still be active

Careful observations of how the Galileo spacecraft moved in Europa's gravity field enabled scientists to determine the ocean thickness (section 9.4). The ocean of liquid water below Europa's icy surface may extend down several tens of kilometers (or more). More importantly, the pressure at the ocean bottom could still be small enough that the liquid water could be contact with the rocky mantle that could supply nutrients for life. Could life forms have developed in the warm waters below

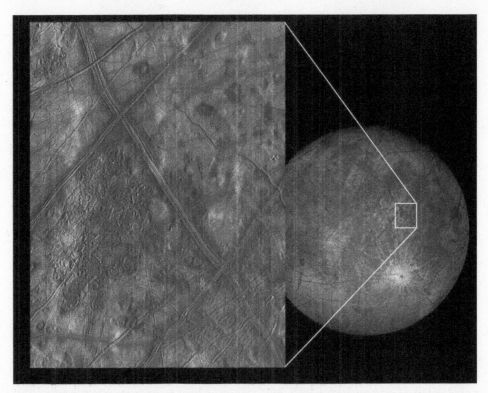

The Galileo spacecraft provided high-resolution images of Europa's surface and showed giant blocks of ice that appear to have been broken off and floated away into new positions. This is a false-color image to highlight the differences in the surface. Reddish brown areas represent non-ice material resulting from geologic activity. Dark blue areas are coarse-grained ice plains and light blue are fine-grained ice plains. The long, dark lines are ridges and fractures, some of which extend more than 3000 kilometers that result from tectonic activity. Image courtesy of NASA/JPL/University of Arizona

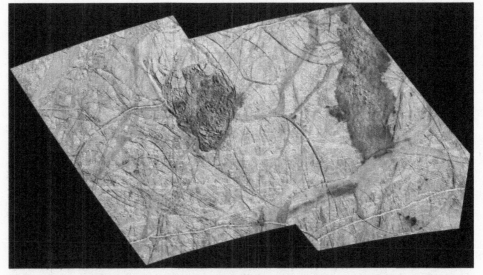

Two dark, reddish regions of strange terrain disrupt the older icy ridged plains of Europa as imaged by NASA's Galileo spacecraft. They are caused either by a complete melt-through of Europa's ice shell from an ocean below or by warm ice welling up from below that partially melted the surface ice. Courtesy of NASA/JPL

the icy surface? Discoveries of fish, albino crabs, and 10-foot-long tube worms huddled around active volcanic vents on the Earth's ocean floor far below where the sunlight energy can penetrate has bolstered the view that Europa could harbor life below its icy surface away from sunlight. Before the discovery of life around the geothermal vents, scientists thought that all life depended on sunlight. Bacteria on Earth have been found to exist in rock a few kilometers *below* the sea floor and land surface. Clearly, life is more versatile than originally thought. *Europa is the most likely place in our solar system for current life to exist beyond the Earth, even more likely than Mars.* *life on Europa?* *life at Europa now?*

A spacecraft orbiting Europa could derive the thickness of the ice shell from how much Europa bulges with the changing tides as it orbits Jupiter. A thicker ice shell is stiffer and will not bulge as much as a thin ice shell. The Europa Clipper mission proposed for the 2020s will use an ice penetrating radar to determine the thickness of the moon's icy shell and search for subsurface lakes similar to those beneath Antarctica. Further investigation of the Galileo data shows that there may be large shallow lakes within the top ice layer that could provide a way of exchanging material between the surface and the ocean beneath. That would make Europa more habitable even if the top ice shell is thick. *measuring thickness of ice shell*

The Hubble Telescope detected signs of possible plumes from geysers erupting on Europa in 2012 similar to what we find on Saturn's moon Enceladus but there was quite a bit of uncertainty with the ultraviolet images used to make the claim. A new analysis in 2018 of data collected by the Galileo orbiter's magnetometer in 1997 shows that a brief, localized bend in the magnetic field could be explained by Galileo passing through a geyser plume. The 2018 analysis also shows that the Plasma Wave Spectrometer's measurements of plasma waves from charged particle in gases around Europa's atmosphere could be explained by Galileo passing through a geyser plume. The Europa Clipper could sample the frozen liquid and dust particles by flying through a plume. *Europa plumes?*

Ganymede and Callisto

The largest of the Galilean satellites (and the largest moon in the solar system) is Ganymede. At 5262 km across, Ganymede is larger than Mercury but because Ganymede orbits a planet, it is classified as a moon. Ganymede orbits Jupiter in 7.15 days. Its density of 1.94× water shows that it is made of half rock and half water ice. Its water ice composition enabled it to be more geologically active than Mercury—ice melts and flexes at a lower temperature than rock and metals of the inner terrestrial planets (and the Moon). Ganymede has bright grooved areas with few craters and much older dark area with more craters (see figure next page). The bright, parallel ridges may have been caused by a plate tectonic process that was short-lived. Water may have gushed forth or ice squeezed up between the plate margins. Craters on the parallel ridges and older dark areas indicate that Ganymede's geological activity probably stopped hundreds of millions of years ago. *icy moon still active*

The Galileo spacecraft detected a magnetic field generated by Ganymede itself as well as an induced one from the varying Jupiter magnetic field strength at Ganymede. The internally generated magnetic field is probably generated by convection in a liquid iron core heated by radioactive decay and tidal heating. Ganymede's orbit is kept slightly eccentric because of the 4:2:1 orbit resonance it shares with Europa and Io so the tides do vary in strength. The induced magnetic field is evidence for a liquid water layer. At great enough pressures, water will turn solid. Ganymede's water layer is hundreds of kilometers thick, so the liquid water part would be a thin layer sandwiched between a regular ice sheet above and a high density ice sheet below. That would mean that the liquid water layer would be cut off from any nutrients from the rocky mantle. *Ganymede's magnetic field* *Ganymede water ocean?*

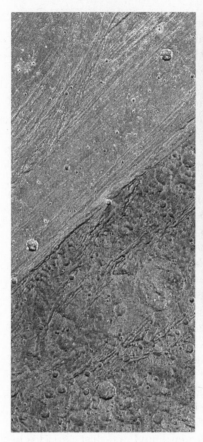 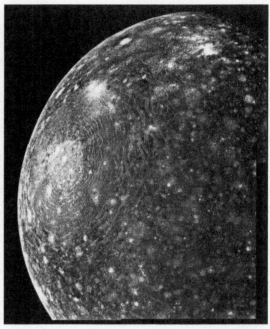

(left) Boundary between an ancient, dark terrain and younger, bright fracture zones (top) on Ganymede. *(right)* The giant impact feature on Callisto called Valhalla (just above center right of the image). Image enhanced to highlight the ripple pattern from the impact. Images courtesy of NASA/JPL

The second largest of the Galilean satellites (4821 km across) and the farthest from Jupiter is the heavily-cratered moon called Callisto. Callisto orbits Jupiter in 16.7 days. It has a density of 1.83× water, so it has proportionally more frozen water surrounding a smaller rocky core than Ganymede. Callisto's surface does not appear to have undergone any sort of geological activity because of the lack of tidal heating. Its interior is partially differentiated—ice layer on top and a rock and ice mixed together core. Callisto has a huge impact site called Valhalla that was produced about 4 billion years ago. When the asteroid hit Callisto, it exploded on impact. The explosion heated the ice to above the melting point and the shock waves produced a ripple pattern away from the impact site. The ripples later froze so Valhalla now looks like a big "bull's eye".

Callisto water ocean?

Callisto has an induced magnetic field, so it may have a salty liquid water ocean layer beneath its ice crust. The side opposite Valhalla shows no grooves or hilly terrain as one would expect for a stiffer material (as for example, what we see on the opposite side of Mercury from its giant Caloris impact basin). A liquid water layer might explain how the shock waves from the Valhalla got dampened out by the time they reached the opposite side of Callisto.

9.7.3   Titan

Saturn's largest satellite (of 60 orbiting Saturn) is the mysterious world called Titan. It has slightly greater diameter (5150 km), density, and mass than Callisto. At 1.22 million kilometers from Saturn, it takes 15.9 days to orbit Saturn. With a density of 1.881× water, Titan is probably half rock, half ice. Careful observations of how the Cassini spacecraft moved in Titan's gravity field (section 9.4 have shown that Titan's interior is only partially differentiated (like Callisto). Below the frozen surface may be an internal ocean of liquid water (or water-ammonia mixture) sandwiched between two thick ice layers surrounding a rock-ice mixture core.

What is special about Titan is that it has a thick atmosphere with a surface air pressure about 1.5 times greater than the Earth's. Even though Titan's mass is even smaller than Mars', it is so cold (just 95 Kelvin) that it has been able to hold on to its primordial atmosphere (see section 9.2.1). The atmosphere is made of cold molecular nitrogen (95%) and methane (about 5%). Other organic molecules have been detected in its atmosphere. They are formed from solar ultraviolet light and high energy particles accelerated by Saturn's magnetic field interacting with the atmospheric nitrogen and methane. The molecules of nitrogen and methane are split apart (photodissociation) and the atoms recombine to make a thick haze layer of mostly ethane that blocks our view of the surface in visible light. When the droplets of the organic molecules get large enough, they rain down to the surface as very dark deposits of liquid methane and ethane. Methane bubbling up from below the surface is thought to replenish the methane lost in its atmosphere from photodissociation. When Voyager 1 and 2 flew by Saturn in the early 1980s, their view of Titan at visible wavelengths showed just an orange fuzz ball because their cameras were tuned to the *wrong* wavelength and they could not peer through the haze layer.

thick atmosphere

Titan revealed: *(left)* Voyager 2 saw only the fuzzy upper layer of Titan's atmosphere. *(right)* Cassini's view at infrared wavelengths revealed the surface. Images courtesy of NASA/JPL

Titan's brew of organic compounds is probably like the early Earth's chemistry. Its very cold temperatures may then have preserved a record of what the early Earth was like before life formed. This possibility and the possibility of lakes or oceans of methane and ethane hidden under a haze of organic compounds made Titan the special subject of a Saturn orbiter mission to follow-up the Voyager fly-by mission. The Cassini spacecraft orbited Saturn for 13 years, flying by its numerous moons including over 100 targeted flybys of Titan. Using infrared wavelengths and radar Cassini was able to peer through the hazy atmosphere. The picture above right is a mosaic of 16 images taken at infrared wavelengths coming from the surface and that pass through the atmosphere easily to Cassini's camera.

Why Titan so important: frozen version of early Earth

Cassini managed to sample particles from the uppermost levels of Titan's atmo-

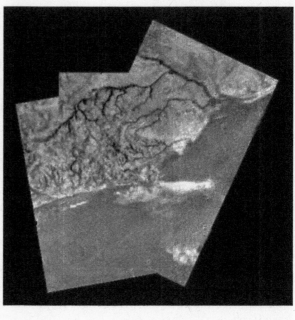

Landing on Titan: *(left)* Titan's surface after the Huygens probe landed on the surface. Titan's rocks are dirty water ice. *(right)* Huygens' view from about 16 km altitude shows methane river drainage channels. Images courtesy of NASA/JPL/ESA/University of Arizona

sphere (many hundreds of kilometers above the surface) and found that there were traces of oxygen in Titan's upper atmosphere, probably from the photodissociation of water escaping Enceladus (see below) into hydrogen and oxygen. The presence of trace amounts of oxygen enables a greater variety of chemical compounds to be made with the energy of sunlight than just nitrogen and methane alone. Scientists simulating the conditions of Titan's upper atmosphere by mixing together simple compounds together under very low densities and bathing them with various wavelength bands of light have been able to create complex organic compounds, and an experiment reported in October 2010 (see the textbook website for the links) produced all five of the nucleotide bases of life (adenine, cytosine, uracil, thymine, and guanine) and two amino acids (glycine and alanine) when a mixture of molecular nitrogen, methane, and carbon monoxide were subjected to microwaves. Early Earth with only trace amounts of oxygen in its atmosphere might have produced the first nucleotides and amino acids in the same way.

Another probe called Huygens, built by the European Space Agency, hitched a ride on Cassini and parachuted down to Titan's surface in January 2005. The "Landing on Titan" figure (left) is Huygen's view from the surface of Titan. The probe settled 10 to 15 centimeters into the surface. The various landscapes of Titan *remarkable Earth simi-* look surprisingly familiar—like landscapes here on Earth. The mechanics of Titan's *larity!* hydrogeological cycle is similar to the Earth's but the chemistry is different: instead of liquid water, Titan has liquid methane and instead of silicate rocks, Titan's rocks are dirty water ice. Liquid methane below the surface is released to the atmosphere to replenish that lost to the formation of the photochemical smog that eventually gets deposited in the soil. Methane rain washes the higher elevations of the dark material and it gets concentrated down in valleys to highlight the river drainage channels (see the right side of the "Landing on Titan" figure). Later images from Cassini revealed huge methane and ethane lakes that change shape, presumably from rainfall of liquid hydrocarbons. Later images showed methane rain falling in the equatorial regions of Titan as spring unfolded in the Saturn system in late 2010. Besides erosion, Titan may have signs of tectonic activity and volcanism (see the textbook's website for links to the evidence). There are, of course, some impact craters but fewer than 100 have been seen—small bodies burn up in Titan's atmosphere and erosion, tectonics, and volcanism erase others. Its icy composition and its eccentric orbit might mean that tidal heating added to radioactive decay are enough to provide the internal heat (recall that water ice melts and flexes at lower temperatures than the rocks of the inner planets).

The montage below includes a radar map of the lakes near the north pole of Titan. They are filled with liquid ethane and methane and are fed from sub-surface seepage and rainfall. Looking a lot like lakes on the Earth, you can see bays, islands, and tributary networks. The large lake at the top of the radar map is larger than Lake Superior on Earth. Kraken Mare, of which a small portion of is visible in the lower left part of the map, is as big as the Caspian Sea on the Earth. There are also lakes near the south pole of Titan.

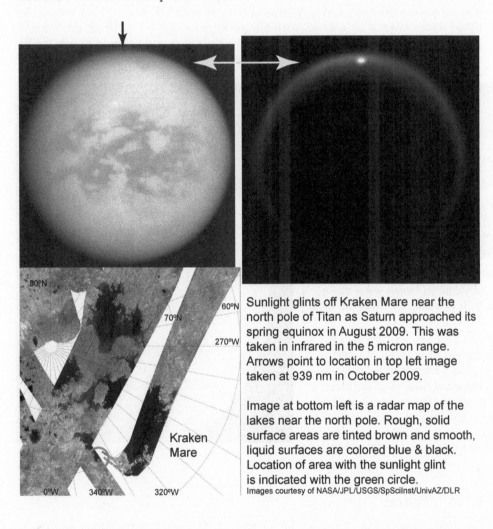

Sunlight glints off Kraken Mare near the north pole of Titan as Saturn approached its spring equinox in August 2009. This was taken in infrared in the 5 micron range. Arrows point to location in top left image taken at 939 nm in October 2009.

Image at bottom left is a radar map of the lakes near the north pole. Rough, solid surface areas are tinted brown and smooth, liquid surfaces are colored blue & black. Location of area with the sunlight glint is indicated with the green circle.
Images courtesy of NASA/JPL/USGS/SpSciInst/UnivAZ/DLR

9.7.4 Enceladus

Enceladus is the fourth largest moon of Saturn at 504 kilometers in diameter. Enceladus orbits 238,000 kilometers from Saturn in 1.37 days. Despite its small size, Enceladus is a moon of large interest because it has the highest albedo of any major moon (1.0) and it is geologically active. Tidal heating supplies only a small amount (about 1/5th) of the internal heat for this moon. Simulations show that if Enceladus has a slight wobble in its rotation of between 0.75 and 2 degrees, the wobbling could generate about five times more heat than tidal heating as well as produce it at the observed locations of greatest heat—in the fissures in its southern hemisphere. Geological activity is helped by Enceladus being mostly ice—its density is 1.61× water. Recall that ices can deform and melt at lower temperatures than silicate and metal rocks.

Enceladus water ocean?

Enceladus has geysers spurting water (vapor and ice) from its south pole that point to a large ocean of liquid water below its icy, mirror-like surface. The geysers can be seen when one is on the other side of Enceladus looking back toward the Sun. The small particles scatter the sunlight forward toward the viewer. Geyser material is able to escape Enceladus and become part of the E-ring of Saturn. Enceladus' activity appears to be localized to the southern hemisphere. Its northern hemisphere has many more craters. Sampling of the geyser material found salts (sodium chloride and potassium chloride) and carbonates mixed in with the water. That means the liquid water layer is in contact with the rocky core instead of being sandwiched

nutrient supply? Life?

between ice layers. If there is an ocean below the icy surface, should Enceladus be another place to look for life besides Europa?

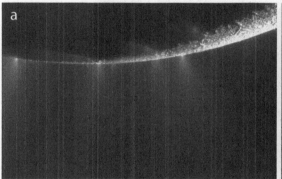

In image a (left) above taken in November 2009, more than 30 individual jets shoot water vapor and ice up hundreds of kilometers from the south pole region.

The south pole region of Enceladus is a stark contrast from regions further north in image b at right. In this enhanced color view, the blue "tiger stripes" stand out. The "tiger stripes" are fissures that spray icy particles, water vapor and organic compounds.
Images courtesy of NASA/JPL/Space Science Institute

9.7.5 Triton

Neptune's large moon, Triton, is about 80% the diameter of the Moon and has a density of 2.1× water. It is probably made of about 75% rock surrounded by a thick layer of frozen water. Triton is even colder than Pluto, about 35 to 40 K. Because of the extremely cold temperatures, nitrogen can be frozen on its surface. On other moons and planets, nitrogen is a gas. Some of the nitrogen on Triton is gaseous and makes up its thin atmosphere. Triton has a young surface with smooth frozen lakes and cantaloupe-textured terrain of unknown cause.

Our Moon compared with Saturn's largest moon (Titan)
and Neptune's largest moon (Triton) all to the same scale.
Images courtesy of NASA/JPL and UCO/Lick Observatory

Triton has many black streaks on its surface that may be from volcanic venting of nitrogen heated to a gaseous state despite the very low temperatures by high internal pressures. The nitrogen fountains are about 8 kilometers high and then move off parallel to the surface by winds in the upper part of its thin atmosphere. Another unusual thing about Triton is its highly inclined orbit (with respect to Neptune's equator). Its circular orbit is retrograde (backward) which means the orbit is decaying—Triton is spiraling into Neptune. Triton's strange orbit and the very elliptical orbit of Neptune's other major moon, Nereid, leads to the proposal that Triton was captured by Neptune when Triton passed too close to it. If it was not captured, Triton was certainly affected by something passing close to the Neptune system.

Triton's strange orbit

9.7.6   Rings

All of the jovian planets have a system of rings. Jupiter has four faint rings: a flattened main ring, a puffier inner ring, and two wispy outer rings that are inside the orbit of Io. The rings are made of very small, dark particles the size of smoke particles. They are produced by dust kicked up from the tiny innermost moons of Jupiter by impacts on the moons.

Saturn's Rings

The planet with the spectacular ring system is Saturn. Icy particles spread out into large, flat rings make up Saturn's ring system that can be seen with even low-power telescopes on the Earth's surface. The rings of the other jovian planets are

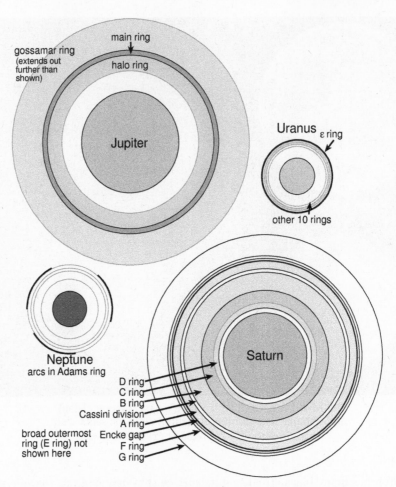

Rings of the jovian planets shown to the same scale

dark and faint, so they were discovered only relatively recently with either powerful telescopes or by spacecraft flybys.

Saturn's rings were discovered by Christian Huygens in 1659. Galileo's telescope was too small to make them look like more than just a couple of bumps on either side of the planet. In 1675 Giovanni Cassini discovered a gap between the two large (A & B) rings, now called the Cassini division in his honor. With improved telescopes, astronomers were able to see that one of the large rings was in fact, two rings (B & C) and there is a gap in the A ring (the Encke division). There is also a hint of another ring closer to the planet than the C ring (the D ring). When the Pioneer and Voyager spacecraft flew by, astronomers found more rings and complex structure in the rings.

The rings that are visible in even low-power telescopes on the Earth (A, B, and C) extend from about 74,000 kilometers to about 137,000 kilometers from Saturn's center (or 1.23 to 2.28 Saturn radii). The rings are very thin, less than a hundred meters thick. A scale model of the rings with the width equal to a single piece of regular paper would be about 100 meters across! Collisions between the ring particles keeps the ring system very flat and all of the particle orbits circular. In 1859 James C. Maxwell (of electromagnetism fame), showed that the rings could not be solid, but, rather a swarm of particles. A solid ring the width of Saturn's

the rings are not solid   ring system would become unstable and break up. James Keeler proved Maxwell correct in 1895 when he measured the doppler shifts of different parts of the rings and found that the outer parts of the ring system orbited at a slower speed than the inner parts. The rings obeyed Kepler's third law and, therefore, must be made of millions of tiny bodies each orbiting Saturn as a tiny mini-moon. Spectroscopy of the rings shows that the particles are made of frozen water.

Computer-generated picture of the particles in
a 3-meter square section of Saturn's A ring.
Image courtesy of NASA/JPL

More recently, astronomers bouncing radar off the rings and analyzing the reflected signal indicated that the ring particles must be from a few centimeters to a few meters across. When the Voyager spacecraft went behind the rings with respect to the Earth, astronomers could measure the particles sizes from how Voyager's radio signal scattered off the particles and from how sunlight scattered through the rings. The Cassini spacecraft that orbited Saturn for 13 years made many such observations. The ring particles range in size from the size of a small grain of sand to the size of a mountain but, on average, they are about the size of your clenched fist.

size and composition of the ring particles

The effect of particle size on how the particles scatter sunlight is nicely illustrated in the iconic image in the middle of the next page as well as in a movie made by Cassini crossing the ring plane from above to below (see the textbook's website). The Sun is behind Saturn and Cassini is in Saturn's shadow.

Very small particles will scatter sunlight forward while larger particles will scatter the sunlight backward. Recall how the very fine dust on the inside of your car's windshield will make it nearly impossible to see through it when you are driving toward the Sun. People on the outside of your car are able to easily see you inside through your windshield because there is not any backscattering of the sunlight. They would have a much harder time seeing you though, if the outside of your windshield was coated with grittier dust and dirt. The Voyager and Pioneer spacecraft confirmed the presence of the inner D ring and discovered two other rings beyond the outer A ring: a narrow F ring just outside the A ring and a broad, but faint E ring. Cassini added another two rings with this image: a ring that shares the same orbit as Janus and Epimetheus and another that shares the same orbit as Pallene. Micro-meteorite impacts on these moons chip off material to feed their namesake rings. The E-ring is supplied by the geysers of Enceladus (see figure three pages over).

The broad rings we see from the Earth are actually systems of thousands of tiny

ringlets each just a few kilometers wide, so the rings look like grooves in a phonograph record (youngsters only familiar with CD's will have to ask their parents or grandparents about them). Voyager also found some unusual things in Saturn's ring system: rings that change shape, eccentric ring shapes (some even twist around each other to make a braid), and dark features that look like spokes extending radially outward across the rings. Cassini studied these features and also discovered features that look like propellers that can get up to several thousand kilometers long (see the figure on the next page). The propellers form by the gravitational interaction of small moonlets in the rings with the surrounding ring material. The moonlets create a wake both behind and in front of the moonlet as it orbits because the ring material nearer Saturn moves faster than the moonlet while the ring material farther from Saturn moves slower.

Saturn's A and B rings are separated by the Cassini Division. The Encke Gap is in the outer part of the A-ring. Darker streaks (spokes) extending across the B-ring are also visible.
Image courtesy of NASA/JPL

The grooved pattern of Saturn's rings are probably the result of *spiral density waves* forming from the mutual gravitational attraction of the ring particles. Narrow gaps in the rings are most likely swept clean of particles by small moonlets embedded in the rings. The tiny moons can also act as *shepherd satellites*. Two shepherd satellites with one orbiting slightly outside the other satellite's orbit can constrain or shepherd the ring particles to stay between the moonlet orbits. The narrow F ring is the result of two shepherd satellites, Pandora and Prometheus, between 80 and 100 kilometers across with orbits about 1000 kilometers on either side of the F ring. Prometheus and Pandora also responsible for the braids and kinks in the F ring. The dark drapes in the image below were created by Prometheus as its gravity tugged on F ring material at its closest approach to the F ring.

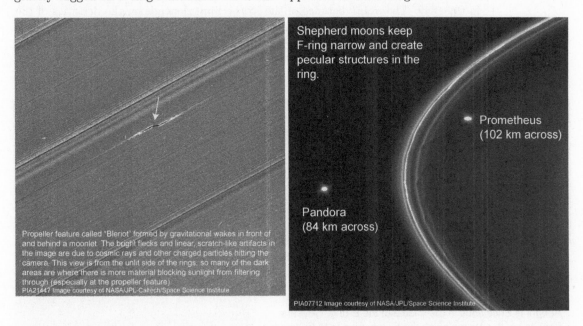

Propeller feature called "Bleriot" formed by gravitational wakes in front of and behind a moonlet. The bright flecks and linear, scratch-like artifacts in the image are due to cosmic rays and other charged particles hitting the camera. This view is from the unlit side of the rings, so many of the dark areas are where there is more material blocking sunlight from filtering through (especially at the propeller feature). PIA21447 Image courtesy of NASA/JPL-Caltech/Space Science Institute

Shepherd moons keep F-ring narrow and create pecular structures in the ring.

Prometheus (102 km across)

Pandora (84 km across)

PIA07712 Image courtesy of NASA/JPL/Space Science Institute

Bigger gaps in the rings (such as the Cassini division) are the result of gravitational **resonances** with the moons of Saturn. A **resonance** happens when one object has an orbital period that is a small-integer fraction of another body's orbital period, e.g., 1/2, 2/3, etc. The object gets a periodic gravitational tug at the same point in its orbit. Just as you can get a swing to increase the size of its oscillation by pushing it at the same point in its swing arc, a resonance can "pump up" the orbital motion of an object. Particles at the inner edge of the Cassini division are in a one-two resonance with the moon called Mimas—they orbit twice for every one orbit of Mimas. The repeated pulls by Mimas on the Cassini division particles, always in the same direction in space, force them into new orbits outside the gap. Other resonances with Mimas are responsible for other features in Saturn's rings: the boundary between the C and B ring is at the 1:3 resonance and the outer edge of the A ring is at the 2:3 resonance. It is amazing what a simple inverse square law force can do!

The dark spokes in Saturn's B ring were a surprise. The different orbital speeds of the ring particles should quickly shear apart any radial structure in the rings, but the spokes clearly survived the shearing! The spokes are probably caused by very tiny dust particles hovering just above the rings by their interaction with Saturn's magnetic field or by electrostatic forces created from ring particle collisions.

Where did the rings of Saturn come from? Studies of the various forces on the ring particles show that the rings are transient—they did not form with Saturn as part of the formation of the main planet, nor will they always be there. Cassini's measurements of the mass of the rings and the rate that dust is accumulating on them to darken them indicate a young age of only about 100 to 200 million years (though the estimates are uncertain). Another study combining results from

shepherd satellites

resonance

spokes

origin of Saturn's rings

Cassini, the Voyager 1 and 2 flybys in the early 1980s and ground-based telescope observations has found Saturn's rings are being drained of material as a dusty rain falls from the rings into Saturn's atmosphere at a rate that means the rings will be gone in about 100 million years. Furthermore, if the observed rate of rain has been the same as today, then the C-ring would have been as dense as the B-ring just 100 million years ago—we're seeing the rings at their mid-life.

The rings of Saturn are within the distance at which a large moon would experience extreme enough tidal stretching to be torn apart. This distance is called the **Roche limit**, after M.E. Roche who developed the theory of tidal break up in the 1849. The exact distance of the Roche limit depends on the densities of the planet and close-approaching moon and how strongly the material of the moon is held together. The classical Roche limit considers a moon held together only by its internal gravity. Such a moon would break up at a distance of about 2.44 planetary radii from the center of the planet.

Roche limit: $2.44\,R_p$

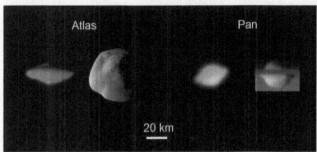

Ring material clumping together can make moonlets with significant equatorial ridges. No, these are not flying saucer spacecraft!

At right is Enceladus in the middle of the E-ring. Geysers from its south pole replenish the E-ring. Also note Enceladus' shadow across the E-ring.

All images courtesy of NASA/JPL/Space Science Institute

Saturn's rings lie within Saturn's Roche limit so it is likely that they were formed by particles too close to Saturn to ever form a large moon. The fact that all of the jovian planets have rings argues against the breakup of a large moon spiraling in toward Saturn from a rare encounter with an object passing through the moon system. (Maybe it could happen with one planet, but with all four jovians?) Another possibility is that large collisions on the large moons outside the Roche limit spewed material into the region inside the Roche limit. One variation of this involves the sun's gravity perturbing small moons inside of Rhea's orbit and getting them to violently collide and break apart. Material from the smashup outside the Roche limit coalesced to form the inner moons while material inside the Roche limit formed the rings. However, that means the inner moons, Enceladus, Dione, and Mimas would have to be just 200 million years old (assuming the ring age given above) and their complex, cratered surfaces appear to be much older than that.

Small moonlets are able to exist in the rings because the tidal stretching across their small diameters are too small. Tidal forces will prevent them from getting large. Collisions among themselves and micro-meteorite impacts can replenish a ring. Some the ring material may be able to clump together to create the moonlets and that may be why some of the moonlets have significant equatorial ridges to make them look like "flying saucers". Saturn's E ring lies outside Saturn's Roche limit and is most concentrated at the orbit of the icy moon, Enceladus. Eruptions of water vapor from Enceladus are the source of the E ring material.

Rings of the jovian planets *scaled to size of the planet*. The distances are from the planet center in units of the planet radius. The classical Roche limit for a moon of equal density as the planet is shown as the dashed line at 2.44 planet radii.

The Rings of Uranus and Neptune

Uranus' rings were discovered in 1977 from measuring the intensity of light from a star as Uranus passed in front of it. Astronomers were originally intending to learn about Uranus' atmosphere from how the light passed through the top cloud layers and to measure both the diameter of Uranus and the star accurately from timings of when the star was totally blocked. They noticed that the star blinked off and on before Uranus itself passed in front of the star. The star also blinked off and on after Uranus itself had moved out of the way. The symmetry of the winking out of the star as the rings passed in front of the star pointed to their existence. Later infrared observations gave astronomers more information about them. Neptune's rings were discovered in the same way a few years after the Uranus' rings discovery. Voyager 2 gave a much better view of the rings when it flew by Uranus in 1986 and Neptune in 1989.

The rings of Uranus and Neptune are much darker than Saturn's rings, reflecting only a few percent of what little sunlight reaches them (they are darker than pieces of black, burned wood) while Saturn's rings reflect over 70% of the Sun's light. The rings are also much narrower than Saturn's rings. Uranus' outermost and most massive ring, called the Epsilon Ring, is only about 100 kilometers wide and probably less than 100 meters thick. The other ten dark and narrow rings have a combined mass less than the Epsilon Ring. The six rings of Neptune are less significant than Uranus' and the ring particles are not uniformly distributed in the rings. Like Saturn's F ring, the rings of Uranus and Neptune are kept narrow by shepherd satellites. The narrowness and even clumpiness of the rings means that the rings can last for only a short time—a million years or so, unless the rings are replenished by material ejected off the moons in large collisions.

Vocabulary

giant impact theory   mare   resonance
Roche limit

Review Questions

1. What do the **mare** look like on the Moon and why are they so smooth?

2. Why does the Moon not have erosion?

3. What *two* reasons explain why the Moon is geologically dead?

4. How can you use the number of craters to determine the age of a planet's or moon's surface?

5. The lunar highlands have about ten times more craters on a given area than do the maria. Does this mean that the highlands are ten times older? Explain your reasoning.

6. In what ways are the Moon and Mercury like each other? In what ways are they different from each other?

7. In what ways are the Moon and the Earth like each other? In what ways are they different from each other?

8. In what ways is the **giant impact theory** better at explaining the formation of the Moon than other Moon formation theories?

9. Why is Io such a geologically-active moon? Describe how its interior is kept molten.

10. What is the interior of Europa like?

11. What is so unusual about Europa's surface?

12. Why is Europa another good place to look for life beyond the Earth?

13. What are four lines of evidence for a liquid water ocean below Europa's surface? Which line is shared with Ganymede and Callisto?

14. What causes the parallel ridges on Ganymede?

15. What about the compositions of the jovian planets' moons enable them to be geologically active despite their small size?

16. What is Callisto like and how do you know the age of its surface?

17. How do we know that Ganymede and Callisto might have a liquid water layer?

18. Compare/contrast Titan with our Moon (size, mass, surface conditions, etc.)

19. What is so special about Titan?

20. What is Titan's atmosphere made of and why is it so thick?

21. How is Titan probably like the early Earth?

22. In what ways is Titan like Earth today?

23. What is a recent surprising discovery about Enceladus? Why is it another possible place to look for life beyond the Earth?

24. How cold is Triton and what is it made of?

25. Is Triton's surface young or old and what causes some of Triton's strange surface features?

26. What is unusual about Triton's orbit?

27. What are Saturn's rings made of and how do we know?

28. How do we know the sizes of the particles in Saturn's rings?

29. How are grooves and gaps made in the rings of Saturn?

30. What unusual things were found in Saturn's rings and what are the likely causes?

31. What formed the rings of Saturn and when were they made?

32. Compare/contrast the rings of Uranus and Neptune with Saturn's rings.

This a flowchart summary of the process of the escape of planet atmospheres.

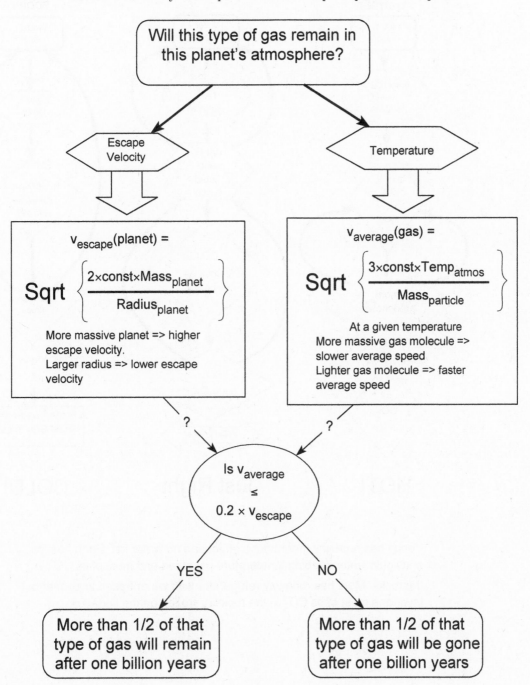

This is a flowchart summary of the histories of the terrestrial planet atmospheres. The chart for Venus up to the dashed arrow describes the runaway greenhouse process that occurred several hundred million to a few billion years ago. The bottom diamond describes the current condition. The chart for Mars up to the dashed arrow describes the runaway refrigerator process that happened a LONG time ago. The bottom rectangle describes the current condition. The chart for the Earth describes the carbon dioxide cycle as it currently operates. The Earth exists balanced between the two extremes of Venus and Mars.

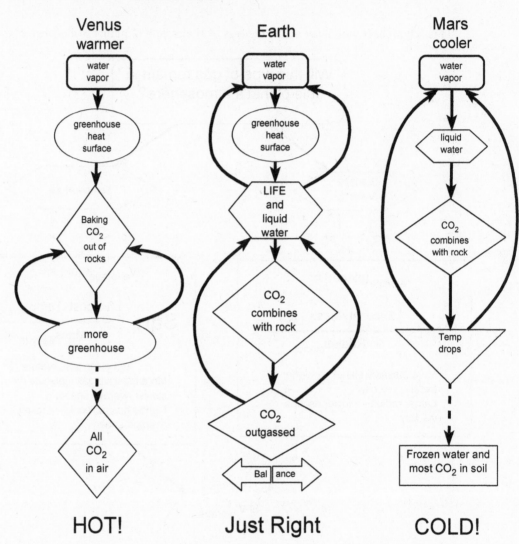

Venus has runaway greenhouse effect and no water left. Earth has life and liquid water keeping temperature balanced and most of its CO_2 in the rocks. Mars has runaway refrigerator with water frozen in permafrost layer and most of its CO_2 in the rocks or frozen on the surface.

Chapter 10

Solar System Fluff

This chapter covers all of the solar system that is not the planets or the Sun: meteorites, asteroids, and comets. I group them all together as "solar system fluff" because the objects are much smaller than planets and most moons. The "fluff" may be small in size but certainly not in importance. We get clues of the origin of the solar system from these small objects. The chapter will end with the current model for the formation of the solar system and explorations of other planetary systems. The vocabulary terms are in boldface.

10.1 Asteroids

There are millions of boulder-size and larger rocks that orbit the Sun, most of them between the orbits of Mars and Jupiter. Some asteroids called *Trojan asteroids* travel in or near Jupiter's orbit about 60 degrees ahead of Jupiter and 60 degrees behind Jupiter (gravity balance points between Jupiter and the Sun). Some asteroids have orbits that bring them close to Earth's orbit, some even crossing the Earth's orbit. These are called *Near-Earth Asteroids (NEA)* and include some 1947 (at the time of writing) "Potentially Hazardous Asteroids" with the greatest potential of very close approaches to Earth. Comets that get near the Earth and NEA are lumped together into *Near-Earth Objects (NEO)*. A link to a plot of the currently known asteroids is given on the textbook's website.

About one million of them are larger than 1 kilometer across. Those smaller than about 300 kilometers across have irregular shapes because their internal gravity is not strong enough to compress the rock into a spherical shape. The largest asteroid is Ceres with a diameter of 1000 kilometers. Pallas and Vesta have diameters of about 500 kilometers and about 15 others have diameters larger than 250 kilometers. The number of asteroids shoots up with decreasing size. The combined mass of all of the asteroids is about 25 times *less* than the Moon's mass (with Ceres making up over a third of the total). Very likely the asteroids are pieces that would have formed a planet if Jupiter's strong gravity had not stirred up the material between Mars and Jupiter. The rocky chunks collided at speeds too high to stick together and grow into a planet.

Though there are over a million asteroids, the volume of space they inhabit is very large, so they are far apart from one another. Unlike the movie *The Empire Strikes Back* and other space movies, where the spacecrafts flying through an asteroid belt could not avoid crashing into them, real asteroids are at least tens of thousands of kilometers apart from each other. Spacecraft sent to the outer planets have travelled through the asteroid belt with no problems (and no swerving about).

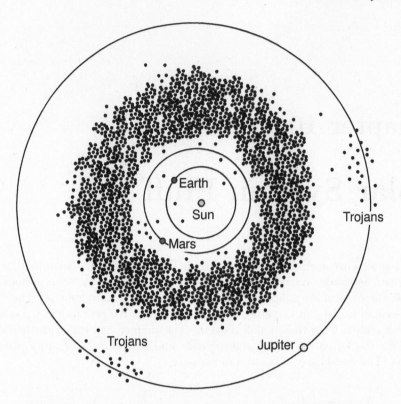

Millions of small rocks lie between Jupiter and Mars in the asteroid belt. The Trojan asteroids are about 60° in front of and behind Jupiter. The orbits of Mercury and Venus are not shown here. Note that some of the asteroid orbits cross the Earth's orbit!

There are several possible ways of grouping asteroids. Astronomers use schemes of varying complexities based on composition, orbit characteristics or some combination of both. The simplest way puts them into three basic types based on their composition:

asteroid types: C, S, M

1. *C*: they are carbonaceous—made of silicate materials with a lot of carbon compounds so they appear very dark. They reflect only 3 to 4% of the sunlight hitting them. You can tell what they are made of by analyzing the spectra of sunlight reflecting off of them. This reflectance spectra shows that they are **primitive**, unchanged since they first solidified about 4.6 billion years ago. A great majority of the asteroids are of this type. The asteroid called Mathilde, explored by the NEAR spacecraft; possibly Lutetia (either C or M-type), explored by the Rosetta spacecraft; near-Earth asteroid Bennu, orbited by OSIRIS-REx; near-Earth asteroid Ryugu, orbited by Hayabusa2; and Ceres, orbited by Dawn for two years are are examples of this type (see picture next page). Mars' moons, Phobos and Deimos, are captured C-type asteroids.

primitive

2. *S*: they are made of silicate materials without the dark carbon compounds so they appear brighter than the C types. They reflect about 15 to 20% of the sunlight hitting them. Most of them appear to be primitive. Although S types make up a smaller fraction of the asteroids than the C types, most of the asteroids that have been visited by spacecraft so far have been the S-type: Gaspra and Ida/Dactyl, explored by the Galileo spacecraft on its way to Jupiter; Eros, orbited by the NEAR spacecraft for a year; Steins, visited by Rosetta; Annefrank, visited by Stardust on its way to Comet Wild; Braille, visited by Deep Space 1; Itokawa, orbited by Hayabusa (see below

for more details), the near-Earth asteroid Toutatis, visited by China's lunar probe Chang'e 2 during one of Toutatis' regular four-year close fly-bys of the Earth in 2012 (see picture next page); and Vesta, orbited by Dawn for a year.

3. *M*: they are made of metals like iron and nickel. These rare type of asteroids are brighter than the S and C types. They are thought to be the remains of the cores of **differentiated** objects such as Vesta and Ceres. Large objects were hot enough in the early solar system so that they were liquid. This allowed the dense materials like iron and nickel to sink to the center while the lighter material like ordinary silicate rock floated up to the top. Smaller objects cooled off quicker than larger objects, so they underwent less differentiation. In the early solar system, collisions were much more common and some of the differentiated large asteroids collided with one another, breaking them apart and exposing their metallic cores. Lutetia may be an M-type asteroid.

differentiated

Some of the asteroids that have been visited by spacecraft are shown in the figure below all to the same scale. Tiny Itokawa is about 0.5 kilometers along its long axis so it is just a speck in the picture. Lutetia is about 130 kilometers in diameter and Vesta is about 530 kilometers in diameter.

Note their irregular shapes! Small bodies can have irregular shapes because their gravity is too weak to crush the material into the most compact shape possible: a sphere. Depending on the strength of the material of which they are made, the largest non-spherical asteroids (and moons) can have diameters of roughly 360 to 600 kilometers. Planets are much too large (have too much gravity) to be anything but round. Ceres, the largest asteroid, is large enough to be round and is now re-classified as a "dwarf planet" (along with Pluto, Charon, Eris, Haumea, and Makemake—see section 10.6.2).

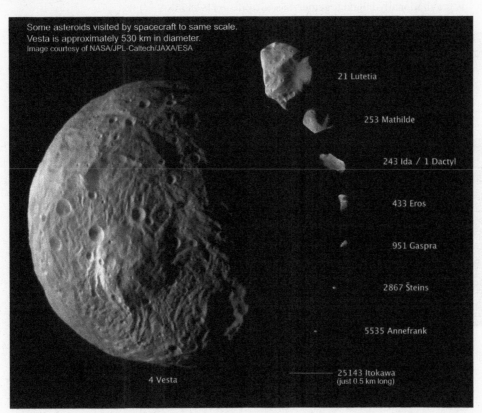

Some asteroids visited by spacecraft to same scale. Vesta is approximately 530 km in diameter. Image courtesy of NASA/JPL-Caltech/JAXA/ESA

21 Lutetia
253 Mathilde
243 Ida / 1 Dactyl
433 Eros
951 Gaspra
2867 Šteins
5535 Annefrank
25143 Itokawa (just 0.5 km long)
4 Vesta

The Japanese Aerospace Exploration Agency launched a spacecraft called Hayabusa to land and extract a sample from Itokawa, a small near-Earth S-type asteroid only half a kilometer in length (535 x 294 x 209 meters). Hayabusa collected at least one sample from the asteroid's surface and returned to Earth in June 2010. At the top of the next page are images of Itokawa from Hayabusa when it was just 7 kilometers from the asteroid. It has a rough surface but very few impact craters. Itokawa is basically a rubble pile formed by the ejecta from a large impact on a larger object coming back together gravitationally. Its composition is very much like the chondrite meteorites with little iron or other metals. JAXA followed up with Hayabusa2 that was sent to Ryugu, a near-Earth C-type asteroid about 865 meters across. Hayabusa2 reached Ryugu in late July 2018 and deployed several small landers in October 2018. Hayabusa2 will collect three samples from Ryugu in 2019 and return them to Earth in December 2020, including one sample from inside a crater created by shooting a copper projectile into Ryugu, so we can get a sample from Ryugu's interior.

Two sides of the asteroid Itokawa, an S-type near-Earth asteroid about 535 x 294 x 209 meters in size. It is probably the result of rubble from an impact on a larger object that is gravitationally bound together. Images courtesy of ISAS/JAXA

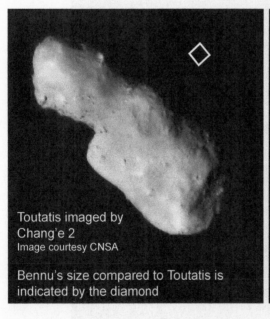

Toutatis imaged by
Chang'e 2
Image courtesy CNSA

Bennu's size compared to Toutatis is
indicated by the diamond

Bennu imaged by OSIRIS-REx
Image courtesy NASA/Goddard/University of Arizona

Above are the near-Earth asteroids Toutatis imaged by the Chinese lunar probe Chang'e 2 and Bennu imaged by OSIRIS-REx. Toutatis was imaged from a distance of just 93 kilometers away, though the spacecraft got to within 3.2 kilometers at closest approach. Toutatis was about 6.9 million kilometers from the Earth when it passed by us in December 2012. Toutatis is 4.5 x 2.4 x 1.9 kilometers in size and like Itokawa, it is probably a rubble pile from the merging of two bodies. The size comparison of Bennu (just 524 meters in diameter) to Toutatis is indicated by the diamond to the upper right of Toutatis. Toutatis passes close to the Earth approximately every four years. The next time it will pass even closer will be in November 2069 but at a still safe distance of 3 million kilometers (7.7 lunar distances).

The Bennu image is from a distance of 24 kilometers. Two large boulders on the southern limb of Bennu are clearly visible. Like Itokawa, Bennu is a rubble pile that formed from one or more breakups in its history but its shape is like Ryugu's (though half the size of Ryugu). Bennu is rich in carbon, organic molecules, and hydrated minerals. Bennu comes very close to Earth every six years and there is a 0.037% of hitting Earth between 2175 and 2199. From an orbit less than two kilometers from Bennu's center, OSIRIS-REx will do very high-resolution mapping and spectroscopy of Bennus surface and its gravity field to determine Bennus interior structure as well as finding the best spot to extract a sample to return to Earth. This intense scrutiny of Bennu before collecting a sample will take about a year and half. In July 2020 OSIRIS-REx will make up to three attempts to collect between 60 grams and 2 kilograms of Bennu material. Further study of Bennu will follow until the window for departing Bennu opens in March 2021. OSIRIS-REx will arrive back at Earth in September 2023 to return the sample.

In late September 2007, NASA launched the Dawn spacecraft to explore the two largest asteroids, Ceres (about 960 km in diameter) and Vesta (530 km in diameter), originally for about six months at each asteroid (Dawn's time at Vesta was extended to a full year). Vesta was explored from August 2011 to August 2012. Dawn the traveled across the asteroid belt for 2.5 years and arrived at Ceres in February 2015. Dawn explored Ceres until November 2018 when it ran out of propellant to keep its radio antenna pointed at Earth. Dawn remains in orbit around Ceres. will be explored from February 2015 to July 2015. Below are the best pictures we have of these asteroids and how they compare to the much smaller Eros asteroid that was explored by the NEAR Shoemaker spacecraft. The Dawn spacecraft's primary goal was to help us figure out the role of size and water in determining the evolution of the planets. Ceres is a primitive and relatively wet protoplanet while Vesta has changed since its formed and is now very dry. At nearly the same distance from the Sun, why did these two bodies become very different?

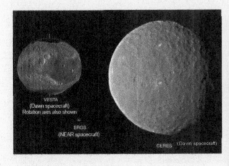

Ceres (960 km diameter) and Vesta (530 km diameter) are the two largest asteroids. Ceres is large enough to be considered a "dwarf planet". Dawn explored Vesta from August 2011 to August 2012 and Ceres from February 2015 to November 2018. Though they are large for an asteroid, they are considerably smaller than a planet as shown on the right.

Some initial findings from Dawn about Vesta include: Vesta once had a subsurface magma ocean—when Vesta was almost completely melted. It has a differentiated interior or a crust, mantle, and core. Dawn confirmed that three classes of meteorites used by meteorite scientists (howardite, eucrite and diogenite meteorites) do in fact come from Vesta. Those types of meteorites account for about 6 percent of all meteorites falling on Earth, making Vesta one of the largest single sources for Earth's meteorites. Vesta does have some minerals that are chemically bound with water ("hydrated minerals") and much of the water was originally delivered as part of Vesta's formation over a small time-frame, rather than primarily as a result of comet collisions later in its history as what produced the water ice found in sheltered craters at the poles of the Moon and Mercury always shut off from sunlight. Vesta also has some very dark patches from impacts with carbon-rich asteroids.

Vesta's topography is steeper and more varied than originally expected. Some of the crater walls are almost vertical instead of sloped like those on the Earth, Moon, and other worlds. It has a huge central peak in one of its impact basins that is much higher and wider, relative to crater size, than the central peaks of craters found on other bodies in the solar system. Two of the largest impact basins on Vesta are much younger than the impact basins found on the Moon. That's geologically speaking, of course. The youngest impact basin on Vesta is about a billion years old while the Moon's impact basins, including the ones making the dark, smooth maria are about 3.8 billion years old. Some of the craters have short, wide, straight gullies in the crater walls formed from flows of sand-like material and some gullies that are much longer, narrower, and curvier than would be formed from sand-like material flowing downward. Such sinuous gullies on the Earth are carved by liquid water and those on Mars are from water, carbon dioxide, or other mechanism. Clearly, the geology of Vesta is more complex than originally thought!

Ceres was originally an ocean world where ammonia and water reacted with silicate rocks (about 25% of its mass is ice). When Ceres cooled and froze, the carbonates and other salts concentrated into deposits that are now exposed in locations across the surface, including the very bright spots in Occator Crater.

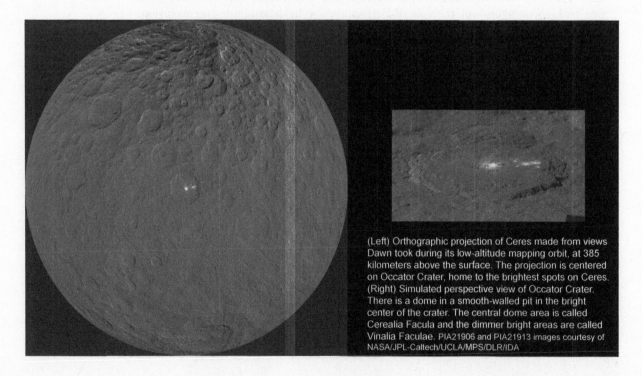

(Left) Orthographic projection of Ceres made from views Dawn took during its low-altitude mapping orbit, at 385 kilometers above the surface. The projection is centered on Occator Crater, home to the brightest spots on Ceres. (Right) Simulated perspective view of Occator Crater. There is a dome in a smooth-walled pit in the bright center of the crater. The central dome area is called Cerealia Facula and the dimmer bright areas are called Vinalia Faculae. PIA21906 and PIA21913 images courtesy of NASA/JPL-Caltech/UCLA/MPS/DLR/IDA

Ceres also has organic molecules on its surface. Ceres has a strong crust made of hydrated salts, rocks, and clathrates on top of a differentiated interior. Ceres also appears to have recent, maybe ongoing, geologic activity despite its small size. Perhaps the salts enable some of the interior water to remain liquid. The presence of ammonia on Ceres suggests that Ceres might have originally come from the outer solar system and then got its orbit changed from the reshuffling events that happened in the early solar system (see section 10.8 for more about that). More discoveries will happen as scientists pore over all of the data beamed back to Earth by Dawn.

A few other asteroids have surfaces made of basalt from volcanic lava flows. When asteroids collide with one another, they can chip off pieces from each other. Some of those pieces, called *meteoroids* if they are less than a meter in size, can get close to the Earth and be pulled toward the Earth by its gravity.

meteoroid

10.2 Meteorites

The quick flashes of light in the sky most people call "shooting stars" are *meteors*— pieces of rock glowing from friction with the atmosphere as they plunge toward the surface at speeds around 20 to 40 kilometers/second. Before the rock hits the Earth's atmosphere it called a *meteoroid*. Most of the meteors you see are about the size of a grain of sand and burn up at altitudes above 50 kilometers (in the mesosphere). If the chunk of rock is a meter or larger in size, it is called an asteroid. Large meteors and asteroids can make the much brighter "fireballs" that may even briefly rival the brightness of the Sun. More meteors are seen after midnight because your local part of the Earth is facing the direction of its orbital motion around the Sun. Meteoroids moving at any speed can hit the atmosphere. Before midnight your local part of the Earth is facing away from the direction of orbital motion, so only the fastest moving meteoroids can catch up to the Earth and hit the atmosphere. The same sort of effect explains why an automobile's front windshield will get plastered with insects while the rear windshield stays clean.

meteor

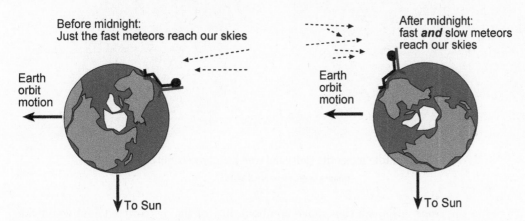

If the little piece of rock makes it to the surface without burning up, it is called a **meteorite**. As with the asteroids, there are many ways of grouping meteorites. Just as was done for the asteroids, you can group the meteorites into three basic types based on their composition.

meteorite

1. *Stones*: they are made of silicate material with a density around 3 times that of water and look like ordinary Earth rocks. This makes them hard to distinguish from Earth rocks so they do not stand out. About 95% to 97% of

types of meteorites

primitive
chondrules

the meteorites are of these type. About 85% of the stones are **primitive,** unchanged since they first solidified about 4.6 billion years ago. Most of the primitive stones have **chondrules**—round glassy structures 0.5 to 5 millimeters across embedded in the meteorites. They are solidified droplets of matter from the early solar nebula and are the oldest part of a primitive meteorite.

carbonaceous mete-
orites

The oldest of the stone meteorites are the **carbonaceous meteorites.** They contain silicates, carbon compounds (giving them their dark color), and a surprisingly large amount of water (about 22% of their mass). They are probably chips of C-type asteroids. Some of the carbonaceous meteorites have organic molecules called amino acids. Amino acids can be connected together to form proteins that are used in the biological processes of life. There is the possibility that meteorites like these may have been the seeds of life on the Earth. In addition, these type of meteorites may have provided the inner planets with a lot of water. The terrestrial planets may have been so hot when they formed that most of the water in them at formation evaporated away to space. The impact of millions to billions of carbonaceous meteorites (and comets, section 10.5) in the early solar system may have replenished the water supply on the terrestrial planets.

About 10% to 12% of the stones are from the crust of differentiated parent objects. Therefore, they are younger (only 4.4 billion years old). The lighter-colored stones are chips from the S-type of asteroids.

2. *Stoney-Irons*: only 1% of the meteorites are of this type. They have a variable mixture of metal (iron and nickel) and rock (silicates) and have densities ranging from 4 to 6 times that of water. They come from a differentiated object at the boundary between the metal core and the rock crust or from objects that were only partially differentiated. They are 4.4 billion years old.

Chondrite meteorite (left) and iron meteorite (right).
Images courtesy of NASA/JPL

3. *Irons*: although they make up about 40% of the meteorites found worldwide, only 2 to 3% of the meteorites are these type. They make up so many of the ones found because they are easily distinguished from Earth rocks. They are noticeably denser than Earth rocks, they have a density around 7 times that of water. They come from the core of a differentiated body and are made of iron and nickel. They are 4.4 billion years old. Irons sometimes have large, coarse-grained crystalline patterns ("Widmanstatten patterns") that is evidence that they cooled *slowly*.

The primitive meteorites are probably the most important ones because they hold clues to the composition and temperature in various parts of the early solar nebula.

Because of this, some astronomers put the meteorites into two groups: primitive and processed (not primitive).

10.2.1 Finding Meteorites

Most stoneys look like Earth rocks and so they are hard to spot. The rare irons are easy to distinguish from Earth rocks and make up most of the ones found worldwide. Usually the meteorites that science museums show off are iron meteorites. Not only does their high density and metal composition set them apart from ordinary rocks, the iron meteorites are stronger. This means they will more likely survive the passage through the atmosphere in one piece to make impressive museum displays. The stone meteorites are more fragile and will break up into several pieces (less impressive for museum displays).

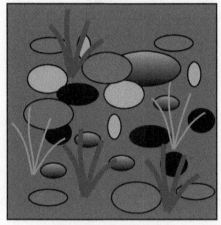
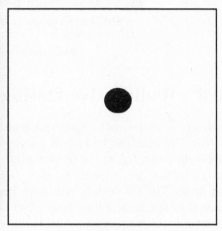
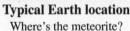

Typical Earth location   **Antarctica**
Where's the meteorite?   Where's the meteorite?

To get an accurate number for the proportion of meteorites that fall to the Earth (an *unbiased sample*), meteorite searchers go to a place where all types of rocks will stand out. The best place to go is Antarctica because the stable, white ice pack makes darker meteorites easy to find. Meteorites that fell thousands of years ago can still be found in Antarctica without significant weathering. Since the 1980s, thousands of meteorites have come from here. For further exploration, check out the *Antarctica Meteorite* website at the *Planetary Materials Curation* office of NASA. Links are given on the textbook's website.

look in Antarctica for un-biased sample

Most (99.8%) meteorites are pieces of asteroids, but 143 (at the time of writing) are from the Moon. A select few (125 at the time of writing), the Shergotty-Nakhla-Chassigny (SNC) meteorites, *may* be from Mars. The relative abundances of magnesium and heavy nitrogen (N-15) gases trapped inside the SNC meteorites is similar to the martian atmosphere as measured by the Viking landers and unlike any meteorites from the asteroids or Moon. Also, the isotope ratios of argon and xenon gas trapped in the meteorites most closely resemble the martian atmosphere and are different than the typical meteorite. The analysis of the soil and rocks by the *Mars Pathfinder* confirm this.

martian meteorites

Most SNC meteorites are about 1.4 Gyr old, but the one with *suggestions* of extinct martian life is about 4.5 Gyr old. Recent studies of the meteorite have cast considerable doubt on the initial claims for fossil microbes in the rock. There is strong evidence of contamination by organic molecules from Earth, so this meteorite does not provide the conclusive proof hoped for. Links to detailed descriptions of SNC meteorites are found on the textbook's website.

A SNC meteorite (piece blasted from Mars that fell to Earth).

Image courtesy of NASA/JPL

10.3   Radioactive Dating

There are several ways to figure out relative ages, that is, if one thing is older than another. For example, looking at a series of layers in the side of a cliff, the younger layers will be on top of the older layers. Or you can tell that certain parts of the Moon's surface are older than other parts by counting the number of craters per unit area. The old surface will have many craters per area because it has been exposed to space for a long time. But how old is "old"? If you assume that the impact rate has been constant for the past several billion years, then the number of craters will be proportional to how long the surface is exposed. However, the crater number relation must be calibrated against something with a known age.

To measure the passage of long periods of time, scientists take advantage of a regularity in certain unstable atoms. In radioactive atoms the nucleus will spontaneously change into another type of nucleus. When looking at a large number of these atoms, you see that a certain fraction of them will change or *decay* in a certain amount of time that depends on the type of atom—more specifically, the type of nucleus. **Radioactive dating** is an *absolute* dating system because you can determine accurate ages from the number of remaining radioactive atoms in a rock sample. Most of the radioactive **isotopes** used for radioactive dating of rock samples have too many neutrons in the nucleus to be stable.

radioactive dating

isotope

Recall from section 7.4 that an **isotope** is a particular form of an element. All atoms of an element have the same number of protons in their nucleus and behave the same way in *chemical* reactions. The atoms of an **isotope** of a given element have same number of protons AND neutrons in their nucleus. Different isotopes of a given element will have the same chemistry but behave differently in *nuclear* reactions. In a radioactive decay, the original radioactive isotope is called a *parent isotope* and the resulting isotope after the decay is called a *daughter isotope*. For example, Uranium-238 is the parent isotope that breaks apart to form the daughter isotope Lead-204.

10.3.1   Radioactive Dating Method

Radioactive isotopes will decay in a regular exponential way such that one-half of a given amount of parent material will decay to form daughter material in a time period called a **half-life**. A **half-life** is NOT one-half the age of the rock! When

half-life

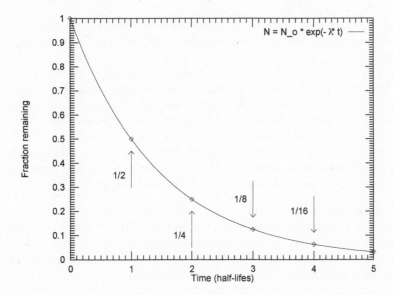

the material is liquid or gaseous, the parent and daughter isotopes can escape, but when the material solidifies, they cannot escape so the ratio of parent to daughter isotopes is frozen in. The parent isotope can only decay, increasing the amount of daughter isotopes. Radioactive dating gives the *solidification age*. When the rock melts, the radioactive dating "clock" gets reset.

There are two simple steps for radioactive dating:

1. Find out how many times you need to multiply (1/2) by itself to get the observed fraction of remaining parent material. Let the number of the times be n. For example $1/8 = (1/2) \times (1/2) \times (1/2)$, so $n = 3$. The number n is the number of **half-lives** the sample has been decaying. If some material has been decaying long enough so that only 1/4 radioactive material is left, the sample is 2 half-lives old: $1/4 = (1/2) \times (1/2)$, $n = 2$.

2. The age of the sample in years $= n \times$ (one half-life in years).

How do you do that?

If 1/8 of the original amount of parent isotope is left in a
radioactive sample, how old is the sample? *Answer:* After 1 half-life, there is 1/2 of original amount of the parent left. After another half-life, there is 1/2 of that 1/2 left = $1/2 \times 1/2 = 1/4$ of the original amount of the parent left. After yet another half-life, there is 1/2 of that 1/4 left = $1/2 \times 1/2 \times 1/2 = 1/8$ of the original amount of the parent left (which is the fraction asked for). So the rock is 1 half-life + 1 half-life + 1 half-life = 3 half-lives old. To get the age in years, simply multiply 3 by the number of years in one half-life.

If you have a fraction that is not a multiple of 1/2, then it is more complicated: The age = [ln(original amount of parent material/current amount of parent material) / ln(2)] × (half-life in years), where ln() is the "natural logarithm" (it is the "ln" key on a scientific calculator).

10.3.2 If Amount of Original Is Not Known

There are always a few astronomy students who ask me the good question (and many others who are too shy to ask), "what if you don't know the original amount of parent material?" or "what if the rock had some daughter material at the very beginning?" The age can still be determined but you have to be more clever in determining it.

One common sense rule to remember is that the number of parent isotope atoms + the number of daughter isotope atoms = an unchanging number throughout time. The number of parent isotopes decreases while the number of daughter isotopes increases but the total of the two added together is a constant. You need to find how much of the daughter isotopes in the rock (call that isotope "A" for below) are *not* the result of a radioactive decay of parent atoms. You then subtract this amount from the total amount of daughter atoms in the rock to get the number of decays that have occurred since the rock solidified. Here are the steps:

1. Find another isotope of the same element as the daughter that is *never* a result of radioactive decay (call that isotope "B" for below). Isotopes of a given element have the same chemical properties, so a radioactive rock will incorporate the NONradioactively derived proportions of the two isotopes in the *same* proportion as any nonradioactive rock.

2. Measure the ratio of isotopes A and B in a nonradioactive rock. This ratio, *R*, will be the **primitive** (initial) proportion of the two isotopes.

3. Multiply amount of the non-daughter isotope (isotope B) in the radioactive rock by the ratio of the previous step: (isotope B) $\times R$ = initial amount of daughter isotope A that was not the result of decay.

4. Subtract the initial amount of daughter isotope A from rock sample to get the amount of daughter isotope A that IS due to radioactive decay. That number is also the amount of parent that has decayed (remember the rule #parent + #daughter = constant). Now you can determine the age as you did before.

The oldest meteorites have ages clustering around 4.55 to 4.57 billion years with *uncertainties* in the age measurements of less than 100 million years. The narrow range of ages is taken to be how long it took the parent bodies of the meteorites to form.

The discussion above is for the case of determining when a *rock* solidified (and it is usually *very old* rocks!). To determine the ages of old, *once-living* material such as plants, then something like carbon-14 will be used. Most carbon atoms are carbon-12 (99%) or carbon-13 (1%). A very small fraction (about 1 part in 10^{12}) are the radioactive carbon-14 isotope that will decay to form nitrogen-14 with a half-life of 5,730 years (see the figure on the next page). Carbon-14 is being produced continuously in our atmosphere when cosmic rays (extremely high-energy particles from space, mostly protons) collide with air molecules. When plants absorb carbon-dioxide in the photosynthesis process, some of the carbon dioxide has the carbon-14 atom in the molecule. Assuming that our atmosphere's composition and the cosmic ray flux has not changed significantly in the last few thousand years, you can find the age of the once-living organic material by comparing its carbon-14/carbon-12 ratios to those of now-living plants. Carbon-14 dating works well for samples less than about 50,000 to 60,000 years old and for things that were getting their carbon from the air.

10.3.3   Is Radioactive Dating Valid?

The long ages (billions of years) given by radioactive dating of rocks seems an impossibly long time for some people. Since radioactive rocks have been observed for only a few decades, how do you know you can trust these long half-lives and the long ages derived? Here are some points to consider:

primitive

carbon dating

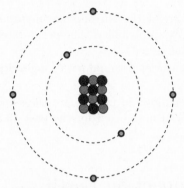

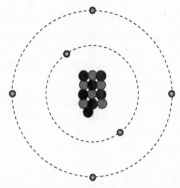

Carbon-12: 99% of carbon atoms

Carbon-13: 1% of carbon atoms

- ● Proton = +1 (nucleus)
- ● Neutron = 0 (nucleus)
- ◉ Electron = -1 (orbitals)

Carbon isotopes

All the same *chemistry* (same outer electron configuration) BUT different *nuclear* properties.

Biochemical reactions slightly prefer C-12 so cells become enriched in C-12 compared to carbon in inorganic materials.

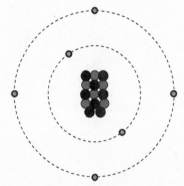

Carbon-14: 1 in a trillion carbon atoms
Radioactive half-life of 5730 years

1. The rate of decay should follow a simple exponential decline based on the simple theory of probability in statistics. This same probability theory is used to figure the odds of winning by gamblers.

2. An exponential decay is seen for short-lived isotopes with half-lives of only a few days.

3. For the decades they have been observed, the long-lived isotopes also follow an exponential decay.

4. The gamma ray frequencies and intensities produced by radioactive elements in supernova remnants (section 13.1.2) change in the same predictable way as they do here on the Earth. One well-studied supernova remnant is SN1987A that is 169,000 light years away in a satellite galaxy of the Milky Way. The predictions for the decay rates have turned out to be correct for all of the radioactive elements we have detected in that remnant. Since the SN1987A is 169,000 light years away, that tells us the decay rates were not different 169,000 years ago. We find similar results for supernova remnants even further away [and therefore, further back in time (section 1.3)].

5. The decay probability should not depend on time because:

   (a) An exponential decay IS observed for short-lived isotopes.

   (b) Decays are *nuclear* reactions. Nuclear reactions only care about size scales of 10^{-13} centimeters (100 million times smaller than the wavelength of visible light). The composition and state of the surrounding material will not affect the rate of decay.

   (c) Tests looking for a variable decay probability by changing the pressure, temperature, and chemical combinations of the surrounding material have *not* found any variation in the decay probability. The decay rates do not change under all of the conditions tested.

(d) The laws of nature or physics at the nuclear level should not change with time (section 1.3).

(e) Astronomical observations show that the laws of physics are the same everywhere in the universe and have been unchanged for the past 13.8 billion years.

10.4   Effects of an Asteroid Impact on Earth

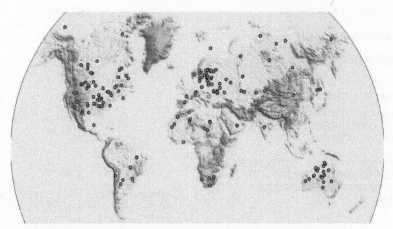

Impact sites on the Earth (on the land masses only). There may be other ones that have not been identified yet.
Image courtesy of the Geological Survey of Canada, Natural Resources Canada

Some asteroids have orbits that cross the orbit of the Earth. That means that the Earth *will* be hit sometime. Recent studies have shown that the Earth has been hit an alarmingly large number of times in the past. One large impact is now thought to have contributed to the quick demise of the dinosaurs about 65 million years ago. What would be the effects of an asteroid hitting the Earth?

What follows is a condensation of an excellent article by Sydney van den Bergh called "Life and Death in the Inner Solar System" in the May 1989 issue of the *Publications of the Astronomical Society of the Pacific* (vol. **101**, pages 500–509). He considers a typical impact scenario of a 10-kilometer object with density = 2.5 times that of water, impacting at speed = 20 kilometers/second. Its mass = 1.31 *trillion* tons (1.31×10^{15} kilograms). A 1-kilometer object has a mass of 1.31 *billion* tons.

10.4.1   Explosion

Obviously, something this big hitting the Earth is going to hit with a lot of energy! In the article van den Bergh uses an old unit of energy of traditional astronomy called an "erg" in which 10 million ergs equals 1 Joule. Since the energy values in ergs are so tremendously large, let's use the energy unit of 1 megaton of TNT ($= 4.2 \times 10^{15}$ Joules = ($= 4.2 \times 10^{22}$ ergs) to describe energy of the impact. This is the energy one million *tons* of dynamite would release if it was exploded and is the energy unit used for nuclear explosions. The largest yield of a thermonuclear warhead is around 50–100 megatons. The kinetic energy of the falling object is converted to the explosion when it hits. The 10-kilometer object produces an explosion of 6×10^7 megatons of TNT (an earthquake of magnitude 12.4 on the Richter scale). The 1-kilometer object produces a milder explosion of "only" 6×10^4 megatons (an earthquake of magnitude 9.4 on the Richter scale).

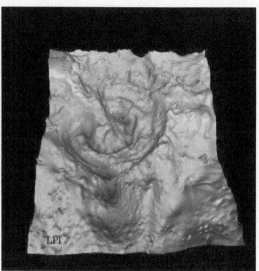

The 1.2-kilometer diameter Meteor Crater (left) in northern Arizona was formed about 50,000 years ago. The 170-kilometer diameter Chicxulub crater (right) at the edge of the Yucatan peninsula of Mexico was made about 64.98 million years ago. This computer-generated picture was made from local gravity and magnetic field variations.

Images courtesy of D. Roddy, V. Sharpton and Lunar Planetary Institute/NASA

On its way to the impact, the asteroid pushes aside the air in front of it creating a hole in the atmosphere. The atmosphere above the impact site is removed for several tens of seconds. Before the surrounding air can rush back in to fill the gap, material from the impact: vaporized asteroid, crustal material, and ocean water (if it lands in the ocean), escapes through the hole and follows a ballistic flight back down. Within two minutes after impact about 10^5 cubic kilometers of ejecta (10^{13} tons) is lofted to about 100 kilometers. If the asteroid hits the ocean, the surrounding water returning over the hot crater floor is vaporized (a large enough impact will break through to the hot lithosphere and maybe even the asthenosphere—section 9.4), sending more water vapor into the air as well as causing huge steam explosions that greatly compound the effect of the initial impact explosion.

There will be a *crater* regardless of where it lands. The diameter of the crater in kilometers is $= 0.765 \times$ (energy of impact in megatons TNT)$^{(1/3.4)}$. Plugging in the typical impact values, you get a 150-kilometer diameter crater for the 10-kilometer asteroid and a 20-kilometer diameter crater for the 1-kilometer asteroid. The initial blast would also produce shifting of the crust along fault lines.

10.4.2 Tsunamis

The oceans cover about 75% of the Earth's surface, so it is likely the asteroid will hit an ocean. The amount of water in the ocean is nowhere near large enough to "cushion" the asteroid. The asteroid will push the water aside and hit the ocean floor to create a large crater. The water pushed aside will form a huge tidal wave, a tsunami. The tidal wave height in meters $= 10.9 \times$ (distance from impact in kilometers)$^{-0.717} \times$ (energy of impact in megatons TNT)$^{0.495}$. What this means is that a 10-kilometer asteroid hitting any deep point in the Pacific (the largest ocean) produces a megatsunami along the entire Pacific Rim.

Some values for the height of the tsunami at different distances from the impact site are given in table 10.1. The heights are given for the two typical asteroids, a 10-kilometer and a 1-kilometer asteroid.

Table 10.1: Tidal wave heights vs. distance from impact site for two different asteroids

Distance (in km)	10 km asteroid	1 km asteroid
300	1.3 km	42 m
1000	540 m	18 m
3000	250 m	8 m
10000	100 m	3 m

The steam blasts from the water at the crater site rushing back over the hot crater floor will also produce tsunamis following the initial impact tsunami and crustal shifting as a result of the initial impact would produce other tsunamis—a complex train of tsunamis would be created from the initial impact (something not usually shown in disaster movies).

10.4.3   Global Firestorm

The material ejected from the impact through the hole in the atmosphere will re-enter all over the globe and heat up from the friction with the atmosphere. The chunks of material will be hot enough to produce a lot of infrared light. The heat from the glowing material will start fires *around the globe*. Global fires will put about 7×10^{10} tons of soot into the air. This would "aggravate environmental stresses associated with the ... impact."

10.4.4   Acid Rain

The heat from the shock wave of the entering asteroid and reprocessing of the air close to the impact produces nitric and nitrous acids over the next few months to one year. The chemical reaction chain is:

(a) $N_2 + O_2 \rightarrow NO$ (molecular nitrogen combined with molecular oxygen produces nitrogen monoxide)

(b) $2NO + O_2 \rightarrow 2NO_2$ (two nitrogen monoxide molecules combined with one oxygen molecule produces two nitrogen dioxide molecules)

(c) NO_2 is converted to nitric and nitrous acids when it is mixed with water.

These are really nasty acids. They will wash out of the air when it rains—a worldwide deluge of acid rain with damaging effects:

- destruction or damage of foliage;

- great amounts of weathering of continental rocks;

- the upper ocean organisms are killed. These organisms are responsible for locking up carbon dioxide in their shells (calcium carbonate) that would eventually become limestone. However, the shells will dissolve in the acid water. That along with the "impact winter" (described below) kills off about 90% of all marine nanoplankton species. A majority of the free oxygen from photosynthesis on the Earth is made by nanoplankton.

- The ozone layer is destroyed by O_3 reacting with NO. The amount of ultraviolet light hitting the surface increases, killing small organisms and plants (key parts of the food chain). The NO_2 causes respiratory damage in larger animals. Harmful elements like Beryllium, Mercury, Thallium, etc. are let loose.

10.4.5 Temperature Effects

All of the dust in the air from the impact and soot from the fires will block the Sun. For several months you cannot see your hand in front of your face! The dramatic decrease of sunlight reaching the surface produces a drastic short-term global reduction in temperature, called *impact winter*. Plant photosynthesis stops and the food chain collapses.

The cooling is followed by a *much more prolonged period* of increased temperature due to a large increase in the *greenhouse effect* (described in the previous chapter). The greenhouse effect is increased because of the increase of the carbon dioxide and water vapor in the air. The carbon dioxide level rises because the plants are burned and most of the plankton are wiped out. Also, water vapor in the air from the impact stays aloft for awhile. The temperatures are too warm for comfort for awhile.

10.4.6 Finding Near-Earth Objects

In the early 1990s astronomers requested funding for an observing program called Spaceguard to catalog all of the near-Earth asteroids and short period comets. The international program would take 10 years to create a comprehensive catalog of all of the hazardous asteroids and comets. The cost for the entire program (building six special purpose telescopes and operation costs for ten years) would be less than what it costs to make a popular movie like *Deep Impact* or *Armageddon*.

In mid-1999 NASA and the US Air Force began a Near-Earth Object search program using existing telescopes to locate 90% of the NEOs larger than 1 kilometer in diameter in ten years. *Near-Earth Objects* are those objects that can approach the Sun to within 1.3 AU. The 1-kilometer diameter size is the lower limit of an impact having a global rather than just a regional effect. As of mid-December 2018, the program had found 894 asteroids larger than 1 kilometer in diameter and there are about 1947 "Potentially Hazardous Asteroids (PHAs)" with diameters greater than 150 meters and have orbits that can get within 0.05 AU (7,480,000 km) of the Earth's orbit. The "potential" in the PHA term does *not* mean the PHA *will* impact the Earth; there is just the *possibility* it could in the future, so we must monitor the PHA closely. See the textbook website for links of current programs to find NEOs.

NEOs

PHAs

One process that affects the orbits of asteroids and, therefore, introduces uncertainty in whether a particular NEA will hit the Earth is the *Yarkovsky effect* (see figure next page). In the Yarkovsky effect, there is a slight mis-alignment of the energy emitted by the asteroid and the energy it receives from the Sun. Because any material takes some time to heat up, the asteroid's afternoon side emits more infrared energy than the morning side. The afternoon emission of infrared energy from solar heating is not pointed right at the Sun, so the thermal radiation from the asteroid is not exactly balanced by the solar photons. This results in a pushing that can move the asteroid inward toward the Sun or away from the Sun. If the asteroid is rotating in the same direction that it moves in its orbit around the Sun ("prograde rotation"), the asteroid will be pushed away from the Sun; if the asteroid is rotating in the opposite direction from its orbital motion ("retrograde rotation"), the asteroid will be pushed toward the Sun. The effect is very small but it is continually acting on the asteroid over many years, so it can have a measurable influence on the asteroid's motion.

Yarkovsky effect

Unfortunately for us, the Yarkovsky effect depends on all sorts of features about the asteroid itself that we do not know: things like the asteroid's size, mass, how the material in the asteroid responds to heat, and most importantly on the orientation of the asteroid's spin axis (remember the mis-alignment of the noon Sun energy input direction vs. the afternoon asteroid energy output direction). If the asteroid

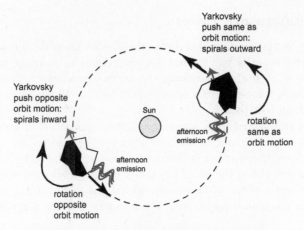

Because any material takes some time to heat up, it emits more infrared energy in the afternoon than in the morning. This extra afternoon emission provides a *small* push like a tiny rocket (from Newton's 3rd law) that's always "on" called the "Yarkovsky effect". The Yarkovsky effect can make the object spiral outward away from the Sun if the object is spinning in the same direction as its orbit motion or spiral inward toward the Sun if the object is spinning in the opposite direction as its orbit motion.

YORP effect

is tumbling about two or more axes, then the afternoon infrared radiation it emits from solar heating is randomly directed instead of being in one consistent direction. Without a consistent direction of the infrared emission, the Yarkovsky effect is eliminated. A related effect called the "YORP effect" arises from the non-uniform shape and reflectivity of various parts of the asteroid that can cause one side of the asteroid to be a better emitter of its infrared energy than another part. The YORP effect can speed up or slow down the asteroid's spin rate and also change the spin axis direction leading to a possible increase in the Yarkovsky effect. The OSIRIS-REx spacecraft has measured the increase in Bennu's rotation speed due to the YORP effect such that Bennu's rotation period is decreasing by one second every century (an hour every 360,000 years). Links to more information about near-Earth objects and asteroid tracking programs are found on the textbook's website.

10.4.7   Deflecting and Using Asteroids

The surprise airburst of an asteroid over Chelyabinsk, Russia in February 2013 followed several hours later by the very close flyby of another but unrelated asteroid called 2012 DA14 were potent reminders that an impact can happen any time. Asteroid 2012 DA14 is a near-Earth stony asteroid about 50 meters in diameter that was discovered just several months before its close flyby of just 27,600 km from the Earth's surface, closer than even the ring of geosynchronous satellites. That was one we were prepared to observe. The smaller Russia asteroid was truly a surprise. The airburst of the 17-meter Russia asteroid released as much energy as nearly 500 kilotons of TNT 20-30 kilometers above the surface, knocking out windows for many kilometers around. If DA14 had hit, it would have released the energy equivalent to 2.4 megatons of TNT. Something like DA14 passes near the Earth every 40 years on average and an impact happens roughly once every 1200 years. Smaller objects are much more numerous, so something the size of the Russia asteroid impact the Earth roughly once every several decades. With most of the Earth's surface covered with oceans of water and humans concentrated in a small fraction of the land area, destructive impacts over population centers are fortunately rare.

Ground-based efforts to find potentially-hazardous asteroids are described in the previous section. The NEOWISE program that used the Wide-field Infrared Survey Explorer spacecraft to discover near-Earth objects in 2011 after the spacecraft's primary mission was completed showed that a space-based infrared telescope would find near-Earth objects more efficiently than any ground-based effort could. A special-purpose NEO search mission called "Sentinel" was proposed by the privately-funded B612 Foundation with a launch date in mid-2018. Fundraising for Sentinel was stopped in 2016 when B612 concluded that NASA's proposed NEO-Cam space telescope and the Large Synoptic Survey Telescope (to be completed in 2022-2023) would be able to find the 100-meter and larger asteroids that could hit Earth. NEOCam would orbit at the Earth-Sun L1 Lagrange point, a gravitational balance point between Earth and the Sun. NEOCam was still in the planning stage in late 2018.

The space-based infrared telescope like NEOCam has a number of advantages over a ground-based search including it would have a wider search field that includes objects interior to the Earth's orbit as well as those outside of Earth's orbit, it would more easily find the dark near-Earth asteroids that are quite common, it could operate 24 hours per day, there would be less confusion from the background stars, and the infrared measurements of the asteroids would provide more accurate estimates of the asteroid sizes and reflectivity. Objects of special interest that get close enough to Earth can be studied with radar to get very precise orbit determinations along with rotation, shape, and surface properties measurements.

NEOcam

Asteroids that are on Earth-impact trajectories can be nudged out of the way by various techniques that are either precise and gradual long-term pulling or pushing or sudden and less precise impulses. Regardless of the technique, the key is to apply them while the asteroid is still quite far from the Earth so the nudge does not have to be as large. In the same way it is easier to change an arrow's path when it is just leaving the bow string than it is when the arrow is near its target, the farther away the asteroid is from the Earth when we apply the nudge, the easier it will be to change the asteroid's path. Despite what is portrayed in the movies, our current capabilities would require the nudge to be given while the asteroid is still several years out from the impact.

nudging asteroid: slow and precise or sudden and imprecise

In the sudden impulse category we could simply run into the asteroid with a massive spacecraft. A sort of trial-run of such a technique was done successfully when the Deep Impact impactor ran into the nucleus of comet Tempel 1 (for scientific purposes discussed in section 10.5.1) in July 2005. That proved we could hit a small body from tens of millions of kilometers away. This technique works if the asteroid is solid rock or metal and not a rubble pile as some (most?) asteroids appear to be. A rubble pile asteroid (fragmented rock) would efficiently absorb the shock without changing course. We also would not want to risk creating multiple large fragments that would later hit the Earth. The method loved by movie makers—detonating nuclear warheads—is in the sudden impulse category. The movies show the warheads striking the asteroid at high speed and blowing it up. Unfortunately, our current warheads cannot survive impact speeds as high as what they show in the movies. Actual nuclear detonations would need to be either just off the asteroid's surface, strongly heating one part of the asteroid and giving the asteroid the needed nudge from the recoil, or from devices embedded within the asteroid with the hope of fragmenting the asteroid enough so that only a much smaller amount of the asteroid reaches the Earth. Like the spacecraft impactor option, how well the nuclear option works depends on the asteroid's composition and structure.

sudden impulse methods

In the gradual long-term applied force category is a technique that has a spacecraft moving alongside the asteroid and adjusting the asteroid's pass by the gravitational pull of the spacecraft, a "slow-pull gravity tractor". The spacecraft gravity method does not depend on the asteroid's structure, composition, or rotation. However, the acceleration supplied by the spacecraft's gravity is extremely small, so it

spacecraft's gravity slowly pulls asteroid away from Earth impact

would need to act over a long time. Other examples in this category include pushing the asteroid with an ion beam, attaching a rocket (chemical or ion) engine to the asteroid, focusing solar energy to enhance the Yarkovsky effect, and a mass driver on the asteroid that ejects small pieces of the asteroid into space to give the slow steady recoil push. Of course, it is always possible to use multiple techniques to deflect the asteroid and the gradual long-term applied force techniques would be most useful if they supplied small course corrections after the more powerful sudden impulses were used. All of these techniques would require an unprecedented amount of cooperation and agreement among the nations in planning and implementing the deflection attempts and deciding when to act and also what happens if the impact site shifts from one country to another because the deflection attempt was not totally successful.

asteroid mining

The near-Earth asteroids are the most worrisome ones for possible impacts but they could also be potentially very beneficial to us if we could mine them for rare metals and use the asteroids as convenient stepping stones to manned exploration of the solar system, especially traveling to Mars. The near-Earth asteroids are relatively abundant in heavy metals like iron and nickel and the platinum-group metals (platinum, palladium, rhodium, ruthenium, osmium, and iridium) used in modern technology. A kilometer-diameter asteroid would have several trillion dollars worth of these materials. In fact, all of the heavy metals (iron on up) in the Earth's crust came from asteroid impacts after the Earth differentiated—the Earth's original supply from its formation is in the Earth's core. For some near-Earth asteroids it would take less fuel to travel to, land on, and return to Earth than would a roundtrip to the Moon's surface. The round-trip asteroid trip would take several months and provide the crucial experience needed to prepare for the more difficult over two-year round-trip to Mars. This experience would include testing of methods of extracting water from the asteroid's minerals, recycling the water for long-duration flights, and using the water as a shield from solar wind, solar eruptions, and cosmic rays. The water from the asteroids could also be broken down into oxygen and hydrogen to be used as rocket fuel. An excellent resource to learn more about the topics discussed in this section is Don Yeomans' book *Near-Earth Objects: Finding Them Before They Find Us*, published in 2013. Yeomans was the manager of NASA's Near-Earth Object Program and supervisor of the Solar System Dynamics Group.

Vocabulary

carbonaceous meteorite	chondrules	differentiated
half-life	isotope	meteorite
primitive	radioactive dating	

Review Questions

1. Where are most of the asteroids found?

2. Why are spacecraft able to pass through the asteroid belt without getting hit?

3. What are the three types of asteroids and what are they made of?

4. Why are more meteors seen after midnight?

5. What are the proportions of the three types of meteorites and what are they made of?

6. What type of asteroid does each type of meteorite correspond to?

7. Which meteorites are **primitive** and why are they particularly important for understanding the origin of the planets?

8. What makes **carbonaceous meteorites** so special?

9. Why are **chondrules** especially important for solar system formation models? What type of meteorite are they likely to be found in?

10. How old are the various types of meteorites and why are they used to find the age of the solar system?

11. Why do iron meteorites make up 40% of the "finds", but are only 2 to 3% of the total meteorites? What causes the biasing of the "finds"?

12. Why is Antarctica a good place to get an unbiased sample of meteorites?

13. What makes SNC meteorites so unique and how are they different than other types of meteorites?

14. Why are iron and stoney-iron meteorites thought to come from a **differentiated** body?

15. Does **radioactive dating** give relative or absolute ages for rocks? What type of "age" does it tell us?

16. How do you use the **half-life** to find the age of radioactive rocks?

17. If the half-life of a radioactive sample is 1 month, is a sample of it completely decayed after 2 months? If not, how much is left?

18. Uranium-235 has a half-life of 700 million years. How long will you have to wait until a 1-kilogram chunk decays so that only 0.0625 kilograms (1/16 kg) is left?

19. How are the very old ages derived for some radioactive rocks known to be correct?

20. If a large asteroid were to hit Earth, how much of the Earth's surface would be affected?

21. What would be the effects on Earth of an impact by an asteroid a kilometer or larger in diameter?

22. What are the current and proposed future programs to search for Near-Earth Objects?

23. What are possible ways of effectively preventing an asteroid impact with Earth?

10.5   Comets

The passage of the comet Hale-Bopp through our part of the solar system created spectacular displays in the spring of 1997. Every newspaper, television and radio station carried some report with photos of the comet. We had a foretaste of the Hale-Bopp show when Comet Hyakutake passed close to the Earth in the spring of 1996. Hale-Bopp was one of the brightest comets to grace our skies this century, coming close to the displays put on by Comet West in 1976 and Halley's Comet in 1910. Many people were justifiably interested in Hale-Bopp—it was a gorgeous site! Many people also tuned into the news and astronomy websites in the summer of 1994 when the comet Shoemaker-Levy 9 smashed into the planet Jupiter. Predictions of Jupiter's demise were, of course, greatly exaggerated—Jupiter took the hits in stride.

Our favorable view of comets is a big change from the dread and fear people held of comets even less than a century ago. Comets were usually thought to be omens of bad events to occur on the Earth. King Harold of England took the passage of Halley's Comet to be a sign of his defeat in 1066. However, William the Conqueror took it as a good sign and led the Normans to victory over King Harold's army. As recently as 1910 people thought the end of the world was near when it was discovered the Earth would pass through the tail of Halley's Comet. Astronomers had discovered the presence of cyanogen molecules in the tail, so the

comet superstition then and now

At left is a depiction of comets as destroyers of worlds from 1857. At right, a piece of the Bayeux Tapestry shows the English people and the king viewing Halley's Comet as a sign of their imminent doom in 1066.

popular media spread tales of cyanide poisoning of the Earth. Even with great effort the astronomers were not able to convince many people that we faced no danger— a comet's tail is extremely diffuse so the minute amounts making it through the atmosphere and being breathed by helpless human beings was much, much less than the noxious stuff they breathed everyday from industrial pollution. The tragedy of the Heaven's Gate cult with Hale-Bopp shows that despite our current knowledge of comets, there are still those who view comets with great superstition or as something much more than the icy bodies they are from the outer limits of the solar system.

Components of Comets

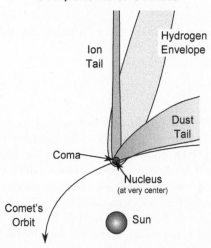

Comets are small "potato-shaped" objects a few hundred meters to about 20 kilometers across. They are made of dust grains embedded in frozen *volatiles* (materials that vaporize at low temperatures) like water, methane, ammonia, and carbon dioxide (they are like "icy dirt balls"). They are **primitive** objects which means they are unchanged since they first solidified from the solar nebula about 4.6 billion years ago. Comets are frozen relics of the early solar system holding valuable information about the formation of the planets.

primitive *object*

When a comet gets close to the Sun, it changes into something more spectacular. The picture at the bottom of the previous page shows the parts of a comet that form when the cold "icy dirt ball" is warmed up by the Sun. This picture is courtesy of David Doody at JPL and is part of the *Basics of Space Flight* manual for all operations personnel. The comets that have exhausted their supply of ices from repeated passages near the Sun or the remaining ices become insulated enough by the dusty or rocky material to no longer vaporize are reclassified as asteroids. Some comet researchers even call the icy bodies in the Kuiper Belt and Oort Cloud (that never get near the Sun) asteroids because the ices do not vaporize. Therefore, the line between what is called a "comet" and what is an "asteroid" is a bit blurry.

comet vs. asteroid

10.5.1 Nucleus

All the material comes from the **nucleus.** This is the "icy dirt ball". Comet nuclei are 0.5 to 20 kilometers in size and are potato-shaped conglomerates of dust (silicates and carbonaceous) embedded in ice (frozen water, carbon dioxide, carbon monoxide, methane, and ammonia). They have a mass of only 10^{14} to 10^{15} kilograms (the Earth has a mass of almost 6×10^{24} kilograms—tens of *billions* to hundreds of *billions* of times larger than a comet). It is less than the size of a period on the scale of the comet drawing above. Because of their small size, comet nuclei have too little gravity to crush the material into a sphere.

nucleus

The nucleus of Halley's Comet as seen by Giotto
Image courtesy of Max Planck Institut fuer Aeronomie

When a comet nears the Sun around the Jupiter–Saturn distance, it warms up. The ices **sublime**—they change from solid to gas without going through a liquid phase (like the white mist coming from a block of frozen carbon dioxide, "dry ice"). Jets of material will shoot out from the nucleus. These jets can alter the comet's orbit (remember Newton's third law of motion?)

sublime

Since the orbit of Halley's Comet is known so well, spacecraft were sent to it when it passed through our part of the solar system in 1986. The spacecraft Giotto launched by the European Space Agency on July 2, 1985 reached Halley's Comet on March 13, 1986. Giotto got to within 596 kilometers of the nucleus passing by at 68 kilometers/*second*. The nucleus of Halley's Comet has dimensions of $8 \times 8 \times 16$ kilometers. The nucleus has a density of only 0.1 to 0.25 times that of water and is very dark—it reflects only 4% of the sunlight (coal reflects about 6%). The density is about that of a loosely-compacted snowball and it is quite fragile—you could break a piece of the nucleus in two with your bare hands!

Comet Hale-Bopp's nucleus is larger than Halley's nucleus—10 to 40 kilometers in size (about twice the size of the Halley's Comet's nucleus) and is dust-rich. It began ejecting material when still at the distance of the outer planets, so it was discovered while still a couple of years from its perihelion passage in March of 1997. Comet Hyakutake (bright comet of spring 1996 that passed within 0.1 A.U. of the Earth) has a nucleus 1 to 3 kilometers in size. Five other comet nuclei that have been imaged up close by spacecraft are shown below. Like Halley, they too are very dark.

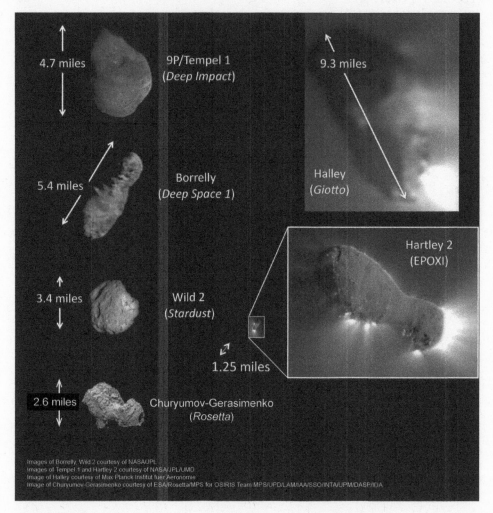

The Deep Impact mission was designed to investigate the *interior* of a comet by crashing a 370-kg copper impactor into the nucleus of Tempel 1 in July 2005 and analyzing the material shot out from the impact (copper is an element not expected to be in comets). Tempel 1 is made of a mixture of materials with high and low melting temperatures which tells us that the early solar nebula was more complex than previously thought. It has silicates like beach sand with olivine and pyroxene that would have come from the inner solar system, carbonates and sulfide that would have come from part of the solar system farther out, and ice (mostly water ice and a little carbon dioxide) from the outer solar system. Tempel 1 has a powdery surface layer a few tens of meters thick with most of the ices missing in that surface layer ("a marshmallow dipped in powered sugar"). There are a few smooth patches of water ice on the surface. Young surfaces right next to old, battered areas with a layered (slabs of ice) interior filled with pockets of empty space tell us the geological history of comets is more complex (and interesting!) than we initially thought.

The Deep Impact spacecraft has been renamed the EPOXI mission. It flew by Comet Hartley 2 on November 4, 2010. Hartley 2 is about a quarter the size of Tempel 1. Its two ends are rough and knobbly from which spew jets of carbon dioxide ("dry ice") and a smooth region between the two ends from which frozen water sublimates through the dust. The images were clear enough that astronomers could see jets spewing out from specific surface features and even the "snow" particles in the jets the size of golf balls to basketballs. This is the first comet for which frozen carbon dioxide has provided the jets—usually the jets are made from the sublimation of frozen water.

The Rosetta mission of ESA was the first mission to orbit a comet, land on its surface, and study a comet up close through its various stages of activity as the comet approaches the Sun. Rosetta rendezvoused with Comet 67P/Churyumov-Gerasinmenko in August 2014 after more than a decade's journey. Along the way to Comet 67P/Churyumov-Gerasimenko, Rosetta flew by Asteroid Steins in September 2008 and Asteroid Lutetia in July 2010. The mission consisted of two spacecraft: the Rosetta Orbiter and Philae Lander. Rosetta began orbiting the comet in early September 2014 while the comet was about 3.5 AU from the Sun, between the orbits of Mars and Jupiter. The comet nucleus looks like two round pieces stuck together with a narrow bridge of ice-rock material, so it is technically known as a "contact binary". The nucleus is about 2.2 by 2.6 miles in dimension and is darker than charcoal, so the images you see on the web have been light stretched in order to see the details. There is a mix of craters and smooth areas on the surface like that found on Comet Tempel 1. The smooth areas are dusty—probably the result of material deposited from outgassing and several of the craters, at least, are vents from which the ice-dust material comes. Other craters are the result of impacts.

The Philae Lander touched down on the surface in November 2014. The lander had a mass of about 100 kilograms but because of the comet's very weak gravity, the gravity force the lander felt on the comet's surface was only about the weight of a piece of paper on the Earth's surface. Therefore, the lander was fitted with a combination of ice screws on its feet and harpoons to secure itself to the surface. However, the landing equipment did not work properly, so it bounced twice and settled against a cliff wall at such an angle that it could not recharge its batteries with its solar panels. Before it went into hibernation, it did manage to make several measurements with its suite of scientific instruments. When the comet got to about Mars' distance from the Sun in June 2015, the lander awoke to resume some investigation of the comet's surface but communication with the Rosetta orbiter was hampered by the increasing activity of the comet. The Rosetta had to remain at a safe distance from the comet due to the very dusty environment of the coma.

Each of the Rosetta mission spacecraft had a whole suite of instruments on board to explore this relic from the solar system's formation 4.6 billion years ago. The Rosetta Orbiter was powered by a huge set of solar panels that span 32 meters, the largest of any interplanetary craft. The name "Rosetta" was chosen because we hope that this mission will be the Rosetta Stone of finally understanding the language of comets. We will better understand the connection between the local features of the interior and surface of the ice-rock nucleus and the environment of the comet's coma and the tail. With that knowledge, we will be able to understand what our past observations of comets from the Earth and brief flyby missions have tried to reveal to us. Some early results from the Rosetta mission include: that a number of the dust jets from the comet can be traced back to active pits that probably form when volatiles under the surface escape into space and the surface material collapses as a sinkhole; extensive layering seems to show that the material accumulated over a lengthy period; the high porosity, low density, and weak strength of the nucleus and dust in the coma show the comet formed from low-speed accretion of material to make a fluffy aggregation of dust particles over an extended period of time in the earliest stages of the solar system's formation; and the double-lobed shape of the comet plays an important role in the cycle of activity of different parts of the comet and how dust is transported among parts of the comet in different parts in its 6.5-year orbit around the Sun.

The Rosetta Orbiter orbited the comet for a two-year period of time that included the perihelion passage on August 13, 2015, so Rosetta explored the various stages of a comet's activity up close. On September 30, 2016, the orbiter became a lander, ending the mission by landing on Churyumov-Gerasinmenko in a region with several active pits. Discoveries will continue to made for many years to come as we continue to analyze the enormous amount of data gathered by Rosetta.

10.5.2   Coma

coma

Gas and dust pouring out from the nucleus forms a huge atmosphere around the nucleus. This is the bright core, called a **coma,** you can see when you observe a comet from the Earth. It is 100,000's of kilometers across. Because the nucleus has such low gravity (you could jump off it!), it cannot hang onto the escaping dust and gas. NASA's StarDust mission captured material from Comet Wild 2's coma in early January 2004 and returned the microscopic dust grains embedded in aerogel to Earth in mid-January 2006. It found that Comet Wild 2, like Comet Tempel 1, is also made of a mixture of materials with high and low melting temperatures. This may be the result of material originally forming near the Sun that got ejected to the outer parts of the solar system nebula via the bipolar jets we see in many young, forming stars (see sections 10.8.2 and 13.1.2). Further analysis of the Comet Wild 2 material has uncovered Glycine, an amino acid. Rosetta also found Glycine in Churyumov-Gerasimenko's coma.

Comets bring water to terrestrial planets?

Almost a year after the EPOXI spacecraft flew by Hartley 2, astronomers using the infrared Herschel Space Observatory were able to measure in the infrared band the ratios of regular water to "*heavy water*" in the comet's coma. Heavy water has one of the normal hydrogen atoms replaced by its heavier isotope cousin, deuterium. The ratio between heavy water and regular water from Hartley 2 matches the ratio of Earth's ocean water. Another team using the Stratospheric Observatory for Infrared Astronomy ("SOFIA", a converted 747 that flies a 2.7-meter infrared telescope into the stratosphere) measured the water isotopes in Comet Wirtanen in December 2018 and found its water matches Earth's ocean water also. The other ten comets that have measured regular water to heavy water ratios (including Hyakutake, Hale-Bopp, Halley, and Churyumov-Gerasimenko) are relatively enriched in heavy water—their heavy water to regular water ratios are twice as great as the Earth's ocean water. Eight of the other comets come from the very distant reaches of our solar system, called the Oort Cloud discussed in the next section, while Hartley 2, comes from a closer region just outside of Neptune's orbit called the Kuiper Belt (also discussed in the next section). Perhaps comets from the Kuiper Belt supplied some of the water found on the terrestrial planets. What is surprising about Hartley 2's water is that the Kuiper Belt comets were expected to have an even higher percentage of heavy water than the Oort Cloud comets. Further uncertainty about the process resulted when the Rosetta mission found that Comet 67P/Churyumov-Gerasimenko could not have supplied the Earth with its water despite the fact that Churyumov-Gerasimenko is probably originally from the Kuiper Belt like Hartley 2. The range of deuterium-to-hydrogen ratios from the various comets studied indicates that comets formed over a wide range of distances from the Sun. Molecular oxygen and nitrogen being outgassed along with the water vapor from Churyumov-Gerasimenko tell us that the comet formed in a very cold region of the solar nebula.

Comet Hale-Bopp was a spectacular comet in the spring 1997 sky.
Image courtesy of Darren Bly

10.5.3   Tails

When the comet gets to around Mars' distance from the Sun, the Sun's radiation pushes the coma gas and dust away from the Sun to form the well-known tails of a comet. Usually, two tails will form, a bluish, straight **ion tail** and a more curved, yellow-white **dust tail.**   **ion tail, dust tail**

The Sun is constantly spewing out charged particles, called the *solar wind*, into the solar system. The solar wind travels along solar magnetic field lines extending radially outward from the Sun. Ultraviolet light from the Sun ionizes some of the   *ion tail—solar wind* gases in the coma. These charged particles (ions) are forced along magnetic field lines to form the ion tail millions of kilometers long. The blue ion tail acts like a "solar" wind sock. The ion tail always points directly away from the Sun, so when the comet is moving away from the Sun, its ion tail will be almost in front of it! The blue color is mostly from the light emitted by carbon monoxide ions but other types of ions also contribute to the light. Since the gas is so diffuse, the observed spectrum is an emission-line spectrum.

The dust tails forms from the solar *photons* colliding with the dust in the coma. The dust forms a long, curved tail that lies slightly farther out from the Sun than   *dust tail—sunlight* the nucleus' orbit. The dust tail has a yellow-white color from reflected sunlight. Both of the tails will stretch for millions of kilometers. Because of the large amount of dust, Hale-Bopp's tail was much brighter and whitish-yellow from reflected sunlight. Hyakutake's tail was dimmer and blue-green in appearance because of the low amount of dust and proportionally more ions.

10.5.4   Hydrogen Cloud

Some of the water vapor ejected in the jets from the nucleus is dissociated by solar ultraviolet light into oxygen and hydrogen. The hydrogen forms a huge cloud around the comet that can be tens of millions of kilometers across. If you include the hydrogen cloud and tails in describing the size of comets, they can be the largest things in the solar system. However, all of this is coming from an icy dirt ball the size of a city.

10.6   Comet orbits

long period comet
short period comet

Comets can be divided into two basic groups depending on their orbital periods. There are **long period comets** with orbital periods that can be thousands to millions of years long, and **short period comets** with orbital periods less than about 200 years. Their alignments with the plane of the planet orbits is also different. The long period comet orbits are oriented in all different random angles while the short period comets orbits are within about 30 degrees of the solar system plane (ecliptic). These orbital characteristics point to two regions beyond the realm of the planets: the Oort Cloud and the Kuiper Belt.

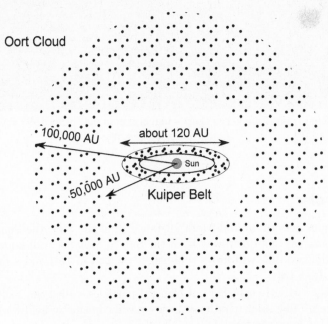

The Oort Cloud and Kuiper Belt (not to scale!). Extent of the two comet reservoirs are indicated. The nearest star is almost three times farther out than the Oort Cloud.

10.6.1   Oort Cloud

Oort Cloud

The **Oort Cloud** is a large spherical cloud with a radius from 50,000 to 100,000 A.U. surrounding the Sun filled with billions to trillions of comets. It has not been directly observed. Its existence has been inferred from observations of **long period**

long period comets

comets. Long period comets have very elliptical orbits and come into the inner solar system from all different random angles (not just along ecliptic). Kepler's third law says that they have orbital periods of 100,000's to millions of years. However, their orbits are so elliptical that they spend only 2 to 4 years in the inner part of the solar system where the planets are and most of their time at 50,000 to 100,000

A.U. With such long orbital periods their presence in the inner solar system is, for all practical purposes, a one-time event. Yet we discover several long period comets every year. This implies the existence of a large reservoir of comets. This was first noted by the Dutch astronomer Jan Oort in 1950 so the spherical comet reservoir was named after him. If Halley's Comet's mass is typical for comets, then the Oort Cloud could have a total mass between 4 and 80 Earth masses. The Oort cloud may extend inward as close as 1000 or so A.U.. One recent visitor from the Oort Cloud is Comet ISON (C/2012 S1).

At the great distances of the Oort Cloud, comets can be affected by the gentle gravitational tugs of nearby passing stars. The passing stars tug on the comets, "perturbing" their orbits, sending some of them into the inner solar system. The comets passing close to a jovian planet are deflected by the planet's gravity into an orbit with a shorter period, only decades to a few thousand years long. Jupiter and perhaps Saturn tend to deflect long period comets completely out of the solar system (or gobble them up as Jupiter did with Shoemaker Levy-9). Uranus and Neptune tend to deflect the long period comets into orbits that stay within the solar system. Halley's Comet may be an example of a deflected comet. Unlike other short period comets, Halley's Comet's orbit is retrograde.

The Oort cloud comets probably formed 4.6 billion years ago at about the same distance as where Saturn and Uranus are today from the Sun and were then deflected outward when they passed to close to the large planets. Comets forming at the distance of Jupiter were either ejected from the solar system by the massive planet in a "gravitationally slingshot" or gobbled up. Comets forming further out than Neptune's current position never coalesced to form a planet and now make up the Kuiper Belt.

10.6.2 Kuiper Belt

Using the observed characteristics of the short period comet orbits, the Dutch-American astronomer Gerard Kuiper proposed the existence of a disk of 100's of millions of comets from 30 to 100 or more A.U. from the Sun orbiting roughly along the ecliptic. This belt of comets is called the **Kuiper Belt** or sometimes the Edgeworth-Kuiper Belt after the British astronomer who also proposed its existence even earlier than Kuiper but unknown to Kuiper. The Kuiper Belt was first observed in 1992. Comets originally from the Kuiper Belt that pass near the Earth have perihelia around the terrestrial planets' distances from the Sun and aphelia beyond Neptune. Interactions with Neptune and Uranus have made their orbits so elliptical. Some examples are Comet Hartley 2, Comet Encke, Comet Giacobini-Zinner, and the former Comet Shoemaker-Levy 9.

Kuiper Belt

The comets observed *in* the Kuiper Belt have more circular orbits and do not stray close to Uranus or Neptune. Many of the Kuiper belt comets observed from the ground are 100 to 300 kilometers in size (but some are Pluto-size) and orbit between 30 and 60 A.U. from the Sun. Another group of objects between Saturn (9.5 A.U.) and Uranus (19.2 A.U.), called "Centaurs", may be an extension of the Kuiper Belt. These objects include Chiron (170 kilometers in diameter) and Chariklo (about 240 kilometers in diameter) and many others.

Further out than the 50 or 60 A.U. limit of the Kuiper Belt is a sort of transition zone between the Kuiper Belt and the inner part of the Oort Cloud called the "*scattered disk*" that includes objects with larger, more eccentric orbits and larger orbit inclinations (angles with respect to the ecliptic) than Kuiper Belt objects. These objects include Eris (about 2300 kilometers in diameter and an elliptical orbit between 38 A.U. and almost 98 A.U.) and Sedna (about 1000 kilometers in diameter and an elliptical orbit between 76 A.U and almost 940 A.U.). On its 1996-97 visit to the inner solar system, Comet Hale-Bopp had its orbit changed by

scattered disk

Jupiter so it now spends most of its time in the scattered disk with an aphelion about 370 A.U. and an orbital period of about 2500 years. Scattered disk objects are probably the result of gravitational interactions with Uranus and Neptune.

The discovery of Pluto's large moon, Charon, in 1978 and then the five-year period of eclipses as Charon's orbit lined up with our line of sight between 1985 and 1990, enabled us to downsize Pluto's diameter and mass considerably. Because of its small size and low density, some astronomers came to view Pluto (2300 km in diameter) as just a large comet. In addition to its size and density, the orbital characteristics of Pluto and its moon Charon (1200 kilometers in diameter) around the Sun clearly show that they are members of the Kuiper Belt. (Pluto is now known to have at least four other smaller moons orbiting it.)

In July 2005 the discovery of a scattered disk object larger than Pluto was announced, called Eris (formerly UB 313). Is Eris the tenth planet? If Pluto is a planet, should not Eris be considered a planet too? How about Ceres in the asteroid belt? Although the discovery of a Kuiper Belt object the size of Pluto or larger was considered likely, Eris' discovery finally forced astronomers to decide what is to be called a "planet", what is a "minor planet", what is an "asteroid", "large comet", etc. (Note that more recent measurements of Eris say that it is about the same diameter as Pluto but 20% larger in mass. It doesn't change the "planet" definition problem.)

definition of "planet" and "dwarf planet"

On August 23, 2006, the International Astronomical Union (IAU, the official authority responsible for naming stars, planets, celestial bodies and phenomena, etc.—the official body of astronomy) re-classified Pluto as a *"dwarf planet"*. A "planet" in our solar system is a celestial body that "(a) orbits the Sun; (b) has sufficient mass for its self-gravity to overcome rigid-body forces so that it assumes a hydrostatic equilibrium (nearly round) shape; and (c) has cleared the neighborhood around its orbit." Pluto fits (a) and (b), but not (c). Pluto, Eris, Ceres, and others will be called "dwarf planets" because although they fit (a) and (b), they have not cleared the neighborhood around their orbits. Also, a "dwarf planet" is not a satellite (which may leave out Charon, but its large mass compared to Pluto may make Charon to be a "dwarf planet").

Pluto is a dwarf planet

The third criteria (c) of a planet from the IAU has caused a considerable amount of debate—what does "cleared the neighborhood around its orbit" mean? One interpretation is to say that the object gravitationally dominates its orbital zone where an orbital zone includes all objects whose orbits cross each other, their orbital periods differ by less than a factor of 10, and they are not in a stable resonance. Within that orbital zone, if a round object is much more massive (say, by at least 100 times) than the other objects combined mass, it will gravitationally dominate its zone. With this interpretation there is a clear separation between the eight "planets" (Mercury, Venus, Earth, Mars, Jupiter, Saturn, Uranus, and Neptune) and the "dwarf planets". All eight planets are at least 5000 times more massive than the other objects in their orbital zones while Pluto is only 0.07 times the mass of the rest of the objects in its orbital zone (Ceres is just 0.33 times the mass of the rest in its orbital zone). At the time of writing, Haumea and Makemake were the only others that had been officially recognized by the IAU as "dwarf planets". However, any body made mostly of ices larger than about 400 kilometers will be round, so the number of dwarf planets is undoubtedly much larger. By the time all of the bodies in the Kuiper Belt are found, the number of dwarf planets will probably number well over 200.

Even smaller objects (comets, most asteroids, etc.) will be called "Small Solar System Bodies". This does leave open the question of how this applies to planets outside the solar system, especially the truly planet-sized objects that are not bound to any star. Another controversial issue behind the IAU 2006 decision was the small proportion of members who voted on the decision. After the initial series of

Pluto and Charon (bottom right) are compared with the Earth and the Moon. Eris is probably about 20% larger than Pluto so it is still smaller than the Moon. Images courtesy of NASA.

Composite of New Horizon's views of Pluto and Charon to highlight the differences between the two. This image shows the two at approximately correct relative sizes but not a true separation distance. Image courtesy of NASA/JHUAPL/SwRI

arguments following the 2006 decision, over time the astronomers came to accept the decision and the planet definition issue did not even come up at the IAU 2009 and 2012 meetings.

diameter is key property: large objects have history of geologic activity

From a planetary geologist's perspective, the crucial measure of a planet, dwarf planet, or moon is its diameter. An object large enough for its own gravity to make it round will also have had enough internal heating to create the geologic activity necessary to reshape its surface from its initial formation 4.6 billion years ago. Also, the internal heating will mean the object has undergone differentiation where the heavier materials have sunk to the core and the lighter materials have risen nearer to the surface. For example, Pluto has a surprisingly geologically complex surface for such a small world, second only to Earth in its diversity: from mountain ranges to smooth plains and nitrogen ice glaciers that appear to still be active, as well as, cryo-volcanism that may also still be active. (Indeed, Pluto has shown us why we explore. Reality is so much cooler than what we can program in our virtual worlds because nature is far more creative than we are.)

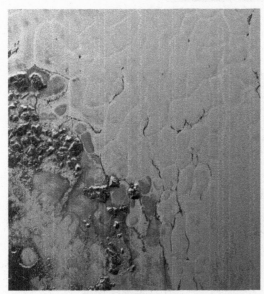

Left: large sections of Sputnik Planum on Pluto are being constantly renewed by the convection of the nitrogen ice.
Right: Tenzig Montes on west side of Sputnik Planum are Pluto's highest mountains. The mounds behind the mountains (in upper left of frame) are volcanic features composed of ices.
Images courtesy of NASA/JHUAPL/SwRI/LPI/Paul Schenk

Technically, the crucial measure should be the object's mass as in the IAU definition above but the diameter of a solar system object can usually be determined more quickly than its mass. The diameter can be determined from as little as a single image while mass determination requires multiple observations of how the object accelerates the motions of other bodies near it. In addition, solid objects of sufficient diameter and made of typical sorts of material will have enough mass to create some interesting geology. Finally, the use of either of the intrinsic properties of mass or diameter is much easier (practical) than whether or not the object has cleared its neighborhood when studying exoplanets (planets orbiting other stars).

The current list of objects of the Kuiper Belt is at the *Minor Planets Center*. A link to the updated list is given on the textbook's website. In mid-January 2006, the New Horizons spacecraft was launched on a 9.5-year trek to Pluto-Charon. After flying by Pluto-Charon in July 2015, it was directed to Kuiper Belt Object 2014 MU69, nicknamed "Ultima Thule". It flew by Ultima Thule on January 1, 2019.

angular momentum

Regardless of where it is in the solar system, the Sun's gravity is always pulling on the comets. When a comet is close to the Sun, it moves quickly because of the great force of gravity it feels from the Sun. It has enough **angular momentum** to avoid crashing into the Sun. **Angular momentum** is a measure of the amount of spin or orbital motion a celestial object has—see appendix A for more on angular momentum. As a comet moves away from the Sun, the Sun's gravity continually slows it down. Eventually, the comet slows down to the aphelion point and the Sun's gravity pulls it back.

A comet's motion around the Sun is sort of like a swing on the Earth. When the swing is closest to the ground, it moves quickly. As the swing moves up, the Earth's gravity is continually pulling on it, slowing it down. Eventually, the swing is slowed down so much that it stops and the Earth's gravity pulls it back down. The swing has enough angular momentum to avoid crashing to the ground.

10.7 Comet Beginnings and Endings

Comets formed 4.6 billion years ago along with the rest of the planets from the same solar nebula material. They were too small and cold to undergo any geologic activity (they did not differentiate), so they preserve the record of the early solar nebula composition and physical conditions. Those forming near the jovian planets were deflected outward, swallowed up or sent careening inward toward the terrestrial planets and the Sun. Some of the water now present on the terrestrial planets may have come from comets crashing into them.

Short period comets make hundreds to thousands of passes around the Sun spewing out gas and dust. Over time a comet will leave bits of dust along its orbit, each piece of dust has an orbit close to the comet's orbit. The dust grains are the size of a grain of sand or smaller. If the Earth passes through the comet's orbit, the dust grains can hit the Earth's atmosphere to make the spectacular displays called **meteor showers.** After many passages around the Sun, the nucleus has no more volatile material and it becomes "dead". Some asteroids are former comets.

meteor shower

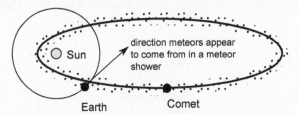

Comets leave dust trails in their orbit from repeated passages close to the Sun. If the Earth passes through the comet's orbit, we get a *meteor shower*.

The famous Perseid meteor shower in mid-August is due to Earth passing through the orbit of Comet Swift-Tuttle and the Leonid meteor shower in mid-November is due to Comet Tempel-Tuttle. The meteor showers appear to be coming from a particular direction in the sky so the meteor showers are named after the constellation they appear to be coming from. The divergence from a point in the sky (called the "*radiant*") is from the same geometric effect you see of straight railroad tracks or the edges of a straight road spreading out toward you from a distant point far away on the horizon. The Perseids appear to diverge from the Perseus constellation and the Leonids diverge from Leo. When the parent comet passes through the inner solar system, the meteor shower display is particularly impressive—several thousand meteors can be seen in one hour. Such events are called *meteor storms*. The last storm was for the Leonids in 2002. While most comet dust particles in meteor showers hit the atmosphere at 30 to 40 kilometers/second, the Leonid particles hit our atmosphere at 72 kilometers/second. Table 10.2 summarizes the characteristics for several impressive showers. A meteor shower will cover a time period of several days before and after the given maximum date.

meteor shower radiant

The meteors not associated with a meteor shower are bits of rock from asteroids.

regular meteors vs. meteor showers

Table 10.2: Some major meteor showers

Meteor shower	Max. Date	Meteors per hour	constellation/ RA :: Dec	comet source	meteor speed
Quadrantids	Jan. 3	40 to 110	Bootes, Hercules, Draco 15h 28m :: +50°	2003 EH1	25.5 km/sec
Lyrids	Apr. 22	8 to 12	Hercules-Lyra 18h 16m :: +34°	C/1861 G1 Thatcher	49 km/sec
Eta Aquarids	May 5	5 to 20	Aquarius 22h 24m :: 0°	Comet Halley	66 km/sec
Delta Aquarids	Jul. 28	15 to 35	Aquarius 22h 36m :: −17°	? (*maybe* 96P Machholz)	41 km/sec
Perseids	Aug. 11 to 12	40 to 70	Perseus 03h 04m :: +58°	Comet 109P/Swift-Tuttle	59 km/sec
Orionids	Oct. 21	13 to 30	Orion 06h 20m :: +15°	Comet Halley	(66 km/sec)
Taurids	Nov. 1 to 8	5 to 12	Taurus 03h 32m :: +14°	Comet Encke	28 km/sec
Leonids	Nov. 17	6 to 10	Leo 10h 08m :: +22°	Comet 55P/Temple-Tuttle	72 km/sec
Geminids	Dec. 13 to 14	50 to 70	Gemini 07h 32m :: +32°	3200 Phaethon (inactive comet?)	35 km/sec

The meteors that *are* associated with a meteor shower are much too fragile to survive their trip through our atmosphere and burn up at altitudes above 50 kilometers. Some of the comet dust intercepts the Earth at much slower speeds than those making the meteors and can make its way to the surface gently. More information about the study of this comet dust is available at the *Planetary Materials Curation* office of NASA (see the textbook's website for the link).

Vocabulary

angular momentum	dust tail	ion tail
Kuiper Belt	long period comet	meteor shower
nucleus (comet)	Oort Cloud	primitive
short period comet	solar wind	sublime

Review Questions

1. What is a comet?

2. How do comets give clues to the original conditions of the solar system?

3. If all of the objects in our solar system (Sun, planets, moons, etc.) formed from the same material, why are most meteorites and comets useful for finding out what the early solar system was like but the planets and the Sun are not?

4. What are the four components of a comet when it is close to the Sun and what are their dimensions?

5. Put the nucleus of a typical comet in the following sequence: stadium, Bakersfield, California, United States, Earth. Why can the nucleus not hang onto its gas and dust?

6. What unexpected things did we find out about the nuclei of comets from recent comet missions? Why were they unexpected?

7. What are comets made of and what is the structure of the nucleus like?

8. What happens to a comet's nucleus as it approaches the Sun?

9. What are the two tails of a comet and what are they made of? What gives them their characteristic colors?

10. Which way do the tails point? Why is a comet's tail *in front* of a comet as it moves away from the Sun?

11. How are **long period comets** associated with the **Oort Cloud**? How is the Oort Cloud known to exist if it has not been observed?

12. What direction can long period comets come from? What causes a comet in the Oort cloud to head toward the inner solar system?

13. How are **short period comets** associated with the **Kuiper Belt**?

14. What direction do most short period comets come from?

15. How were the Oort Cloud and Kuiper Belt formed?

16. What is the difference between a dwarf planet and a planet? Why is Pluto now considered a dwarf planet?

17. How are the meteors in a meteor shower different from the ordinary meteors you can see on any night of the year?

18. Why does a meteor shower happen at the same time every year?

10.8 Solar System Formation

The radioactive dating of meteorites says that the Sun, planets, moons, and solar system fluff formed about 4.6 billion years ago. What was it like then? How did the solar system form? There are some observed characteristics that any model of the solar system formation must explain.

10.8.1 Observables

a. All the planets' orbits lie roughly in the same plane.

b. The Sun's rotational equator lies nearly in this plane.

c. Planetary orbits are slightly elliptical, very nearly circular.

d. The planets revolve in a west-to-east direction. The Sun rotates in the same west-to-east direction.

e. The planets differ in composition. Their composition varies roughly with distance from the Sun: dense, metal-rich planets are in the inner part and giant, hydrogen-rich planets are in the outer part.

f. Meteorites differ in chemical and geologic properties from the planets and the Moon. Comets sampled by spacecraft are made of a mixture of rock/metals and hydrogen-rich compounds.

g. The Sun and most of the planets rotate in the same west-to-east direction. Their obliquity (the tilt of their rotation axes with respect to their orbits) are small. Uranus and Venus are exceptions.

h. The rotation rates of the planets and asteroids are similar—5 to 15 hours, unless tides slow them down.

i. The planet distances from the Sun obey Bode's law—*a descriptive* law that has no theoretical justification. However, Neptune is a significant exception to Bode's "law".

j. Planet-satellite systems resemble the solar system.

k. The Oort cloud and Kuiper Belt of comets.

l. The planets contain about 90% of the solar system's angular momentum (see appendix A), but the Sun contains over 99% of the solar system's mass.

10.8.2   Condensation Model

The model that best explains the observed characteristics of the present-day solar system is called the *Condensation Model*. The solar system formed from a large gas nebula that had some dust grains in it. The nebula collapsed under its own gravity to form the Sun and planets. What triggered the initial collapse is not known. Two of the best candidates are a shock wave from a nearby supernova or from the passage through a spiral arm. The gas cloud that made our solar system was probably part of a large star formation cloud complex. The stars that formed in the vicinity of the Sun have long since scattered to other parts of the galactic disk. Other stars and planets in our galaxy form in the same basic way as will be described here. The figure below summarizes the basic features of the *Condensation Model*. On the following pages is further explanation of the model and how it explains the observable items in the previous section.

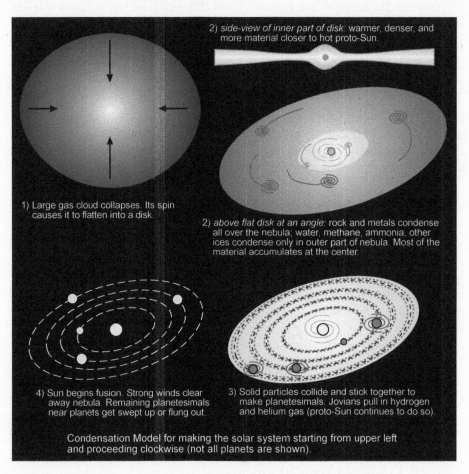

2) *side-view of inner part of disk:* warmer, denser, and more material closer to hot proto-Sun.

1) Large gas cloud collapses. Its spin causes it to flatten into a disk.

2) *above flat disk at an angle:* rock and metals condense all over the nebula; water, methane, ammonia, other ices condense only in outer part of nebula. Most of the material accumulates at the center.

4) Sun begins fusion. Strong winds clear away nebula. Remaining planetesimals near planets get swept up or flung out.

3) Solid particles collide and stick together to make planetesimals. Jovians pull in hydrogen and helium gas (proto-Sun continues to do so).

Condensation Model for making the solar system starting from upper left and proceeding clockwise (not all planets are shown).

A. A piece of a large cloud complex started to collapse about five billion years ago. The cloud complex had already been "polluted" with dust grains from previous generations of stars, so it was possible to form the rocky terrestrial planets. As the piece, called the *solar nebula* collapsed, its slight rotation increased. This is because of the conservation of angular momentum (see appendix A).

B. Centrifugal effects caused the outer parts of the nebula to flatten into a disk, while the core of the solar nebula formed the Sun. The planets formed from material in the disk and the Sun was at the center of the disk. This explains

solar nebula

items (a) and (b) of the observables above. Disks are seen around most of the young lower-mass stars in our Galaxy today, so we know that this part of the model is a common process in star formation.

C. Most of the gas molecules and dust grains moved in circular orbits. Those on noncircular orbits collided with other particles, so eventually the noncircular motions were dampened out. The large scale motion in the disk material was parallel, circular orbits. This explains items (c) and (d) of the observables above.

D. As the solar nebula collapsed, the gas and dust heated up through collisions among the particles. The solar nebula heated up to around 3000 K so everything was in a gaseous form. The solar nebula's composition was similar to the present-day Sun's composition: about 93% hydrogen, 6% helium, and about 1% silicates and iron, and the density of the gas and dust increased toward the core where the proto-Sun was. The inner, denser regions collapsed more quickly than the outer regions.

When the solar nebula stopped collapsing it began cooling, though the core forming the Sun remained hot. This meant that the outer parts of the solar nebula cooled off more than the inner parts closer to the hot proto-Sun. Only metal and rock materials could condense (solidify) at the high temperatures close to the proto-Sun. Therefore, the metal and rock materials could condense in all the places where the planets were forming. Volatile materials (like water, methane and ammonia) could only condense in the outer parts of the solar nebula. This explains item (e) of the observables above.

Around Jupiter's distance from the proto-Sun the temperature was cool enough to freeze water (the so-called "snow line"). Further out from the proto-Sun, ammonia and methane were able to condense. There was a significant amount of water in the solar nebula. Because the density of the solar nebula material increased inward, there was more water at Jupiter's distance than at the distances of Saturn, Uranus, or Neptune. The greater amount of water *ice* at Jupiter's distance from the proto-Sun helped it grow larger than the other planets. Although, there was more water closer to the Sun than Jupiter, that water was too warm to condense.

Material with the highest freezing temperatures condensed to form the *chondrules* that were then incorporated in lower freezing temperature material. Any material that later became part of a planet underwent further heating and processing when the planet differentiated so the heavy metals sunk to the planet's core and lighter metals floated up to nearer the surface. The first part of observables item (f) is explained.

The inner planets were not totally devoid of volatile material, though. Water could still be incorporated into the minerals to form hydrated minerals that could survive the extreme heat of the inner part of the solar system without all being vaporized away, even during the phase of numerous, large impacts in the early solar system. The three comets sampled up close by spacecraft, Tempel 1, Wild 2 and Churyumov-Gerasimenko, are made of a mixture of materials with high and low melting temperatures (second part of observables item (f)). Therefore, the materials making them up would have come from different parts of the early solar system and there was more mixing in the solar nebula than previously thought. The still-forming proto-Sun probably produced strong winds as seen in young, protostars today and those winds could be responsible for at least part of the mixing of solar nebula materials.

E. Small eddies formed in the disk material, but since the gas and dust particles

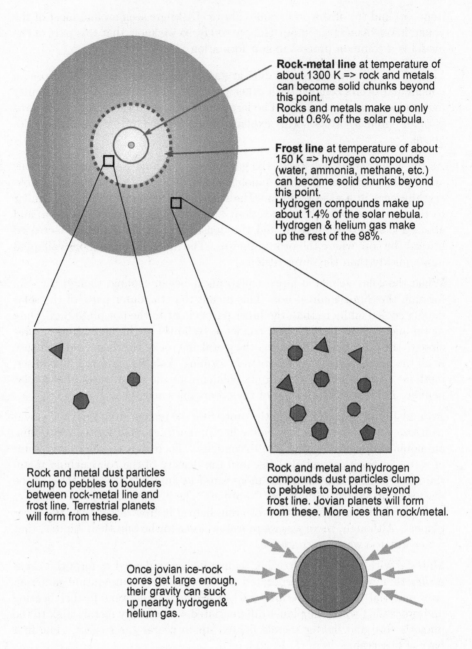

Rock-metal line at temperature of about 1300 K => rock and metals can become solid chunks beyond this point.
Rocks and metals make up only about 0.6% of the solar nebula.

Frost line at temperature of about 150 K => hydrogen compounds (water, ammonia, methane, etc.) can become solid chunks beyond this point.
Hydrogen compounds make up about 1.4% of the solar nebula.
Hydrogen & helium gas make up the rest of the 98%.

Rock and metal dust particles clump to pebbles to boulders between rock-metal line and frost line. Terrestrial planets will form from these.

Rock and metal and hydrogen compounds dust particles clump to pebbles to boulders beyond frost line. Jovian planets will form from these. More ices than rock/metal.

Once jovian ice-rock cores get large enough, their gravity can suck up nearby hydrogen& helium gas.

moved in almost parallel, near-circular orbits, they collided at low velocities. Instead of bouncing off each other or smashing each other, they were able to stick together through electrostatic forces to form *planetesimals*. The larger planetesimals were able to attract other planetesimals through gravity and increase in size. This process is called *accretion*.

The coalescing particles tended to form bodies rotating in the same direction as the disk revolved. The forming planet eddies had similar rotation rates. This explains items (g) and (h) above. The gravity of the planetesimals tended to divide the solar nebula into ring-shaped zones. This process explains item (i) above.

F. More massive planetesimals had stronger gravity and could pull in more of the surrounding solar nebula material. Some planetesimals formed mini-solar nebulae around them which would later form the moons. This explains item (j) above. The Jupiter and Saturn planetesimals had a lot of water ice mass, so they swept up a lot of hydrogen and helium. The Uranus and Neptune planetesimals were smaller so they swept up less hydrogen and helium (there was also less to sweep up so far out). The inner planetesimals were too small to attract the abundant hydrogen and helium.

G. The small icy planetesimals near the forming Jupiter and perhaps Saturn were flung out of the solar system. Those near Uranus and Neptune were flung to very large orbits. This explains the Oort Cloud of item (k) above, though some of the gravitational flinging by Uranus and Neptune would have been weaker to form the closer scattered disk. There was not enough material to form a large planet beyond Neptune. Also, accretion of material at these great distances progressed more slowly than material closer to the Sun. The icy planetesimals beyond Neptune formed the Kuiper Belt. The large planets were able to stir things up enough to send some of the icy material near them careening toward the terrestrial planets. The icy bodies gave water to the terrestrial planets.

Recent sophisticated computer simulations have shown that gravity interactions between the giant planets themselves could have changed their orbits from the ones they originally had. Jupiter would have slowly spiraled inward while Saturn, Neptune, and Uranus would have slowly spiraled outward until Saturn reached the point where it took twice as long to orbit the Sun as Jupiter. This 1-2 resonance would have greatly changed the orbits of Neptune and Uranus, even to the point of shifting Neptune's closer orbit to a much larger one outside of Uranus' orbit. Older versions of the Condensation Model had difficulty explaining the formation of a planet the size of Neptune at Neptune's current distance from the Sun because of the amount of available material in the solar disk would have been too small at that distance from the forming Sun. If Neptune had formed much closer in than it is now and later moved to its present position, then the problem goes away. In addition, the onset of the 1-2 Jupiter-Saturn resonance would have led to a sudden scattering of planetesimals which would explain the possible spike in the number of giant impacts throughout the solar system about 3.8 billion years ago (as well as halting Jupiter's inward spiral).

H. The planets got big enough to retain heat and have liquid interiors. The heavier materials like iron and nickel sank to the planet cores while the lighter materials like silicates and gases rose toward the surface, in a process called *differentiation*. The sinking of the heavy material created more heat energy. The planets also had sufficient radioactive decays occurring in them to melt rocky material and keep it liquid in the interior. The small planetesimals that were not incorporated into the large planets did not undergo differentiation. This explains the first part of item (f) of the observables.

I. The proto-Sun had a magnetic field and spewed out ions. The ions were dragged along by the magnetic field that rotated with the proto-Sun. The dragging of the ions around slowed down the proto-Sun's rotation rate. Also, *accretion disks* like the solar nebula tend to transfer angular momentum outward as they transfer mass inward. This explains item (l) above.

J. Because of its great compression, the core of the proto-Sun core reached about 10 million Kelvin and the hydrogen nuclei started fusing together to produce helium nuclei and a lot of energy. The Sun "turned on." The Sun produced strong winds called *T-Tauri winds* that swept out the rest of the nebula that was not already incorporated into the planets. This whole process took just a few hundred million years and was finished by about 4.6 billion years ago.

After forming the disk, the disk would have cooled as the heat was radiated to space. However, before ices could condense and clump closer to the proto-Sun than the "frost line", the Sun went through the T-Tauri stage and the strong winds swept out the remaining gas including the hydrogen compounds. If the nebula had cooled more quickly, the inner planets might have been able to get bigger and have more hydrogen compounds in them. If the nebula was warmer, then the "frost line" would have been further out, so Jupiter would have been a terrestrial planet. The ice cores forming beyond about Neptune's distance never got big enough to capture the surrounding hydrogen and helium gas—they stayed small to become the dwarf planets such as Pluto, Eris, Makemake, Haumea, etc. and the other Kuiper Belt Objects.

observing other plane-tary systems

Although the Condensation Model explains a number of observed facts of the properties of the present-day solar system, we have been looking at a sample size of just one: our solar system. It has been only relatively recently that we have been able to test the theory with other forming and fully-developed planetary systems with the placement of powerful telescopes above the Earth's atmosphere. Observations in the infrared and sub-millimeter wavelengths have enabled us to peer through the thick dust that shields forming stars and their planetary disks. In some cases some of the dust/gas cocoons have been stripped away by ultraviolet from nearby very hot stars so we can study them in optical wavelengths. These star formation processes will be explored a bit more fully in another chapter, but I will note briefly here that the processes described above are seen in other forming planetary systems and a great majority of forming stars have flattened disks with them so planet formation (or at least the "solar nebula" disk formation part) is a common process. We have used those observations to modify and improve the Condensation Model. In particular our observations of other planetary systems has forced us to seriously explore how planets can migrate inward from where they first started forming. Perhaps, one should not be surprised that that could happen. As described in item G above, gravitational interactions flung chunks of material all about. On the other hand, those chunks were much smaller than the forming planets. As described in the next section, the observations show that gravitational interactions could also shift things as big as the planets themselves.

Review Questions

1. What observed facts does the *Condensation Model* of the solar system formation explain?

2. From what did the solar system form?

3. Why are the inner terrestrial planets small and rocky while the outer jovian planets are large and gaseous?

4. Why does a disk form in the collapsing cloud?

5. What role do dust particles play in planet formation?

6. If the disk was moving so quickly, how did it create big enough clumps to make planets?

7. What drove out the rest of the nebula after the planets formed?

8. Why are the planet interiors made of layers of increasing density closer to their cores?

9. How do we test the Condensation Model of the solar system?

10.9   Other Planetary Systems

Nearly 4000 planets (at the time of writing) have been found orbiting other stars—**exoplanets** (sometimes also called *extrasolar planets*)—in nearly 3000 exoplanet systems (over 600 are multi-planet systems).   This section will first look at how we find exoplanets and then I will draw some preliminary conclusions based on the statistics of the orbits and masses of the exoplanets.

exoplanet

10.9.1   Finding Exoplanets

Detecting exoplanets around other stars is a difficult project requiring very careful observations.   At first finding exoplanets might seem a simple thing to do—take pictures of stars and look for small faint things orbiting them. An exoplanet would indeed be a faint: a billion or more times fainter than a star in the visible band—the glare of the starlight would wash out the feeble light of an exoplanet.   The **direct imaging technique** of finding exoplanets would be better accomplished in the infrared band because the exoplanet's thermal spectrum would have maximum emission in the infrared band. Also, stars produce less infrared energy than visible band energy—an exoplanet would only be ten *thousand* to a hundred *thousand* times fainter than the star. The exoplanet would still be very faint, but at least the contrast ratio is improved by many thousands of times. Forty-five exoplanets (as of the time of writing) have been found this way.

imaging exoplanets is hard to do
direct imaging technique

less contrast in the infrared band

Visible (optical) band — Planet lost in glare of star that is very bright in the visible band.

Infrared band — Planet more luminous in the infrared band and star not so bright.

Some of the exoplanets imaged are very young and still quite warm from their formation.   Therefore, the young exoplanets are quite bright in the infrared and easier to detect.   Some exoplanets have been imaged by blocking the light from the much brighter star with a device called a *coronagraph* so that the feeble light from the exoplanet can be detected.   Use of a coronagraph was essential to create the first visible light (optical) image of an exoplanet: that orbiting the very bright star, Fomalhaut, shown below. The black area in the center is the coronagraph, the white dot shows the location of the star, the ring is a dusty debris disk analogous to our solar system's Kuiper Belt (but much further out), the small white box shows the location of the exoplanet some 115 AU from its star, and the inset shows its motion over eight years of its entire 1522-year orbit. Its motion proved it was an object orbiting the star.

Astronomers have detected disks of dust and gas around young stars using sensitive infrared detectors on the largest telescopes in the world. An equivalent amount of material locked up into a single object will have a smaller total surface area than if it was broken up into many tiny particles. The disks have a lot of surface area

dust disks emit a lot of infrared energy

Fomalhaut System
Hubble Space Telescope • STIS

NASA and ESA   STScI-PRC13-01a

and, therefore, can emit a lot of infrared energy. Some bright stars in our sky have dust around them: Vega, Beta Pictoris, and Fomalhaut. These are systems possibly in the beginning stages of forming planets. One disk around the star HR 4796A appears to be in between the dust disk stage and a fully-fledged planet system. The inner part of the disk has been cleared away. Presumably, the dust material has now coalesced into larger things like planets. The exoplanets would have a smaller surface area than if the material was still in tiny particles form, so the exoplanets will be much fainter. The Hubble Space Telescope has also detected disks of gas and dust around 50% of the stars still forming in the Orion Nebula. It appears that the formation of planet systems is a common process in the universe.

exoplanet makes star wobble
center of mass
astrometric technique

Another way to look for exoplanets around other stars is to notice their gravitational effect on the stars they orbit. One signature of an exoplanet would be that the star would appear to wobble about as the star and the exoplanet orbit a point situated between them, proportionally closer to the more massive star, called the **center of mass**. This technique is called the **astrometric technique**. Our Sun wobbles because of the gravity of the planets orbiting it. Most of the wobble is due to Jupiter which contains more mass than all of the other planets combined. However, the wobble is tiny! Because the Sun is over a thousand times more massive than Jupiter, the **center of mass** is over a thousand times closer to the Sun, or about 47,000 kilometers above the surface of the Sun (this distance is less than 7% the radius of the Sun). Despite the tiny wobble, astronomers on planets orbiting nearby stars could detect this wobble using the same technology we have here on Earth if they observed the Sun's motion very carefully over a couple of decades. The stronger the gravity between the star and exoplanet, the larger will be the wobble of the star and the easier to detect. Therefore, the **astrometric technique** is well-suited to finding massive jovian exoplanets close to their parent stars. Not only is the wobble larger but it is also happens more quickly, so one can see the periodic motion in a short amount of time. Because of the distorting effect of the Earth's atmosphere, only one exoplanet has been found using this technique using ground-based telescopes (at the time of writing). The now-canceled SIM Lite mission was to use this technique and the Gaia mission, launched in December 2013, uses this technique.

doppler shift technique *easiest way to find planets*

Another signature of an exoplanet would be doppler shifts in the star's spectral lines as they orbit their common center of mass. This **doppler shift technique** (also sometimes called the *radial velocity technique*) has been the easiest and most prolific way to find exoplanets so far. As of the time of writing 751 exoplanets have been found using the **doppler shift technique**. Like the *astrometric technique*, the *doppler shift technique* is well-suited to finding jovian exoplanets close to their parent stars. However, in 2016 astronomers were able to refine the technique enough to detect an exoplanet around Proxima Centauri (the closest of the three stars in the nearest star system to us) that is just 1.3 times the mass of the Earth. It produces a doppler star wobble of just 1.38 meters per second or about the speed of a person walking. Proxima Centauri b orbits within Proxima Centauri's *habitable zone*. The *habitable zone* is the region around a star in which an exoplanet's *surface* would be not too hot nor too cold for liquid water to exist on the *surface* (see chapter 17).

pick up star wobble with doppler effect

habitable zone

In another milestone of the technique, astronomers announced in late June 2013 after several years of radial velocity measurements of a nearby star Gliese 667C (just 22 light years away), the discovery of three exoplanets orbiting in the *habitable zone* of the star. While other exoplanets have been found in the habitable zones of stars, especially by the Kepler mission discussed below, this was the largest number of exoplanets in a habitable zone up to that time (TRAPPIST-1 took the title in 2016), and for Gliese 667C, very likely the largest number of exoplanets possible in its habitable zone (so the habitable zone is said to be "dynamically packed"). In our solar system there is just one habitable planet, Earth. Mars might have been habitable if it was bigger to retain a thicker atmosphere and have plate tectonics working on it for long-term habitability (section 9.6.3). Gliese 667C is a low-mass star, smaller than our Sun and those cooler, lower mass stars are more common in the Galaxy than stars like the Sun.

The period of the star wobble is measured and then the distance (semi-major axis of the orbit) is derived from Kepler's third law (section 4.5). The star's velocity change is measured and then the total mass of the system is derived from Newton's Laws of Motion (section 5.1). We can estimate the mass of the star from its spectral type, estimate the exoplanet velocity from the star wobble period and then derive the exoplanet's mass. However, the doppler effect tells you about the motion along the line of sight only. The exoplanet orbits are undoubtedly inclined, or tipped, to our line of sight and the amount of inclination is uncertain. This introduces an uncertainty in the derived masses of the exoplanets. Usually, astronomers will quote the masses as "mass×sin(orbit inclination angle)", so the actual exoplanet masses could be higher. The star-wobble techniques can also give us the orbit eccentricity (section 4.5) if we have observations from the entire orbit. The three exoplanets in the habitable zone of Gliese 667C have minimum masses ("M sin(i)") of 2.7 to 3.8 times the mass of the Earth, so they are called "super-Earths". Because of the uncertainty in inclination of their orbits, their masses may be up to two times larger based on computer models of what gravitationally stable planet orbits would be possible.

star wobble gives orbit size and exoplanet mass

orbit inclination uncertainty

star wobble gives orbit shape
super-Earths

In the context of exoplanet research, a "super-Earth" is usually defined by mass only: a world between about 1.9 to ten times the mass of Earth (the lower bound value of 1.9 Earth masses is not universally agreed upon, so you will find a variety of mass and diameter ranges in the research papers). The term does not necessarily mean the planet is habitable. The upper limit of ten times the mass of Earth is used because it is thought that planets larger than 10 times the mass of Earth will have enough gravity to suck up the hydrogen and helium surrounding it as it is forming and become a jovian planet. The Kepler spacecraft mission defined super-Earth by diameter instead of mass because it used the transit method (defined below) to find exoplanets. For Kepler, a super-Earth is any exoplanet between 1.25 and 2 Earth diameters. If the super-Earth has a density the same as Earth, then that corresponds to a mass range of 1.95 to 8 Earth masses. However, the discovery of

super-Earth: 1.9 to 10 Earth mass

Kepler super-Earth: 1.25 to 2 Earth diameter

Kepler 10c announced in June 2014 with a mass of 17.2 times the Earth but just 2.35 times the diameter of the Earth means it has a density = 7.1 times water, so it is definitely a rocky world instead of something like Neptune or Jupiter. (Nature doesn't always fit into our nice, neat boxes.)

super-Earth vs. mini-Neptune

A research group headed by Benjamin Fulton might have found the dividing line between super-Earths and mini-Neptunes. In this refinement of "super-Earth", a super-Earth is a planet that is primarily a rock-iron world while a mini-Neptune planet has a much greater proportion of lighter hydrogen compounds—water, ammonia, methane—and hydrogen and helium. If the exoplanet is less than about 1.75 times the diameter of Earth, it is a super-Earth. If it is above two times the diameter of Earth, the forming exoplanet has enough mass to pull in enough hydrogen and helium from its surrounding environment nebulae to become something like Neptune. Fulton's group has sharply defined the upper size for a habitable world. Worlds larger than two times the size of Earth will either have no surface or the surface is under an extremely deep atmosphere with such a crushingly high pressure (far more than that found at the deepest point of the Marianas Trench on Earth) that no life we know of could exist.

Astronomers cannot yet determine both the diameters and masses of most of the giant exoplanets, so their densities, and, therefore, their composition is still unknown. Before the Kepler mission, only a small fraction of the giant exoplanets had been observed to move in front of their stars and cause an eclipse or dimming of the starlight from ground-based telescopes. This is called a *transit* so this means of detecting exoplanets is called the **transit technique**. A transit means that the exoplanet's orbit is aligned with our line of sight (and the inclination angle is nearly 90 degrees). From the exoplanet transit, astronomers have been able to accurately measure the diameter of the exoplanet. Using the exoplanet mass from the star wobble methods, you can then determine the density.

transit technique

transit gives exoplanet diameter

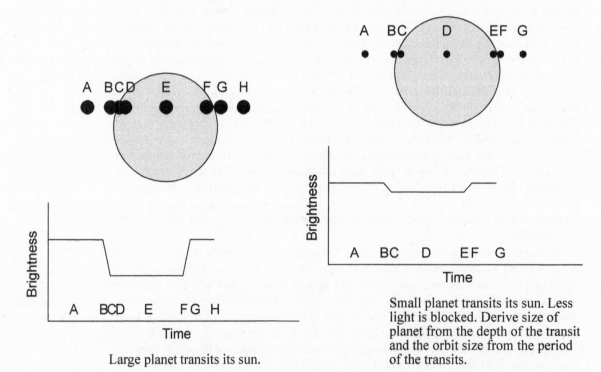

Large planet transits its sun.

Small planet transits its sun. Less light is blocked. Derive size of planet from the depth of the transit and the orbit size from the period of the transits.

Careful observations of the spectrum of the star while the exoplanet is transiting across will enable astronomers to determine the chemical composition of the exoplanet's atmosphere using spectroscopy. In other cases, the exoplanet's spectrum is found from taking the spectrum of the star plus exoplanet, then taking the spectrum of just the star when the exoplanet is behind the star and subtracting it from the star plus exoplanet spectrum. One exoplanet, HD 189733b, has water, methane and carbon dioxide in its atmosphere but the exoplanet is much too hot and massive to support life. It was not until January 2010 that astronomers had been able to take the spectrum of an exoplanet directly—an important step in eventually being able to analyze the spectrum of a terrestrial exoplanet to see if it is supporting life on it.

transit may give us spectrum of exoplanet

Most of the transiting exoplanets discovered in the early years were first detected via the doppler shift technique, but with the exquisite instrumentation on the Kepler spacecraft, the transit technique became a very prolific way of searching for exoplanets around other stars. By the end of the mission in October 2018, Kepler had found 2687 exoplanets with another 2898 candidates still to be confirmed. Candidate exoplanets are those that have not been verified yet through follow-up observations to make sure the star dimming is not due to another star as in an eclipsing binary system or a dead star called a white dwarf. As of the time of writing, a total of 3059 confirmed exoplanets had been found by the transit technique, including fifteen (so far) by the successor to Kepler, the TESS spacecraft. Most planetary systems do not have their orbits so exquisitely aligned with our line of sight so *a lot* of stars would need to be looked at to improve the chances of finding even a few transits. One advantage of the transit technique over the star-wobble methods for exoplanet detection is that you would be able to detect terrestrial exoplanets (i.e., small exoplanets). Small exoplanets like the Earth produce too small a wobble in their parent star to be detected by the star-wobble methods. The COROT mission (ESA) has found an exoplanet less than twice the diameter of the Earth. However, this exoplanet is so close to its star that the exoplanet's surface temperature is 1000 to 1500 deg C! Kepler was able to detect exoplanets as small as the Moon.

The NASA Kepler spacecraft mission looked at 156,000 stars *simultaneously* to look for Earth-sized exoplanets during four-year period of time. The spacecraft focused on exoplanets that could be in the stars' habitable zones. Only 0.5% of the stars are expected to have their planets orbits in the habitable zones properly aligned for detection by Kepler. A terrestrial exoplanet with mass between 0.5 to 10 Earth masses will cause its star to dim by a fractional amount of between 0.00005 to 0.0004, respectively, and the transits will last just a few hours. Each exoplanet transit must be repeatable at least two more times after the first detected transit with the same time interval between transits and depth of transit. Such repeatability of the transits would mean that something was orbiting the star and not just some chance occurrence of an unrelated object passing in front of the star. For a solar-type star with an exoplanet in the habitable zone, the exoplanet would transit the star once a year. However, this assumes that the stars are calm and steady like our Sun. The Kepler team found that a number of the stars are a bit more active, more variable, than our Sun, so they got an extension on the mission to get more observations in order to tease out the dimmings due to transiting exoplanets from those due to the intrinsic variability of the stars themselves. The mission extension was to carry the mission through to the year 2016 but hardware failure of a couple of its stabilizer reaction wheels brought the observing to an end in early 2013. Although the Cygnus observing is finished, the Kepler team still has many thousands of transits to sift through, so there are plenty of discoveries still to be made. Using the number of confirmed exoplanets from the candidate list along with the numbers of candidates that were later rejected, we now have a very good idea of how well the Kepler team's transit vetting process works in finding possible planets. Just ten percent of the exoplanet candidates turn out to be something else. That leaves 90% of the exoplanet candidates as actual exoplanets.

Kepler mission: search for Earth-sized exoplanets in the habitable zone

three identical transit events needed

Beginning in June 2014, the Kepler mission employed a clever technique that used the pressure of sunlight to help point the telescope with the remaining two stabilizer reaction wheels. This mission called "K2" looked at objects near the ecliptic. In the K2 phase, Kepler looked at other objects in addition to hunting for exoplanets such as variable stars, star clusters, and galaxies.

At least sixty-five of the confirmed exoplanets in the Exoplanet Archive (at the time of writing) are definitely rocky exoplanets with densities 3.0 times or greater than that of water. The first rocky exoplanet discovered, called Kepler-10b, has a density of 8.8 times that of water. However, Kepler-10b orbits less than 0.017 AU from its star (Mercury orbits our Sun at 0.39 AU), so its surface temperature is over 1800 K! The oceans there would be liquid iron. Another confirmed exoplanet, Kepler-22b, is the first one from the Kepler mission known to be in its star's habitable zone. At 2.4 times the diameter of Earth, Kepler-22b is considered to be a "mini-Neptune", instead of a "super-Earth".

Kepler-10b

Kepler-22b

super-Earth up to 1.75 Earth diameters Kepler 186f

The first confirmed exoplanet the size of Earth in a star's habitable zone is Kepler 186f at just 1.1 times the size of the Earth. **If** Kepler 186f has the same density as the Earth, it would be a little over 1.3 times the mass of the Earth. The statistics of the known densities of exoplanets plus sophisticated modeling tells us that about 75% of the exoplanets smaller than 1.5 Earth-radii are rocky worlds. Therefore, it is very likely that Kepler 186f is a rocky world composed mostly of silicates, iron, nickel, and magnesium like the Earth.

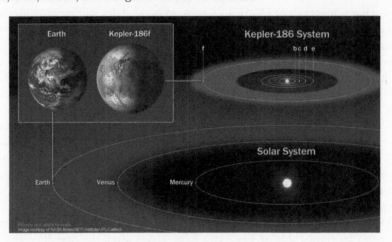

Kepler 20

Kepler 37

Another confirmed exoplanet system, Kepler 20, has five exoplanets including two exoplanets that are the size of Earth. Kepler-20e is smaller than Venus and Kepler-20f is just 3% larger than the Earth. Unfortunately, both of them orbit well inside Kepler-20's habitable zone but this discovery clearly shows that the Kepler spacecraft can detect Earth-sized exoplanets and that such exoplanets definitely exist. Yet another confirmed exoplanet system, Kepler 37, has one exoplanet just slightly larger than the Moon, a second slightly smaller than Venus, and a third that is twice the size of the Earth. In the last data release for the Cygnus field project (before the K2 phase), the Kepler team gave a list of forty-eight exoplanets (28 confirmed and 20 candidates) with diameters less than 1.8 times Earth's diameter that reside within their star's habitable zone. The planet most like the Earth-Sun system is the candidate KOI 7711.01 with a diameter 1.31 times Earth's diameter orbiting its star every 302.8 days. It receives 87% of the energy that Earth receives from the Sun and the star is slightly cooler than the Sun. Although the Kepler team has not found the exact Earth analog of an exoplanet of identical size to the Earth orbiting a star with the same temperature as the Sun at the exact same distance as the Earth is from the Sun, it has become quite clear that there are *plenty* of small rocky-world exoplanets orbiting within the habitable zone of their star in just this one small section of the Milky Way we have searched.

Other statistical results from the Kepler mission include: nature makes planets of a variety of sizes up to 3 Earth diameters with equal ease and has more difficulty with larger planets like Saturn or Jupiter; 22% of sun-like stars (that's 1 in 5) have a planet of 1 to 2 Earth diameters in size orbiting in the star's habitable zone; at least 70% of ordinary stars including those hotter than the Sun and the great majority cooler than the Sun have a planet of some size orbiting them; and about 50% or so of the very common cool stars have a planet between 0.5 to 1.4 Earth diameters orbiting within their habitable zone. That last statistic means that the closest Earth-size exoplanet having its orbit aligned just right with our line of sight so the exoplanet transits its star is just 29 light years away—within very easy reach of the TESS mission that is looking for transiting exoplanets around stars in all directions but at closer distances than the Kepler mission.

exoplanet statistics from Kepler

The transit method can usually find just the exoplanet's diameter and the doppler shift technique must be used to determine the exoplanet's mass. In a few systems with multiple exoplanets it may be possible to find the exoplanet masses. The precision of the Kepler measurements are high enough that the Kepler team has been able to detect changes in the exoplanet periods caused by the exoplanets pulling on each other. The exoplanet mass follows from observing the amount of acceleration changes in the exoplanets' motions. This also requires the exoplanets to have closely spaced orbits. One last thing to note is that in order to even see a system with multiple transiting exoplanets at all requires the exoplanets to have very closely aligned orbits, even more closely aligned than the planets in our own solar system—there are some very flat systems out there!

While the Kepler mission was getting most of the media attention, the Spitzer Space Telescope using the transit technique revealed in early 2017 that the TRAPPIST-1 red-dwarf star, just 40 light years away, has seven Earth-size exoplanets orbiting it (see figures next page). Three of the planets (TRAPPIST-1e, f, g) are in the middle of the habitable zone and the four others could have liquid water if they had just the right atmospheric conditions. The TRAPPIST-1 exoplanets are within 0.062 AU of the star (that is just one-sixth the distance that Mercury is from the Sun), so they are very close to each other. Standing on one planet, its neighbor would appear larger than the Moon in our sky. Their closeness to each other also enables us to get their masses. A year after the announcement, NASA released results from Spitzer, Kepler, and Hubble observations of the TRAPPIST-1 system that showed all the planets are made of rock and some may have much more water than Earth. Hubble observations show that the inner five planets do not have thick, hydrogen-rich like Neptune. TRAPPIST-1e is the densest of the bunch with a density 1.02 times that of Earth. It receives about 60% of the energy Earth receives from the Sun.

TRAPPIST-1

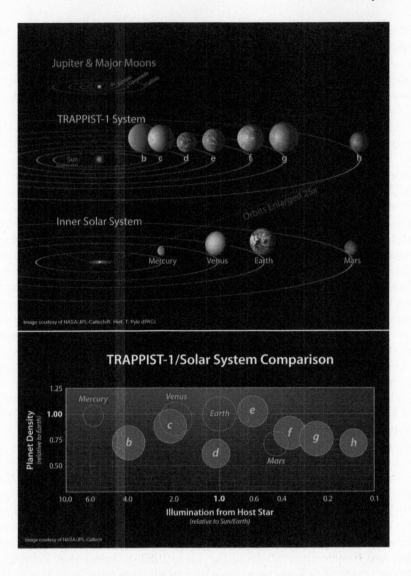

Image courtesy of NASA/JPL-Caltech/R. Hurt, T. Pyle (IPAC)

Image courtesy of NASA/JPL-Caltech

finding exoplanets using gravitational lenses

Another method of exoplanet detection uses the gravitational lensing effect discussed in chapter 6. It is summarized in the figure on the next page. When a star passes almost in front of another more distant star as seen from the Earth (the stars are not orbiting each other), the light from the distant star can be warped and focused toward us by the gravity of the nearer star to produce multiple images of the distant star or even a ring of light if they are aligned exactly right. This lensing effect is too small and the resolving powers of telescopes are too small to see the multiple images. The multiple images will blend together into a single blurry blob that is brighter than when the multiple images are not present (a **microlens** event). As the nearer star moves in front of the distant star, the nearer star's blurry blob will appear to brighten and then dim as the nearer star moves out of alignment. The microlens event for typical stars in our galaxy moving at typical speeds will last a few weeks to a few months and the amount of the brightness magnification will depend on how closely the near and distant stars are aligned with our line of sight. See the textbook website for an animation of this effect.

If the nearer star has a planetary system with an exoplanet at the right position, a smaller and briefer microlens event will happen superimposed on top of the star's microlens. By looking for brief deviations in the otherwise smooth increase, then smooth decrease of a stellar microlens event, you could detect the presence of an

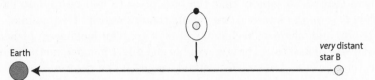

Earth

very distant
star B

Closer but still distant star A with planet in small orbit begins to move between us and
very distant star B.

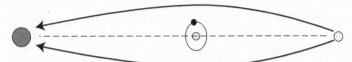

Closer star A warps space so additional light from *very* distant star B reaches us: *very* distant
star B appears to brighten.

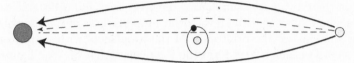

Closer star A's planet warps space less than closer star A so a little extra light from
very distant star B added to already lensed light.

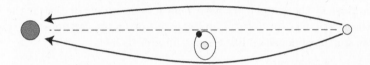

Closer star A's planet now enough out of the way to not lens the very distant star B's light
but closer star's gravity still enough to lens some of the light: we see extra short-lived
increase or other noticeable deviation in the otherwise symmetric, larger and longer-lived
brightening then dimming in the *very* distant star B's brightness caused by the closer star.

exoplanet. This method is called the **microlens technique**. The exoplanet's mass and orbit size could be determined from careful measurements of the brief deviations. The microlens event method can be used to detect jovian-mass and terrestrial-mass exoplanets near their parent stars and the parent stars are distant from the Earth. Like the transit method, *a lot* of stars must be monitored to pick up even a single stellar microlens event. The microlens events are due to chance alignments that are not repeatable. Seventy-five exoplanets orbiting stars have been found using the **microlens technique** (as of the time of writing).

microlens gives exoplanet mass and orbit size

In May 2011, two teams using the microlens technique announced the discovery of several other exoplanets that are not orbiting a star—"free floaters". The teams had observed about 50 million stars in the direction of the Milky Way's bulge every 10 to 50 minutes in 2006 and 2007 looking for those chance alignments. They found a surprisingly large number of brightenings caused by planet mass objects alone. A statistical extrapolation of the results says that the free floater planets could be almost twice as numerous as normal main sequence stars in the Galaxy!

free floaters

The searches have so far focused on stars similar to the Sun, but exoplanets have also been found around other types of stars, from those much larger and hotter than the Sun to stars much smaller and cooler than the Sun, and even four systems have exoplanets orbiting a pulsar (a type of ultra-compact, dead star discussed in chapter 13—exoplanets found using a variation of the doppler shift technique called the *timing technique*). The number of systems discovered and the details

exoplanets are found around all types of stars

microlens technique

about them changes so rapidly that the best place to find up-to-date information on exoplanets is on the internet (see the textbook's website for the links).

The transit and microlens techniques are not good for looking exoplanets around a particular star of interest. The star-wobble and direct imaging methods are better. However, the transit and microlens methods are useful for determining the statistics of planetary systems in our galaxy, particularly the number of star systems with terrestrial exoplanets in the habitable zones. Another possible exoplanet detection method uses the amount of lithium in a star. A comparison of stars with planets and those stars without planets shows that the stars with planets have about 1% of the lithium in the star than in stars without planets. Such a detection method could offer a much more cost-effective to search for planetary systems than the other techniques being used now.

lithium amount as a way to find exoplanets

10.9.2   Results and Testing the Theory

The figures on these two pages summarize the orbit sizes and orbit eccentricities of the other planetary systems with known orbit properties (as of the time of writing). The first set summarizes the orbit sizes of the exoplanets with known orbit sizes and masses as of December 2018 from the Exoplanet Archive. The figure below is for the exoplanets with masses greater than 0.5 times Jupiter's mass and the top figure on the next page is for the less massive exoplanets. Note that the low-mass exoplanets farther from their star are going to be *much* harder to detect with our current techniques, so the bars for the larger orbits are very likely shorter than they should be. Most of the exoplanets with known orbit eccentricities in the bottom figure on the next page are Saturn-Jupiter mass or larger and most of those that transit their star have densities like Saturn-Jupiter or less.

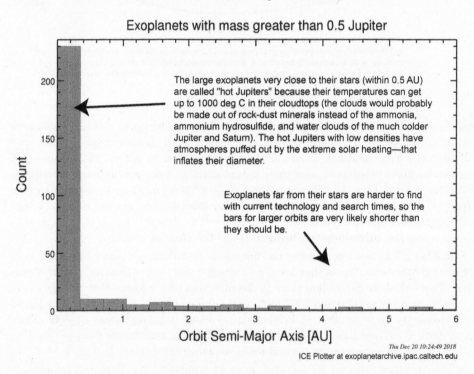

Two things to notice are how close the large exoplanets (50% Jupiter's mass or larger) are to their stars and the large eccentricities of some of the exoplanet orbits. The exoplanets very close to their stars are called *"hot Jupiters"* because their temperatures can get up to 1000 deg C in their cloud tops (the clouds would probably

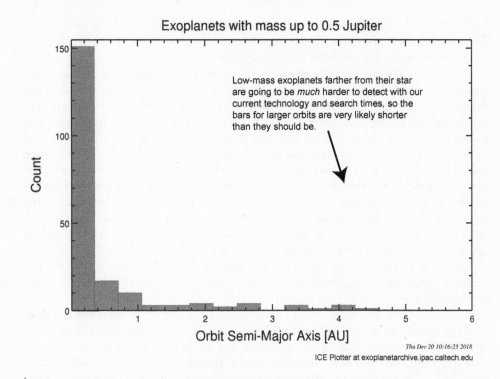

Exoplanets with mass up to 0.5 Jupiter

Low-mass exoplanets farther from their star are going to be *much* harder to detect with our current technology and search times, so the bars for larger orbits are very likely shorter than they should be.

Thu Dec 20 10:16:25 2018
ICE Plotter at exoplanetarchive.ipac.caltech.edu

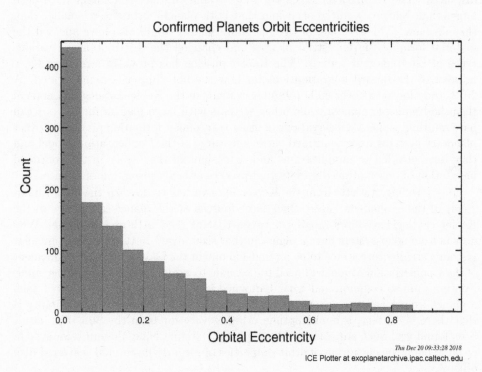

Confirmed Planets Orbit Eccentricities

Thu Dec 20 09:33:28 2018
ICE Plotter at exoplanetarchive.ipac.caltech.edu

be made out of rock-dust minerals instead of the ammonia, ammonium hydrosulfide, and water clouds of the much colder Jupiter and Saturn). The hot Jupiters with low densities have atmospheres puffed out by the extreme solar heating—that inflates their diameter.

The Condensation Model outlined in the previous section predicts that large planets will only form far from the young star. Giant planets start from a core of rock and ice that was able to solidify far from the intense heat of the young star. The rock-ice cores then pull in surrounding gas by their gravity. Near the star, the temperature is too high to form the rock-ice cores.

planet migration

Over a decade before the discovery of the first exoplanets, astronomers predicted as part of the Condensation Model that large gas/rock clumps would form far from a young star and spiral inward toward the star because of friction with the gas remaining in the disk around the forming star. The gas/rock clumps can also interact with each other sending one into a small orbit while the other is ejected out of the system. Such interactions may explain the elliptical orbits we see. Some astronomers working on planet formation models are looking for ways to halt the inward spiral of the gas giant planets near the star through tidal interactions between the planet and star. Perhaps the gas giant planets we see are simply the ones that did not have time to spiral completely into the stars before the gas disk was cleared away by the strong T-Tauri winds that accompany the start of nuclear fusion. Perhaps in our solar system other giant planets had formed but did not survive or were ejected. Evidence for the ejection possibility comes from the potentially large number of free floater planets that the microlens surveys are saying must exist in the Galaxy.

planet migration in our early solar system

Recent computer simulations of the dynamical history of our solar system show that the gravity of Saturn helped prevent Jupiter from spiraling into the Sun and that their orbits may have started further out than they are now, then moved closer in than they are now, and then finally moved further out to their present distances. The simulations also show that Uranus' initial orbit might have been larger than Neptune's initial orbit and that both planets' orbits were smaller than they are now. This shuffling of the gas giant planets would also have affected the material forming the terrestrial planets and changed the distributions of various types of asteroids and comets. The Kepler mission has provided strong evidence in favor of the inward migration idea for how the hot Jupiter systems formed. A 2012 study looked at over 60 hot Jupiter systems in the Kepler catalog and none of them had multiple planets while other systems with large planets further out can have multiple planets. Observations of other star/planet formation places and other planetary systems have confirmed various features of the Condensation Model and they have also led to modifications and extensions of the theory in the continual interaction of observation-theory-testing process of error correction of science.

One puzzling statistic from the Kepler mission has to do with the sizes (diameters) of the exoplanets. More than three-fourths of the planet candidates in the Kepler catalog have sizes ranging between that of the Earth and Neptune. Why does not our solar system have a planet in that size range? In that respect, our solar system's architecture seems to be an unusual one in the Galaxy. Further refinement of the Condensation Model will need to be made to explain why super-Earths/mini-Neptunes are so common and what happened in our solar system to prevent such a planet from forming or continue to exist in our solar system. One possibility is that there is, in fact, a mini-Neptune orbiting very far from the Sun that hasn't been found yet. Such a distant but large planet ("Planet Nine") in our solar system could explain the clustering of orbit properties of recently-discovered scattered disk objects.

Planet Nine?

how determine if exoplanet has life

In the next few years, ground-based interferometers will be completed that can image large exoplanets. It is unlikely that life could arise on a gas giant planet because of the strong convection in their atmospheres that would move organisms vertically between huge extremes of temperatures. What about Earth-like planets? NASA's proposed Terrestrial Planet Finder (TPF), a space-based mission, would be able to obtain infrared or optical pictures of life-bearing planets. With TPF, astronomers would also be able to analyze the spectrum of the planets to determine the composition of their atmospheres. The upcoming James Webb Space Telescope

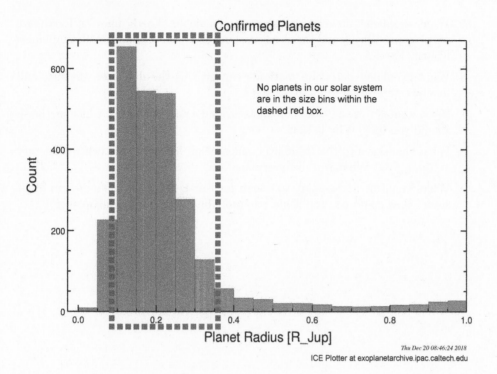

Confirmed Planets

No planets in our solar system are in the size bins within the dashed red box.

Thu Dec 20 08:46:24 2018
ICE Plotter at exoplanetarchive.ipac.caltech.edu

should be able to take spectra of nearby exoplanet atmospheres. Spectral lines from water would say that a planet has a vital ingredient for life but it does not mean that life is present. If oxygen, particularly ozone (a molecule of three oxygen atoms), is found in the atmosphere, then it would be possible that life is indeed on the planet. This is discussed further in section 17.4 of the Life in the Universe chapter along with the possibility of oxygen being a "false-positive" sign of life. The setup and technologies TPF will employ will be based on the experience gained from previous projects such as the Keck Interferometer, the Large Binocular Telescope Interferometer, Kepler, CoRot, NESSI spectroscopy of nearby exoplanets, and the Gaia Mission. Unfortunately, there are now no plans to develop TPF for at least the next decade.

The number of stars with detected planets and the details about them changes so rapidly that the best place to find up-to-date information on exoplanets is on the internet. The textbook's website has a list of exoplanets websites that have continually updated databases at end of the solar system fluff chapter.

Vocabulary

astrometric technique   center of mass   direct imaging technique
doppler shift technique   exoplanet   microlens technique
transit technique

Review Questions

1. What are *two* signatures of an exoplanet in the starlight?

2. Why is it better to search for exoplanets in the infrared, rather than the optical band?

3. What sort of exoplanets are the star wobble methods best suited to find? Why?

4. What exoplanet properties and orbit properties can you find with the star wobble methods?

5. What exoplanet detection methods could detect Earth-mass or Earth-size exoplanets? Why would the other methods not be able to find small exoplanets like the Earth?

6. What exoplanet detection methods can give us the diameter, density, and maybe composition of an exoplanet?

7. If you wanted to search for exoplanets around a particular star, which method(s) should you use? Why is that?

8. What challenges to the standard condensation model do the other planetary systems give? What is a likely explanation?

9. What would be a good way to search for Earth-like exoplanets around other stars? How could you tell if life was probably present on an exoplanet?

Chapter 11

Stellar Properties

Stars are *hundreds of thousands* of times farther away from us than the planets are from us. The *nearest* star (other than the Sun) is so far away that the fastest spacecraft the human race has built so far would take tens of thousands of years to get there. Yet we are a curious and ambitious species, and we want to know how those stars are born, live out their lives, and die. How can we learn about objects that are so remote and beyond our physical grasp? This chapter gives you an idea of how we learn about the stars and what we find about the stars. Because the stars in our galaxy are so far away, they appear as just pinpoints of light in even the most powerful of telescopes on the ground or in space. We have to rely on the information encoded in the feeble starlight. Before continuing with this chapter, be sure to review carefully the concepts in the Electromagnetic Radiation (Light) chapter (chapter 7) so that you will understand this Stellar Properties chapter.

By the end of the chapter you will see there is an internal consistency of star properties and that these points of light are very different from the other points of light that wander among them (the planets). Once we were able to measure the distances to the stars, we found that they are very luminous compared to the planets. There are like our Sun. We also discovered that there is a depth to our universe—the stars are not all at the same distance from us. And we found that the universe is a lot bigger than we thought before.

The stars are very luminous things like our Sun but are they really like our Sun? Are they hot like the Sun? Temperature measurements show us that the star are hot compared to the planets and more like the Sun. The red ones are cooler—only 2500 to 3500 K, the yellow ones are 5000 to 7000 K, the white ones are 9000 to 15000 K, and the blue ones are 20,000 to 50,000 K. Are the stars large in diameter like the Sun? Size measurements show that the stars are big compared to the planets; they are large like the Sun. Things that are big and hot should also be massive like the Sun if they are like the Sun. Mass measurements show the stars do have a lot more material in them than the planets and are more like the Sun.

This chapter is the most math intensive of the chapters in this book (chapter 5 is the next most math intensive one), but remember to keep your eye on the "bigger picture": how we know what we know and don't get bogged down with the formulae. If your math skills are rusty, study appendix B and do not hesitate to ask your astronomy instructor for help. The vocabulary terms are in boldface.

11.1 Stars—What Are They Like?

11.1.1 Distances—Trigonometric Parallax

Unlike the other sciences, astronomy is entirely observational. You cannot run experiments on things. You cannot manipulate the objects to see how they work. In order to compare the objects you see from the Earth, you must first know how far away they are. Obviously, you cannot use a tape measure or send spacecraft out to the stars and measure how far they travelled. Bouncing radar off the surfaces of stars would not work because: (1) stars are glowing balls of hot gas and have no solid surface to reflect the radar beam back and (2) the radar signal would take *years* to reach even the nearest stars.

A favorite way to measure great distances is a technique used for thousands of years: look at something from two different vantage points and determine its distance using trigonometry. The object appears to shift positions compared to the far off background when you look at it from two different vantage points. The angular shift, called the *parallax*, is one angle of a triangle and the distance between the two vantage points is one side of the triangle. Basic trigonometric relations between the lengths of the sides of a triangle and its angles are used to calculate the lengths of all of the sides of the triangle. This method is called **trigonometric parallax.** Modern surveyors use this method to measure great distances, so the method is sometimes called "the surveyor's method".

parallax

trigonometric parallax

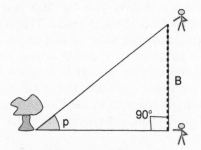

If we know one side (B) and one
angle (p) of a right triangle, we
can derive the length of the other
two sides.

The side of the triangle between the observers, labelled "B" in the figure above, is called the *baseline.* The size of the parallax angle p is proportional to the size of the baseline. If the parallax angle is too small to measure because the object is so far away, then the surveyors have to increase their distance from each other. Ordinarily, you would have to use trigonometric functions like a *tangent* or a *sine*, but if the angle is small enough, you find a very simple relation between the parallax angle p, baseline B, and the distance d:

$$p = \frac{206,265 \times B}{d},$$

smaller parallax means greater distance

where the angle p is measured in the tiny angle unit called an *arc second*. The farther away the object is, the less it appears to shift. Since the shifts of the stars are so small, arc seconds are used as the unit of the parallax angle. There are 3,600 arc seconds in just one degree. The ball in the tip of a ballpoint pen viewed from across the length of a football field is about 1 arc second.

Trigonometric parallax is used to measure the distances of the nearby stars. The stars are so far away that observing a star from opposite sides of the Earth would produce a parallax angle much, much too small to detect. As large a baseline

observe from opposite sides of orbit

as possible must be used. The largest one that can be easily used is the orbit of the Earth. In this case the baseline is the distance between the Earth and the Sun—an **astronomical unit** (A.U.) or 149.6 million kilometers! A picture of a nearby star is taken against the background of stars from opposite sides of the Earth's orbit (six months apart). The parallax angle p is one-half of the total angular shift.

However, even with this large baseline, the distances to the stars in units of astronomical units are huge, so a more convenient unit of distance called a **parsec** is used (abbreviated with "pc"). A parsec is the distance of a star that a *par*allax of one arc *sec*ond using a baseline of 1 astronomical unit. Therefore, one parsec equals 206,265 astronomical units. The nearest star is about 1.3 parsecs from the solar system. In order to convert parsecs into standard units like kilometers or meters, you must know the numerical value for the astronomical unit—it sets the scale for the rest of the universe. Its value was not known accurately until the early 20th century (see chapter 9). In terms of light years, one parsec equals 3.26 light years.

Which unit should you use to specify distances: a light year or a parsec? Both are fine and are used by astronomers (including myself) all of the time, just as you may use "feet" and "yards" in everyday talk. However, when the parsec unit is used in this book, the equivalent in light years will usually be given as well, but when the light year unit is used, the parsec equivalent will usually not be given. Using a parsec for the distance unit and an arc second for the angle, the simple angle formula above becomes extremely simple for measurements from Earth:

$$p = \frac{1}{d}.$$

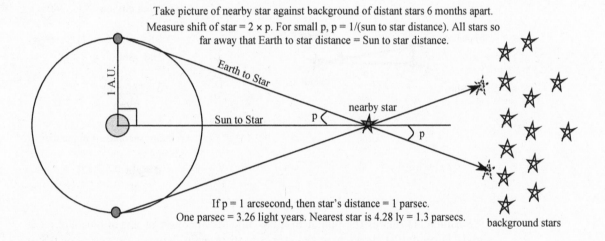

Take picture of nearby star against background of distant stars 6 months apart.
Measure shift of star = 2 × p. For small p, p = 1/(sun to star distance). All stars so far away that Earth to star distance = Sun to star distance.

If p = 1 arcsecond, then star's distance = 1 parsec.
One parsec = 3.26 light years. Nearest star is 4.28 ly = 1.3 parsecs.

Parallax angles as small as 1/50 arc second can be measured from the *surface* of the Earth. This means distances *from the ground* can be determined for stars that are up to 50 parsecs away. If a star is further away than that, its parallax angle p is too small to measure and you have to use more indirect methods to determine its distance. Stars are about a parsec apart from each other on average, so the method of trigonometric parallax works for just a few thousand nearby stars. The Hipparcos mission greatly extended the database of trigonometric parallax distances by getting above the blurring effect of the atmosphere. It measured the parallaxes of 118,000 stars to an astonishing precision of 1/1000 arc second (about 20 times better than from the ground)! It measured the parallaxes of 1 million other stars to a precision of about 1/20 arc seconds.

The actual stellar parallax triangles are much longer and skinnier than the ones

astronomical unit

parallax angle is half *total shift*

parsec

nearby stars are 100,000's of times farther away than the planets

from Earth formula

Sun-star distance = Earth-star distance

Star parallax triangles are *very* l o n g and skinny
Earth
                                                                                                    star
○━━○
○━━○
Sun   The *nearest* star is actually 4,513 times further away than shown here.

typically shown in astronomy textbooks. They are so long and skinny that you do not need to worry about which distance you actually determine: the distance between the Sun and the star or the distance between the Earth and the star. Taking a look at the skinny star parallax triangle above and realizing that the triangle should be over 4,500 times longer(!), you can see that it does not make any significant difference which distance you want to talk about. If Pluto's entire orbit was fit within a quarter (2.4 centimeters across), the nearest star would be 80 meters away! But if you are stubborn, consider these figures for the planet-Sun-star star parallax triangle (where the planet-star side is the hypotenuse of the triangle):

the Sun–nearest star distance =   267,068.23022*0* A.U. =   1.2948 pc;
the Earth–nearest star distance =   267,068.23022*2* A.U. =   1.2948 pc;
Pluto–nearest star distance =   267,068.23*3146* A.U. =   1.2948 pc!

If you are super-picky, then yes, there is a slight difference but no one would complain if you ignored the difference. For the more general case of parallaxes observed from any planet, the distance to the star in parsecs $d = ab/p$, where p is the parallax in arc seconds, and ab is the distance between the planet and the Sun in A.U.

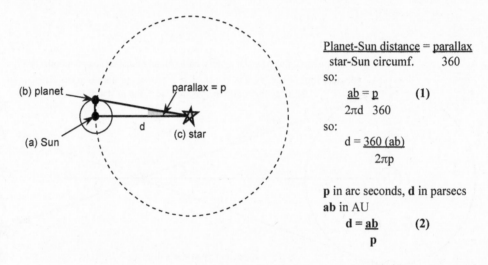

$$\frac{\text{Planet-Sun distance}}{\text{star-Sun circumf.}} = \frac{\text{parallax}}{360}$$

so:

$$\frac{ab}{2\pi d} = \frac{p}{360} \quad \textbf{(1)}$$

so:

$$d = \frac{360\,(ab)}{2\pi p}$$

p in arc seconds, **d** in parsecs
ab in AU

$$d = \frac{ab}{p} \quad \textbf{(2)}$$

Formula (1) relates the planet-Sun baseline distance to the size of parallax measured. Formula (2) shows how the star-Sun distance d depends on the planet-Sun baseline and the parallax. In the case of Earth observations, the planet-Sun distance $ab = 1$ A.U. so $d = 1/p$. From Earth you simply flip the parallax angle over to get the distance! (Parallax of 1/2 arc seconds means a distance of 2 parsecs, parallax of 1/10 arc seconds means a distance of 10 parsecs, etc.)

Vocabulary

astronomical unit   parsec   trigonometric parallax

Formulae

- small angle relation: *angle p* in arc seconds $= (206{,}265 \times B)/d$. The *baseline B* and *distance d* must be in the same units of length.

- star parallax relation: *parallax angle p* in arc seconds $= B/d$. The *baseline B* is in units of A.U. and the *distance d* is in units of parsecs. For measurements from the Earth, $B = 1$.

- star distance $d = B/p$. For measurements from the Earth, $B = 1$.

Review Questions

1. Describe the procedure used to find distances to the nearby stars.

2. What do you need to know in order to get the scale of interstellar space in terms of kilometers or meters?

3. If the star-Sun distance = 30 parsecs, how far is the star from the Earth?

4. If you measure the parallax of a star to be 0.1 arc second on Earth, how big would the parallax be for an observer on Mars (Mars-Sun distance = 1.5 A.U.)?

5. If you measure the parallax of a star to be 0.5 arc second on Earth and an observer in a space station in orbit around the Sun measures a parallax for the same star of 1 arc second, how far is the space station from the Sun?

6. If you can measure angles as small as 1/50 arc second, how far out can you measure star distances from the Earth using the trigonometric parallax method? How long do you have to wait between observations?

7. If you can measure angles as small as 1/50 arc second, how far out can you measure star distances from Jupiter (Jupiter-Sun distance = 5.2 A.U.) using the trigonometric parallax method? However, how long do you have to wait between observations? (Use Kepler's third law to find Jupiter's orbital period and divide by two.)

11.1.2 Distances—Inverse Square Law

When the direct method of trigonometric parallax does not work for a star because it is too far away, an indirect method called the **Inverse Square Law of Light Brightness** is used. This method uses the fact that a given star will grow dimmer in a predictable way as the distance between you and the star increases. If you know how much energy the star emits (its **luminosity**), then you can derive how far away it must be to appear as dim as it does. Stars become fainter with increasing distance because their energy is spread out over a larger and larger surface.

A star's apparent brightness (its **flux**) decreases with the *square* of the distance. The **flux** is the amount of energy reaching each square centimeter of a detector (e.g., your eye, CCD, piece of the sphere) every second. Energy from any light source radiates out in a radial direction so concentric spheres (centered on the light source) have the same amount of energy pass through them every second. As light moves outward it spreads out to pass through each square centimeter of those spheres.

The same total amount of energy must pass through each sphere surface. Since a sphere has a surface area of $4\pi \times$ (its radius)^2, the flux of energy on sphere #1 = (the flux of energy on sphere #2) × [(sphere #2's radius)/(sphere #1's radius)]^2. Notice that the radius for the *reference* flux (sphere #2) is on the top of the fraction while the radius for the unknown flux (sphere #1) is on the bottom—this is an inverse square law! *As the distance INcreases, the flux DEcreases with the square of the distance.* In formula form, this means the star's flux = star's luminosity / $(4\pi \times$ (star's distance)^2). See appendix B for help on when to multiply and when to divide the distance factor.

Put another way: As the flux DEcreases, the star's distance INcreases with the square root of the flux. *If you know how much energy pours through the star's surface and you measure how much energy you detect here on the Earth, then you can derive the star's distance from you.*

Inverse Square Law of Light Brightness
luminosity

flux = apparent brightness

flux = luminosity / $4\pi d^2$

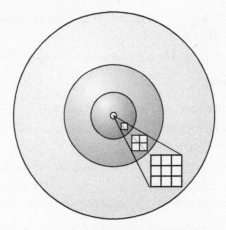

Light spreads out with the **square** of the distance.
Through a sphere twice as large, the energy covers an
area **four** times larger. Through a sphere three times
as large, the energy covers an area **nine** times larger.

Inverse square law: the energy we receive is inversely proportional
to square of the distance.

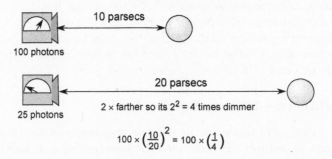

$$100 \times \left(\tfrac{10}{20}\right)^2 = 100 \times \left(\tfrac{1}{4}\right)$$

Vocabulary

flux   Inverse Square Law of Light Brightness   luminosity

Formulae

- **Inverse Square Law:** Brightness at distance A = (brightness at distance B) × [(distance B)/(distance A)]^2. Position (B) is the reference position.

- **flux = luminosity** / $(4\pi \times \text{distance}^2)$

- Unknown distance = reference distance $\times \sqrt{(\text{reference flux})/(\text{measured flux})}$.

Review Questions

1. Two identical stars have different apparent brightnesses (**fluxes**). One star is 10 parsecs away from you and the other is 30 parsecs away from you. Which star is brighter and by how many *times*?

2. Two identical stars have different **fluxes**. One star is 5 parsecs away from you and appears 81 times brighter than the other star. How far away is the dimmer star?

3. The Earth receives about 1380 Watts/meter^2 of energy from the Sun. How much energy does Saturn receive from the Sun (Saturn-Sun distance = 9.5 AU)? (A Watt is a unit for the amount of energy generated or received every second.)

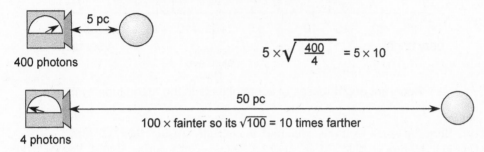

The distance is inversely proportional to
the *square root* of the energy we receive.

5 pc

400 photons

$5 \times \sqrt{\dfrac{400}{4}} = 5 \times 10$

50 pc

$100 \times$ fainter so its $\sqrt{100} = 10$ times farther

4 photons

4. What is the **luminosity** of star in Watts that has a **flux** of 2.7×10^{-8} Watts/meter^2 and is 4.3 light years away from us? A light year is 9.461 trillion kilometers or 9461 trillion meters.

11.1.3 Magnitude System

magnitude

The brightness of stars are specified with the **magnitude** system. The Greek astronomer Hipparchus devised this system around 150 B.C.E. He put the brightest stars into the first magnitude class, the next brightest stars into second magnitude class, and so on until he had all of the visible stars grouped into six magnitude classes. The dimmest stars were of sixth magnitude. The magnitude system was based on how bright a star appeared to the unaided eye.

By the 19th century astronomers had developed the technology to objectively measure a star's brightness. Instead of abandoning the long-used magnitude system, astronomers refined it and quantified it. They established that a *difference of 5 magnitudes corresponds to a factor of exactly 100 times in intensity*. The other intervals of magnitude were based on the 19th century belief of how the human eye perceives differences in brightnesses. It was thought that the eye sensed differences in brightness on a logarithmic scale so a star's magnitude is not directly proportional to the actual amount of energy you receive. Now it is known that the eye is not quite a logarithmic detector.

defining rule of magnitudes

Your eyes perceive equal *ratios* of brightness as equal *intervals* of brightness. On the quantified magnitude scale, a magnitude *interval* of 1 corresponds to a *factor* of $100^{1/5}$ or approximately 2.512 *times* the amount in actual intensity. For example, first magnitude stars are about $2.512^{2-1} = 2.512$ *times* brighter than 2nd magnitude stars, $2.512 \times 2.512 = 2.512^{3-1} = 2.512^2$ *times* brighter than 3rd magnitude stars, $2.512 \times 2.512 \times 2.512 = 2.512^{4-1} = 2.512^3$ *times* brighter than 4th magnitude stars, etc. (See appendix B for what is meant by the terms "factor of" and "times".) Notice that you raise the number 2.512 to a power equal to the *difference* in magnitudes.

ratios of brightness for intervals of magnitude

Also, many objects go beyond Hipparchus' original bounds of magnitude 1 to 6. Some very bright objects can have magnitudes of 0 or even negative numbers and very faint objects have magnitudes greater than +6. The important thing to remember is that brighter objects have *smaller* magnitudes than fainter objects. The magnitude system is screwy, but it's tradition! (Song from *Fiddler on the Roof* could be played here.)

Apparent Magnitude

The apparent brightness of a star observed from the Earth is called the **apparent magnitude**. The apparent magnitude is a measure of the star's *flux* received by

apparent magnitude

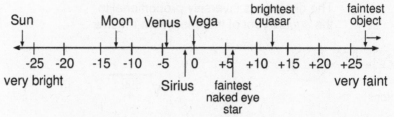

Apparent brightnesses of some objects in the magnitude system.

us. Here are some example apparent magnitudes (using the "V" filter, see section 11.1.4): Sun = −26.7, Moon = −12.6, Venus = −4.4, Sirius = −1.4, Vega = 0.00, faintest naked eye star = +6.5, brightest quasar = +12.8, faintest object = +30 to +31.

How do you do that?

Star A has an apparent magnitude = 5.4 and star B has an apparent magnitude =2.4. Which star is brighter and by how many times? Star B is *brighter* than star A because it has a lower apparent magnitude. Star B is brighter by 5.4 − 2.4 = 3 magnitudes.

In terms of intensity, star B is $2.512^{(5.4-2.4)} = 2.512^{3.0}$ = approximately 15.8 times brighter than star A. The amount of energy you receive from star B is almost 16 times greater than what you receive from star A.

Absolute Magnitude and Luminosity

absolute magnitude
luminosity

If the star was at 10 parsecs distance from us, then its apparent magnitude would be equal to its **absolute magnitude**. The absolute magnitude is a measure of the star's **luminosity**—the total amount of energy radiated by the star every second. If you measure a star's apparent magnitude and know its absolute magnitude, you can find the star's distance (using the inverse square law of light brightness). If you know a star's apparent magnitude and distance, you can find the star's luminosity (see the table below). The luminosity is a quantity that depends on the star itself, not on how far away it is (it is an "intrinsic" property). For this reason a star's luminosity tells you about the internal physics of the star and is a more important quantity than the apparent brightness.

"intrinsic" = belonging to a thing by its very nature

Luminosity is proportional to the *fourth* power of temperature.

Sun

6000 K
L = 1

12,000 K
L = 16
$\left(\dfrac{12,000}{6000}\right)^4 = 2^4$

2000 K
L = $\dfrac{1}{81}$
$\left(\dfrac{2000}{6000}\right)^4 = (1/3)^4$

A star can be luminous because it is hot or it is large (or both!). The luminosity of an object = the amount of energy every square meter produces multiplied by its surface area. Recall from section 7.3.1 that the amount of energy pouring through every square meter $= \sigma \times$ (object's surface temperature)^4, where σ is the Stefan-Boltzmann constant. Because the temperature is raised to the fourth power, it means that the luminosity of a star increases very quickly with even slight increases in the temperature.

Luminosity is also proportional to the surface area.

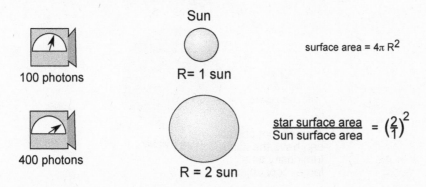

Because the surface area is also in the luminosity relation, the luminosity of a bigger star is larger than a smaller star at the same temperature. You can use the relation to get another important characteristic of a star. If you measure the apparent brightness, temperature, and distance of a star, you can determine its size.

The figure below illustrates the inter-dependence of measurable quantities with the derived values that have been discussed so far. In the left triangular relationship, the apparent brightness, distance, and luminosity are tied together such that if you know any two of the sides, you can derive the third side. For example, if you measure a glowing object's apparent brightness (how bright it appears from your location) and its distance (with trigonometric parallax), then you can derive the glowing object's luminosity. Or if you measure a glowing object's apparent brightness and you know the object's luminosity without knowing its distance, you can derive the distance (using the inverse square law). In the right triangular relationship, the luminosity, temperature, and size of the glowing object are tied together. If you measure the object's temperature and know its luminosity, you can derive the object's size. Or if you measure the glowing object's size and its temperature, you can derive the glowing object's luminosity—its electromagnetic energy output.

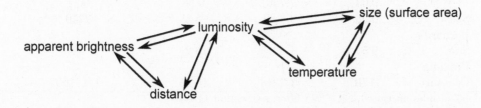

Finally, note that a **small, hot object can have the same luminosity as a large, cool object.** So if the luminosity remains the same, an increase in the size (surface area) of the object must result in a DEcrease in the temperature to compensate.

Most famous apparently bright stars are also intrinsically bright (luminous). They can be seen from great distances away. However, most of the nearby stars are intrinsically faint. If you assume we live in a typical patch of the Milky Way Galaxy (using the Copernican principle), then you deduce that most stars are puny emitters of light. The bright stars you can see in even the city are the odd ones

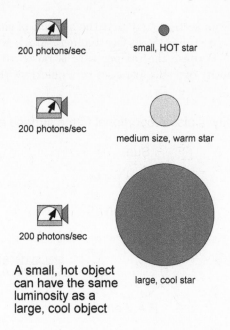

200 photons/sec

small, HOT star

200 photons/sec

medium size, warm star

200 photons/sec

large, cool star

A small, hot object can have the same luminosity as a large, cool object

in our galaxy! The least luminous stars have **absolute magnitudes** = +19 and the most luminous stars have **absolute magnitudes** = –8. This is a huge range in luminosity! See the "How do you do that?" box on the next page for how you determine star distances and luminosities from their apparent and absolute magnitudes.

Even the intrinsically faintest star's luminosity is much, much greater than all of the power we generate here on the Earth so a "watt" or a "megawatt" are too tiny a unit of power to use for the stars. Star luminosities are specified in units of **solar luminosity**—relative to the Sun (so the Sun generates one solar luminosity of power). One solar luminosity is about 4×10^{26} watts.

solar luminosity

Magnitudes and Distances for some well-known Stars (from the precise measurements of the Hipparcos mission)

Star	App. Mag.*	Distance (pc)	Abs. Mag.	Luminosity (rel. to Sun)
Sun	-26.74	4.84813×10^{-6}	4.83	1
Sirius	–1.44	2.6371	1.45	22.5
Arcturus	–0.05	11.25	–0.31	114
Vega	0.03	7.7561	0.58	50.1
Spica	0.98	80.39	–3.55	2250
Barnard's Star	9.54	1.8215	13.24	1/2310
Proxima Centauri	11.01	1.2948	15.45	1/17700

*magnitudes measured using "V" filter, see section 11.1.4

11.1.4   Color and Temperature

Stars are dense, hot balls of gas so their spectra are similar to that of a perfect thermal radiator, which produce a smooth continuous spectrum. (Although, stars are not perfect thermal radiators, their spectra are similar enough to the smooth continuous spectrum for what follows.) Therefore, the color of stars depends on their temperature—hotter stars are bluer and cooler stars are redder. You can observe the star through different **filters** to get an approximate temperature. A filter

filter

How do you do that?

A quantity that uses the inverse square law and the logarithmic magnitude system is the "distance modulus". The distance modulus = the apparent magnitude − absolute magnitude. This is equal to $5 \times \log(\text{distance in parsecs}) - 5$. The "log()" term is the "logarithm base 10" function (it is the "log" key on a scientific calculator). If you measure a star's apparent magnitude and its distance from its trigonometric parallax, the star's absolute magnitude = the apparent magnitude − $5 \times \log(\text{distance}) + 5$. For example, Sirius has an apparent magnitude of −1.44 and Hipparcos measured its distance at 2.6371 parsecs, so it has an absolute magnitude of $-1.44 - 5 \times \log(2.6371) + 5 = -1.44 - (5 \times 0.421127) + 5 = 1.45$.

If you know a star's absolute magnitude, then when you compare it to calibration stars, you can determine its distance.

$$\text{Its distance} = 10^{(\text{apparent magnitude} - \text{absolute magnitude} + 5)/5}.$$

For example, Spica has an apparent magnitude of 0.98 and stars of its type have absolute magnitudes of about −3.55, so Spica is at a distance of $10^{(0.98 - (-3.55) + 5)/5} = 10^{1.906} = 80.54$ which is very close to the trig. parallax value measured by Hipparcos (Spica's absolute magnitude of −3.546 was rounded to −3.55 in the table on the next page).

If you know two stars' absolute magnitudes, you can directly compare their luminosities. The ratio of the two stars luminosities is

$(\text{Lum.}_{*_1})/(\text{Lum.}_{*_2}) = 10^{-0.4(\text{abs mag*1} - \text{abs mag*2})}$ or in an approximate relation:

$(\text{Lum.}_{*_1})/(\text{Lum.}_{*_2}) = 2.512^{(\text{abs mag*2} - \text{abs mag*1})}$. Remember the more luminous star has an absolute magnitude that is *less than* a fainter star's absolute magnitude! Try out this relation on the stars given in the table on the next page.

allows only a narrow range of wavelengths (colors) through. By sampling the star's spectrum at two different wavelength ranges ("bands"), you can determine if the spectrum is that for a hot, warm, cool, or cold star. Hot stars have temperatures around 60,000 K while cold stars have temperatures around 3,000 K. The filter diagrams are shown below.

Color Index and Temperature

Hot stars appear bluer than cooler stars. Cooler stars are redder than hotter stars. The "B–V color index" is a way of quantifying this using two different filters; one a blue (B) filter that only lets a narrow range of colors or wavelengths through centered on the blue colors, and a "visual" (V) filter that only lets the wavelengths close to the green-yellow band through.

A hot star has a B–V color index close to 0 or negative, while a cool star has a B–V color index close to 2.0. Other stars are somewhere in between. Here are the steps to determine the B–V color index:

1. Measure the apparent brightness (flux) with two different filters (B, V).

2. The flux of energy passing through the filter tells you the magnitude (brightness) at the wavelength of the filter.

3. Compute the magnitude difference of the two filters, B–V.

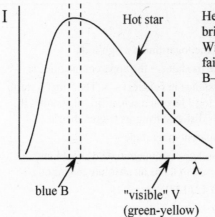

Here with the Blue (B) filter, the star will appear brighter —> smaller, more negative magnitude. With the Visible (V) filter, the star will appear fainter —> larger, more positive magnitude. So B–V = small # – large # = negative number.

blue B

"visible" V
(green-yellow)

Here with the Blue (B) filter, the star will appear fainter —> larger, more positive magnitude. With the Visible (V) filter, the star will appear brighter —> smaller, more negative magnitude. So B–V = large # – small # = positive number.

blue B

"visible" V
(green-yellow)

Wien's Law and Temperature

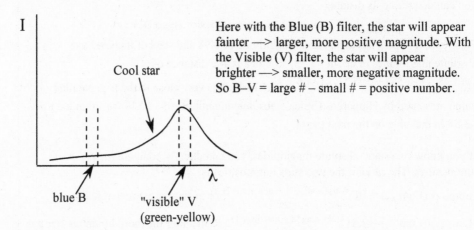

Measuring temperature: Wien's Law

Cool star

large λ_{peak}

small λ_{peak}

Hot star

$$\text{Temperature} = \frac{2.9 \times 10^6}{\lambda_{peak}} \text{ Kelvin} \qquad (\lambda \text{ is in nanometers})$$

Another way to measure a star's temperature is to use Wien's law described in chapter 7. Cool stars will have the peak of their continuous spectrum at long (redder) wavelengths. As the temperature of a star increases, the peak of its continuous spectrum shifts to shorter (bluer) wavelengths. The final way to measure a star's temperature is more accurate than the previous two methods. It uses the strength of different absorption lines in a star's spectrum. It is described in full a little later in the chapter. The temperatures of different types of stars are summarized below in table 11.1 of section 11.2.2.

Vocabulary

absolute magnitude	apparent magnitude	filter
luminosity	magnitude	solar luminosity

Formulae

- **Luminosity** = (surface area of star) × flux of energy through its surface. This is: $[4\pi \times (\text{star's radius})^2] \times [\sigma \times (\text{star's surface temperature})^4]$, where σ is the Stefan-Boltzmann constant.

- **Magnitudes:** star A brightness $\approx$ star B brightness $\times 2.512^{(\text{mag B} - \text{mag A})}$. Star B is the reference star.

Review Questions

1. What does a magnitude *interval* of 5 correspond to in brightness? How about an interval of 1? How about an interval of 3?

2. Do bright things have larger or smaller magnitudes than fainter things?

3. How is **apparent magnitude** different from **absolute magnitude?**

4. Put the following objects (given with their apparent magnitudes) in order of brightness as seen from Earth (*faintest first*): Sun (–26.7), Venus (–4.4), Barnard's Star (9.5), Sirius (–1.4), Proxima Centauri (11.0).

5. You receive 8×10^{-9} Watts/meter^2 of energy from a star 2 parsecs away with an apparent magnitude = 1.3. What is the energy you receive from a star with an apparent magnitude = 5.3?

6. Two identical stars but star B is 10× farther away than star A. What is the difference in magnitudes between the two stars?

7. What two things does **luminosity** depend on?

8. If our Sun has **luminosity** = 1 solar luminosity, what is the luminosity of the following stars if they have the same diameter as the Sun (fill in the table):

star	temperature (K)	luminosity
Sun	6,000	1
A	12,000	
B	2,000	
C	36,000	

9. Some stars have temperatures of only 3000 K but have over 100× more luminosity than the Sun. How is this possible?

10. Would a red giant have a smaller or larger magnitude in a "V" filter than in a "B" filter? (Remember the first rule of magnitudes!)

11.1.5   The Composition of Stars

The compositions of stars are determined through **spectroscopy. Spectroscopy** is the study of something using spectra. Recall from chapter 7 that a spectrum is what results when you spread starlight out into its individual colors. By noting what absorption lines (or sometimes, emission lines) are present and their strengths, you can find out a tremendous amount of information. Stars have absorption line patterns similar to the Sun. This means that they are composed mostly of hydrogen and helium with traces of other elements.

spectroscopy

From these absorption lines you learn some important things beside the star's composition:

1. *Structure of stars:* From the simple fact that you see absorption lines in most stellar spectra, you know that the stars must have a hot dense part that produces a continuous spectrum and an outer layer, or atmosphere, made of cooler, low density gas. The general trend is density and temperature of stars decreases as the distance from the star's center increases. The hot dense part is also gaseous because of the extreme temperatures. Stars have no molten rock in them like the interiors of some of the planets. The next two things have already been noted in section 7.6 but they are important enough to state again.

Same physical laws everywhere and every time

2. *Universality of physical laws:* The same pattern of hydrogen lines are seen in the in spectra of the Sun, stars, distant galaxies, and quasars (active galaxies at very great distances from us). This is a sensitive test of whether or not the laws of physics used in the structure of atoms works everywhere in the universe. Even slight differences in the rules of quantum mechanics that govern the interactions of the protons, electrons, and neutrons or differences in the strengths of the fundamental forces of natures from that observed on the Earth would produce noticeable changes in the spacing and strength of the spectral lines. If the subatomic particles had different amount of charge or mass, the pattern of lines would be different than what you see on the Earth.

Because the same patterns are seen in the spectra, regardless of where the light comes from, the physics used on Earth must work everywhere else in the universe! All of the absorption lines seen in celestial objects can be seen in laboratories on Earth. The charge and mass of the electron and proton are the same everywhere you look. *Physical laws are the same everywhere!*

3. *Permanence of physical laws:* Since light has a finite speed and the distances are vast, the light received from very distant galaxies and quasars has been travelling for billions of years. The light from those remote regions tells about the physical laws way back then. The spectra seen can be explained with the same physical laws in operation here on Earth at the present time. *Physical laws are the same throughout time!*

11.1.6   The Velocities of Stars

doppler effect

spectral lines get shifted to new wavelengths

The velocity of stars are determined by using the **doppler effect** (see section 7.7). The motion of a star causes a shift in the wavelengths *received*. The star *emits* the same spectrum it would emit if it was at rest. The pattern of lines depends on the internal physics of the star itself. But the doppler effect depends on the external property of the star's motion through space relative to us. The wavelength shift $\Delta\lambda = \lambda_{new} - \lambda_{rest}$, where λ_{new} is the observed wavelength and λ_{rest} is the wavelength you would observe if the star was not moving relative to us. The amount of the shift depends on the velocity of the star in this way: $\Delta\lambda/\lambda_{rest} = $ (radial velocity)$/c$, where c is the speed of light and the **radial velocity** is the component of the star's motion that is *along the line of sight*. Rearranging the terms you find the radial velocity $= (\Delta\lambda/\lambda_{rest}) \times c$.

greater speed makes greater shift

radial velocity

If the star is moving away from you, then you see the wavelengths stretched out and $\Delta\lambda$ is a positive number. The spectral lines appear shifted to the red end of the spectrum, so the shift is called a **redshift**. If the star is moving toward you, then the wavelengths appear to the compressed and $\Delta\lambda$ is a negative number. The spectral lines are shifted to the blue end of the spectrum, so the shift is called a **blueshift**. The doppler effect tells you only about the motion *relative to you*. If

redshift: motion away

blueshift: motion toward

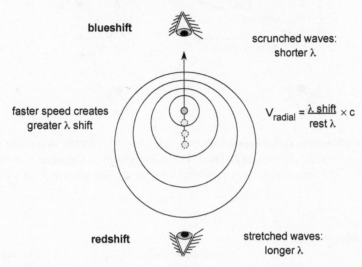

Radial Velocity measured from the *doppler effect*

blueshift

scrunched waves:
shorter λ

faster speed creates
greater λ shift

$$V_{radial} = \frac{\lambda \text{ shift}}{\text{rest } \lambda} \times c$$

redshift

stretched waves:
longer λ

you move toward the star or it moves toward you, the doppler effect will be the same. The Earth is in motion relative to the star because it is orbiting the Sun, so you have to take the Earth's orbital motion into account when figuring the star's velocity from the doppler effect.

Also, the doppler effect gives you only the speed *along the line of sight*. Most stars move at an angle to our line of sight. The part of a star's *total velocity* that is perpendicular to the line of sight is called the **tangential velocity.**

tangential velocity

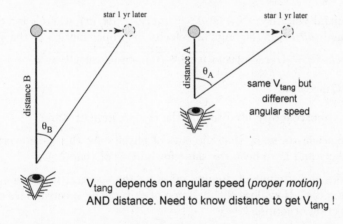

Tangential Velocity measured from the *proper motion*

star 1 yr later

star 1 yr later

distance B

distance A

θ_A

same V_{tang} but
different
angular speed

θ_B

V_{tang} depends on angular speed (*proper motion*)
AND distance. Need to know distance to get V_{tang} !

To get the tangential velocity, you need to first measure the *angular velocity* of the star across the sky ($d\theta/dt$). This is how many degrees on the sky the star moves in a given amount of time and is called the **proper motion** by astronomers. If you determine the star's distance from its trigonometric parallax or the inverse square law method, you can convert the angular velocity (proper motion) to tangential velocity in physical units such as kilometers/second. The tangential velocity = $k\times$ the star's distance × the proper motion, where k is a conversion factor that will take care of the conversion from arc seconds, parsecs and years to kilometers/second.

proper motion

Using Pythagoras' theorem for right triangles, you find that the star's *total velocity* = $\sqrt{(\text{radial velocity})^2 + (\text{tangential velocity})^2}$.

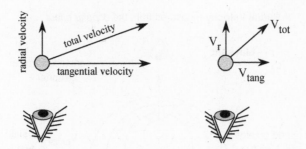

Two stars with the same **radial velocity** (line-of-sight) but very different **tangential velocities** and, therefore, very different **total velocities**. The radial velocity is measured from the doppler effect. The tangential velocity is derived from the angular speed and star's distance.

Vocabulary

blueshift	doppler effect	proper motion
radial velocity	redshift	spectroscopy
tangential velocity		

Formulae

- **redshift:** $\Delta\lambda > 0$. Object moving away from you.

- **blueshift:** $\Delta\lambda < 0$. Object moving toward you.

- **Radial velocity** $= (\Delta\lambda/\lambda_{rest}) \times c$, where $\Delta\lambda$ is the doppler shift, λ_{rest} is the wavelength you would see if the star was at rest. The rest wavelength is also the wavelength of light *emitted by the star*. Larger doppler shift means greater radial velocity.

- **Tangential velocity** $= k\times$ (star's distance) $\times(d\theta/dt)$, where k is a conversion factor and $(d\theta/dt)$ is the angular velocity or proper motion of the star.

- *Total velocity* $= \sqrt{(\text{radial velocity})^2 + (\text{tangential velocity})^2}$.

Review Questions

1. How is **spectroscopy** used to find the composition of stars?

2. How do scientists know that the laws of physics are the same everywhere in the Galaxy and have been the same for billions of years?

3. How does the amount of doppler effect in the spectral lines depend on the relative speed? How does the direction of shift of the spectral lines depend on the direction of motion?

4. Given three stars moving with the same total speed of 40 kilometers/second but in three different directions: (A) moving away at an angle=45° from our line of sight, (B) moving directly away from us, (C) moving perpendicular to our line of sight, put the stars in order of increasing amount of shift you see in their spectral lines (the smallest shift first).

5. The $H\alpha$ spectral line is at 6563Å. Star (A) has that line at 6568Å, star (B) has that line at 6560Å, star (C) has that line at 6563Å. Which star is moving the fastest (along the line of sight) and what is the three stars' directions of motion?

6. What must you first know about a star before you can convert its angular velocity to a tangential velocity in kilometers/second?

7. Two stars have **proper motions** of 0.5 arc seconds/year. Star (A) is 20 parsecs away and star (B) is 30 parsecs away. Which one is moving faster in space?

8. Two stars orbit about a common point in a plane that is oriented parallel to our line of sight. What will you see happening to the spectral lines of each star? If there is a change, will both stars' spectra be changing in the same direction at the same time?

11.1.7 The Masses of Stars

To determine the masses of stars, Kepler's third law is applied to the motions of binary stars—two stars orbiting a common point. The greater the *combined* mass of the two stars, the greater the gravity acceleration is, and, therefore, the smaller their orbital period. A majority of the several hundred billion stars in the Galaxy are in a system with two or more stars orbiting each other. Usually the binary stars are **spectroscopic binary** stars. A spectroscopic binary system is two stars orbiting a common point at too great a distance away from us to resolve the two stars individually, but whose binary nature is indicated in the periodic shift of their spectral lines as they orbit around each other. Spectroscopic binary stars are used because (a) there are a lot more far away stars than nearby ones and (b) more importantly, you can easily measure their speeds from the doppler shifted lines.

smaller orbital period means greater combined mass

spectroscopic binary

Spectroscopic binary: binary too far away to resolve individual stars but whose binary nature is detected by periodic shifts in its spectral lines.

Image

Newton's form of Kepler's third law gives the *combined* mass of the two stars: (mass 1 + mass 2) = (separation distance)^3/(orbital period)^2 if you use solar mass units, the A.U. for the distance unit between the stars, and the time unit of years for the orbital period. The total distance between the two stars is used in Kepler's third law, but their individual distances from the common point they orbit is used to determine the stars' individual masses.

Kepler's 3rd: combined mass only

Since stars have about the same mass (within a factor of 20), they both orbit around a common point, called the **center of mass**, that is significantly different from each of the stars' center. The **center of mass** (C.M.) is the point where (mass star 1) × (C.M. distance 1) = (mass star 2) × (C.M. distance 2), or the point they would be balanced upon if the stars were on a stellar seesaw. The massive star is proportionally closer to the center of mass than the low-mass star and the massive star also moves proportionally slower than the low-mass star so its spectral lines have a smaller doppler shift (see the figure at the top of the next page) .

center of mass

use balance point to get individual masses

more massive star proportionally closer to C.M. & proportionally slower than companion

Newton's Law of Gravity with Newton's second law of motion explains why this is. Both stars are experiencing the same gravity force between them [since (mass star 1) x (mass star 2) = (mass star 2) x (mass star 1)]. Given the same gravity force at work between the two stars, the lower-mass star will experience a greater acceleration than the more massive star (which star would be like Andre the Giant and which would be like Tom Thumb of section 5.1?). The lower-mass star moves faster and has a larger orbit. The more massive star's orbital speed is less and its orbit is smaller so that the two stars always stay on opposite sides of the center of

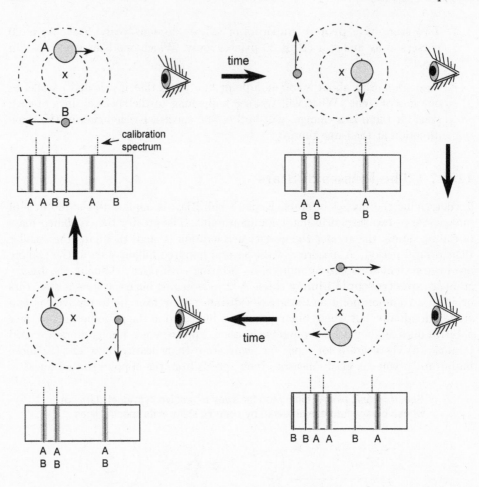

mass. The two stars inside the binary system have the *same orbital period* around
the center of mass.

caution note

   Note of caution about comparisons: When comparing two separate binary
systemS of the same separation distance, the two stars in the binary system that has
larger *combined* mass will move faster than the two stars in the binary system with
less *combined* mass. The larger *combined* mass binary has greater gravity force
acting between the two stars. When comparing the two stars *within* a particular
binary system, the larger mass star will move slower than the less massive star. The
gravity force acting on the two stars *within* the binary is the same for both of the
stars.

   The *distance* travelled by an object = *velocity* × the *time* it takes. The distance
travelled by the star is just the circumference of the orbit = $2\pi \times$ the radius of a
circular orbit and something similar for an elliptical orbit. Therefore, each star's
*C.M.-distance r = the star's velocity × the star's orbital period / (2π). This allows
you to use the easily measured velocity in Kepler's third law and in the center of
mass relations*. The doppler shifts of the spectral lines can be used to construct
a **radial velocity curve**—a plot of the radial velocity (line of sight velocity) vs.

radial velocity curve

time. The low-mass star will move proportionally faster than the massive star.

   Uncertainty arises, though, if the binary orbital plane is inclined to our line of
sight by an angle amount i. In that very common case, the radial velocity = total
velocity × sin(i). The orbit's inclination angle, i, ranges from $i = 0°$ for a *face-on*
orbit (viewing the orbit from directly above the system) to $i = 90°$ for an *edge-on*
orbit (viewing the orbit along its plane). The inclination angle can be approximately
determined from the radial velocity curve. If the binary is an eclipsing binary, then

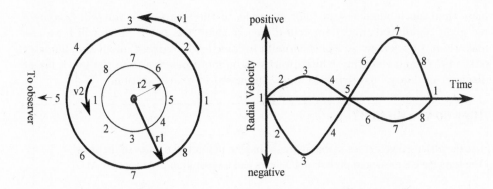

you know that $i = 90°$ because you see the two stars periodically pass in front of each other. Eclipsing binaries also allow you to accurately determine the diameters of stars (discussed in the next section). The radial velocity measurement technique has also been used to find planets around other stars and to locate black holes from the doppler shifts they produce in the spectra of the visible stars they orbit around.

Remember these rules:

1. Stars stay on the opposite side of the center of mass from each other.

2. The massive star moves *slower* than the low-mass star.

3. The center of mass is also the point where mass1 × velocity1 = mass2 × velocity2.

Using the distance of the center of mass from each star, you can proportion out the total mass to each star. Here are the steps to figure out each star's mass:

1. Find the total mass (mass star A + mass star B) from Kepler's 3rd law.

2. Find the proportion of each star's mass to the total mass from the center of mass: (mass star A)/(mass star B) = (C.M. distance B)/(C.M. distance A) or (mass star A)/(mass star B) = (velocity star B)/(velocity star A). Note which star's values are on top of the fraction and which are on the bottom! Simplify the fraction down as far as possible.

3. If you set the mass of star A = (mass of star B)×(the fraction of the previous step) and substitute this for the mass of star A in the first step (Kepler's 3rd law step), you will find star B's mass = the total mass/(1 + the fraction from step 2).

4. Star A's mass = star B's mass × (the fraction from step 2).

5. Check that the proportions add up to the total mass!

(By the way, you can use this proportion idea in cooking if you need to have a 32-ounce mixture and the recipe calls for 3 parts sugar to 2 parts flour or if a recipe is for 6 people but you need to serve 8 people.) The masses of different types of stars are summarized below in table 11.1 of section 11.2.2. An example of a derivation of a binary system's individual star masses is given on the next page in a "How do you do that?" box.

Even the smallest star's mass is much, much greater than a planet's so a "kilogram" is too tiny a unit of mass to use for the stars. Star masses are specified in units of **solar mass**—relative to the Sun (so the Sun has one solar mass of material). One solar mass is about 2×10^{30} kilograms.

solar mass

One final caution: There is a difference between the mass of a star and its size (diameter)! Just because something is large in size (diameter) does not necessarily mean that it is more massive. Some stars are very large in diameter but have less

caution note

mass than much smaller stars. For example, in the future, our Sun will become a red giant about 100 times larger in diameter than it is now, but it will have less mass than it does now. It will eventually become a white dwarf about the diameter of the Earth and that tiny white dwarf will be more massive than the much larger diameter ordinary "red dwarf M stars" discussed in a later section.

How do you do that?

Use the observed velocities in the figure to find the individual masses of the stars. The stars have a measured period of 4/3 years and a separation distance of 4 AU.

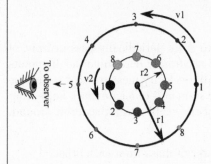
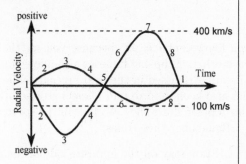

Step 1: Kepler's third law says the total mass = $4^3/(4/3)^2 = 64/(16/9) = 36$ solar masses.

Step 2: I will let the massive star be "star A". So (mass star A)/(mass star B) = $400/100 = 4$.

Step 3: mass star B = 36 solar masses/(1 + 4) = 7.2 solar masses.

Step 4: mass star A = mass star B × 4 = 28.8 solar masses.

Step 5: *Check:* 28.8 solar masses + 7.2 solar masses does equal 36 solar masses. This step makes sure you did not make an arithmetic error in the previous steps. If the sum does not equal the value in step 1, then re-check your math!

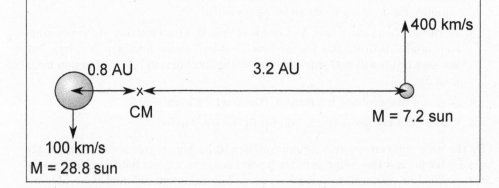

Vocabulary

center of mass   radial velocity curve   spectroscopic binary
solar mass

Formulae

- **Center of mass distance:** mass star A / mass star B = distance B / distance A, where the distances are each measured from the center of mass. Notice which star's distance is in the top of the fraction!

- separation distance = distance A + distance B, where the distances are each measured from the center of mass.

- **Center of mass velocity:** mass star A / mass star B = velocity star B / velocity star A. Notice which star's velocity is in the top of the fraction!

- **Kepler's 3rd law:** (mass star A + mass star B) = (separation distance)^3 / (orbital period)^2 if use solar mass units, A.U. for the distance unit between the stars, and the time unit of years for the orbital period.

Review Questions

1. How are the masses of stars found? What kind of star systems are used and which famous law of orbital motion is used?

2. How many times closer to the **center of mass** is the massive star than the low-mass star?

3. How do you use the **radial velocity curve** to find the mass proportions and separation distance? How much faster or slower does the low-mass star move than the massive star?

4. Three binary systems with a separation of 2 A.U. between the two stars in each system. System (1) has the two stars orbiting the center of mass in 1 year, system (2) has the two stars orbiting the center of mass in 5 months, and system (3) has the two stars orbiting the center of mass in 2 years. Put the binary systems in the correct order by *increasing* total mass (least massive first and ignore the inclination angle i).

5. Star A is 0.2 A.U. from the center of mass and its companion star B is 0.6 A.U. from the center of mass. Which star is more massive?

6. If the two stars in the previous question have orbital periods of 0.35777 years, what are the individual masses of the two stars? (Hint: find their combined mass from Kepler's third law and then use their relative center of mass distances to find how many times more massive one star is than the other.)

7. Use the radial velocity curve graph in the text above. Assume that star A reaches a velocity of 90 kilometers/second and star B reaches only 10 kilometers/second. If the separation distance = 10 A.U. and the orbital period = 10 years, what is the combined mass of the two stars? From the center of mass relation also find (star A mass)/(star B mass) and their individual masses.

8. Which star system(s) would you be able to measure the radial velocity: (a) stars orbiting in a plane that is along our line of sight ($i = 0°$); (b) stars orbiting in a plane that is perpendicular to our line of sight (face-on, $i = 90°$); (c) stars orbiting in a plane with $i = 30°$.

11.1.8   The Sizes of Stars

All but a few stars appear as mere pinpoints in even the largest telescopes. They are much too far away to derive their diameters from measuring their angular diameters and distances. **Eclipsing binaries** are used to determine indirectly the diameters of stars. These are two stars orbiting each other in a plane that is parallel to your line of sight so you see their orbits edge-on. This means that one star will periodically cover up the other star. During the eclipse the total brightness measured for the binary will decrease. The amount of the dip in brightness depends on the luminosity and relative size of the two stars.

eclipsing binary

A star's diameter is found from *speed = (distance travelled)/(time it takes)*. The speed comes from the doppler shift and the time is the length of the eclipse.

light curve

diameter= speed× eclipse time

The distance travelled during the eclipse is equal to the diameter of the star = 2×radius. The **light curve**—a plot of the brightness vs. time—is used to derive the star diameters. Below is an example of two stars orbiting each other in circular orbits seen edge-on with one star small and hot and the other large and cool.

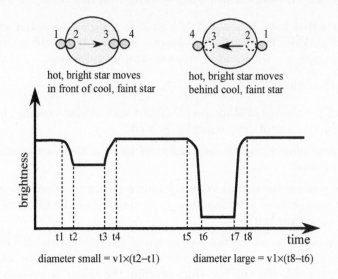

hot, bright star moves in front of cool, faint star   hot, bright star moves behind cool, faint star

diameter small = v1×(t2–t1)   diameter large = v1×(t8–t6)

When the small star moves from position 1 to position 2 (or from position 3 to position 4), it has moved a distance equal to its diameter. When the small star moves from position 1 to position 3 (or from position 2 to position 4), it has moved a distance equal to the diameter of the large star.

diameter from the luminosity

Star sizes can also be found (less accurately) from the luminosity and the apparent brightness. Recall from section 11.1.3 that the luminosity = [4π×(star radius)^2] × [σ×(star's surface temperature)^4], where σ is the Stefan-Boltzmann constant. If you compare the star with the Sun, you can cancel out the constants to get (star's radius)/(Sun's radius) = (Sun's temperature/star's temperature)^2 × $\sqrt{\text{star's luminosity/Sun's luminosity}}$. See the "How do you do that?" box below for an example. The sizes of different types of stars are summarized below in table 11.1 of section 11.2.2.

How do you do that?

Antares is 9120 times more luminous than the Sun (Antares' luminosity/Sun's luminosity = 9120) and has a temperature of only 3340 K and the Sun's temperature is 5840 K.

Antares's size/Sun's size = $(5840/3340)^2 × \sqrt{9120}$ = 3.057 × 95.5 = 292. Antares is almost 300 times the size of the Sun! If the Sun were replaced by Antares, Mercury, Venus, and Earth would be *inside* Antares! It is a red giant star—a star close to death.

Vocabulary

light curve   eclipsing binary

Formulae

- **Eclipsing binary:** diameter = speed × time of eclipse.

- Size from luminosity: star's radius/Sun's radius = (Sun's temperature/star's temperature)^2 × $\sqrt{\text{star's luminosity/Sun's luminosity}}$.

Review Questions

1. How do you use the **light curve** to find the diameters of stars?

2. What special type of binary star system is used to find the diameters of stars?

3. Use the light curve in the figure in the section above. Assume that when star A is behind star B, the small dip in brightness is seen. When star B is behind star A, the big dip in brightness is seen. Which star is more luminous?

4. From the previous problem, if t1 = 45 minutes, t2 = 60 minutes, t3 = 105 minutes, t4 = 120 minutes, what is (star A diameter)/(star B diameter)? [Hint: find which star is brighter and in this circular orbit system (t8 − t6) = (t4 − t2).]

5. From the previous problem, if the velocity is 750 kilometers/second, what is the diameter of the *larger* star? (Hint: you need to convert the minutes to seconds.)

6. The white dwarf Sirius B has a temperature of 14,000 K and a luminosity only 0.00794 times the Sun's luminosity. What is the *diameter* of Sirius B in kilometers? (The Sun's *radius* = 696,000 kilometers.)

11.2   Types of Stars and the HR diagram

This section presents the results of using the tools described above. In order to get a better idea of what stars are like, put them into groups of some sort. Then you can see how the other quantities differ among the various groups. Astronomers group stars into general types based on their temperature. Temperature is chosen because the color of a star depends on the temperature and color is an easily seen characteristic, regardless of the distance.

temperature groups

However, using color as a temperature probe gives only a crude measurement of the star's temperature. Astronomers use another method of determining the temperature more accurately. It uses the strength of different absorption lines in a star's spectrum. Once astronomers developed this method, they began to look for correlations of temperature with other quantities such as mass, size, and luminosity in the hope that the underlying physical principles of stars could be understood. But are the stars you easily see from Earth typical of other stars in other parts of the universe? You will see how that important question can be answered.

use spectral lines to get temperature

11.2.1   Temperature Dependence of Absorption Lines

The strength and pattern of the absorption lines does vary among the stars. Some stars have strong (dark) hydrogen lines, other stars have no hydrogen lines but strong calcium and sodium lines. Are their abundances different? No. When scientists learned more about the physics of the atom, they discovered that the *temperature* of the star's photosphere determines what pattern of lines you will see. Because of this, you can determine the temperature of a star from what pattern of absorption lines you see and their strength. As a way to check this, the spectra from all of the gas clouds from which stars form show approximately the same abundances everywhere.

Before reading further, you will need to have a good grasp of the concepts in sections 7.4 and 7.5. Please review those sections before continuing so that you will understand what follows. While the temperature does not change the energy levels of an atom—they are fixed, the temperature certainly does affect how many electrons are in which energy levels. Measuring the strength of the hydrogen absorption lines is usually the first step for determining a star's temperature. If the star is too hot or too cold, the hydrogen lines will be weak. To produce strong, dark hydrogen lines, the star's temperature must be within a certain range. To produce a hydrogen absorption line in the *visible (optical) band* of the electromagnetic spectrum, the atom's electron *must be in the second energy level* when it absorbs a photon. If the temperature is too high, most of the hydrogen atoms will have their electrons starting out at higher energy levels. If the temperature is too low, most of the hydrogen atoms will have their electrons starting out from the ground state.

Ultra-hot **O-type** star: electron not bound to atom: no H lines

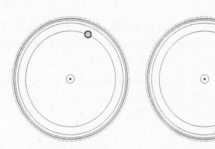

Very hot **B-type** star: some H atoms have electron in prime **2nd energy level**, other atoms have electron in *higher* energy levels: detectable H lines

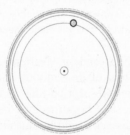

Hot **A-type** star: most H atoms have electron in prime **2nd energy level**: very strong, dark H lines.

warm **F & G-type** star: some H atoms have electron in prime **2nd energy level**, other atoms have electron in *ground state*: detectable H lines

Cool **K & M-type** star: electron is stuck in *ground state* : no H lines.

To produce strong, dark hydrogen absorption lines in the **visible band**, the electron must be in the **2nd energy level**. Most stars are too hot or too cool to have atoms in the proper setup so they have weak, light hydrogen lines.

Other elements behave in the same way: star needs to have just the right temperature to produce dark lines of the other elements.

If the hydrogen atoms are heated to high temperatures, the atomic collisions can ionize the hydrogen atoms. If there are no electrons bound to the nuclei, there are no hydrogen absorption lines. If the star's temperature is too low, then there are few electrons in the second energy level. Most of the electrons are in the ground state because there are not that many atomic collisions.

Hydrogen lines will be strong for temperatures = 4,000 to 12,000 K. Helium atoms hang onto their electrons more strongly and, therefore, require higher temperatures of 15,000 to 30,000 K to produce absorption lines in the visible band. Calcium atoms have a looser hold on their electrons so calcium lines are strong for cooler temperatures of 3000 to 6000 K. The strengths of each element's absorption lines are sensitive to the temperature. A given strength of an element's lines will give you either two possible temperatures for the star or a range of possible temperatures. But using two or more element's line strengths together narrows the possible temperature range. Cross-referencing each elements' line strengths gives an accurate temperature with an uncertainty of only 20 to 50 K. This technique is the *most accurate* way to measure the temperature of a star.

why spectral line method is best

A star's temperature found from the continuous spectrum is not as accurate. One reason for this is that some stars have the peaks of their thermal spectrum outside of the visible band so you cannot use Wien's law (see section 11.1.4) to determine the temperature. Also, stars are not perfect thermal radiators and have many absorption lines in their spectra, so the continuum spectrum (Wien's law) gives only a rough temperature (within a few hundred Kelvin). The spectral lines seen for different temperatures of stars are summarized below in table 11.1.

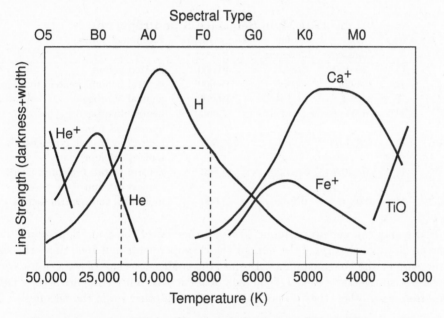

Cross-referencing different line strengths narrows the possible temperature range. A given strength for the Hydrogen line could mean two possible temperatures (hot or warm). If Helium line is present, then the choice is the hot temperature. If the ionized Calcium line is present (and Helium not present), then the choice is the warm temperature.

11.2.2   Spectral Types

Stars are divided into groups called **spectral types** which are based on the strength of certain absorption lines. The A-type stars have the strongest (darkest) hydrogen lines, B-type next strongest, F-type next, etc. Originally there was the whole alphabet of types, based on just hydrogen line strengths, but then astronomers discovered that the *line strengths depend on the temperature*. Also, the discussion in the previous section and the figure above show that more than just the hydrogen

spectral type

lines must be used because a very hot star and a cool star can have the same hydrogen lines strength. The presence of other atomic or ion lines are used in conjunction with the hydrogen spectrum to determine the particular temperature of the star.

spectral class sequence

After some rearranging and merging of some classes, the class sequence is now O-B-A-F-G-K-M when ordered by *temperature*. The O-type stars are the hottest stars and the M-type stars are the coolest. Each class is subdivided into 10 intervals, e.g., G2 or F5, with 0 hotter than 1, 1 hotter than 2, etc. The Sun is a G2-type star and it is hotter than Tau Ceti, a G8-type star. About 90% of the stars are called **main sequence** stars. The other 10% are either red giants, supergiants, white dwarfs, proto-stars, neutron stars, or black holes. The characteristics of these types of stars will be explored in the following chapters. The table below gives some basic characteristics of the different spectral classes of *main sequence* stars. Notice the trends in the table: as the temperature of the main sequence star increases, the mass and size increase. Also, because of the relation between luminosity and the size and temperature of a star, hotter main sequence stars are more luminous than cooler main sequence stars. However, there are limits to how hot a star will be, or how massive and large it can be. Understanding why the constraints exist is the key to understanding how stars work.

main sequence: *90% of stars*

Table 11.1: **Main Sequence Star Properties**

Color	Class	solar masses	solar diameters	Temperature	Prominent Lines
bluest	O	20–100	12–25	40,000	ionized helium
bluish	B	4–20	4–12	18,000	neutral helium, neutral hydrogen
blue-white	A	2–4	1.5–4	10,000	neutral hydrogen
white	F	1.05–2	1.1–1.5	7,000	neutral hydrogen, ionized calcium
yellow-white	G	0.8–1.05	0.85–1.1	5,500	neutral hydrogen, strongest ionized calcium
orange	K	0.5–0.8	0.6–0.85	4,000	neutral metals (calcium, iron), ionized calcium
red	M	0.08–0.5	0.1–0.6	3,000	molecules and neutral metals

Red giants can get up to about 50 times the size of the Sun. Supergiants are between 20 times the size of the Sun for the B0 supergiants and 1000 times the size of the Sun for the M0 supergiants. Despite the tremendous size of some stars, even the largest supergiant is only 1/7000 light years across. Since stars are *several* light years from each other, they do not collide with each other (even the fat ones!).

Vocabulary

main sequence   spectral type

Review Questions

1. What is the main reason why some stars have strong (dark) hydrogen lines and others have weak (light) hydrogen lines?

2. Why do very hot stars have no hydrogen lines?

3. Why do very cool stars have no hydrogen lines?

4. What is the grouping of stars by **spectral type** based on?

5. A star of spectral type A has the strongest hydrogen lines. What is its temperature?

6. Two stars have equal strengths of their hydrogen lines. Star A has lines from helium present while star B has lines of ionized calcium present. Which star

is hotter? Explain your reasoning.

7. What are *two* reasons why determining a star's temperature from Wien's law (chapter 7) is usually not as accurate as using the spectral lines?

8. What are the 7 basic spectral types in order of temperature (hottest to coldest)?

9. If our Sun has a surface temperature of 5840 K, how many times hotter than the Sun is the hottest O-type star? How many times cooler than the Sun is the coolest M-type star?

10. What fraction of the stars are **main sequence** stars?

11. What is the range of temperatures found on the surface of main sequence stars?

12. What is the range of luminosities produced by main sequence stars? Compare them to the Sun (Watts are ridiculously small energy units to use).

13. What is the range of diameters for main sequence stars? Compare them to the Sun (miles and kilometers are ridiculously small length units to use). Red giants, supergiants, white dwarfs are not main sequence stars.

14. What is the *trend* in the stellar diameters vs. temperature for main sequence stars? (As temperature increases, the diameter _____.)

15. What is the *trend* in the stellar luminosities vs. temperature for main sequence stars? (As temperature increases, the luminosity _____.)

16. What is the likelihood that even the largest supergiant stars will run into another star (of any size)?

17. What is the range of stellar masses for main sequence stars? Compare them to the Sun (pounds and kilograms are ridiculously small mass units to use).

18. What is the *trend* in the stellar masses vs. temperature for main sequence stars? (As temperature increases, the mass _____.)

19. What is the *trend* in the stellar masses vs. luminosity for main sequence stars? (As luminosity increases, the mass _____.)

11.2.3 Hertzsprung-Russell Diagram

In order to better understand how stars are constructed, astronomers look for *correlations* between stellar properties. The easiest way to do this is make a plot of one intrinsic property vs. another intrinsic property. An *intrinsic* property is one that does not depend on the distance the star is from the Earth (e.g., temperature, mass, diameter, composition, and luminosity). By the beginning of the 20th century, astronomers understood how to measure these intrinsic properties. In 1912, two astronomers, *Ejnar Hertzsprung* (lived 1873–1967) and *Henry Norris Russell* (lived 1877–1957), independently found a surprising correlation between temperature (color) and luminosity (absolute magnitude) for 90% of the stars. These stars lie along a narrow diagonal band in the diagram called the **main sequence.** This plot of luminosity vs. temperature is called the **Hertzsprung-Russell diagram** or just **H-R diagram** for short. See the next page for an example.

intrinsic property

correlation of temperature and luminosity
main sequence

Hertzsprung-Russell diagram

Before this discovery astronomers thought that it was just as easy for nature to make a hot dim star as a hot luminous star or a cool luminous one or whatever other combination you want. But nature prefers to make particular kinds of stars. *Understanding why enables you to determine the rules nature follows.* A correlation between mass and luminosity is also seen for main sequence stars: Luminosity = Mass$^{3.5}$ in solar units. The hot, luminous O-type stars are more massive than the cool, dim M-type stars. The mass-luminosity relationship tells about the structure

mass-luminosity relation

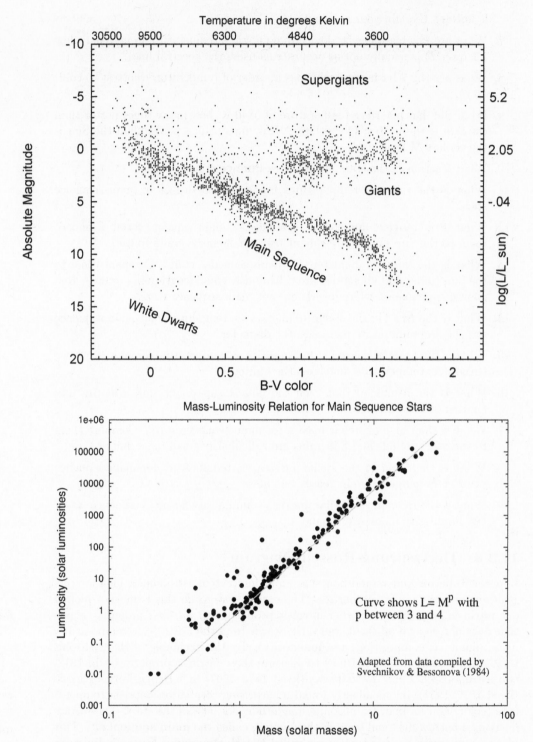

The mass-luminosity relation for 192 stars in double-lined spectroscopic binary systems.

of stars and how they produce their energy. The cause of the mass-luminosity relation will be explored further in the next chapter.

The other ten percent of the stars in the H-R diagram do not follow the mass-luminosity relationship. The giant and supergiant stars are in the upper right of the diagram. These stars must be large in diameter because they are very luminous even though they are cool. They have a huge surface area over which to radiate their energy. The white dwarfs are at the opposite end in the lower left of the diagram. They must be very small in diameter (only about the diameter of the Earth) because even though they are hot, they are intrinsically dim. They have a small surface area and so the sum of the total radiated energy is small.

The H-R diagram is also called a **color-magnitude diagram** because the absolute magnitude is usually plotted vs. the color. The H-R diagram at the top of this page is for all stars visible to the naked eye (down to apparent magnitude = +5) plus all stars within 25 parsecs. Luminous stars are easier to observe because they can be seen from great distances away but they are rarer in the galaxy. They tend to reside in the top half of the H-R diagram. Faint stars are harder to see but they are more common in the galaxy. They tend to reside in the bottom half of the H-R diagram.

color-magnitude diagram

11.2.4 Spectroscopic Parallax

You can use the correlation between luminosity and temperature (spectral type) for *main sequence* stars to get their distances. This method is called **spectroscopic parallax** because a distance is found from knowledge of a star's spectral type. Distances for stars too far away to show a detectable trigonometric parallax are found this way. Here are the steps you use to find a star's distance using the spectroscopic parallax method:

spectroscopic parallax

1. Determine the star's spectral type from spectroscopy and measure the star's apparent brightness (flux).

2. Use a calibrated main sequence to get the star's luminosity. The Hyades cluster's main sequence in the Taurus constellation is the standard calibrator.

3. Use the Inverse Square Law for Brightness to get the distance: unknown distance = calibrator distance $\times \sqrt{\text{calibrator flux}/\text{unknown star's flux}}$.

How do you do that?

A G2 star appears 25 times dimmer than it would if it was at the standard distance of 10 parsecs used for the absolute magnitude. The G2 star is at a distance of $10 \times \sqrt{[1/(1/25)]} = 10 \times \sqrt{25/1} = 50$ parsecs from us.

Distances to red giant and supergiant stars are found in a similar way but you need to investigate their spectra more closely to see if they are the very large stars you think they are. Their position in the calibrated H-R diagram is found and their apparent brightness gives you their distance. Also, this process can be used to find the distance of an entire cluster. The entire color-magnitude diagram for the cluster is compared with a calibration cluster's color-magnitude diagram. The calibration cluster is a known distance away. Some adjustments for the cluster's age and composition differences between the stars in the cluster and the calibration cluster must be made. Such fine-tuning adjustments are called "main sequence fitting".

11.2.5 What is a "Typical" Star?

The Sun is often said to be an "average" or "typical" middle-aged star. What is "average" depends on how you choose your sample!

1. Compared to the nearby stars, the Sun is luminous, hot, and big.

2. Compared to the *apparently* bright stars, the Sun is dim, cool, and small.

3. Compared to the stars in globular clusters, the Sun is very young.

4. Compared to the stars in open (galactic) clusters, the Sun is very old.

If you picked stars at random from our galaxy, what would they tend to look like? How the stars are selected can give you very different answers of what a typical star is like. The figure below shows where the 100 apparently brightest stars in our sky would be plotted and where the 100 nearest stars would be plotted on the H-R diagram. Both data sets are from the Hipparcos survey. The stars that *appear* bright in our sky also are intrinsically luminous for the most part. They are the diamonds in the diagram. The near stars are all within 7.63 parsecs of the Sun. They are plotted with the upside-down triangles. A great majority of the near stars are cool and faint.

brightness-limited sample

distance-limited sample

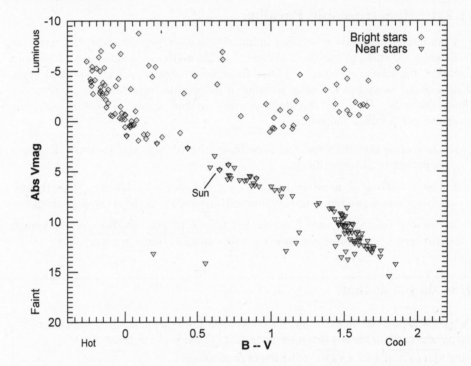

Another way to compare them is to plot the proportions of the spectral types for each group. As shown in the bar chart on the next page, most of the apparently bright stars are the hot and luminous A and B-type stars. The sample includes a few of the very hot O-type stars. All but one of the K-type stars in the bright star sample are giants or supergiant stars. All of the M-type stars are giants or supergiants. The graph for the near star sample looks very different: the majority of stars are the cool and faint K and M-type stars. Only one star in the entire sample is a giant star. The rest are main sequence stars.

Which of these samples is more *representative* of the entire population of stars in our galaxy? A **representative sample** includes all parts of the population of the objects you are investigating in their proper proportions. The relative proportion of common things will be greater than the relative proportions of rare things. In fact, the uncommon things may not be found in a small representative sample because they are so rare!

A poorly selected sample that is unrepresentative of the larger set can lead to biased results. Such biases can be found in any sample of objects or people. Public

representative sample
unbiased sample

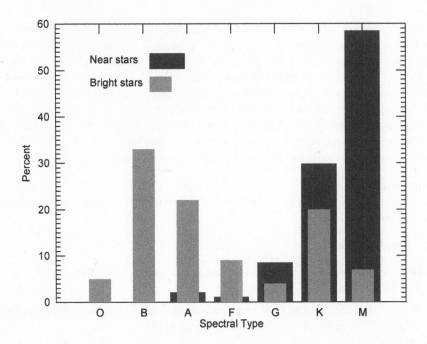

officials and politicians who base their decisions on what the polls say people believe or think about different issues, are usually working with biased samples of opinions. The pollsters will interview between 1000 to 2000 people across the nation and from that set, they get an idea of what the entire nation of several hundred million people believe. They get accurate results only if they have a sample of people that properly represents the entire population. It is extremely difficult (if not impossible) to get a representative sample for political polls. The situation for astronomy is easier and standard statistical methods can be used to find a representative sample of stars.

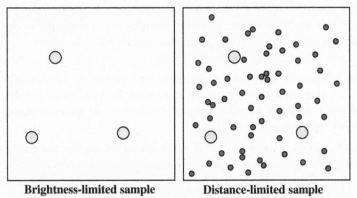

Brightness-limited sample   **Distance-limited sample**

What you would see if you could only detect the apparently bright stars is shown on the left. What you see **in the same volume of space** if you have a good telescope is shown on the right.

In our example of the types of stars, the bright star sample is very biased. The average distance between each star in the bright star sample is about 20 times greater than the average distance between each star in the near star sample. This gives you a rough idea of how spread out the luminous stars and faint stars are—the luminous stars are much more spread out than the cool faint stars. Therefore, in a given volume of space, there will be many more cool faint stars than luminous stars. The faint stars cannot be seen from the great distances the luminous stars are seen, so a sample based on the apparent brightness biases against the very numerous faint stars.

brightness-limited sample is biased

The situation is analogous to using meshes of different spacings between the mesh lines for sifting pieces of minerals on a beach. A coarse mesh with large spacings between the mesh lines will let the sand fall through so all you get are the large rocks. The sample of minerals you would get with the coarse mesh would be just the rare large rocks. A fine mesh with narrow gaps between the mesh lines will collect all the sand grains and the large rocks. The sample of minerals you would get with the fine mesh would be all of the pieces of mineral (sand + rocks) in that plot of beach and you would reach a much more accurate conclusion of the proportion of small mineral chunks (sand grains) to large mineral chunks (large rocks).

Vocabulary
color-magnitude diagram   Hertzsprung-Russell diagram   representative sample
spectroscopic parallax

Review Questions

1. How is it known that luminosity and temperature are correlated for about 90% of the stars?

2. Where are luminous and faint stars plotted in the H-R diagram (color-magnitude diagram)? Where are cool and hot stars plotted?

3. Where are red giants, **main sequence** stars, and white dwarfs plotted in the H-R diagram?

4. Which main sequence stars are hotter and which are cooler? Which ones are more massive and which ones are the lightweights?

5. Which main sequence stars are bigger in diameter than others? How can you tell that they are bigger?

6. What is the relation between stellar luminosity and stellar mass?

7. Which spectral classes are more common than others? How do you know without having to survey the entire galaxy?

8. Of the two ways of selecting stars, grouping by proximity or by apparent brightness, which gives you a **representative sample** of stars? Why is the other way a *biased* way of selecting stars?

9. If you wanted to find out an accurate proportion of the galaxies that are faint and the proportion of the galaxies that are luminous, should you select all galaxies within a certain volume of space or all galaxies above a certain apparent brightness? Explain why!

10. Which telescope should you use if you want to get a more accurate proportion of faint stars to luminous stars: a 15-centimeter telescope or a 90-centimeter telescope? Explain why!

Chapter 12

Our Sun and Stellar Structure

Much of what is known about the stars comes from studying the star closest to us, the Sun. At a distance of almost 150 million kilometers, the Sun is a few hundred thousand times closer to us than the next nearest star. Because of its proximity, astronomers are able to study our star in much, much greater detail than they can the other stars.

The Sun is a G2-type main sequence star that has been shining for almost 5 billion years. It is known from radioactive dating of the Earth, Moon, and meteorites, that these objects have been around for about that length of time and temperatures on the surface of the Earth have been pleasant since it formed. The Sun's energy has made this possible. What could power something as big as the Sun for so long? The process called nuclear fusion is now known to be the source of the Sun's enormous energy, as well as, other stars. This is a relatively recent discovery. However, using simple physical principles of gas physics, astronomers knew about the density and temperature structure of the interior of the stars long before they unlocked the secret to what could power them for so long. This chapter will cover these topics. I will first give a brief description of the Sun to give you an idea of what a star is like and then go into the basic principles of what the interiors of stars are like and what powers them. The vocabulary terms are in boldface.

12.1   The Sun—An Average Star

The Sun is by far the biggest thing in the solar system (see the figure at the beginning of chapter 1). From its angular size of about 0.5° and its distance of almost 150 million kilometers, its diameter is determined to be 1,392,000 kilometers. This is equal to 109 Earth diameters and almost 10 times the size of the largest planet, Jupiter. All of the planets orbit the Sun because of its enormous gravity. It has about 333,000 times the Earth's mass and is over 1,000 times as massive as Jupiter. It has so much mass that it is able to produce its own light. This feature is what distinguishes stars from planets.

12.1.1   Composition

What is the Sun made of? Spectroscopy shows that hydrogen makes up about 94% of the solar material, helium makes up about 6% of the Sun, and all the other elements make up just 0.13% (with oxygen, carbon, and nitrogen the three most abundant "metals"—they make up 0.11%). In astronomy, any atom heavier than helium is called a "metal" atom. The Sun also has traces of neon, sodium, magnesium, aluminum, silicon, phosphorus, sulfur, potassium, and iron. The percentages quoted here are by the relative number of atoms. If you use the percentage *by mass*, you find that hydrogen makes up 78.5% of the Sun's mass, helium 19.7%, oxygen 0.86%, carbon 0.4%, iron 0.14%, and the other elements are 0.54%.

12.1.2   The Sun's Interior

Here are the parts of the Sun starting from the center and moving outward.

Core

The **core** is the innermost 10% of the Sun's mass. It is where the energy from nuclear fusion is generated. Because of the enormous amount of gravity compression from all of the layers above it, the core is very hot and dense. Nuclear fusion requires extremely high temperatures and densities. The Sun's core is about 16 million K and has a density around 160 times the density of water. This is over 20 times denser than the dense metal iron which has a density of "only" 7 times the density of water. However, the Sun's interior is still gaseous all the way to the very center because of the extreme temperatures. There is no molten rock like that found in the interior of the Earth.

Radiative Zone

radiative zone

The **radiative zone** is where the energy is transported from the superhot interior to the colder outer layers by photons. Technically, this also includes the core. The radiative zone includes the inner approximately 85% of the Sun's radius.

Convection Zone

Energy in the outer 15% of the Sun's radius is transported by the bulk motions of gas in a process called convection. At cooler temperatures, more ions are able to block the outward flow of photon radiation more effectively, so nature kicks in convection to help the transport of energy from the very hot interior to the cold **convection zone** space. This part of the Sun just below the surface is called the **convection zone**.

12.1.3   The Sun's Surface

photosphere

The deepest layer of the Sun you can see is the **photosphere**. The word "photosphere" means "light sphere". It is called the "surface" of the Sun because at the top of it, the photons are finally able to escape to space. The photosphere is about 500 kilometers thick. Remember that the Sun is totally gaseous, so the surface is not something you could land or float on. It is a dense enough gas that you cannot see through it. It emits a continuous spectrum. Several methods of measuring the temperature all determine that the Sun's photosphere has a temperature of about 5840 K.

Measuring the Sun's Temperature

One method, called Wien's law (see section 11.1.4), uses the wavelength of the peak emission, λ_{peak}, in the Sun's continuous spectrum. The temperature in Kelvin = 2.9×10^6 nanometers$/\lambda_{peak}$.

flux

Another method uses the *flux* of energy reaching the Earth and the inverse square law. Recall from the previous chapter that the *flux* is the amount of energy passing through a unit area (e.g., 1 meter^2) every second. From the *inverse*

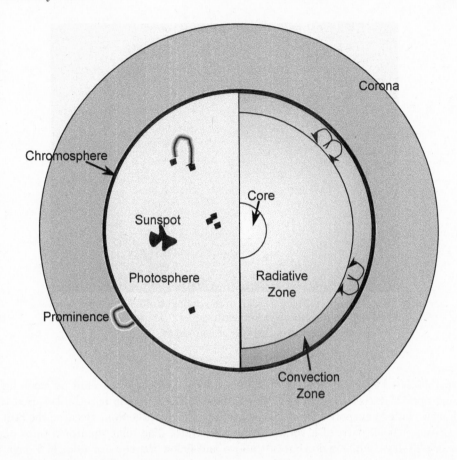

Energy is generated in the **core** where the temperature reaches 16 million K and the density is 160 g/cm³ and then transported outward by radiation. In the **convection zone** rising and falling gas is used to tranfer the energy to the **photosphere** (''surface'' of the Sun). **Sunspots** are cooler, dimmer regions with strong magnetic fields. Some sunspots have **prominences** forming over them. The **chromosphere** is a thin pink layer above the photosphere that is hotter than the photosphere. The temperature increases outward into the **corona**, the very hot (1–2 million K) but tenuous atmosphere of the sun. Fast moving ions in the corona escape the Sun to form the **solar wind.**

square law of light brightness (see section 11.1.2), you find that the solar flux at the Earth's distance = the Sun's surface flux×(Sun's radius/Earth's distance)² = 1380 Watts/meter². Since the Sun's photosphere is approximately a thermal radiator, the flux of energy at its surface = $\sigma \times$ (the Sun's surface temperature)⁴, where σ is the Stefan-Boltzmann constant. Rearranging the equation, the photosphere's temperature = [(solar flux at Earth/σ)× (Earth distance/Sun's radius)²]¹ᐟ⁴.

inverse square law

These two methods give a rough temperature for the Sun of about 5800 K. The upper layers of the photosphere are cooler and less dense than the deeper layers, so you see absorption lines in the solar spectrum. Which element absorption lines are present and their strength depends sensitively on the temperature. You can use the absorption line strengths as an accurate temperature probe to measure a temperature of about 5840 K.

Features on the Photosphere

Galileo discovered that the Sun's surface is sprinkled with small dark regions called **sunspots.** Sunspots are cooler regions on the photosphere. Since they are 1000

sunspots: cooler spots

The Sun's photosphere as seen in the optical band. Notice the dark sunspots, each larger than the Earth.
Image courtesy of NASA/MSFC

to 1500 K cooler than the rest of the photosphere, they do not emit as much light and appear darker. They can last a few days to a few months. Galileo used the longer-lasting sunspots to map the rotation patterns of the Sun. Because the Sun is gaseous, not all parts of it rotate at the same rate. The solar equator rotates once every 25 days, while regions at 30° above and below the equator take 26.5 days to rotate and regions at 60° from the equator take up to 30 days to rotate.

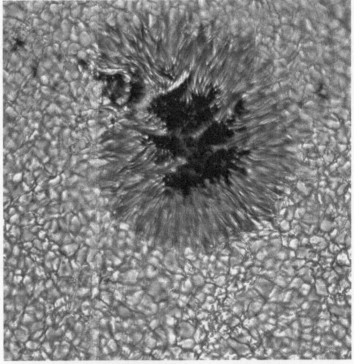

Sunspot and surrounding granulation.
Image from NSO Sacramento Peak Vacuum Tower Telescope courtesy of NOAO

Hundreds of years of observing the sunspots on the Sun shows that the number of sunspots varies in a cycle with an *average* period of 11 years. At the start of a sunspot cycle the number of sunspots is at a minimum and most of them are at around 35° from the solar equator. At solar maximum when the sunspot number peaks about 5.5 years later, most of the sunspots are within just 5° of the solar equator.

sunspot cycle

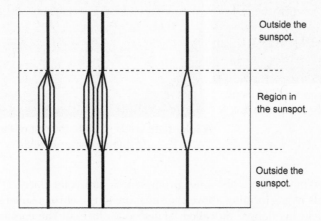

The Zeeman effect: a strong magnetic field splits the spectral lines into two or more components. The strength of the magnetic field can be measured from the amount of separation of the components. Sunspots are regions of strong magnetic fields.

Sunspots are regions of strong magnetic fields. This affects the spectral lines in the sunspot spectra. Each absorption lines will split up into multiple components. The amount of separation between the components measures the strength of the magnetic field. The magnetic field is somehow responsible for the sunspot cycle. In one 11-year cycle the leading sunspot in a sunspot group will have a north magnetic pole while the trailing sunspot in the group will have a south magnetic pole. In the next 11-year cycle the poles will switch so the total cycle is 22 years long. Sunspots form where twisted magnetic field lines rise out of the photosphere and then loop back down into the photosphere and deeper layers. The magnetic field lines suppress the convection at those points on the photosphere so energy has a harder time leaking out at those points on the photosphere—they are cooler than the rest of the photosphere.

magnetic field connection

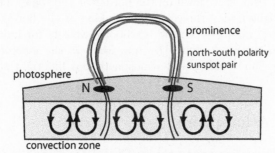

Tightly wound magnetic field lines loop into and out of the photosphere. Convection suppressed => *sunspots.* Trapped gas in magnetic field lines => *prominences.* Twisted magnetic field lines snap => *flares.*

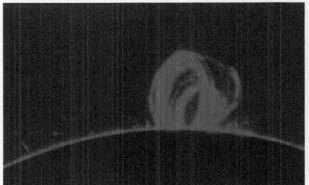

Hot gas in a prominence follows magnetic field loops.
Image courtesy of National Solar Observatory/Sacramento Peak

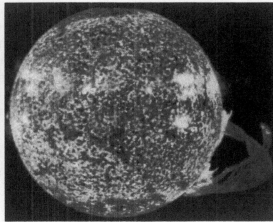

A solar flare sends gas into the rest of the solar system.
Image courtesy of NASA

prominences

At solar maximum there are more prominences and solar flares. Prominences are bright clouds of gas forming above the sunspots in the chromosphere that follow the magnetic field line loops. So-called "quiet" ones form in the corona (the Sun's atmosphere) about 40,000 kilometers above the surface. Sometimes they form loops of hydrogen gas as the gas follows the loops in the magnetic field. Quiet prominences last several days to several weeks. "Surge" prominences lasting up to a few hours shoot gas up to 300,000 kilometers above the photosphere.

solar flares

Solar flares are eruptions that are more powerful than surge prominences. They will last only a few minutes to a few hours. They probably form when the magnetic field lines get so twisted, that they snap violently, releasing the trapped material. A lot of ionized material is ejected in a flare. Unlike the material in prominences, the solar flare material moves with enough energy to escape the Sun's gravity. When this burst of ions reaches the Earth, it interferes with radio communication. Sometimes a solar flare will cause voltage pulses or surges in power and telephone lines. Brownouts or blackouts may result. Humans traveling outside the protection of the Earth's magnetic field will need to have shielding from the powerful ions in a flare.

granulation

High-resolution observations of the solar surface show a honeycomb pattern called **granulation** made of bright spots of convection 700 to 1000 kilometers across. Hot gas rises in the middle of each granule bringing energy from the interior to the surface and sinks back down on the border of a granule. The hot gas rising in the center is brighter than the cooler gas sinking at the borders. Each granule will last for about 8 minutes. See the textbook's website for links to images and movies from the spacecraft studying the Sun. Many of the spacecraft websites will show you what the Sun's surface and atmosphere look like right now.

12.1.4   Solar Atmosphere

Moving outward from the core to the surface of the Sun, the temperature and density of the gas decreases. This trend in the density continues outward in the Sun's atmosphere. However, the temperature *increases* above the photosphere. The cause of the temperature increase is not well known but it involves some combination of sonic waves and magnetic waves from shaking magnetic loops above sunspots, numerous nanoflares, and wiggling jets in the chromosphere known as spicules to heat the atmosphere.

Chromosphere

During solar eclipses a thin pink layer can be seen at the edge of the dark Moon. This colorful layer is called the **chromosphere** (it means "color sphere"). The chromosphere is only 2000 to 3000 kilometers thick. Its temperature rises outward away from the photosphere. Because it has a low density and it is hotter than the photosphere, you see *emission lines* of hydrogen (mostly at the red wavelength of 656.3 nanometers). See the textbook website for images of the chromosphere.

chromosphere

Corona

When the new Moon covers up the photosphere during a total solar eclipse, you can see the pearly-white **corona** around the dark Moon. This is the rarefied upper atmosphere of the Sun. It has a very high temperature of one to two million Kelvin. Despite its high temperature, it has a low amount of *heat* because it is so tenuous.

corona

The corona is known to be very hot because it has ions with many electrons removed from the atoms. At high enough temperatures the atoms collide with each other with such energy to eject electrons. This process is called **ionization**. At very high temperatures, atoms like iron can have 9 to 13 electrons ejected. Nine-times ionized iron is only produced at temperatures of 1.3 million K. The 13-times ionized iron means the temperature gets up to 2.3 million K! During strong solar activity the temperature can reach 3.6 million K and lines from 14-times ionized calcium are seen.

ionization

Image courtesy of Fred Espenak

Total Solar Eclipse August 21, 2017
Nick Strobel

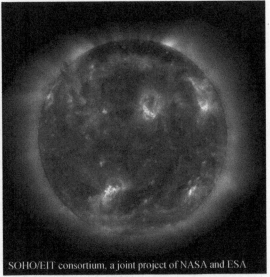

SOHO/EIT consortium, a joint project of NASA and ESA

(Left) Visible light images of the corona near solar maximum activity (top) and near solar minimum activity (bottom). During solar maximum the corona looks more uniform around the entire sun while during solar minimum the corona has bright bulbs closer to the equator, called helmet streamers, and fainter, straight structures at the poles called polar plumes. (Right) An extreme-ultraviolet image of the corona shows more detail in its structure.

Most of the corona is trapped close to Sun by loops of magnetic field lines. In X-rays, those regions appear bright. Some magnetic field lines do not loop back to the Sun and will appear dark in X-rays. These places are called "coronal holes".

solar wind

Fast-moving ions can escape the Sun's gravitational attraction. Moving outward at hundreds of kilometers/second, these positive and negative charges travel to the farthest reaches of the solar system. They are called the **solar wind.** The solar wind particles passing close to a planet with a magnetic field are deflected around the planet. Fluctuations in the solar wind can give energy to the trapped charged particles in the planet's radiation belts. Particles with enough energy can leave the belts and spiral down to the atmosphere to collide with molecules and atoms in the thermosphere of the planet. When the charged particles hit the planet's atmosphere, they make the gas particles in the atmosphere produce emission spectra—the **aurorae** (see section 9.3.1 for more details). During solar maximum the increased number and energy of the solar wind particles produce more extensive auroral displays in the Earth's atmosphere—the aurorae can even be seen by those near latitudes near 30° N or S! Usually, the aurorae are seen by only those above about 50° N latitude (or 50° S latitude for the aurora australis). See the textbook's website for links to spacecraft observing the Sun's atmosphere.

Vocabulary

aurorae	chromosphere	convection zone
core (stellar)	corona	granulation
ionization	photosphere	radiative zone
solar wind	sunspots	

Formulae

- Temperature from Wien's Law: T (in K) = 2.9×10^6 nanometers/λ_{peak}, where λ_{peak} is the wavelength of peak emission in a star's spectrum given in nanometers.

- Temperature from solar flux: T (in K) = $[(\text{solar flux at Earth}/\sigma)\times(\text{Earth distance/Sun's radius})^2]^{1/4}$, where σ is the Stefan-Boltzmann constant and the solar flux at Earth = 1380 Watts/meter^2.

Review Questions

1. What are the two main gases in the Sun? How does the Sun's mass and size compare with Jupiter?
2. What goes on in the **core, radiative zone,** and **convection zone** of the Sun?
3. Describe the three ways astronomers use to find that the **photosphere** is about 5800 K.
4. What are some of the characteristics of **sunspots**? What is the sunspot cycle?
5. Do all surface layers of the Sun rotate at the same rate? How can you tell?
6. What produces the **granulation** on the surface of the Sun?
7. What are prominences and flares? How are they associated with solar activity? How is their number correlated with the number of sunspots?
8. How can you tell that the **chromosphere** and **corona** are over 6000 K (some parts reaching a few million degrees). What are "coronal holes"?
9. What is the association of the magnetic field with the sunspots and solar atmosphere?
10. How is the **solar wind** associated with **aurorae**?

12.2   The Sun's Power Source

The Sun produces a lot of light every second and it has been doing that for billions of years. How does it or any other star produce so much energy for so long? This section will cover how stars produce their energy. Astronomers have known for a long time that the Sun produces a tremendous amount of energy. The first part of this section will try to give you an idea of how much energy it produces. Do not feel bad if you have trouble grasping the amount. It is mind-boggling! There are several ways to generate the amount of energy coming from the Sun. What distinguishes the correct explanation from the other models is *how long* it can power the Sun.

12.2.1   Solar Luminosity—huge energy output!

The first basic question about the Sun is how bright is it? It puts out A LOT of energy every second. How much? The answer from our measurements is 4×10^{26} watts. Such a large number is beyond most of our comprehension, so let's put the Sun's total energy output (ie., its **luminosity**) in more familiar units. It is equal to 8×10^{16} of the largest power plants (nuclear or hydroelectric) on the Earth. Our largest power plants now can produce around 5,000 Megawatts of power. Another way to look at this is that the Sun puts out every *second* the same amount of energy as 2.5×10^9 of those large power plants would put out every *year*—that's over two billion!

luminosity

12.2.2   Possible Sources of Energy

What could produce that much energy every second? Let's first rule out other likely candidates. How about chemical reactions? The most efficient chemical reaction is combining two hydrogens atoms and one oxygen atom to make a water molecule plus some energy. Such a reaction has a very small "efficiency" (something like 1/66000000 of one percent). The *efficiency* = amount of energy released/(mass$\times c^2$), where "mass" is the total mass of all of the atoms involved and c is the speed of light. The amount of energy the Sun has stored = the efficiency $\times$ (the mass of the fuel source) $\times c^2$.

   To find out how long the Sun would last, you need to find out how much energy the Sun has stored in its account and know how fast it makes withdrawals on its account. The amount of time it would last is the amount of energy stored divided by the rate of withdrawal: *lifetime = energy stored/consumption rate = E stored/Luminosity*. Makes sense, yes? If the Sun could use all of its hydrogen to make water, the chemical reactions would only power the Sun for about 18,000 years. However, the amount of oxygen is much less than the hydrogen, so the chemical reactions can power the Sun for only 30 years.

why chemical reactions (burning) do not work

   A reaction with a higher efficiency is needed. How about the ultimate in efficiency—a complete matter to energy conversion with 100% efficiency. Such a reaction could power the Sun for 10^{13} years. Unfortunately, there are problems with this because the number of heavy particles (protons + neutrons) in the Sun must stay the same and protons are extremely stable—they do not spontaneously change into energy (photons).

12.2.3   Gravitational Contraction Doesn't Power the Sun Long Enough

How about gravitational settling? This is a fancy way of referring to the converting of the potential energy of the falling layers to kinetic energy. When you hold a rock above the ground it has stored energy ("potential energy"—it has the potential to do some work). The stored energy is released as you let it fall. The rock gets kinetic energy because it is moving. Kinetic energy can heat things up. This is what would happen to the layers of the Sun if they were to fall inward toward the center of the Sun. The gas would be compressed and, therefore, would heat up. In addition to the expected heating, the gas would also radiate light.

Until the beginning of this century, this was the idea physicists strongly argued for. This gravitational energy (with an efficiency of 1/10000 of one percent) could power the Sun for 30 million years—a nice long time except for the nagging but ever louder criticism of the biologists who needed more time for evolution to occur and the geologists who preferred the idea of an unlimited age for the Earth but would stomach something like a few billion years for the age of the Earth. A good article on the age-of-the-Earth debate is in *Scientific American* August 1989 pages 90 to 96. Eventually, physicists had to change their minds about the age of the Sun (and the Earth) as radioactive dating indicated a 4.6 *billion* year age for the solar system and, therefore, the Sun. It was the fact that the Sun could not last long enough being powered by gravitational contraction that motivated the search for nuclear power sources.

Time scale is the key: nuclear fusion is only one that lasts long enough

12.2.4   Nuclear Fusion Needs Extreme Temperatures and Densities

Nuclear power is the only thing left to power the Sun for as long as it has been shining. There are two types of nuclear reactions possible: fusion and fission. They both transform the *nucleus* of an atom into another type of nucleus. *Fission* produces energy by *breaking up* massive nuclei like uranium into less massive nuclei like helium and lead. *Fusion* produces energy by *fusing together* light nuclei like hydrogen to make more massive nuclei like helium. Atomic power plants and the Atom Bomb use fission to get the energy. Stars and the Hydrogen bomb use fusion.

difference between fission and fusion

To get the positively-charged nuclei to fuse together, their electrical repulsion must be overcome (remember that like charges repel and opposite charges attract—something that rarely happens in human interactions). Once the positively-charged nuclei are close enough together (within several 10^{-13} centimeters of each other), another fundamental force of nature called the *strong nuclear force* takes over. It is much more powerful than the electric force and makes the nuclei stick together.

strong nuclear force

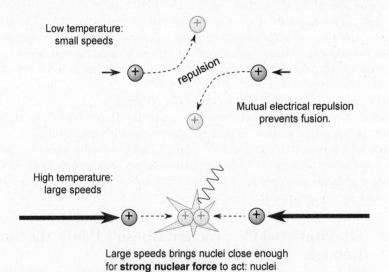

To get those nuclei close enough together requires high temperatures *and* high densities. At high temperatures the nuclei move fast enough to be driven close enough together for them to fuse. The high densities ensure that there are enough nuclei within in a small volume for the collisions to take place at all. The only place these extreme conditions occur naturally is in the cores of stars.

The temperatures in the cores of stars are above the approximately 8 million K needed to fuse hydrogen nuclei together. The amount of repulsion is larger for nuclei with more positive charge so the fusion of elements with greater positive charge requires greater temperatures and densities than that needed for fusing elements with small positive charge. This is why stars fuse hydrogen nuclei before they fuse other nuclei. For example, the fusion of helium nuclei requires temperatures above 100 million K and heavier nuclei require even higher temperatures. You will see in the next chapter that these ultra-extreme conditions occur in the final stages of a star's life cycle after the main sequence stage.

more massive nuclei need higher temperatures for fusion

12.2.5 Some Mass Is Converted to Energy in Fusion Reactions

Fusion involves low-mass nuclei whose combined mass is *more* than the resulting fused massive nucleus. The mass that was given up to form the massive nucleus was converted to energy. Remember $E = mc^2$? That tells you how much energy (E) can be made from matter with mass m. Remember that c is the speed of light and it's squared (!) so a little bit of mass can make a lot of energy.

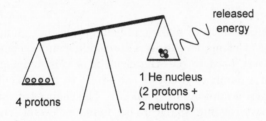

Some mass is converted into energy ($E=mc^2$)

In the cores of main sequence stars, four hydrogen nuclei, each with the mass of one proton, are fused together to form a single helium nucleus (two protons and two neutrons) that has a mass of 3.97 times the mass of one proton. An amount of mass equal to 0.03 times the mass of one proton was given up and converted to energy equal to $0.03 \times$ (mass one proton) $\times c^2$. The efficiency of this reaction is about 4/5 of one percent. The Sun could last for about 10 billion years on hydrogen fusion in its core. This is plenty long enough to satisfy the modern geologists.

12.2.6 Why Stars Use a Complicated Chain Reaction

The fusion process in stars is a little more complicated than what was described above. Rather than creating the helium nucleus in a single reaction, nature uses a series of reactions to build up the helium nucleus step-by-step. In most stars a three-step chain reaction, called the "proton-proton chain", is used (see figure next page). Massive stars also use a reaction that uses carbon, nitrogen, and oxygen nuclei in a chain process, called the Carbon-Nitrogen-Oxygen chain, with several more steps. Regardless of the chain process used, the net result of the fusion process is to fuse four hydrogen nuclei (protons) to create one helium nucleus (2 protons + 2 neutrons) plus some energy.

Why does nature use a long complicated chain reaction process to fuse four protons into one helium nucleus? Would it not be much simpler if four protons

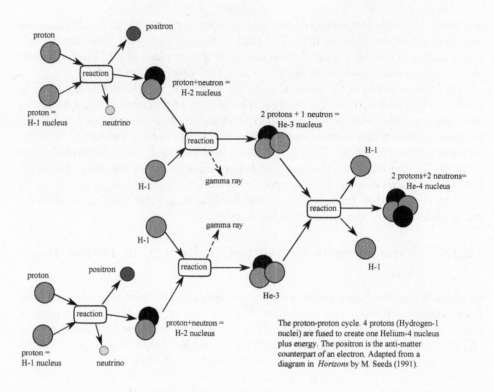

The proton-proton cycle. 4 protons (Hydrogen-1 nuclei) are fused to create one Helium-4 nucleus plus energy. The positron is the anti-matter counterpart of an electron. Adapted from a diagram in *Horizons* by M. Seeds (1991).

increase probability

would collide simultaneously to make one helium nucleus? Simpler, but not very likely is the answer. Getting four objects to collide simultaneously each with high enough energy is very hard to do—the chances of this happening are very, very small (as one from a family of 8 boys I can attest to the difficulty of getting just half of us together for a mini-family reunion!). The chances of this type of collision are too small to power the Sun, so nature has found a cleverer scheme. The chances of two particles colliding and fusing is much higher, so nature slowly builds up the helium nucleus.

Nuclear fusion is something of a holy grail for utility companies because it produces no nasty waste products and has the potential of getting more energy out of it than you put in—free energy! Unfortunately, the conditions to get fusion to happen are very extreme by our standards. A major problem is containing the very hot gas for extended periods of time to provide a sustained energy source. We have been only able to tap the fusion process with the Hydrogen bomb, but that is a one shot deal. The Hydrogen bomb still needs an atomic bomb trigger to create the extreme temperatures needed for the fusion process. At least you can get the waste product of the Sun's fusion process for free with solar power collectors. The Sun can have a controlled fusion process and not blow up all at once because of the hydrostatic equilibrium "thermostat".

12.2.7   Hydrostatic Equilibrium Controls the Reaction Rates

Hydrostatic equilibrium is the balance between the thermal pressures from the heat source pushing outwards and gravity trying to make the star collapse to the very center. I will discuss hydrostatic equilibrium in more depth (no pun intended) in a later section. The nuclear fusion rate is very sensitive to temperature. It increases as roughly temperature^4 for the proton-proton chain and even more sharply (temperature^{15}) for the Carbon-Nitrogen-Oxygen chain. So a slight increase in the temperature causes the fusion rate to increase by a large amount and a slight decrease in the temperature causes a large decrease in the fusion rate.

Now suppose the nuclear fusion rate speeds up for some reason. Then the following sequence of events would happen: 1) the thermal pressure would increase causing the star to expand; 2) the star would expand to a new point where gravity would balance the thermal pressure; 3) but the expansion would lower the temperature in the core—the nuclear fusion rate would slow down; 4) the thermal pressure would then drop and the star would shrink; 5) the temperature would rise again and the nuclear fusion rate would increase. Stability would be re-established between the nuclear reaction rates and the gravity compression.

A similar type of scheme would occur if the nuclear fusion rate were to slow down for some reason. The fusion rate stays approximately constant for stars that are fusing hydrogen to make helium + energy in the core. Once the hydrogen fuel in the core has been used up, hydrostatic equilibrium can no longer stabilize the star. What happens next will have to wait until I talk about stellar evolution.

12.2.8 Summary

A. Stars need an energy source that lasts a long time: *lifetime = energy stored/luminosity*. Nuclear fusion is the only process that can do this. With **nuclear fusion**, lower-mass nuclei fuse together to form a single more massive nucleus + energy. The sum of the low-mass nuclei masses = the single massive nucleus mass + energy/c^2 (remember $E = mc^2$). The "c" is the symbol for the speed of light. Nuclear fusion can power a star like the Sun for about 10 billion years.

nuclear fusion

B. To overcome the mutual electrical repulsion of positively-charged nuclei, a star needs extremely high temperatures and densities. These conditions are found only in the core of a star. Under these extreme conditions, particles move fast enough to get close enough for strong nuclear force to overcome electrical repulsion. Repulsive force increases with more positive charges. Hydrogen is fused first because it requires less extreme conditions, than the fusion of more massive nuclei.

C. Stars use a chain process to fuse four hydrogen nuclei to create one helium nucleus. A chain process is much more probable than a process that fuses four hydrogen nuclei simultaneously. Most stars use a **proton-proton chain** that is described in the figure on the previous page. Stars with enough mass will also use the "Carbon-Nitrogen-Oxygen chain" process. The net process for either chain is the fusion of four hydrogen nuclei to make one helium nucleus plus some energy.

proton-proton chain

D. The balance between gravity compression and outward thermal pressure controls the rate of the nuclear fusion reactions. The star does not blow up like a bomb.

12.3 Neutrino

Helium is produced in the fusion of hydrogen. As shown in the proton-proton fusion chain diagram on the previous page, there are two other particles produced. One is the "positron" and the other is a "neutrino". A positron is the antimatter counterpart of the electron. It has the same mass as an electron but the opposite charge. When it collides with an electron, they annihilate each other converting all of their mass into energy.

The photons produced in nuclear reactions take about a million years to move from the core to the surface. The photons scatter off the dense gas particles in the interior and move about a centimeter between collisions. In each collision they

solar photons made a million years ago

transfer some of their energy to the gas particles. By the time photons reach the photosphere, the gamma rays have become photons of much lower energy—visible light photons. Because the photons now reaching the surface were produced about a million years ago, they tell about the conditions in the core as it was a million years ago. The other particle produced in nuclear reactions has a less tortuous path out of the core.

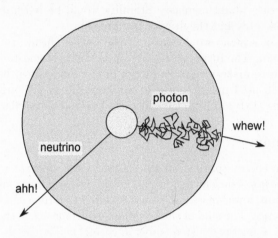

Photons take tortuous paths out of the Sun's interior.
Neutrinos pass right on through in just two seconds.

neutrino

solar neutrinos made only 8.5 minutes ago

A **neutrino** is a very low-mass particle that rarely interacts with ordinary matter. Neutrinos travel extremely fast—slightly less than the speed of light. Because they travel so fast and interact so rarely with matter, neutrinos pass from the core of the Sun to the surface in only two seconds. They take less than 8.5 minutes to travel the distance from the Sun to the Earth. If you could detect them, the neutrinos would tell you about the conditions in the Sun's core as it was only 8.5 minutes ago (much more current information than the photons!).

The problem with neutrinos is that they have a very low probability of interacting with matter. A neutrino could pass through a light year of lead and not be stopped by any of the lead atoms! However, there are A LOT of neutrinos produced by the Sun. Take a look at your pinky finger. In one second several *trillion* neutrinos passed through your pinky (did you feel them?). Do not worry, the neutrinos did not damage anything. The great majority of neutrinos pass right through the materials around you.

use LARGE detector

A few of them will interact with some matter on the Earth. You can increase the odds of detecting a few of them by using a LARGE amount of a material that reacts with neutrinos in a certain way. A chlorine isotope will change to a radioactive isotope of argon when a neutrino interacts with it. In the same way a gallium isotope will change to a radioactive isotope of germanium. Water molecules will give off a flash of light when struck by a neutrino. Neutrino detectors use hundreds of thousands of liters of these materials in a container buried under many tens of meters of rock to shield the detectors from other energetic particles from space called *cosmic rays*. Even the largest detectors detect only several hundred neutrinos in a *year* (compare that to the *trillions* of neutrinos that pass through you every *second*).

12.3.1 Solar Neutrino Problem

As shown in the figure describing the proton-proton chain above, the number of neutrinos produced in the Sun is directly proportional to the number of nuclear

A large container of cleaning fluid (C_2Cl_4) is used to detect neutrinos in the Homestake Gold Mine.

Image courtesy of R. Davis, Brookhaven National Laboratory

reactions that are taking place in the Sun's core. The same can also be said of the number of neutrinos produced via the Carbon-Nitrogen-Oxygen chain. The more reactions there are, the more neutrinos are produced and the more that should be detected here on the Earth. The number of neutrinos detected coming from the Sun was *smaller* than expected. Early experiments detected only 1/3 to 1/2 of the expected number of neutrinos. These experiments used hundreds of thousands of liters of cleaning fluid (composed of chlorine compounds) or very pure water. They were sensitive to the high-energy neutrinos produced in less than one percent of the nuclear fusion reactions. Later experiments using many tons of gallium were able to detect the more abundant low-energy neutrinos. However, those experiments also found the same problem—too few neutrinos (the gallium experiments found about 2/3 the expected number). The puzzling lack of neutrinos from the Sun was called the **solar neutrino problem.** There were several possible reasons for this discrepancy between the observations and our predictions:

too few neutrinos

solar neutrino problem

1. Nuclear fusion is not the Sun's power source. This reason was not supported by other observations, so it was not likely to be the correct reason.

2. The experiments were not calibrated correctly. It was unlikely that all of the carefully-tuned experiments were tuned in the same wrong way. The experiments used three very different ways to detect neutrinos and produced the same lack of neutrinos. The experiments were independently verified by many other scientists, so astronomers think that the results are correct, even if they were disappointing.

3. The nuclear reaction rate in the Sun is lower than what our calculations say. This was possible but many people checked and re-checked the physics of the reaction rates. There are some strong constraints in how much you can lower the temperature in the core of the Sun to slow down the reactions. Astronomers know how much total energy is emitted by the Sun, so they know very accurately how many nuclear reactions are needed to produce all of those photons seen coming from the Sun. Those reactions also produce the

The inside of the Super-Kamiokande neutrino detector before it was filled with water. The wall is lined with thousands of light detectors, each about the size of a large beach ball (50 cm), that detect the flashes of light made when a few neutrinos hit the water molecules.

Image courtesy of Institute for Cosmic Ray Research
University of Tokyo, Japan

neutrinos. Astronomers think they have a good idea of how stars produce their energy. That left another alternative.

4. Neutrinos produced in the core of the Sun change into other types of neutrinos during their flight from the Sun to the Earth. Our neutrino detectors can detect a certain kind of neutrino, called the "electron neutrino", that are produced from nuclear fusion. Some of these electron neutrinos can change into another of two types of neutrino (the "muon neutrino" or the "tau neutrino") that do not interact with the detection material as well as the electron neutrino. Some experiments in high-energy particle accelerators and the water tank Super-Kamiokande neutrino detector (Japan) suggested that the neutrinos could change into other types. The Sudbury Neutrino Observatory (Canada), using almost 900,000 liters of heavy water, was built to detect all three types of neutrinos. It firmly established that some of the electron neutrino produced by the nuclear fusion in the Sun do change into the other neutrino types and that the solar nuclear fusion models do predict the correct number of neutrinos. It looks like the 30-year mystery has been solved! The chief scientists for the Super-Kamiokande and the Sudbury Neutrino Observatory received the 2015 Nobel Prize in Physics for their discovery of neutrino oscillation.

A neutrino can change into another type of neutrino only if the neutrino has some mass. If the neutrino has mass, then it cannot travel at the speed of light, but it can get darn close. Recent experiments have shown that the neutrino does have a tiny amount of mass (several million times less than an electron). A neutrino with even as small a mass as this has important consequences for the evolution of the universe (more about that later) and our understanding of the structure of matter. It is amazing that in their effort to check their nuclear fusion theory, astronomers have learned totally unexpected things about fundamental physics and this has changed what is known about the structure and behavior of the entire universe itself. Wow!

There are several excellent sites on the world wide web that discuss neutrinos and the instruments used to detect them. Links to them are found on the textbook's website—go to the end of the neutrino section of the online "Our Sun and Stellar Structure" chapter .

12.4   Helioseismology

Another probe of the Sun's interior uses the pulsating motions of the Sun. The pulsations are too small to be seen just by looking at the Sun. But the pulsations can be seen if the doppler shifts are measured across the face of the Sun. Some parts of the Sun expand towards the Earth and adjacent regions contract away from the Earth. These regions are several thousands of kilometers across and the pulsation periods are just a few minutes long. Different types of oscillating waves combine to produce the complicated patterns of pulsation seen.

measure blueshifts and redshifts across the Sun

If you disentangle the different oscillation modes from each other, you can use these waves to probe the solar interior. How those waves propagate through the Sun and interact with each other depends on the temperature, density, and composition of the material they pass through. By observing the effects of these waves on the photosphere of the Sun, you can determine the temperature, density, and composition of the different layers inside the Sun. Geologists on the Earth use similar techniques to study the interior of our planet from earthquake waves in the research field called *seismology* (see chapter 9). Modifying the name for solar studies, the study of the Sun's interior using the solar oscillations is called **helioseismology**.

helioseismology

Solar astronomers have set up a global network of stations to continuously monitor the Sun's pulsations. This network is called the Global Oscillations Network Group (GONG). Links to more information about GONG are found at the text's web site. Select the "Our Sun and Stellar Structure" chapter and go to the end of the Helioseismology section to find the links. Instruments to detect solar oscillations have also been placed on satellites. The text's web site has links to those sites as well.

12.5   Asteroseismology

We can apply the same techniques of helioseismology to the pulsations of other stars. **Asteroseismology** is the study of the internal structure of stars from their pulsations. We can determine the temperature, pressure, density, and composition of the different layers inside the stars from very careful measurements of minute brightness changes (*microvariability*) of the stars. From the ground, these pulsations can be seen for only a few brighter stars because of the distorting effects of the Earth's atmosphere. In space much more precise observations are possible so asteroseismology can be extended to smaller, very stable stars, including solar-type stars.

asteroseismology

The particular oscillation modes seen also depend on the total mass and diameter of the stars. Smaller stars have higher frequency modes and smaller amplitudes. This means, though, that the stars must have greater apparent brightnesses (smaller apparent magnitudes) than larger stars such as red giants to pick out the microvariability above the statistical noise fluctuations inherent in any measurement. Even still, many thousands of stable, smaller stars lie within the stringent photometric limits required for asteroseismology using space telescopes such as COROT, Kepler, and MOST. Asteroseismology provides another way of measuring the overall masses and diameters of stars in addition to the classical techniques described in the previous chapter. With the hundreds of eclipsing binaries discovered by the Kepler

finding star masses and diameters

mission, asteroseismology predictions can be cross-checked extremely well with the classical techniques using eclipsing binaries.

finding star ages

A bonus feature of asteroseismology is that it enables us to determine the ages of stars as well. As described in the next chapter, the interior structure of a star changes in predictable ways as the stars ages. We can use the stellar evolution models to pick out the density, temperature, and mass of stars at particular ages that match the observed parameters derived from their oscillation modes to get the age of the star.

Vocabulary

helioseismology	luminosity	neutrino
nuclear fusion	proton-proton chain	solar neutrino problem

Review Questions

1. How does **nuclear fusion** produce energy?

2. Why does nuclear fusion need high temperatures and densities?

3. Why is it so hard to develop nuclear fusion as a dependable power source on Earth?

4. Why will chemical reactions or gravitational contraction not work for powering the Sun?

5. What is the net result of the nuclear fusion chain process? Why does nature use the complicated chain process instead of a one-step fusion procedure?

6. Where are **neutrinos** produced? What information can they tell you about interior conditions in the Sun?

7. What was the **solar neutrino problem**? How was the problem solved and what are the implications of that solution?

8. How can you use pulsations of the Sun to find out about the structure and composition of its interior?

12.6   Interior Structure of Stars

Observations of the stars in all regions of the electromagnetic spectrum and careful observations of the Sun's pulsation modes and neutrinos provide the data needed to construct models of the interiors of stars. This section is about how to find out what the interior of a star is like without physically taking one apart (a rather difficult thing to do).

12.6.1   Mathematical Models

Astronomers construct **mathematical models** of the interior of a star using the information pouring from the surfaces of stars (especially the Sun) and their knowledge of how gases behave under different conditions. The **mathematical models**

mathematical models

are a set of equations that describe how things work layer by layer in a star. Fortunately, the interior of stars is completely gaseous all the way to the center, so the equations are relatively simple (whew!). The physics of gases can be described with just three parameters:

temperature

1. **Temperature**—a measure of the random motion energy (the *average* kinetic energy) of the gas particles. The higher the temperature, the more random kinetic energy is present.

2. **Pressure**—the amount of force/area. Hot gas expands to create pressure on its surroundings. For example, the gas inside a hot air balloon pushes out on the material of the balloon enclosing the gas.

3. **Mass Density**—the amount of mass/volume. Gaseous material can be compressed to smaller volumes and higher densities.

mass density

12.6.2 Equation of State

How the three parameters work together to describe the material you are studying is determined by the **equation of state** of the material. This is an equation that relates density, pressure, and temperature. The equation of state for solids and liquids is very complex and uncertain. The equation of state for the gas in stars is simple: the pressure = (a constant × the mass density × the temperature) / (the *molecular weight* of the gas). The *molecular weight* of a particular type of gas is the combined mass of all of the isotopes of that type of gas in the proportions found in nature. For hydrogen, the molecular weight is very close to 1; for helium, the molecular weight is very close to 4. For a gas made of different types of atoms (such as that found in stars), the molecular weight is the weighted mean of the different atomic types, taking into account the relative proportions of the different types of atoms. This equation of state for simple gases is also called the **ideal gas law**.

equation of state

ideal gas law

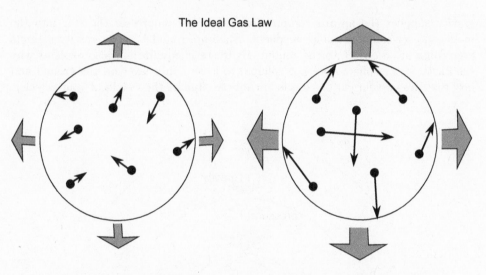

The Ideal Gas Law

Cool gas produces low pressure   Hot gas produces high pressure

$$\text{Pressure} = \frac{\text{constant} \times \text{density} \times \text{temperature}}{\text{molecular weight}}$$

12.6.3 Gravity Holds a Star Together

Stars are held together by gravity. Gravity tries to compress everything to the center. What holds an ordinary star up and prevents total collapse is thermal and radiation pressure. The thermal and radiation pressure tries to expand the star layers outward to infinity.

In any given layer of a star, there is a *balance* between the thermal pressure (outward) and the weight of the material above pressing downward (inward). This balance is called **hydrostatic equilibrium**. A star is like a balloon. In a balloon the gas inside the balloon pushes outward and the elastic material supplies just enough inward compression to balance the gas pressure. In a star the star's internal

gravity inward

thermal + radiation pressure outward

hydrostatic equilibrium

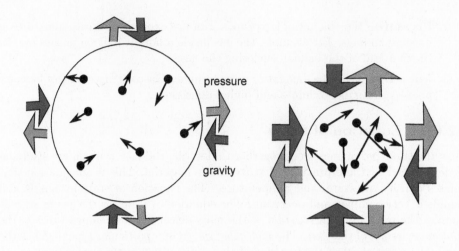

Hydrostatic equilibrium: gravity compression balanced by pressure outward. Greater gravity compresses gas making it denser and hotter, so the outward pressure increases.

gravity supplies the inward compression. Gravity compresses the star into the most compact shape possible: a sphere. Stars are round because gravity attracts everything in an object to the center. Hydrostatic equilibrium also explains why the Earth's atmosphere does not collapse to a very thin layer on the ground and how the tires on your car or bicycle are able to support the weight of your vehicle.

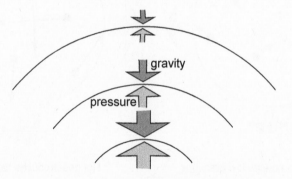

Deeper layers have more gravity compression, so they have greater outward pressure to compensate.

Long before astronomers knew about nuclear fusion, they had a good idea of how the density and temperature of stars increased toward their cores. Deeper layers have *more gravity* compression from the overlying layers. The greater gravity compression raises the density of the gas. In order to balance the greater gravity compression, the outward pressure of the gas and radiation is increased by raising the temperature. Calculating the change in density and temperature layer by layer toward the center of a star, you find the temperature at the core of a star = 8 to 28 million K and the densities = 10 to 130 times the density of water. As stars age, these numbers increase! You have already seen in the previous section that hydrostatic equilibrium also provides a "thermostatic control" on the energy generation inside a star and keeps the star stable.

12.6.4 Other Pieces

Other basic physical principles are put into the mathematical models:

1. *Continuity of Mass*: the total stellar mass = sum of all of the shell layer masses. Mass is distributed smoothly throughout star's interior (there are no gaps or pockets of "negative" mass). Also, the law of the conservation of mass says that the total amount of mass does not change with time.

2. *Continuity of Energy*: the amount of energy flowing out the top of each shell layer in a star = the amount of energy flowing in at bottom of the shell layer. No energy is magically destroyed or created from nothing. A star's luminosity = sum of all of the shell layer energies. Also, the law of the conservation of energy says that the total amount of energy does not change with time. Energy can change from one form to another form of energy, but the total amount is a constant.

3. *Energy Transport*: Recall from the discussion about how energy flows in planetary atmospheres that energy moves from hot to cold via conduction, radiation, or convection. Nature will first try to use radiation (photons) to move energy from the very hot interior to the very cold space. If radiation cannot transport all of the energy over the distance from the center to the surface of the star, then nature will also use convection. Convection is the bulk motion of gases used to transport energy. Hot gases rise to the upper levels and radiate their extra energy at the upper levels while cooler gases sink to pick up more energy from the hot interior. Conduction transports energy by having each atom transfer its energy to the atom next to it. Conduction is not an efficient process in a gas so it transports a very small amount of energy in stars and is usually ignored.

4. **Opacity**: It takes a LONG time for photons produced by nuclear reactions in the core to reach the surface. In the opaque interior a photon travels only about 1 centimeter before it runs into an atom or ion and is absorbed. A measure of the gas' ability to absorb the photons is called its **opacity**. You cannot see into the interior of a star because the gas has a high opacity. **opacity**

   The photon is later re-emitted but in a random direction. It may be re-emitted in the direction it came from! So the photon travels a very zig-zag sort of path outward. It takes about a million years for a photon to travel from where it was created in the core to the surface where it is finally released into space. Along the way the photon has transferred some its energy to the gas particles, so the photon has changed from very high energy gamma rays to the lower energy visible light photons. Some of the radiation is also in the form of neutrinos. The gas has almost zero opacity with the neutrinos so they pass right on through the star's gas in just a few seconds.

5. The equation of state, hydrostatic equilibrium and the other physical principles are put together for each layer in a star. The equations are solved for each layer starting from the layer there is direct information of, the surface. That result gives the conditions for the next layer's equations. Solving the layer's equations gives the conditions for the layer below it and this process continues on down toward the center layer by layer. In order to get sufficient detail for accurate results, the star's interior is divided into hundreds of layers. To save on time, the equations are solved using a computer.

12.6.5   Mass-Luminosity Relation Explained

Observations of thousands of main sequence stars show that there is definite relationship between their mass and their luminosity. The more massive main sequence stars are hotter and more luminous than the low-mass main sequence stars. Furthermore, the luminosity depends on the mass raised to a power that is between three and four (Luminosity $\sim$ Mass^p, where p is between 3 and 4). This means that even a slight difference in the mass among stars produces a large difference in their luminosities. For example, an O-type star can be only 20 times more massive than the Sun, but have a luminosity about 10,000 times as much as the Sun. Putting together the principle of hydrostatic equilibrium and the sensitivity of nuclear reaction rates to temperature, you can easily explain why.

Massive stars have greater gravitational compression in their cores because of the larger weight of the overlying layers than that found in low-mass stars. The massive stars need greater thermal and radiation pressure pushing outward to balance the greater gravitational compression. The greater thermal pressure is provided by the higher temperatures in the massive star's core than those found in low-mass stars. *Massive stars need higher core temperatures to be stable!*

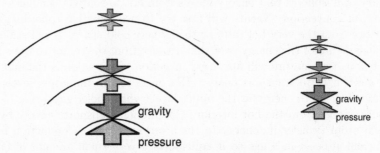

More massive stars have greater gravity compression. They need higher core temperatures to be stable and have very many more nuclear reactions. A slight change in mass produces a large change in luminosity.

The nuclear reaction rate is *very* sensitive to temperature so that even a slight increase in temperature makes the nuclear reactions occur at a *MUCH* higher rate. This means that a star's luminosity increases a lot if the temperature is higher. This also means that a slight increase in the mass of the star produces a large increase in the star's luminosity.

12.6.6   Mass Cutoff Explained

The principle of hydrostatic equilibrium and nuclear fusion theory also explain why stars have a certain range of masses. The stars have masses between 0.08 and about 100 solar masses.

Stars with too little mass do not have enough gravitational compression in their cores to produce the required high temperatures and densities needed for fusion. The lowest mass is about 0.08 solar masses or about 80 Jupiter masses. A star less massive than this does not undergo fusion of ordinary hydrogen but if it is more massive than about 13 Jupiters it can fuse the heavier isotope of hydrogen, deuterium, in the first part of its life. Stars in this boundary zone between ordinary stars and gas planets are called **brown dwarfs**. After whatever deuterium fusion it does while it is young, a brown dwarf then just slowly radiates away the heat from that fusion and that is left over from its formation. Among the first brown dwarfs discovered is the companion orbiting the star Gliese 229 (see figure next page).

With the discovery of several hundred brown dwarfs in recent infrared surveys, astronomers have now extended the spectral type sequence to include these non-

brown dwarf

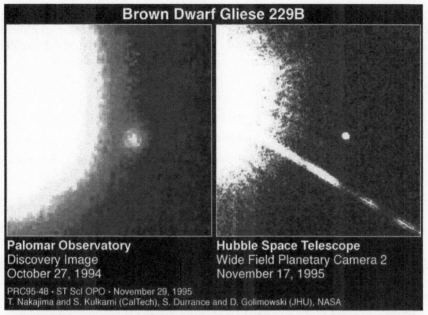

The feeble light of the cooling brown dwarf is almost lost in the glare of its main sequence star companion.

planets. Just beyond the M-stars are the L dwarfs with surface temperatures of about 1400 K to 2200 K with strong absorption lines of metal hydrides and alkali metals. Cooler than the L dwarfs are the T dwarfs. At their cooler temperatures, methane lines become prominent.

Stars with too much mass have so much radiation pressure inside pushing outward on the upper layers, that the star is unstable. It blows off the excess mass. The limit is roughly about 100 to perhaps 150 solar masses. Stars like Eta Carinae and the "Pistol star" are examples of these supermassive stars.

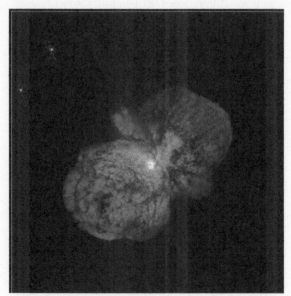

The hot supergiant Eta Carinae has ejected some of its material into dumbbell-shaped lobes. It is one of the most massive stars known.

Image courtesy of Jon Morse and NASA

Vocabulary

brown dwarfs	equation of state	hydrostatic equilibrium
ideal gas law	mass density	mathematical models
opacity	pressure	temperature

Review Questions

1. How can you determine what the interiors of stars are like?

2. What three quantities does an **equation of state** relate?

3. What is the equation of state for gases? (Almost any gas has this equation of state, even the air in your automobile tires or air-filled ball.)

4. Use the equation of state of a gas to explain in what way the temperature of the gas changes as the pressure exerted on the gas is increased. Explain why the pressure in your automobile tires is slightly less when they are cold than right after a long drive.

5. What is being equilibrated in **hydrostatic equilibrium**? How does hydrostatic equilibrium explain why the temperature and density increases inward toward the core of a star?

6. How does hydrostatic equilibrium control the fusion rate in the Sun?

7. What would happen to the size of a star if its core *steadily* produced more energy than it did at some earlier time (e.g., when a main sequence star becomes a red giant)?

8. What would happen to the size of a star if its core *steadily* produced less energy than it did at some earlier time (e.g., when a star stops fusing nuclei in its core)?

9. Do photons produced in the core zip right out from the Sun or does it take longer? Explain why.

10. Why do **brown dwarfs** not undergo fusion?

11. What are some basic differences between stars and planets?

Chapter 13

Lives and Deaths of Stars

Stars live for a very long time compared to human lifetimes. Your great, great grandparents saw the same stars as you will see tonight (if it's clear). Our lifetimes are measured in years. Star lifetimes are measured in millions of years. Even though star timescales are enormous, it is possible to know how stars are born, live, and die. This chapter covers the stages a star will go through in its life and how it was figured out. The last part of the chapter will cover the remains of stars, white dwarfs, neutron stars, and the Hollywood favorite: black holes. The vocabulary terms are in boldface.

13.1   Stellar Evolution

In the previous chapter you found that mass is an important quantity for determining what stars are like. In fact, all of the other aspects of a star such as its luminosity, temperature, size, density, etc., can be explained using the fundamental property of a star: its mass. There is also a slight dependence of the luminosity, temperature, size, etc. on the composition of the star, but because stars are all mostly hydrogen and helium, the star's mass is the important quantity.

13.1.1   Mass Dependence

The stages a star will go through and how long it will last in each stage also depend on the *mass* (with just little bit of dependence on composition). Massive stars evolve quicker than light stars. In the previous chapter, the relationship between the luminosity and mass was explained using basic principles of how compressed gases behave. Slight increases produce large increases in the luminosities of stars.

Stars shine because of nuclear fusion reactions in their core. The more luminous they are, the more reactions are taking place in their cores. Massive stars live shorter lives than the common small stars because even though they have a larger amount of hydrogen for nuclear reactions, their rate of consuming their fuel is very much greater. The massive stars are analogous to the big, gas-guzzling automobiles with big gas tanks of a few decades ago and the small stars are analogous to the small economy automobiles of today that are frugal with their gasoline.

It is a simple calculation to find out how long something can continue consuming fuel. The *lifetime = amount of fuel/consumption rate*. If your car has a full 15-gallon gas tank and it consumes 2 gallons/hour on the highway, then your car can travel for 15 gallons/(2 gallons/hour) = 7.5 hours. Stars are the same way. The amount of fuel for nuclear fusion is proportional to the total mass of the star when it first started producing energy from nuclear reactions, so the amount of fuel = k × initial mass. The consumption rate is simply the star's luminosity, so the star will

how long it can last

live as a main sequence star for an amount of time = k × initial mass/luminosity. If the star masses and luminosity are relative to the Sun, then the star's lifetime = mass/luminosity ×10^{10} years. Recall that the Sun's will live for ten billion (10^{10}) years before it runs out of hydrogen in its core.

mass-luminosity relation
In order to remain in hydrostatic equilibrium, a star's luminosity increases with mass as (the star's mass)^p. The value of the exponent p varies between 3 and 4. For the rare massive stars ($M_* > 30$ solar masses), $p = 3$ and for the more common low-mass stars ($M_* < 10$ solar masses), $p = 4$. You can use the mass-luminosity relation to find the star's lifetime in terms of just its initial mass. The *lifetime = mass/luminosity* ×10^{10} *years* is simply = (star's mass)/[(star's mass)^p] × 10^{10} years = 1/(star's mass)$^{p-1}$ × 10^{10} years (remember that the star's mass is in solar units).

star lifetime

How do you do that?

A 5 solar mass star has only five times more hydrogen fuel than the Sun, but
(the star's luminosity)/(the Sun's luminosity) = $(5/1)^4 = 625$!
Its lifetime = $1/(5/1)^{(4-1)} \times 10^{10}$ years = $(1/125) \times 10^{10}$ years = 8.0×10^7 years.

Some representative lifetimes for other stars are given in the table below. Stars that have fewer elements heavier than helium in them compared to other stars, will have slightly shorter lifetimes than those given in the table.

star mass (solar masses)	time (years)	Spectral type
60	3 million	O3
30	11 million	O7
10	32 million	B4
3	370 million	A5
1.5	3 billion	F5
1	10 billion	G2 (Sun)
0.1	1000's billions	M7

13.1.2 The Basic Scheme

All stars follow the same basic series of steps in their lives: Gas Cloud →Main Sequence →Red Giant →(Planetary Nebula or Supernova) →Core Remnant. How long a star lasts in each stage, whether a planetary nebula forms or a spectacular supernova occurs, and what type of remnant will form depends on the initial mass of the star.

Evolution of stars depends on Mass (at start of fusion) only*
* with a tiny bit of dependence on chemical composition

What follows is a description of each of these stages.

Stage 1: Giant Molecular Cloud

giant molecular cloud
A **giant molecular cloud** is a large, dense gas cloud (with dust) that is cold enough for molecules to form. Thousands of giant molecular clouds exist in the disk part of our galaxy. Each giant molecular cloud has 100,000's to a few million solar masses of material.

One nearby example is the Orion Molecular Cloud Complex that stretches from the belt of the Orion constellation to his sword of which the Orion Nebula is a part.

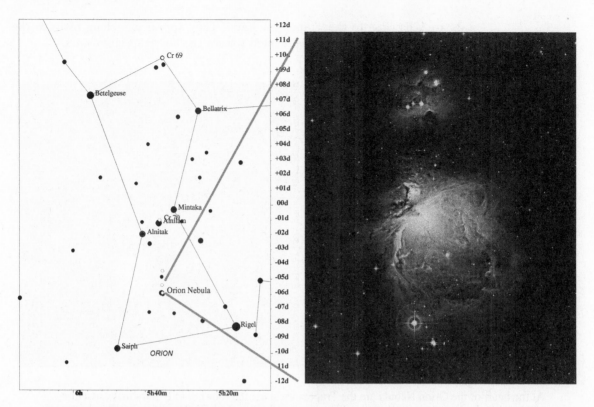

The Orion Nebula is the H II region protruding out one side of the giant molecular cloud complex in the sword part of the Orion constellation.

Orion Nebula image courtesy of David Malin/Anglo-Australian Observatory/Royal Observatory, Edinburgh

The Orion Complex is about 1340 light years away, several hundred light years across, and has enough material to form many tens of thousands of suns. The giant molecular clouds have dust in them to shield the densest parts of them from the harsh radiation of nearby stars so that molecules can form in them. Therefore, they are very dark and very cold with a temperature of only about 10 K. In addition to the most common molecule, molecular hydrogen, over 80 other molecules have been discovered in the clouds from simple ones like carbon monoxide to complex organic molecules such as methanol and acetone. Radio telescopes are used to observe these very dark, cold clouds. The clouds are dense relative to the rest of the gas between the stars but are still much less dense than the atmosphere of a planet. Typical cloud densities are 100 to 1000 molecules per cubic centimeter while each cubic centimeter of the air you breath has about 2.5×10^{19} molecules—a molecular cloud is tens to hundreds of times "emptier" than the best vacuum chambers we have on Earth!

In the parts of a giant molecular cloud where very hot stars (O and B-type) have formed, the hydrogen gas surrounding them can be made to glow in the visible band to make what is called a *H II region*. The Orion Nebula is an example of this. It is the fuzzy patch you can see in the sword part of the Orion constellation. It is a bubble about 26 light years across that has burst out of one side of the Orion Complex. The nebula is lit up by the fluorescence of the hydrogen gas around a O-type star in the Trapezium cluster of four stars at the heart of the nebula. The O-type star is so hot that it produces a large amount of ultraviolet light. The ultraviolet light ionizes the surrounding hydrogen gas. When the electrons recombine with the hydrogen nuclei, they produce visible light. Several still-forming

H II region lit up by O & B stars and shows where a lot of stars are forming

stars are seen close to the Trapezium stars. They appear as oblong blobs in the figure below with their long axis pointed toward the hot Trapezium stars.

At the heart of the Orion Nebula are the Trapezium stars: the four hot O,B stars that cause the surrounding hydrogen gas to fluoresce. The "comets" are actually material surrounding lower-mass stars that is being evaporated away by the intense energy of the Trapezium stars.
Images courtesy of John Bally, Dave Devine, and Ralph Sutherland
and STScI/AURA

H II regions show where stars are forming

H II regions mark sites of star formation because they are formed by hot, young stars. Recall from the table at the beginning of the chapter that O-type stars live just a few million years, a very short time for a star! These hot stars do not live long enough to move out from where they were formed. Behind the visible part of the Orion Nebula is a much denser region of gas and dust that is cool enough for molecules to form. Several hundred stars are now forming inside the Orion Nebula.

Fragments of giant molecular clouds with tens to hundreds of solar masses of material a piece will start collapsing for some reason all at about the same time. Possible trigger mechanisms could be a shock wave from the explosion of a nearby massive star at its death or from the passage of the cloud through regions of more intense gravity as found in the spiral arms of spiral galaxies. These shock waves compress the gas clouds enough for them to gravitationally collapse. Gas clouds may start to collapse without any outside force if they are cool enough and massive enough to spontaneously collapse. Whatever the reason, the result is the same: gas clumps compress to become protostars.

Stage 2: Protostar

As a gas clump collapses it heats up because the gas particles run into each other. The energy the gas particles had from falling under the force of gravity gets converted to heat energy. The gas clump becomes warm enough to produce a lot of infrared and microwave radiation. At this stage the warm clump is called a **protostar**. The gas clump forms a disk with the protostar in the center. Other material in the disk may coalesce to form another star or planets.

protostar glows in the infrared

A protostar will reach a temperature of 2000 to 3000 K, hot enough to glow a dull red with most of its energy in the infrared. The cocoon of gas and dust surrounding them blocks the visible light. The surrounding dust warms up enough to produce copious amounts of infrared and the cooler dust further out glows with microwave energy. This longer wavelength electromagnetic radiation can pass through the dust. The infrared telescopes are able to observe the protostars themselves and their cocoons in dust clouds in our galaxy while the microwave telescopes probe the surrounding regions. The power of infrared detectors is illustrated in the images below. The part of the nebula above and to the right of the Trapezium stars is actually forming many stars. They can only be seen in the infrared image on the right side of the figure.

use infrared & microwave telescopes to see forming stars

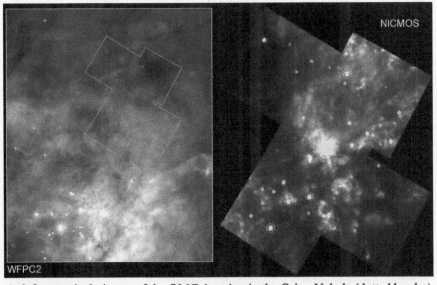

At left an optical picture of the OMC-1 region in the Orion Nebula (dotted border) does not show much. An infrared detector (NICMOS, right) is needed to peer through the thick gas that enshrouds the active star formation region.
Image courtesy of R. Thompson & S. Stolovy (University of Arizona), C.R. O'Dell (Rice University) and STScI/AURA

The low-mass protostars (those up to about 5 solar masses) are initially much more luminous than the main sequence star they will become because of their large surface area. As these low-mass protostars collapse, they decrease in luminosity while staying at roughly a constant surface temperature. A star remains in the protostar stage for only a short time, so it is hard to catch many stars in that stage of their life. Fusion starts in the core and the outward pressure from those reactions stops the core from collapsing any further. But material from the surrounding cloud continues to fall onto the protostar. Most of the energy produced by the protostar is from the gravitational collapse of the cloud material.

Young stars are social—fragmentation of the giant molecular cloud produces protostars that form at about the same time. *Stars are observed to be born in clusters.* Other corroborating evidence for this is that there are no isolated young stars. This observation is important because a valuable test of the stellar evolution models is the comparison of the models with star clusters. That analysis is based on the assumption that the stars in the clusters used to validate the models all formed at about the same time.

stars form in clusters

The Hubble Space Telescope has directly observed protostars in the Orion Nebula and the Eagle Nebula (in the Serpens constellation). The protostars it has observed have been prematurely exposed. The intense radiation from nearby hot O or B-type stars has evaporated the dust and driven away the gas around the smaller still-forming stars. In at least one case in the Orion Nebula, all of the gas has been

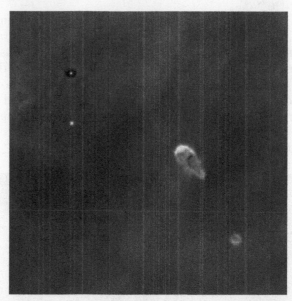

The gas surrounding these protostars is being evaporated by the intense radiation from the Trapezium stars. One of the dusty disks (top left) about the size of Pluto's orbit is now totally exposed and another is seen edgewise in the teardrop-shaped cocoon at center (aligned with the Trapezium stars in the upper left direction).

Images courtesy of John Bally, Dave Devine, and Ralph Sutherland
and STScI/AURA

blown away to leave just the dark dust disk with the protostar in the center. One example of a totally exposed dust disk seen almost face-on is shown in the figure above. It is the black spot to the right of the prominent cocoon nebula around the protostar at the center. The teardrop-shaped cocoon nebula around the center protostar is oriented toward the Trapezium stars to the upper left of the figure. The evaporation of the dark, dense fingers of dust & gas in the Eagle Nebula is captured in the famous "gaseous pillars" picture on the right side of the figure at the top of the next page. Note that the tiniest fingers you see sticking out of the sides of the pillars are larger than our entire solar system!

Stage 3: T-Tauri

T-Tauri

The young star will produce strong winds in the **T-Tauri** stage, named after the prototype star in the constellation Taurus. These strong winds eject much of the surrounding cocoon gas and dust. The winds are constrained to flow preferentially along the rotation axes by the disk of dust and gas. With most of the cocoon gas blown away, the forming star itself becomes visible to the outside for the first time. The HST images in the middle of the next page show jets shooting out from three young stars. The disk around one star is seen in the top left frame. The scale in the bottom left corner of each frame represents 150 billion kilometers, or 1,000 times the distance between Earth and the Sun (over twelve times Pluto's entire orbit).

The central gas/dust pillars of the Eagle Nebula (left) as seen through the Hubble Space Telescope (right).

Eagle Nebula image courtesy of David Malin/Anglo-Australian Observatory

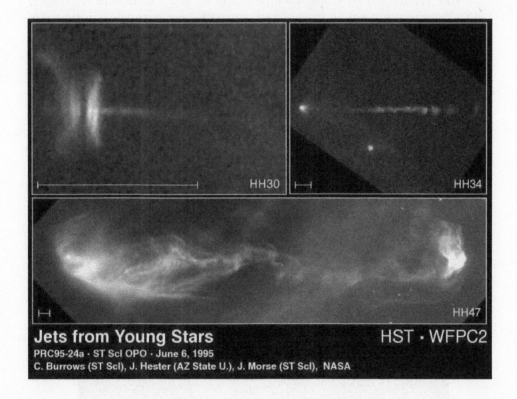

Stage 4: Main Sequence

Eventually the star becomes stable because hydrostatic equilibrium has been established. The star settles down to spend about 90% of its life as a **main sequence** star. It is fusing hydrogen to form helium *in the core*.

    Stars initially begin their lives near other stars in a cluster. After a few orbits

main sequence: hydrogen fusion in core

around the galactic center, gravitational tugs from other stars in the galaxy cause the stars in the cluster to wander away from their cluster and live their lives alone or with perhaps one or two companions. The Pleiades (figure below) are a young cluster of stars easily visible in the shoulder of the Taurus (the Bull) constellation during the winter months. They are about 80 million years old (compare that to the Sun which is 4,600 million = 4.6 billion years old!). The gas and dust around the stars is probably just interstellar clouds the cluster is passing through.

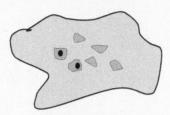 

Stellar "nursery" cloud
Some fragments have proto-stars,
other fragments not dense enough yet

T-Tauri stage
strong bi-polar winds

Main sequence

A star remains at a given spectral type during the entire main sequence stage—the main sequence is *not* an evolutionary sequence. For example, a F-type star formed as an F-type star and will remain a F-type star during the entire main sequence stage. Only if the star has a very close companion may a change occur if gas is transferred between the stars in the system. The main sequence star does *slowly* increase in luminosity with only a slight change in its surface temperature as the helium builds up in its core. Our Sun's luminosity is now about 30% greater than when it formed.

The Pleiades are a beautiful example of a young open cluster.
Image courtesy of David Malin/Anglo-Australian Observatory/Royal Observatory, Edinburgh

Stage 5: Subgiant, Red Giant, Supergiant

All through the long main sequence stage, the relentless compression of gravity is balanced by the outward pressure from the nuclear fusion reactions in the core. Eventually the hydrogen in the core is all converted to helium and the nuclear reactions stop. Gravity takes over and the core shrinks. The layers outside the core collapse too, the ones closer to the center collapse quicker than the ones near the surface. As the layers collapses, the gas compresses and heats up.

Eventually, the layer just outside the core called the "shell layer" gets hot and dense enough for fusion to start. The fusion in the layer just outside the core is called **shell burning.** This fusion is very rapid because the shell layer is still compressing and increasing in temperature. The luminosity of the star increases from its main sequence value. The gas envelope surrounding the core puffs outward under the action of the extra outward pressure. As the star begins to expand, it becomes a **subgiant** and then a **red giant.**

shell burning

subgiant, red giant

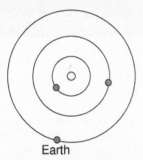 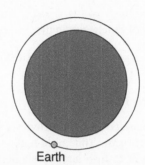

Now: hot core + warm surface; small size.

Future: very hot core + cool surface. Large size but less mass; very bright.

At the bloated out surface, the increased amount of energy is spread out over a larger area so each square centimeter will be cooler. The surface will have a red color because it is so cool and it will be much further from the center than during the main sequence. Despite its cooler surface temperature, the red giant is very luminous because of its *huge* surface area. When the Sun becomes a red giant, Mercury and Venus will be swallowed up by the Sun and perhaps the Earth will too. Even if the Earth is not swallowed up, conditions on its surface will become impossible for life to exist. The Sun's increased luminosity will heat the Earth's surface so much that the water oceans and atmosphere will evaporate away. Massive main sequence stars will expand much further to become **supergiants.** Betelgeuse, the bright red star in the top left corner of the Orion constellation, is an example of a supergiant star (see the figure on the next page). If placed at the center of our solar system, all of the planets out to Jupiter would be inside Betelgeuse. A few supergiants are even larger than Betelgeuse!

supergiant

Red giants can have strong "winds" that dispel more mass than all of the stellar winds that occurred during the long main sequence stage. However, most of the star's mass will be lost in the "last gasp" stage (planetary nebula or supernova) described below. All through the star's life after it first started nuclear reactions, it has been losing mass as it converted some mass to energy and other mass was lost in the winds. This means that even though a red giant is large in terms of linear size, it is *less massive* than the main sequence star it came from. A red giant has the extremes in temperature and density: its surface is cold and has a very low density, while its core is very hot and extremely dense.

red giant stage large in size but smaller in mass than main seq stage

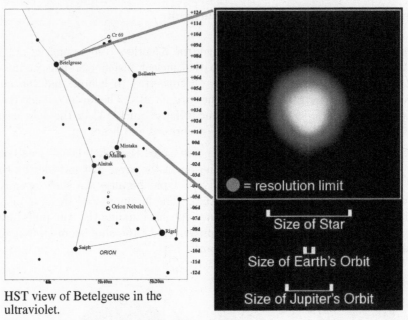

HST view of Betelgeuse in the ultraviolet.

Betelgeuse image courtesy of A. Dupree (CfA) and STScI/AURA

Stage 6: Core Fusion

If the star is massive enough, gravity can compress the core enough to create high enough temperatures, 100 million K, to start fusing helium, or temperatures of billions of Kelvin to fuse heavier elements if it is repeating this stage. In low mass stars (like the Sun), the onset of helium fusion can be *very* rapid, producing a burst of energy called a **helium flash**. Eventually the reaction rate settles down. Fusion in the core during this stage releases more energy/second than the core fusion of the main sequence stage, so the star is bigger, but stable! Hydrostatic equilibrium is restored until the core fuel runs out.

Stars entering and leaving this stage can create conditions in their interiors that trap their radiated energy in their outer layers. The outward thermal pressure increases enough to expand the outer layers of the star. The trapped energy is able to escape when the outer layers are expanded and the thermal pressure drops. Gravity takes over and the star shrinks, but it shrinks beyond the equilibrium point. The energy becomes trapped again and the cycle continues.

In ordinary stars hydrostatic equilibrium works to dampen (diminish) the pulsations. But stars entering and leaving stage 6 can briefly (in terms of star lifetimes!) create conditions where the pressure and gravity are out of sync and the pulsations continue for a time. The larger, more luminous stars will pulsate with longer periods than the smaller, fainter stars because gravity takes longer to pull the more extended outer layers of the larger stars back. The *period-luminosity relation* can be used to determine the distances of these luminous stars from the inverse square law of light brightness. Stars of this type are called *Cepheid variables*, a very important kind of star for setting the scale of the universe, discussed in the next chapter.

Stage 7: Red Giant or Supergiant

When the core fuel runs out again, the core resumes its collapse. If the star is massive enough, it will repeat stage 5. The number of times a star can cycle through stages 5 to 6 to 7 depends on the mass of the star. Each time through the cycle, the star creates new heavier elements in its core (stage 6) from the ash of fusion reactions in the previous cycle. This creation of heavier elements from

helium flash

Cepheid variable

lighter elements is called **stellar nucleosynthesis.** For the most massive stars, this continues up to the production of iron in the core. Stars like the Sun will synthesize elements only up to carbon and oxygen in their cores. Each repeat of stages 5 to 6 to 7 occurs over a shorter time period than the previous repeat.

stellar nucleosynthesis

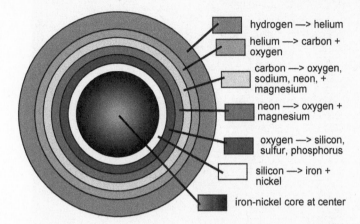

hydrogen —> helium

helium —> carbon + oxygen

carbon —> oxygen, sodium, neon, + magnesium

neon —> oxygen + magnesium

oxygen —> silicon, sulfur, phosphorus

silicon —> iron + nickel

iron-nickel core at center

The "onion layers" of an evolved core of a high-mass star at the end of its red giant stage. Each shell of material is fusing to make the material in the shell inside it; from hydrogen in the outermost shell to iron at the very center.

Up to the production of iron in the most massive stars, the nuclear fusion process is able to create extra energy from the fusion of lighter nuclei. But the fusion of iron nuclei *absorbs* energy. The iron core forms in just the last *year* of the supergiant stage. The core of the massive stars implodes and the density gets so great that protons and electrons are combined to form neutrons + neutrinos and the outer layers are ejected in a huge supernova explosion. The more common low-mass stars will have a gentler death, forming a planetary nebula.

iron marks the end

Stage 8: Planetary Nebula or Supernova

In this next-to-last stage of a star's life, the outer layers are ejected as the core shrinks to its most compact state. A large amount of mass is lost at this stage as the outer layers are returned to the interstellar medium. For the common low-mass stars (those with masses of 0.08 to about 6 or 7 solar masses during the main sequence stage), the increased number of photons flowing outward from the star's hot, compressed core will push on the carbon and silicon grains that have formed in the star's cool outer layers to eject the outer layers and form a **planetary nebula.** The ultraviolet from the hot exposed core, called a white dwarf, causes the gases to fluoresce. Most noticeable is the red emission from the excited hydrogen and nitrogen, the green emission from doubly-ionized oxygen, and the blue emission from excited helium. Planetary nebulae can be distinguished from H II regions by their compact shape and strong emission lines of doubly-ionized oxygen (that give them their green color), doubly-ionized neon, and singly-ionized helium.

low mass star death

planetary nebula

how different from H II region

Planetary nebulae get their name because some looked like round, green planets in early telescopes. They are now known to be entirely different than the planets and are one or more light years across (much larger than our solar system!). Originally, we thought planetary nebulae were simple expanding spherical shells that look like rings on the sky because when you look along the edge of the expanding spherical shell, you look through more material than when you look toward the center of the shell. The round soap bubbles you made as a child (or still do!) look like rings for the same reason. Indeed, many of the planetary nebulae first seen, like the Ring Nebula in Lyra and the Helix Nebula in Aquarius look like rings.

This picture of NGC 3603 from the Hubble Space Telescope captures the life cycle of stars in a single view. From lower right to upper left you see: dark clouds and a giant gaseous pillar with embryo stars at the tip to circumstellar disks around young stars to main sequence stars in a cluster at center to a supergiant with a ring and bipolar outflow at upper left of center near the end of the life cycle.
Image courtesy of Wolfgang Brandner (JPL/IPAC), Eva K Grebel (UW), You-Hua Chu (UI Urbana-Champaign), and NASA

More complete surveys of the planetary nebulae, high-resolution images from the Hubble Space Telescope, and careful analysis of the various parts of the planetary nebulae have shown that planetary nebulae have much more complex structures. Many have bipolar outflows like the Dumbbell Nebula, Hourglass Nebula, and Eskimo Nebula whose different orientations of their poles with our line of sight cause the differences in their appearance as seen from the Earth.

These nebula probably have equatorial rings or disks of material ejected during the red giant phase that force the material to flow perpendicular to the rings/disks. The two rings of the Hourglass Nebula (see the picture next page) are centered along the star's poles that are oriented around 60° to our line of sight. The upper ring is around the pole that is coming towards us and the lower ring is around the pole that is oriented away from us. There is evidence that the Ring Nebula in Lyra is actually bipolar in shape with a torus or doughnut shape around the equator and a roughly cylindrical (hotdog shape) outflow along the poles and that we are viewing it from right along one of the poles, so it looks like a simple ring. Also, the Helix Nebula is probably two disks oriented perpendicular to each other. Companion stars may also be affecting the shapes and may explain why some, like Hourglass Nebula, have the central white dwarf not centered. Complex ones like the Cat's Eye Nebula seem to show that the star ejected its layers in a series of spherical pulses separated by about 1500 years. There are also jets of high-speed gas and shockwaves of gases of different speeds running into each other. While we

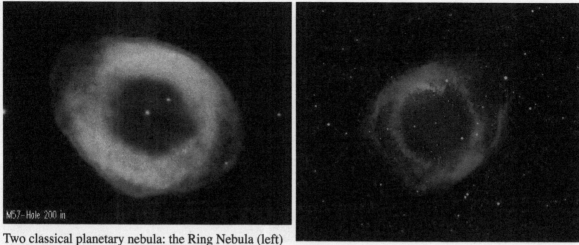

Two classical planetary nebula: the Ring Nebula (left)
and the Helix Nebula (right). At their centers is a white dwarf.

Ring Nebula image courtesy of Palomar Observatory, California Institude of Technology
Helix Nebula image courtesy of David Malin/Anglo-Australian Observatory

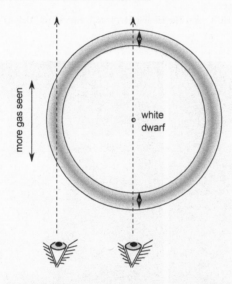

The ``soap bubble effect'' for spherical shells of
gas. More gas is seen along the line of sight at
the edges of the shell, so shell appears more
transparent when looking through the center.

have just some rough ideas of the causes of their shapes, we certainly can marvel
at their beauty!

The rare high-mass stars (those with masses of about 8 to 50 solar masses during
their main sequence stage) will go the explosive supernova route. When a massive
star's iron core implodes, the protons and electrons fuse together to form neutrons
and neutrinos. The core, once the size of the Earth, becomes a very stiff neutron
star about the size of a small town in less than a second. The collapsing outer
layers hit the core and heat up to billions of degrees from the impact. Enough of
the huge number of neutrinos produced when the core collapses interact with the
gas in the outer layers, helping to heat them up. During the supernova outburst,
elements heavier than iron are produced as free neutrons produced in the explosion

high mass star death

rebound off neutron core

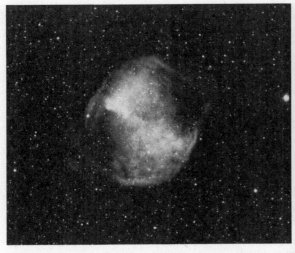

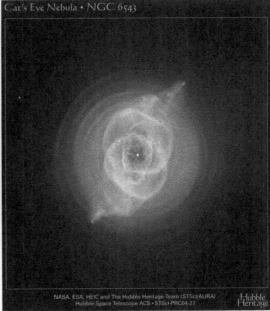

The Dumbbell Nebula (left) and the Cat's Eye Nebula (right) show that planetary nebulae can exhibit asymmetric outflow.

Dumbbell Nebula image courtesy of David Malin/Institute de Astrofisicas de Canarias/Royal Greenwich Observatory

Cat's Eye Nebula image courtesy of NASA, ESA, HEIC, and The Hubble Heritage Team (STScI/AURA)

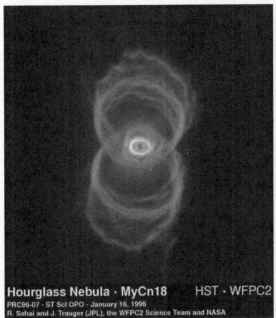

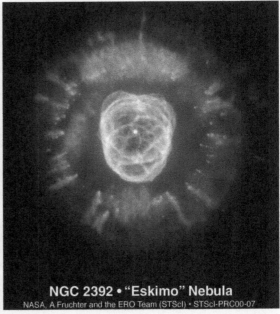

(left) Hourglass Nebula: Two rings centered along the star's poles that are oriented around 60° to our line of sight. Upper ring around the pole pointed towards us; lower ring around the pole pointed away from us. *(right)* Eskimo Nebula: Two elliptical bubbles stream from the star run into a dense ring ejected in red giant phase. Each bubble is made of filaments of denser material. Comet-shaped features in the "parka" may be the result of the collision of slow- and fast-moving gases.

gamma-ray bursts

rapidly combine with heavy nuclei to produce heavier and very rare nuclei like gold, platinum, uranium among others. This happens in about the first 15 *minutes* of the supernova. The most massive stars may also produce very powerful bursts of gamma-rays that stream out in jets at the poles of the stars at the moment their cores collapse to form a black hole (source of the long *gamma-ray bursts*—we see only the jets pointed towards us).

The superheated gas is blasted into space carrying a lot of the heavy elements produced in the stellar nucleosynthesis process. This explosion is a **supernova.** As the expanding gas crashes into the surrounding interstellar gas at thousands of kilometers/*second*, the shock wave heats up the interstellar gas to very high temperatures and it glows. Strong emission lines of neutral oxygen and ionized sulfur distinguish their spectra from planetary nebulae and H II regions. Also, the ratio of the strengths of the individual doubly-ionized oxygen is that expected from shock-wave heating. Planetary nebulae and H II regions are lit up by the action of ultraviolet light on the gas, while supernova glow from shock-wave heating. The gas from supernova explosions also has strong radio emission with a non-thermal continuous spectrum that is produced by electrons spiraling around magnetic field lines. Gas from recent explosions (within a few thousand years ago) are visible with X-ray telescopes as well. A famous supernova remnant is the Crab Nebula. Chinese astronomers recorded the explosion on July 4, 1054 and the Anasazi Indians painted at least one picture of it.

supernova

how different from H II region and planetary nebula

The Crab Nebula exploded in 1054 and could be seen in broad daylight for several months. Shockwave heating and radiation from a pulsar light up the expanding gas.

Image courtesy of D. Malin/J. Pasachoff/California Institute of Technology

The *neutrinos* formed when the neutron core is created fly away from the stiff core, carrying most of the energy (over 99%) from the core collapse away with them. Some energy (less than 1%) goes into driving the gas envelope outward. The rest of the energy (less than only 0.01%) goes into making the supernova as bright as 10^{11} Suns (as bright as an entire galaxy)! When a supernova occurred in a satellite galaxy of the Milky Way at the beginning of 1987 (SN1987a shown on the next page), the Kamiokande neutrino detector in Japan detected a huge burst of neutrinos from the direction of the satellite galaxy. This provided confirmation of the supernova models.

neutrino burst has most of the energy

Supernovae are very rare—about one every hundred years in any given galaxy—because the stars that produce them are rare. However, there are billions of galaxies in the universe, so simple probability says that there should be a few supernovae happening *somewhere in the universe* during a year and that is what is seen! Because supernovae are so luminous and the energy is concentrated in a small area, they

Part of the Large Magellanic Cloud before (left) and during (right) the explosion of SN1987A. A supernova can be as bright as an entire galaxy.
Image courtesy of David Malin/Anglo-Australian Observatory

stand out and can be seen from hundreds of millions of light years away.

The bright gas nebula of a planetary nebula or supernova does not last long, only a few tens of thousands of years. As the nebula expands, it cools and dims. The processed material becomes part of the interstellar medium in the Galaxy.

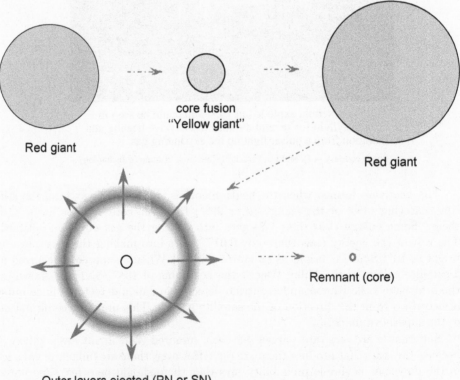

Red giant

core fusion
"Yellow giant"

Red giant

Remnant (core)

Outer layers ejected (PN or SN)
and core collapses

Stage 9: Core Remnant

What remains after the outer layers are thrown off depends on the mass of the core. The core remnants are described fully in the next section. A brief description of each type of core remnant is given here. If the core has a mass less than 1.4 solar masses, it will shrink down to a **white dwarf** the size of the Earth. The electrons in compressed gas bump right against each other to form a strange sort of gas called a degenerate gas (explained further below). The electrons prevent further collapse of the core.

white dwarf

If the core has a mass between 1.4 solar masses and 3 solar masses, the neutrons will bump up against each other to form a degenerate gas in a **neutron star** about the size of small city. The neutrons prevent further collapse of the core. Nothing can prevent the highest mass *cores* (greater than 3 solar masses) from collapsing to a point. On the way to total collapse, it may momentarily create a neutron star and the resulting supernova rebound explosion and powerful bursts of gamma-rays in bipolar jets (probably the source of the long *gamma-ray burst* objects). Gravity finally wins. Nothing holds it up. The gravity around the collapsed core becomes so great that Newton's law of gravity becomes inadequate and the gravity must be described by the more powerful theory of General Relativity developed by Albert Einstein. This will be discussed further below.

neutron star

The super-compact point mass is called a **black hole** because the escape velocity around the point mass is greater than the speed of light. Since the speed of light is the fastest that any radiation or any other information can travel, the region is totally black. The distance at which the escape velocity equals the speed of light is called the **event horizon** because no information of events occurring inside the event horizon can get to the outside. The radius of the event horizon in kilometers = 3 × core mass in solar masses.

black hole

event horizon

13.1.3   Stellar Nucleosynthesis

Hydrogen and helium and some lithium, boron, and beryllium were created when the universe was created. All of the rest of the elements of the universe were produced by the stars in nuclear fusion reactions. These reactions created the heavier elements from fusing together lighter elements in the central regions of the stars and through the explosion of white dwarfs or the merging of neutron stars. When the processed material from these processes are thrown back into space, it can be incorporated into gas clouds that will later form stars and planets. The material that formed our solar system incorporated some of the remains of previous stars. *All of the atoms on the Earth except hydrogen and most of the helium are recycled material—they were not created on the Earth. They were created in the stars.*

The use of the word "created" here is different than what is normally meant by scientists. In chemical reactions, different atoms or combinations of atoms are said to be produced or created when a reaction takes place. For example, in section 9.6.3, I said that oxygen in the Earth's atmosphere was produced in the photosynthesis process of plants. That oxygen then goes into the air and you breathe it in. To be more correct I should have said that the oxygen atoms are moved or broken off from one set of compounds [carbon dioxide (CO_2) and water (H_2O)] to form a molecule of two oxygen atoms bound together (O_2) and a molecule of carbohydrate made of carbon atoms, hydrogen atoms, and oxygen atoms ($C_6H_{12}O_6$). Each atom is rearranged or re-used. It was much simpler to say that oxygen is "created" as a by-product of the photosynthesis process. I hope you did not mind. In defense I want you to know that practically everyone, except for the astronomer researching stellar evolution, uses this loose meaning of "creation".

stellar nucleosynthesis creates atoms, chemical reactions merely recycle atoms

However, now that you know about stellar nucleosynthesis, I need to be more careful about what is being created from scratch and what is being re-used. Except

The Vela supernova remnant is an expanding cloud of processed material
that will be incorporated into future generations of stars and planets.
Image courtesy of David Malin/Anglo-Australian Observaotry/Royal Observatory, Edinburgh

"We are made of starstuff"

for the hydrogen and most of the helium atoms, all of the materials around you,
in the food you eat and drink, in the air you breathe, in your muscles and bones,
in the paper and ink or toner of this book, everything (!) are made of atoms that
were created in the stars. Those atoms are rearranged to produce the vast variety
of things around and in you. In the cores of stars, in supernova explosions, and
merging neutron stars, new atoms are manufactured from nuclear fusion reactions.
You will find out where the hydrogen and most of the helium atoms came from in
the cosmology chapter.

massive red giants make atoms up to iron
supernovae make atoms heavier than iron

The atoms heavier than helium up to the iron and nickel atoms were made
in the cores of stars (the process that creates iron also creates a smaller amount
of nickel too). The lowest mass stars can only synthesize helium. Stars around
the mass of the Sun can synthesize helium, carbon, and oxygen. Massive stars
($M_* > 8$ solar masses) can synthesize helium, carbon, oxygen, neon, magnesium,
silicon, sulfur, argon, calcium, titanium, chromium, and iron (and nickel). Elements
heavier than iron are made in supernova explosions from the rapid combination of
the abundant neutrons with heavy nuclei as well as from the merger of neutron stars.
Massive red giants are also able to make small amounts of elements heavier than
iron (up to mercury and lead) through a slower combination of neutrons with heavy
nuclei but supernovae and merging neutron stars probably generate the majority

of elements heavier than iron and nickel (and certainly those heavier than lead up to uranium). The synthesized elements are dispersed into the interstellar medium during the planetary nebula or supernova stage (with supernova being the best way to distribute the heavy elements far and wide). These elements will be later incorporated into giant molecular clouds and eventually become part of future stars and planets (and life forms?)

A color-coded periodic table on the textbook website summarizes the processes that have made the various elements in our solar system while the one on the next page outlines the elements created in stellar processes. Although the particulars of various nucleosynthesis processes are beyond the scope of this book (see links on the textbook website for the particulars), it is important to note a couple of things:

1. The stellar nucleosynthesis theory correctly predicts the observed abundances of all of the naturally occurring heavy elements seen on the Earth, meteorites, Sun, other stars, interstellar clouds—everywhere in the universe. (In the cosmology chapter you will see where the hydrogen and most of the helium came from.) We understand now why some elements like carbon, oxygen, silicon, and iron are common and the heaviest elements like gold, mercury, and uranium are so rare.

2. In order to create a terrestrial planet like the Earth (and life on such a planet), enough of the heavy elements have to be created in previous generations of stars and then concentrated in the interstellar clouds to collect into sizable chunks around forming stars. There is necessarily a "lag" between the beginning of the universe and the beginning of life.

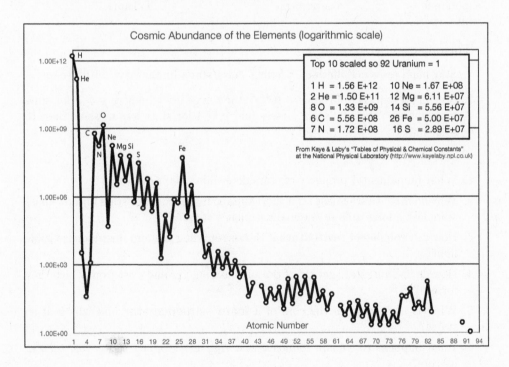

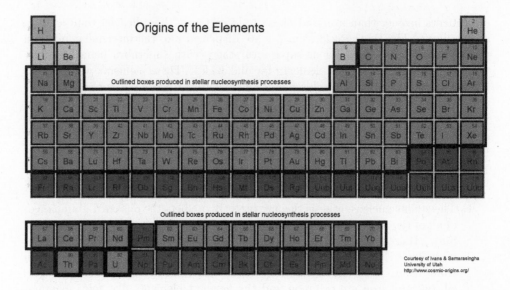

Vocabulary

black hole	event horizon	giant molecular cloud
helium flash	main sequence	neutron star
planetary nebula	protostar	red giant
shell burning	stellar nucleosynthesis	subgiant
supergiant	supernova	T-Tauri
white dwarf		

Formulae

1. Star main sequence lifetime = [star's mass/star's luminosity] $\times 10^{10}$ years.

2. Star main sequence lifetime = $10^{10}/(\text{star's mass})^{(p-1)}$, where $p = 3$ for stars more massive than 30 solar masses and $p = 4$ for stars less massive than 10 solar masses.

Review Questions

1. What fundamental property of stars determines their evolution?

2. Why do massive stars last for a short time as main sequence stars but low-mass stars last a long time in the main sequence stage?

3. How can you detect **protostars** if the surrounding gas and dust blocks visible light?

4. How do T-Tauri stars get rid of the surrounding gas and dust from which they formed?

5. What is happening in the core of a **main sequence star** and why is it so stable?

6. What happens to a main sequence star that has stopped fusing *hydrogen* in its core?

7. Are all red giants or supergiants very massive stars? Why are red giants so big and red? What is going on inside the giants?

8. What is the evolution sequence for stars around the mass of the Sun? How long is the Sun's main sequence lifetime?

9. What will happen to a hot, blue star (> 10 solar masses) during its *entire* lifetime?

10. What will happen to a cool, red star (< 0.5 solar masses) during its *entire* lifetime?

11. In which stage is most of a star's mass lost?

12. How is a **planetary nebula** formed? What is formed at the center of the planetary nebula? Which main sequence stars will eventually form planetary nebulae?

13. What happens in a **supernova** explosion? Which main sequence stars will eventually go supernova?

14. How can you distinguish planetary nebulae and supernovae from each other and from ordinary H II regions?

15. About how often does a supernova occur in a typical galaxy? Why is it better to look for supernovae in other galaxies?

16. How does the concept of **stellar nucleosynthesis** explain where all of the elements on the Earth came from?

17. Why is iron the limit for stellar nucleosynthesis in red giants? Where did heavier elements than iron come from?

13.2   Confirmation of Stellar Evolution Models

Even the shortest-lived massive stars last longer than the entire span of human history, so how can astronomers test the predictions of their stellar evolution models? In science the sole judge of scientific truth is experiments or observation. Regardless of how nice or beautiful a scientific theory may appear, if it does not make accurate testable predictions, it is invalid. When color-magnitude (HR) diagrams for star clusters are constructed, there is a convincing confirmation of the stellar evolution models.

HR diagrams of clusters

What is nice about clusters is that differences in the stars can be explained in terms of only one variable: mass. Stars in a cluster all form at about the same time, so age differences is not a factor in the analysis. The stars form from the same gas cloud, so their chemical composition is the same and all of them are at about the same distance from the Earth (relative to their huge distance from us), so any differences in apparent brightness are due to *luminosity* (intrinsic brightness) differences. *More luminous main sequence stars are more massive than dimmer main sequence stars.*

mass is the only variable

Comparison of the theories with reality is easy since you need to only consider how mass affects the cluster stars' evolution. The predictions from the stellar evolution models as to what the characteristics of the stars in different clusters should be are compared with reality. *Star formation and stellar evolution models are confirmed by observations of real clusters.* By observing clusters of different ages, you can piece together how a star will form, live, and die.

13.2.1   Finding the Ages of Clusters

The diagrams on the following three pages show how cluster color-magnitude diagrams change with age. More massive stars evolve quicker than low-mass stars. The hot, luminous main sequence stars will die before the cool, dim main sequence stars. This means that an old cluster will have only the low-mass stars still in the main sequence stage, but a young cluster will have both high and low-mass stars in the main sequence stage.

The most massive star still in the main sequence stage tells you the age of the cluster. That point on the main sequence is called the **main sequence turnoff**. All

main   sequence turnoff

stars in a cluster are assumed to have formed at about the same time (observations of current star formation do show that stars form in batches). Stars slightly more massive than the turnoff point have already evolved "away" from the main sequence. The main sequence turnoff is analogous to a candle burning—a candle that has been lit longer will be shorter than an identical candle lit more recently.

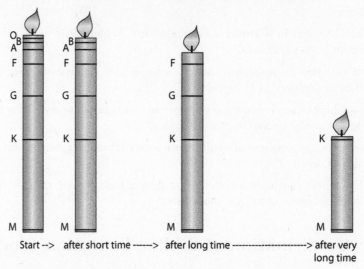

Candle analogy for main sequence turnoff: as candle burns (= cluster ages),
the candle gets shorter (= cluster main sequence remaining gets less)

The age of the cluster equals the lifetime of the stars with masses at the main sequence turnoff.

1. For the common lower mass stars (< 10 solar masses),

$$\text{age of the cluster} = \frac{10^{10}}{\text{MST mass}^3} \text{ years.}$$

Use solar masses!

2. For the *rare* massive stars (> 30 solar masses), use

$$\text{age of the cluster} = \frac{10^{10}}{\text{MST mass}^2} \text{ years.}$$

The most accurate age for a cluster is found from fitting the entire cluster HR diagram (main sequence, sub-giant, red giant, & horizontal branch) to a stellar evolution model of a specific age and chemical composition.

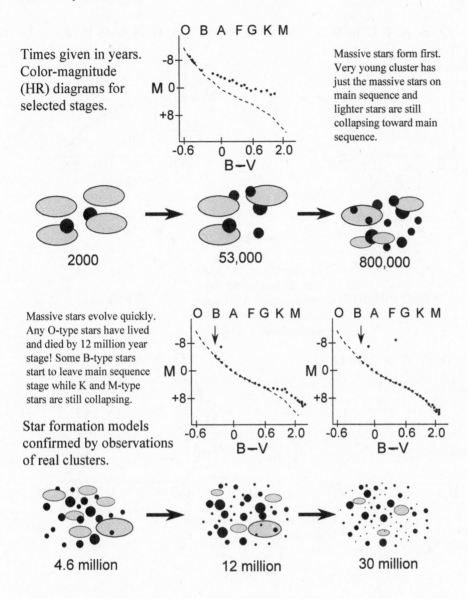

Times given in years.
Color-magnitude
(HR) diagrams for
selected stages.

Massive stars form first.
Very young cluster has
just the massive stars on
main sequence and
lighter stars are still
collapsing toward main
sequence.

Massive stars evolve quickly.
Any O-type stars have lived
and died by 12 million year
stage! Some B-type stars
start to leave main sequence
stage while K and M-type
stars are still collapsing.

Star formation models
confirmed by observations
of real clusters.

Vocabulary
main sequence turnoff

Review Questions

1. How do cluster H-R diagrams confirm the stellar evolution models?

2. How can you use a cluster's H-R diagram to find the age of the cluster? What can the **main sequence turnoff (MST)** tell you?

3. What assumptions are made in the age-dating method of the main sequence turnoff?

4. How do you know that a cluster with a MST of 3 solar masses is younger than a cluster with a MST of 2.8 solar masses and older than a cluster with a MST of 3.2 solar masses?

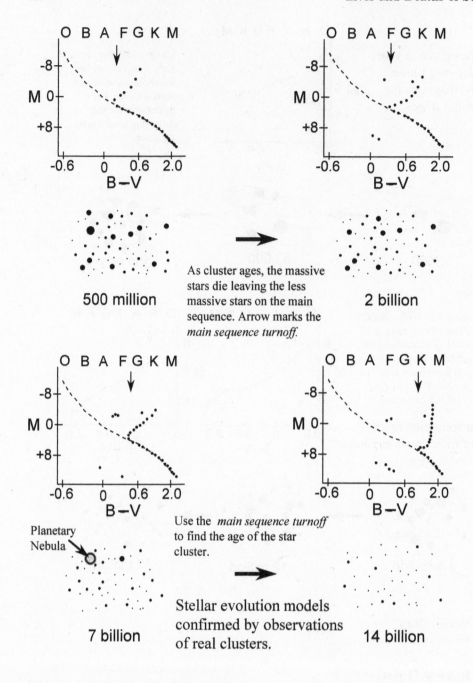

As cluster ages, the massive stars die leaving the less massive stars on the main sequence. Arrow marks the *main sequence turnoff.*

500 million

2 billion

Use the *main sequence turnoff* to find the age of the star cluster.

Planetary Nebula

Stellar evolution models confirmed by observations of real clusters.

7 billion

14 billion

13.3   Stellar Remnants

All that is left of the star after the outer layers are ejected to space is the core remnant. The core's gas is super-compressed by gravity to form a strange type of gas made of "degenerate matter". It is important to remember that what happens to the core depends on the mass of the *core*, rather than the original mass of the main sequence star from which it came, because the only thing left for gravity to really compress is the core.

13.3.1   Degenerate Matter

degenerate gas

When gas become super-compressed, particles bump right up against each other to produce a kind of gas, called a **degenerate gas**, that behaves more like a solid.

Normal gas exerts higher pressure when it is heated and expands, but the pressure in a degenerate gas does not depend on the temperature. The laws of quantum mechanics must be used for gases of ultra-high densities.

The first rule is that only certain energies are permitted in a closely confined space. The particles are arranged in energy levels like rungs of an energy ladder. In ordinary gas, most of the energy levels are unfilled and the particles are free to move about. But in a degenerate gas, all of the lower energy levels are filled. The second rule is that only two particles can share the same energy level in a given volume at one time. For white dwarfs the degenerate particles are the electrons. For neutron stars the degenerate particles are neutrons. The third rule is that how close particles can be spaced depends *inversely* on their masses. Electrons are spaced further apart in a degenerate electron gas than the neutrons in a degenerate neutron gas because electrons are much less massive than neutrons.

Let's see how these rules affect the core remnant.

1. Degenerate gases strongly resist compression. The degenerate particles (electrons or neutrons) are locked into place because all of the lower energy shells are filled up. The only way they can move is to absorb enough energy to get to the upper energy shells. This is *hard* to do! Compressing a degenerate gas requires a change in the motions of the degenerate particle. But that requires A LOT of energy. Degenerate particles have no "elbow room" and their jostling against each other strongly resists compression. The degenerate gas is like hardened steel!

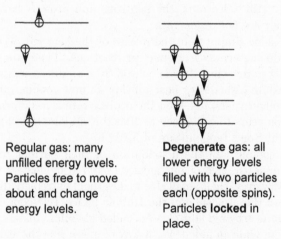

Regular gas: many unfilled energy levels. Particles free to move about and change energy levels.

Degenerate gas: all lower energy levels filled with two particles each (opposite spins). Particles **locked** in place.

2. The pressure in a degenerate gas depends only on the speed of the degenerate particles NOT the temperature of the gas. But to change the speed of degenerate particles requires A LOT of energy because they are locked into place against each other. Adding heat only causes the non-degenerate particles to move faster, but the degenerate ones supplying the pressure are unaffected.

3. Increasing the mass of the stellar core increases the compression of the core. The degenerate particles are forced closer together, but not much closer together because there is no room left. A more massive stellar core remnant will be *smaller* than a lighter core remnant. This is the opposite behavior of regular materials: usually adding mass to something makes it bigger!

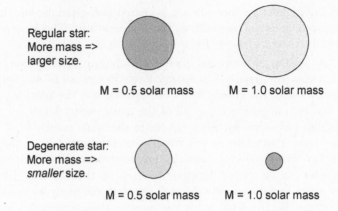

Regular star:
More mass =>
larger size.

M = 0.5 solar mass   M = 1.0 solar mass

Degenerate star:
More mass =>
smaller size.

M = 0.5 solar mass   M = 1.0 solar mass

13.3.2   White Dwarfs

White dwarfs form as the outer layers of a low-mass red giant star puff out to make a planetary nebula. Since the lower mass stars make the white dwarfs, this type of remnant is the most common endpoint for stellar evolution. If the remaining mass of the core is less than 1.4 solar masses, the pressure from the degenerate electrons (called **electron degeneracy pressure**) is enough to prevent further collapse.

electron degeneracy pressure

Because the core has about the mass of the Sun compressed to something the size of the Earth, the density is tremendous: around a million times denser than water (one sugar cube volume has greater mass than a car)! A higher mass core is compressed to a smaller radius so the densities are even higher. Despite the huge densities and the "stiff" electrons, the neutrons and protons have room to move around freely—they are not degenerate.

white dwarf cools off

White dwarfs shine simply from the release of the heat left over from when the star was still producing energy from nuclear reactions. There are no more nuclear reactions occurring so the white dwarf cools off from an initial temperature of about 100,000 K. The white dwarf loses heat quickly at first cooling off to 20,000 K in only about 100 million years, but then the cooling rate slows down: it takes about another 800 million years to cool down to 10,000 K and another 4 to 5 billion years to cool down to the Sun's temperature of 5,800 K.

Their rate of cooling and the distribution of their current temperatures can be used to determine the age of our galaxy or old star clusters that have white dwarfs in them. However, their small size makes them extremely difficult to detect. Because it is above the atmosphere, the Hubble Space Telescope can detect these small dead stars in nearby old star clusters called globular clusters. Analysis of the white dwarfs may provide an independent way of measuring the ages of the globular clusters and provide a verification of their very old ages derived from main sequence fitting.

13.3.3   Novae and Supernovae Type Ia

An isolated white dwarf has a boring future: it simply cools off, dimming to invisibility. White dwarfs in binary systems where the companion is still a main sequence or red giant star can have more interesting futures. If the white dwarf is close enough to its red giant or main sequence companion, gas expelled by the star can fall onto the white dwarf. The hydrogen-rich gas from the star's outer layers builds up on the white dwarf's surface and gets compressed and hot by the white dwarf's gravity.

Eventually the hydrogen gas gets dense and hot enough for nuclear reactions to start. The reactions occur at an explosive rate. The hydrogen gas is blasted

White Dwarf Stars in M4 HST · WFPC2
PRC95-32 · ST ScI OPO · August 28, 1995 · H. Bond (ST ScI), NASA

outward to form an expanding shell of hot gas. The hot gas shell produces a lot of light suddenly. From the Earth, it looks like a new star has appeared in the sky. Early astronomers called them **novae** ("new" in Latin). They are now known to be caused by old, dead stars. The spectra of a nova have blue-shifted absorption lines showing that a hot dense gas is expanding towards us at a few thousands of kilometers per second. The continuum is from the hot dense gas and the absorption lines are from the lower-density surface of the expanding cloud. After a few days the gas has expanded and thinned out enough to just produce blue-shifted emission lines.

After the nova burst, gas from the regular star begins to build up again on the white dwarf's surface. A binary system can have repeating nova bursts. If enough mass accumulates on the white dwarf to push it over the 1.4 solar mass limit, the degenerate electrons will not be able to stop gravity from collapsing the dead core. The collapse is sudden and heats the carbon and oxygen nuclei left from the dead star's red giant phase to temperatures great enough for nuclear fusion. The carbon and oxygen quickly fuse to form silicon nuclei. The silicon nuclei fuse to create nickel nuclei. A huge amount of energy is released very quickly with such power that the white dwarf blows itself apart. This explosion is called a *Type Ia supernova* to distinguish them from the other types of supernova that occurs when a massive star's core implodes to form a neutron star or black hole.

Type I supernovae happen in close binary systems and do not show strong hydrogen emission lines. Type I (especially Ia) supernova create most of the iron and nickel found in the interstellar medium. Type II supernovae happen in single star systems (or at least far enough away from any companion star to retain their hydrogen outer layers) and have strong hydrogen emission lines. Type II create most of the oxygen found in the interstellar medium. Type Ia supernovae are several times more luminous than Type Ib, Ic, and Type II supernovae, leave no core remnant behind, and result from when a low-mass star's core remnant (a white dwarf) detonates. They have a strong ionized silicon emission line at 615 nm. Type Ib and Ic supernovae result from the collapse of a massive star's core whose outer hydrogen layers have been transferred to a companion star or blown off from strong winds which is why they do not show hydrogen emission lines. Type Ib have strong helium emission lines and Type Ic do not.

Since the Type Ia supernova form from the collapse of a stellar core of a particular mass, rather than the range of core masses possible for the other types of supernova, the Type Ia supernova are expected to have the same luminosity. The distances to very luminous objects can be derived using the inverse square law of light brightness if their luminosity is known. Because of their huge luminosities, the

nova
nova spectra

Type I vs. Type II

Type Ia

Type Ib & Ic

Type Ia supernovae could be used to measure distances to very distant galaxies. In practice there is a range of luminosities for the Type Ia, but the luminosity can be derived from the *rate* at which the supernova brightens and then fades—the more luminous ones take longer to brighten and then fade. Astronomers using Type Ia supernova to measure distances to very distant galaxies have come to some surprising conclusions about the history and future of the universe (see chapter 16 for more about that).

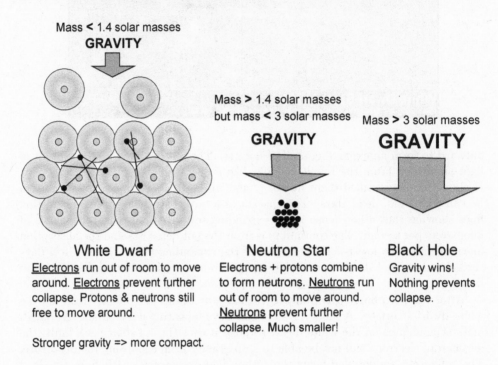

13.3.4   Neutron Stars

If the core mass is between 1.4 and 3 solar masses, the compression from the star's gravity is so great that the protons fuse with the electrons to form neutrons. The core becomes a super-dense ball of neutrons. Only the rare, massive stars (about 8 to 25 solar masses) will form these remnants in a supernova explosion. Neutrons can be packed much closer together than electrons so even though a neutron star is more massive than a white dwarf, it is only about the size of a city.

neutron degeneracy pressure

The neutrons are degenerate and their pressure (called **neutron degeneracy pressure**) prevents further collapse. Neutron stars are about 30 kilometers across, so their densities are much larger than even the incredible densities of white dwarfs: 200 *trillion* times the density of water (mass of one sugar cube volume = mass of humanity)! The closest known neutron star is about 200 light years away.

13.3.5   Pulsars

In the late 1960's astronomers discovered radio sources that pulsated very regularly with periods of just fractions of a second to a few seconds. The periods are extremely regular—only the ultra-high precision of atomic clocks can show a very slight lengthening in the period. At first, some thought they were picking up signals from extra-terrestrial intelligent civilizations. The discovery of several more pulsars discounted that idea—they are a natural phenomenon called **pulsars** (short for "pulsating star").

Normal variable stars (stars near the end of their life in stages 5 to 7) oscillate brightness by changing their size and temperature. The density of the star determines the pulsation period—denser stars pulsate more quickly than low density variables. However, normal stars and white dwarfs are not dense enough to pulsate at rates of under one second. Neutron stars would pulsate too quickly because of their huge density, so pulsars must pulsate by a different way than normal variable stars. A rapidly rotating object with a bright spot on it could produce the quick flashes if the bright spot was lined up with the Earth. Normal stars and white dwarfs cannot rotate fast enough because they do not have enough gravity to keep themselves together; they would spin themselves apart. Neutron stars are compact enough and strong enough to rotate that fast. The pulsar at the center of the Crab Nebula rotates 30 times every second. In the figure below, it is the left one of the two bright stars at the center of the Hubble Space Telescope image (right frame).

pulsar

usual pulsation method not work for neutron stars

rapidly rotating neutron stars

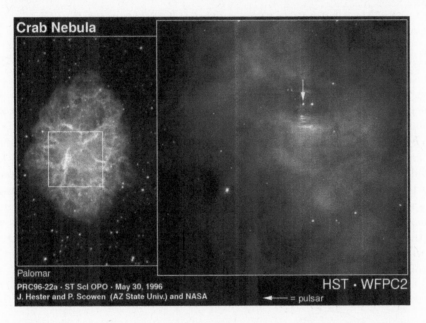

Another clue comes from the length of each pulse itself. Each pulse lasts about 1/1000th of a second (the time *between* pulses is the period mentioned above). An important principle in science is that an object cannot change its brightness faster than it takes light to cross its diameter. Even if the object could magically brighten everywhere simultaneously, it would take light from the far side of the object longer to reach you than the near side. As shown in the figure on the next page, the observed change in brightness would be smeared out over a time interval equal to the time it would take the light from the far side of the object to travel to the near side of the object. If the object did not brighten everywhere simultaneously, then a *smaller* object could produce a pulse in the same interval. The brightness fluctuation timescale gives the *maximum* size of an object. Since the diameter = (fluctuation time) × speed, the *maximum* possible diameter = (fluctuation time) × (speed of light).

fluctuation time gives maximum diameter

The 1/1000th of second burst of energy means that the pulsars are *at most* (300,000 kilometers/second) × (1/1000 second) = 300 kilometers across. This is too small for normal stars or white dwarfs, but fine for neutron stars (they are actually less than 30 kilometers across). When neutron stars form, they will be spinning rapidly and have very STRONG magnetic fields (10^9 to 10^{12} times the Sun's). The magnetic field is the relic magnetic field from the star's previous life

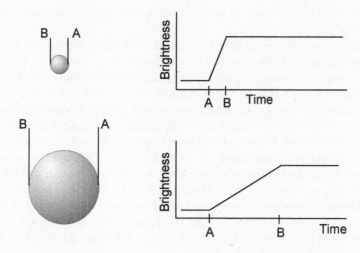

The light from side A reaches us before the light from side B
so even if the object could brighten everywhere simultaneously,
there is still a delay in brightening observed by us.

stages. The magnetic field is frozen into the star, so when the core collapses, the magnetic field is compressed too. The magnetic field becomes very concentrated and much stronger than before.

angular momentum

Why would neutron stars be fast rotators? Conservation of *angular momentum*! Just as a spinning ice skater can spin very fast by pulling in her arms and legs tight about the center of her body, a star will spin faster when it brings its material closer to its center. The *angular momentum* of an object = its mass × its equatorial spin speed × its radius. The mass remains constant. In order to keep the angular momentum constant the spin speed must increase if the radius decreases. This will keep the product of spin speed × radius the same value. A slowly rotating red giant star will have the same angular momentum when it becomes a tiny, fast rotating neutron star. See appendix A for other examples.

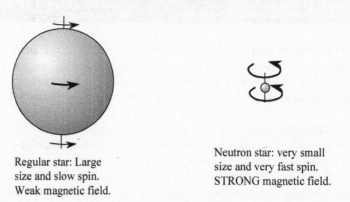

Regular star: Large
size and slow spin.
Weak magnetic field.

Neutron star: very small
size and very fast spin.
STRONG magnetic field.

lighthouse model

The spinning neutron star produces beams of radiation that sweep across your line of sight like a lighthouse beam does for ships at sea. In the **lighthouse model** the neutron star's strong magnetic field creates a strong electric field. The electric field makes charged particles (mostly electrons) flow out of the magnetic poles. As the charged particles spiral around the magnetic field lines, they produce electromagnetic radiation (recall from chapter 7 that any moving charge will create electromagnetic radiation). The energy is called *non*-thermal radiation because it is not produced by a hot, dense object, but by accelerated charges. The shape of

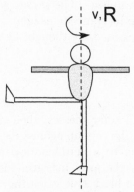 

Rotation axis is dotted line. Part of body mass is far from rotation axis. Spinning slowly (v is small).

Rotation axis is dotted line. All of body mass is close to rotation axis. Spinning quickly (v is large).

Angular momentum BEFORE = Angular momentum AFTER

the continuous spectrum is different from a normal thermal spectrum and does not depend on the temperature. A type of particle accelerator in physics laboratories here on Earth called a "synchrotron" produces this kind of radiation too, so it is sometimes called "synchrotron radiation".

The neutron star's magnetic field lines converge at the magnetic poles, so the charges get focused and a narrow cone of non-thermal radiation is beamed outward. If the beam sweeps past Earth, you see a flash of light. However, given the wide range of angles the magnetic poles could be aligned in space, it is more likely that the beam will miss the Earth. There are probably many more pulsars out there that cannot be detected because their beams do not happen to cross our line of sight.

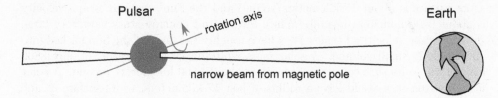

If the narrow synchrotron beam passes over the Earth, we see the neutron star flash on and off like a lighthouse beam does for ships at sea.

The energy of the non-thermal radiation beam comes from the rotational energy of the pulsar. Since the light energy escapes, the production of the energy beam robs energy from the pulsar, so the pulsar's rotation slows down (angular momentum does *slowly* decrease). Another equivalent way to view the process is from Newton's 3rd law of motion. The magnetic field exerts a force on the charged particles, speeding them up. The charged particles exert a reaction force on the magnetic field slowing it and the pulsar down. Eventually, the pulsar dies away when the neutron star is rotating too slowly (periods over several seconds long) to produce the beams of radiation.

Every now and then, a "glitch" is seen in the pulse rate of a pulsar. The pulsar suddenly increases its spin rate. What causes this is the neutron star suddenly shrinks by about 1 millimeter. The spin rate suddenly increases to conserve angular momentum. The spin rate can be greatly increased if the pulsar is in a close binary system and its companion dumps gas onto the pulsar. The pulsar gains angular momentum from the incoming gas and ramps up its spin rate as more gas falls onto it. The pulsars that spin hundreds of times per second are thought to be the result of such a transfer.

13.3.6   Black Holes

black hole

If the core remnant has a mass greater than 3 solar masses, then not even the super-compressed degenerate neutrons can hold the core up against its own gravity. Gravity finally wins and compresses everything to a mathematical point at the center. The point mass is a **black hole**. Only the most massive, very rare stars (greater than about 25 solar masses) will form a black hole when they die. As the core implodes, it briefly makes a neutron star for just long enough to produce the supernova explosion.

Ultra-strong gravity

The gravity of the point mass is strong enough close to the center that nothing can escape, not even light! Within a certain distance of the point mass, the **escape velocity** is greater than the speed of light. Remember from the gravity chapter (ch. 5) that the **escape velocity** is the speed an object needs to avoid being pulled back by the gravity of a massive body. The escape velocity

escape velocity

$$v_{escape} = \sqrt{\frac{2G \times \text{Mass}}{\text{distance to the center}}},$$

where G is the gravitational constant.

Since the mass is in the top of the fraction, the escape velocity is greater for larger masses. The escape velocity is smaller for larger distances from the center because the distance is in the bottom of the fraction. The Earth's escape velocity at its surface is about 11 kilometers/second and the Sun's surface escape velocity is about 620 kilometers/second. White dwarfs and neutron stars have very large surface escape velocities because they have roughly the mass of the Sun packed into an incredibly small volume. A solar mass white dwarf has a radius of only 8800 kilometers, so its surface escape velocity is about 5500 kilometers/second. A solar mass neutron star would have a radius of just 17 kilometers, so its surface escape velocity would be an incredible 125,000 kilometers/second! (Real neutron stars have masses above 1.4 solar masses and *smaller* radii, so their escape velocities are even larger!)

A black hole probably has no surface, so astronomers use the distance at which the escape velocity equals the speed of light for the size of the black hole. This distance is called the **event horizon** because no messages of events (via electromagnetic radiation or anything else) happening within that distance of the point mass make it to the outside. The region within the event horizon is black from our viewpoint outside (if you were inside the event horizon, you could see all sorts of light). Rearranging the formula above for the escape velocity and putting in the speed of light c for the escape velocity, you find the event horizon is at a distance of

event horizon
nothing from inside the event horizon

$$r = \frac{2G \times \text{Mass}}{c^2}$$

from the point mass. This approximately equals $3 \times M_{bh}$ kilometers, where the black hole mass M_{bh} is in units of solar masses (a solar mass black hole would have a radius of 3 kilometers, a 10 solar mass black hole would have a radius of 30 kilometers, etc.).

Black holes have been portrayed as cosmic vacuum cleaners in Hollywood films, sucking up everything around them. Black holes are dangerous only if something gets too close to them. Because all of their mass is compressed to a point, it is possible to get very close to them and still be outside all of the mass. Recall that gravity is an inverse square law force, so at very small distances, the strength of gravity around a point mass becomes very large. But objects far enough away will not sense anything unusual. If the Sun were replaced by a black hole of the *same* mass, the orbits of the planets would remain unchanged (it would be much colder on the Earth, though!).

dangerous only very close

13.3.7   General Relativity

For very strong gravitational fields, Newton's description of gravity becomes inadequate. Einstein's theory of **General Relativity** must be used to describe the gravitational effects. Einstein found that gravity is not a force in the usual Newtonian description of force. Gravity is the result of a warping or distortion of **spacetime** by a massive object. The stronger the gravity is, the more the spacetime is warped or curved. I discuss the developments of the concept of spacetime and the theory of General Relativity in chapter 6. That chapter also gives several observations of curved spacetime. The definite discovery of a black hole would provide more evidence for General Relativity.

General Relativity

warping of **spacetime**

Within the event horizon of a black hole, spacetime is so curved that any light emitted inside the event horizon is bent back to the central point mass. Karl Schwarzschild worked out the equations in General Relativity for a non-rotating black hole and found that the light rays within a certain distance of the point mass would be bent back to the point mass. The derived distance is the same as the event horizon value above. The event horizon is sometimes called the **Schwarzschild radius** in his honor.

Schwarzschild radius

Falling toward a black hole would not be a pleasant experience. If you fell in feet-first, your body would be scrunched sideways and stretched along the length of your body by the tidal forces of the black hole. Your body would look like a spaghetti noodle! The stretching happens because your feet would be pulled much more strongly than your head. The sideways scrunching happens because all points of your body would be pulled directly toward the center of the black hole. Therefore, your shoulders would be squeezed closer and closer together as you fell closer to the center of the black hole. The tidal stretching/squeezing of anything falling into a black hole is an effect conveniently forgotten by Hollywood movie writers and directors. [However, the tidal effect at the event horizon of a supermassive black hole (one with at least a million times the mass of the Sun) is much less than at the event horizon of a stellar-mass black hole, so an astronaut could still be alive crossing the event horizon of a supermassive black hole. *At their respective event horizons*, the tidal strength scales as (small black hole mass / big black hole mass)^2.]

Your friend watching you from a safe distance far from the black hole as you fell in would see your clock run slower and slower as you approached the event horizon. This is the effect of "time dilation" (see chapter 6). In fact, your friend would see you take an infinite amount of time to cross the event horizon—time would appear to stand still. However, in your reference frame your clock would run forward normally and you would reach the center very soon. If you beamed back the progress of your journey into a black hole, your friend would have to tune to progressively longer wavelengths (lower frequencies) as you approached the event horizon. This is the effect of "gravitational redshift" (see chapter 6). Eventually, the photons would be stretched to infinitely long wavelengths.

13.3.8   Detecting Black Holes

Since the (stellar-mass) black holes themselves (their event horizons) are only several miles across, they are too small be visible from a even short distance away. Looking for black circles silhouetted against a background of stars would be an impossible task. You detect their effect on surrounding material and stars. If the black hole is in a binary system and its visible companion is close enough to the black hole, then the effects will be noticeable. There are two signatures of a black hole in a binary system:

1. The black hole and visible star will orbit around a center of mass between them. You look at how the black hole moves its visible companion around. Applying Kepler's 3rd law to the system, you can determine the *total mass*, visible star mass + black hole mass = (separation distance)^3/(orbital period)^2. After making an educated guess of the mass of the visible companion from the correlation of the luminosity, mass, and temperature for normal stars, the rest of the total mass is the unseen object's mass. If the mass of the unseen object is too big for a neutron star or a white dwarf, then it is very likely a black hole!

Binary star system

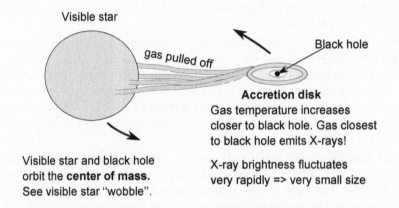

Visible star

gas pulled off

Black hole

Accretion disk
Gas temperature increases
closer to black hole. Gas closest
to black hole emits X-rays!

Visible star and black hole
orbit the **center of mass.**
See visible star "wobble".

X-ray brightness fluctuates
very rapidly => very small size

However, measuring the masses of all of the binary systems in the Galaxy would take much too long a time—there are over a hundred billion binary systems in the Galaxy! Even if it took you just one *second* to somehow measure a binary's total mass and subtract out one star's mass, it would take you over 3000 years to complete your survey. How could you quickly hone on the binary system that might have a black hole? Fortunately, black holes can advertise their presence loud and clear with X-rays.

accretion disk

2. If the visible star is close enough to the black hole, some of its gas will be attracted to the black hole. The gas material will form an **accretion disk** around the black hole as it spirals onto the black hole. The gas particles in the disk will rub against each and heat up from the friction. The amount of friction increases inward causing increasing temperature closer to the event horizon. The disk will produce a wide spectrum of radiation. Close to the event horizon, the disk will be hot enough to emit X-rays. X-ray sources in the Galaxy are *rare*. Stars are bright in the optical band. A very small percentage of them can also put out significant amounts of ultraviolet radiation, but all stars are faint in the X-ray band. If you find an X-ray source, then you know something strange is happening with the object. Therefore, a bright X-ray source is actually the *first* signature that you look for. Once you have found

*look for X-rays first, then
measure mass*

a bright X-ray source, then you measure its mass (the *second* signature) to rule out a white dwarf or neutron star. If the unseen companion is very small, then the X-ray brightness of the disk will be able to change rapidly.

To make rapidly varying X-rays, the unseen companion must be *small!* The fluctuation timescale gives the *maximum* possible diameter of the object. Since the speed of light is finite, it takes a given amount of time for light to travel across the object. The time it takes for any interaction to occur is diameter/speed, where the speed can be up to the speed of light if the object could somehow brighten everywhere simultaneously. The diameter = (fluctuation time interval) × speed. The maximum diameter possible is for a speed equal to the speed of light. The quicker the fluctuations are, the *smaller* the object must be.

fluctuation time gives maximum diameter

Black holes themselves are invisible, but they produce very visible effects on nearby objects. Several stellar-mass black hole candidates have been found. Examples include Cygnus X-1 and V404 Cygni in the constellation of Cygnus, LMC X-3 in the constellation Dorado, V616 Mon in the Monocerotis constellation, J1655-40 in Scorpius, and the closest one, V4641 Sgr in Sagittarius, is about 1600 light years away. Recently, astronomers have used the differences in how neutron stars and black holes accrete material from their accretion disks to show that black holes exist. Material falling toward a neutron star will emit x-rays as it spirals inward and also as it impacts onto the neutron star's surface. But material falling toward a black hole does not impact a surface; it vanishes through the event horizon. Comparing the brightness of compact objects heavier than 3 solar masses with those lighter than 3 solar masses, shows that the heavier masses are dimmer than the lighter masses even if they have the same orbital periods. Since the accretion rate should be the same for two objects with the same orbital period, the faintness of the heavier masses can only be explained if they are swallowing matter and energy like a black hole would do. In chapter 15 more strong evidence is given for the existence of black holes in that "supermassive" black holes provide a simple explanation for the extremely energetic nuclei of peculiar galaxies called "active galaxies".

Finally, the characteristics of the gravitational waves we detect from the merger of binary black holes or black hole and neutron star merger are what would be produced if the merging objects had such extreme densities. The gravitational waves would have a different shape if they were not produced by black holes. The black holes detected by the gravitational wave observatories are significantly larger than the black holes detected by X-ray observatories (see figure next page). It is possible that black hole mergers could explain the apparent gap between typical stellar-mass black holes and supermassive black holes residing at the centers of many galaxies.

Vocabulary

accretion disk	degenerate gas	electron degeneracy pressure
event horizon	General Relativity	gravitational lens
gravitational redshift	lighthouse model	neutron degeneracy pressure
nova	pulsar	Schwarzschild radius

Formulae

1. Escape velocity = $\sqrt{2G \times \text{Mass}/(\text{distance to the center})}$, where G is the gravitational constant.

2. Event horizon radius (Schwarzschild radius) = $2G \times (\text{black hole mass})/c^2$, where G is the gravitational constant, and c is the speed of light.

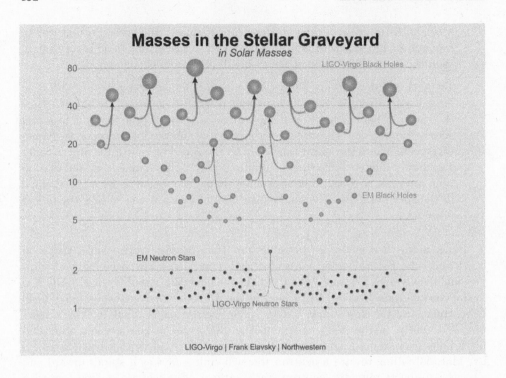

3. Event horizon radius = [3× black hole mass] kilometers, where the black hole mass is measured in solar masses.

4. *Maximum* size of an object = fluctuation time interval × speed of light.

Review Questions

1. What type of star will become a **white dwarf**? Describe the characteristics of a white dwarf.

2. How does **electron degeneracy pressure** keep the white dwarf from collapsing any further?

3. What is the upper bound for the mass of a white dwarf? How would the fact that stars up to 5 solar masses become white dwarfs show that stars lose mass to the interstellar medium as they evolve? How is most of this mass lost?

4. How is a **neutron star** created? What type of star will become a neutron star? Describe the characteristics of a neutron star.

5. How does **neutron degeneracy pressure** keep the neutron star from collapsing to a point at the center?

6. What is the upper bound for the mass of a neutron star?

7. What are the ingredients for a **pulsar**?

8. Why does a pulsar spin so fast?

9. Why could a collapsed star spinning many times each second not be a regular star or white dwarf?

10. What type of star will become a **black hole**? Does anything keep it from collapsing to a point at the center? Describe the characteristics of a black hole.

11. What is the sole determining thing that specifies the size of the **event horizon**?

12. What are the signatures of a black hole—observations indicating the presence of a super-compact nearly invisible object?

13. How do the rapid fluctuations of the X-rays from a black hole's **accretion disk** show that the object at the center has a small diameter? If the fluctuations were slower (taking longer to brighten and then fade), would the implied diameter be smaller or larger?

Chapter 14

The Interstellar Medium and the Milky Way

Our solar system is inside a large galaxy known as the **Milky Way.** All of the stars you can see at night and several hundred billion more are all bound together gravitationally into a huge cluster called a **galaxy.** Most of the stars in our galaxy are far enough away that they blend together in a thin band across the sky. If you are fortunate enough to view a dark sky outside of the glare of the city lights, you will see this milky band running through the constellations Cassiopeia, Perseus, Taurus, Monoceros, Vela, Crux, Norma, Sagittarius, Scutum, Aguila, Cygnus, and Lacerta. To people of long ago, this band looked like milk had been spilled along a pathway, so it was called the Milky Way. This chapter covers the radical discoveries made in the 20th century of the nature of the Milky Way and our place in it. The vocabulary terms are in boldface.

Milky Way

galaxy

14.1 The Interstellar Medium

If you are sitting in an ordinary chair, lean over and look at the ground directly below your head. A cylinder the diameter of your eye drawn from your eye to the ground would enclose about as many particles of air as there are interstellar particles in a cylinder of the same diameter but extending between our solar system and the center of our galaxy 27,000 light years away. Though the space between the stars is emptier than the best vacuums created on the Earth (those are enclosed spaces devoid of matter, not the household cleaning appliances), there is some material between the stars composed of gas and dust. This material is called the **interstellar medium**. The interstellar medium makes up between 10 to 15% of the visible mass of the Milky Way. About 99% of the material is gas and the rest is "dust". Although the dust makes up only about 1% of the interstellar medium, it has a much greater effect on the starlight in the visible band—we can see out only roughly 6000 light years in the plane of the Galaxy because of the dust. Without the dust, we would be able to see through the entire 100,000 light year disk of the Galaxy. Observations of other galaxies are done by looking up or down out of the plane of the Galaxy. Dust provides a place for molecules to form. Finally, probably the most of important of all is that stars and planets form from dust-filled clouds. Therefore, let us look at the dust first and then go on to the gas. The structure of the Galaxy is mapped from measurements of the gas.

interstellar medium

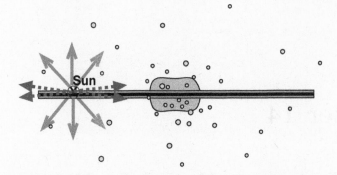

Look out of the plane of the Galaxy to see beyond the Milky Way Galaxy.
Dust blocks our view along the plane of the Galaxy (red arrows).

14.1.1   Dust

The dust is made of thin, highly flattened flakes or needles of graphite (carbon) and
silicates (rock-like minerals) coated with water ice (probably mixed with traces of
ammonia and methane). Each dust flake is roughly the size of the wavelength of
blue light or smaller. The dust is probably formed in the cool outer layers of red
giant stars and dispersed in the red giant winds and planetary nebulae.

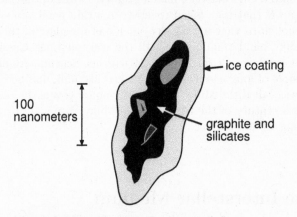

A typical dust grain (note the tiny scale!).

Extinction

Starlight passing through a dust cloud can be affected in a couple of ways. The light
can be totally blocked if the dust is thick enough or it can be partially scattered by
an amount that depends on the color of the light and the thickness of the dust cloud.
All wavelengths of light passing through a dust cloud will be dimmed somewhat.
This effect is called **extinction**.

extinction

Trumpler

The discovery of the dust is relatively recent. In 1930 *Robert J. Trumpler* (lived
1886–1956) plotted the angular diameter of star clusters vs. the distance to the
clusters. He derived the distances from the inverse square law of brightness: clusters
farther away should appear dimmer. *IF* clusters all have roughly the same *linear*
diameter L, then the angular diameter θ should equal (a constant L) / distance.
But he found a *systematic* increase of the linear size of the clusters with distance.

This seemed unreasonable! It would mean that nature had put the Sun at a
special place where the size of the clusters was the smallest. A more reasonable
explanation uses the Copernican principle: the Sun is in a typical spot in the
Galaxy. It is simply that more distant clusters have more stuff between us and the

Copernican principle

 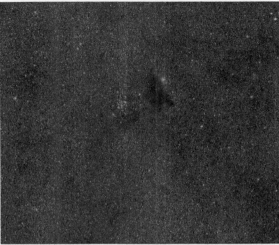

Dark dust clouds like these "Bob globules" in IC 2948 were once thought to be holes in the sky. The dark clouds block the light from the emission nebula behind.

A dark cloud, Barnard 86, is silhouetted against a starry background. Stars form in the dark clouds. A young cluster, NGC 6520, probably associated with Barnard 86 is seen just to the left of it.

Images courtesy of David Malin/Anglo-Australian Observatory

cluster so that they appear fainter (farther away) than they really are. Trumpler had shown that there is dust material between the stars! The extinction of starlight is caused by the scattering of the light out of the line of sight, so less light reaches us. Now, of course, it is much easier to detect the dust once you know it is there and we can directly image it with infrared telescopes and millimeter-wavelength telescopes such as the Atacama Large Millimeter/submillimeter Array (ALMA) in Chile.

Reddening

Not all wavelengths are scattered equally. Just as our air scatters the bluer colors in sunlight more efficiently than the redder colors, the amount of extinction by the interstellar dust depends on the wavelength. The amount of extinction is proportional to 1/(wavelength of the light). Bluer wavelengths are scattered more than redder wavelengths.

The $1/\lambda$ behavior of the scattering indicates that the dust size must be about the wavelength of light (on the order of 10^{-5} centimeters). Less blue light reaches us, so the object appears redder than it should. This effect is called **reddening**, though perhaps it should be called "de-blueing". If the dust particles were much larger (say, the size of grains of sand), reddening would not be observed. If the dust particles were much smaller (say, the size of molecules), the scattering would behave as $1/\lambda^4$. Trumpler showed that a given spectral type of star becomes *increasingly* redder with distance. This discovery was further evidence for dust material between the stars. If the Sun is in a typical spot in the Galaxy, then Trumpler's observation means that more distant stars have more dust between us and them.

You see the same effect when you observe the orange-red Sun close to the horizon. Objects close to the horizon are seen through more atmosphere than when they are close to zenith. At sunset the blues, greens, and some yellow are scattered out of your line of sight to the Sun and only the long waves of the orange and red light are able to move around the air and dust particles to reach your eyes (see figure in section 8.3.2).

At near-infrared (slightly longer than visible light) the dust is transparent. At longer wavelengths you can see the dust itself glowing and you can probe the struc-

reddening
bluer colors scattered away

Reddening and Extinction

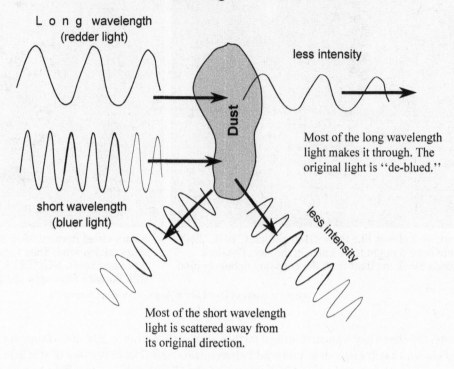

ture of the dust clouds themselves as well as the stars forming in them (young stars that are hidden from us in the visible band). The Spitzer Space Telescope observes in the infrared and has opened up a new universe to us. Although it is not the first infrared space telescope, it is the largest infrared space telescope still in operation, so it has the greatest light-gathering power and resolution of any infrared telescope. The Herschel Space Observatory had an even larger mirror than Spitzer but observed in longer infrared wavelengths. Herschel was active from 2009 to 2013. Spitzer, launched in 2003, remains active today. Movies contrasting the views at visible with infrared of places in the Galaxy as well as other galaxies are available from links on the textbook's website. The superior resolution at millimeter wavelengths of ALMA has enabled us to see planets forming in the dust-filled protoplanetary disks around young stars.

Vocabulary

dust   extinction   interstellar medium
reddening

Review Questions

1. What is the **interstellar medium** composed of?

2. How do astronomers know that the non-gaseous part of the ISM cannot be made of rocks but, rather, of small "dust" particles?

3. How does dust make stars appear redder than they actually are?

4. How does dust cause the **extinction** of starlight?

5. Where is the dust thought to come from?

14.1.2 Gas

About 99% of the interstellar medium is gas with about 90% of it in the form of hydrogen (atomic or molecular form), 10% helium, and traces of other elements. At visible wavelengths, however, dust has a greater effect on the light than the gas. The presence of interstellar gas can be seen when you look at the spectral lines of a binary star system. Among the broad lines that shift as the two stars orbit each other, you see narrow lines that do not move. The narrow lines are from much colder gas in the interstellar medium between us and the binary system.

The hydrogen gas is observed in a variety of states: in ionized, neutral atomic, and molecular forms. The ionized hydrogen emits light in the visible band as the electrons recombine with the protons and the neutral atomic and molecular hydrogen emits light in the radio band of the electromagnetic spectrum.

H II Regions

H II regions are regions of hot (several thousand K), thin hydrogen emission nebulae that glow from the fluorescence of hydrogen atoms. The roman numeral "II" of H II means that hydrogen is missing one electron. A He III nebula is made of helium gas with two missing electrons. A H I nebula is made of neutral atomic hydrogen. Ultraviolet light from hot O and B stars ionizes the surrounding hydrogen gas. When the electrons recombine with the protons, they emit light mostly at visible wavelengths, and primarily at a wavelength of 656.3 nanometers (giving the hydrogen emission nebulae their characteristic red color). In this conversion of the ultraviolet energy, each ultraviolet photon produces a visible photon. The temperature of the stars causing the nebula to fluoresce can be estimated from this even though the O and B stars are hidden inside the nebula. Fluorescent light bulbs operate on the same basic principle except they use mercury vapor to produce ultraviolet light. The ultraviolet light is then converted to visible light by the phosphor layer on the inside of the glass bulb. Below is a picture of a famous H II region called the Orion Nebula (M 42). It is the fuzzy patch you can see in the sword part of the Orion constellation. It is the closest large star formation factory to us and is explored in more detail in chapter 13.

H II region

fluorescence process

M42 (and M43)   © Anglo-Australian Observatory   Photo by David Malin

The Lagoon Nebula in Sagittarius is a large H II region about four times the diameter of the Orion Nebula.

Image courtesy of David Malin/Anglo-Australian Observatory/ Royal Observatory, Edinburgh

Next to the Lagoon on our sky but closer to us in space is the Trifid Nebula: a H II region with a reflection nebula next to it.

Image courtesy of David Malin/ Anglo-Australian Observatory

reflection nebula

Another large H II region is the Lagoon Nebula in the constellation Sagittarius. It is about 5000 light years away and spans 90 by 40 arc minutes in our sky. Converting the angular size to a linear size, the Lagoon Nebula is about 130 by 60 light years in extent (the Orion Nebula is only 29 by 26 light years in size). Next to the Lagoon Nebula on our sky (but closer to us in space) is the Trifid Nebula, so-called because of the dust lanes that trisect the H II region behind them. Just above the Trifid Nebula is a *reflection nebula,* a bright dust cloud seen by reflected light from a luminous star in front of the cloud. Reflection nebulae have a blue color because of the preferential scattering of shorter wavelengths of light.

star formation sites

O and B-type stars are only found in regions of star formation because they are young stars. These hot, very luminous stars do not live long enough to move away from where they were formed. Since stars form in clusters, where O and B stars are found, there are sure to be smaller, lower-mass stars still forming. The spectra of H II regions are much simpler than star spectra so they are easier to decipher. The composition and conditions inside the H II regions are easier to determine and understand than for stars, so H II regions provide a valuable tool for understanding the history of star formation in a galaxy.

H II regions also provide a convenient way to map the structure of a galaxy because they are so large and luminous. In our galaxy the H II regions are distributed in a spiral pattern. The best wavelengths to use to map the distribution of hydrogen, however, are in the radio band. Most of the hydrogen gas is not ionized because O and B stars are rare. Also, energy in the form of radio passes easily through dust.

21-cm Line Radiation

Most of the hydrogen gas in the interstellar medium is in cold atomic form or molecular form. In 1944 Hendrik van de Hulst predicted that the cold atomic hydrogen (H I) gas should emit a particular wavelength of radio energy from a slight energy change in the hydrogen atoms. The wavelength is 21.1 centimeters

van de Hulst

(frequency = 1420.4 MHz) so this radiation is called **21-cm line radiation**. Seven years after van de Hulst's prediction, the 21-cm line radiation was detected from hydrogen gas clouds. The atomic hydrogen gas has temperatures between 100 K to about 3000 K.

Most of the hydrogen in space (far from hot O and B-type stars) is in the ground state. The electron moving around the proton can have a spin in the same direction as the proton's spin (i.e., *parallel*) or spin in the direct opposite direction as the proton's spin (i.e., *anti-parallel*). The energy state of an electron spinning anti-parallel is slightly lower than the energy state of a parallel-spin electron. Remember that the atom always wants to be in the lowest energy state possible, so the electron will eventually flip to the anti-parallel spin direction if it was somehow knocked to the parallel spin direction. The energy difference is very small, so a hydrogen atom can wait on average a few million *years* before it undergoes this transition.

21-cm line radiation

cold, neutral atomic hydrogen makes 21-cm line radiation

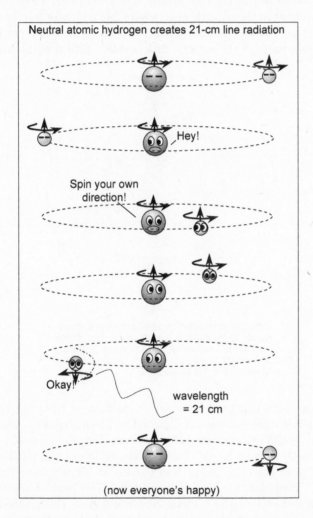

Even though this is a RARE transition, the large amount of hydrogen gas means that enough hydrogen atoms are emitting the 21-cm line radiation at any one given time to be easily detected with radio telescopes. Our galaxy, the Milky Way, has about 3 billion solar masses of H I gas with about 70% of it further out in the Galaxy than the Sun. Most of the H I gas is in the disk component of our galaxy and is located within 720 light years from the midplane of the disk. What is very nice is that 21-cm line radiation is not blocked by dust! The 21-cm line radiation provides the best way to map the structure of the Galaxy.

Using 21-cm Line Radiation to Map the Galaxy

The intensity of the 21-cm emission line depends on the density of the neutral atomic hydrogen along the line of sight. Atomic hydrogen all along the line of sight will contribute to the energy received. You need a way to determine the distance to each clump of hydrogen gas detected. Then when you observe the Galaxy in different directions, you can get a three-dimensional picture of the Galaxy. Using the **rotation curve**, the doppler-shifted radio emission can be converted into distances to the hydrogen clouds.

rotation curve

The **rotation curve** is a plot of the orbital speed of the clouds around the galactic center vs. their distance from the Galaxy center. The term "rotation" in this context refers to the motion of the galactic disk as a whole—the disk made of stars and gas clouds appears to spin. *The gas clouds are assumed to move in the plane of the disk on nearly circular orbits. Jan Oort* (lived 1900–1992) found in 1927 that stars closer to the galactic center complete a greater fraction of their orbit in a given time than stars farther out from the center. This difference in the *angular* speeds of different parts of the galactic disk is called **differential rotation**.

Oort

differential rotation

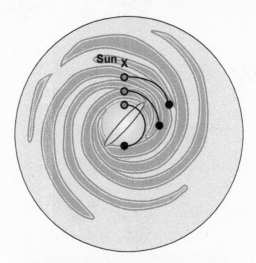

Differential rotation: greater **angular** speeds closer to the galactic center. Each star (black dot) started out along the same line, but the one closer to galactic center completes more of its orbit in the same time.

The rotation curve can be determined by looking at the doppler velocities of hydrogen gas along different lines of sight. The 21-cm emission will include contributions of hydrogen at different distances from the galactic center and different doppler shifts with respect to us. Some of the emission will be from gas clouds just inside the orbit the orbit of the Sun moving at slightly faster angular speeds than the Sun. They will have a small redshift. The part of the total emission coming from gas closest to the galactic center will have the greatest redshift because that gas is moving at the greatest angular speed. In the figure on the next page, the line from the galactic center to the fast moving gas (called "Rmin") makes a 90° angle with respect to our line of sight. Using basic trigonometry, the distance of the fast moving gas (at "A") from the galactic center = (the Sun's distance) × sin (galactic longitude), where the galactic longitude is the angular separation between the cloud and the galactic center and sin () is the "trigonometric sine" function (it is the "sin" key on a scientific calculator). Angle by angle, strip by strip, the rotation curve is constructed from the maximum doppler velocity along different lines of sight. Among the highest resolution HI maps of the entire sky, the

HI4PI survey released in late 2016, required more than a million observations over thousands of hours and the processing of ten billion data points over several years.

Once the rotation curve is determined, the Galaxy's structure can be mapped. The 21-cm line profile has several doppler shifted peaks that are narrow and well-defined. Using the known rotation curve, you can convert the doppler speeds of the peaks to get the distance to the hydrogen producing each peak. The intensity of each peak depends on the density of the hydrogen gas cloud. The mapping surveys show that the hydrogen gas is distributed in a spiral pattern in a thin disk for almost all of the Galaxy.

Use rotation curve to convert doppler shifts to distance from Galaxy center

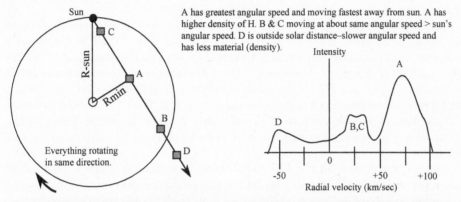

Four clouds all in the same direction. Use doppler shifts to distinguish one cloud from the other. Use the rotation curve to convert the doppler shifts of each cloud to distances from the center of the Galaxy. Do this for other directions to build up a map of the Galaxy strip by strip.

Molecules

Different types of atoms can combine in the coldest regions of space (around 10 K) to make molecules. The cold molecules are detected in the radio band. Most of the molecules are hydrogen molecules (H_2) and carbon monoxide (CO). Actually, molecular hydrogen does not emit radio energy but it is found with carbon monoxide, so the radio emission of CO is used to trace the H_2. Other molecules include such familiar ones as H_2O (water), OH (hydroxide), NH_3 (ammonia), SiO (silicon monoxide), CO_2 (carbon dioxide) and over a hundred other molecules. Many of the molecules have carbon in them and are called *organic molecules*. The organic molecules and the water and ammonia molecules are used in biochemical reactions to create the building blocks of life: amino acids and nucleotides. The presence of these molecules in the interstellar medium shows that some of the ingredients for life exist throughout the Galaxy. Some carbonaceous meteorites reaching the Earth have amino acids in them—apparently, amino acids can be created in conditions too harsh for normal biological processes.

organic molecules in the ISM

Molecular Clouds

Based primarily on observations of the CO emission, astronomers find that the molecules in the interstellar medium are clumped together into clouds with masses anywhere from just a few solar masses to over a million solar masses with diameters ranging from several light years to over 600 light years. Molecules need to have some sort of shielding from the high-energy light from stars. Otherwise, the energetic photons would dissociate the molecules. Molecular clouds have dust in them. The dust grains may provide the shelter for molecules to form. Compared to the size of atoms, the dust grains are enormous and have many pits and recesses for atoms to congregate and combine.

Stars form in the molecular clouds. If the molecular cloud is cold and dense enough, it can collapse under its own gravity. Smaller fragments can form and produce stars (see chapter 13 for further details). The Milky Way has about 2.5 billion solar masses of molecular gas with about 70% of it in a ring extending from 13,000 to 26,000 light years from the center. Not much molecular gas is located at 4,900 to 9,800 light years from the center but about 15% of the total molecular gas mass is located within 4,900 light years from the center. Most of the molecular clouds are clumped in the spiral arms of the disk and stay within 390 light years of the disk mid-plane.

Molecular Hydrogen and Carbon Monoxide Connection

CO traces the H_2

Molecular hydrogen H_2 does not produce radio emission. It produces absorption lines in the ultraviolet. However, the gas and dust become so thick in a molecular cloud that the ultraviolet extinction is too large to accurately measure all of the H_2 in the interior of the cloud. Fortunately, there is evidence of a correlation between the amount of CO and H_2, so the easily detected CO radio emission lines (at 2.6 and 1.3 millimeters) are used to infer the amount of H_2. The CO emission is caused by H_2 molecules colliding with the CO molecules. An increase in the density of the H_2 gas results in more collisions with the CO molecules and an increase in the CO emission.

Another nice feature of the CO radio emission is that its wavelength is small enough (about 100 times smaller than 21-cm line radiation) that even medium-sized radio telescopes have sufficient resolution to map the distribution of the molecular clouds. The higher resolution of large radio telescopes can be used to probe the structure of individual molecular clouds. There is some controversy about how the molecules are clumped together in the clouds. Is one gas cloud actually made of many smaller gas clouds? There is some evidence that indicates that 90% of the H_2 is locked up in 5000 giant molecular clouds with masses greater than 10^5 solar masses and diameters greater than 60 light years. The largest ones, with diameters greater than 160 light years, have more than a million solar masses and make up 50% of the total molecular mass. Other studies indicate that the giants are actually made of smaller clouds grouped together into larger complexes.

Vocabulary

differential rotation	H II region	rotation curve
21-cm line radiation		

Review Questions

1. What are the characteristics of the gaseous part of the ISM? Is the gas all at the same temperature and density? How do you know?

2. What are **H II regions** and how are they produced? What is going on at the atomic level?

3. Why would the presence of a H II region indicate the site of star formation?

4. How does the gas far from any star make its presence seen in the optical wavelengths and radio wavelengths?

5. How is the **21-cm line radiation** produced?

6. Why is the 21-cm line radiation so important for determining galactic structure and mass?

7. How is the 21-cm line radiation used to determine galactic structure and mass?

8. Which part of the Galaxy has greater angular speed? How do you determine the **rotation curve** of the Galaxy from the doppler shifts of the gas?

9. Where are most of the interstellar molecules found and how are they detected?

10. What is the importance of the discovery of organic molecules in the interstellar medium?

11. If the hydrogen molecules produce no radio emission, how do you map its distribution over the entire galaxy?

14.2 Galactic Structure

Determining the structure of our galaxy is not an easy task because the solar system is stuck inside the Galaxy and we can only look in all different directions. Our situation is like you having to determine the layout of your hometown from just looking out on your front porch (or back porch) and not being able to move even across the street. The fact that you see a narrow band of stars tells you that our galaxy is shaped like a thin disk. If we lived in a more spherical galaxy, the stars would be distributed more uniformly across the sky. If we lived in an irregular galaxy, there would be patchier distribution of material in various parts of the sky instead of the narrow band of stars. There is a hint of a bulge in the direction of the Sagittarius constellation (toward the Galaxy center). Careful star counts and determining their distances shows hints of a spiral pattern in the disk. The interstellar dust limits our view to a small section of the Galaxy. However, clear evidence of the spiral structure in the disk comes from the 21-cm line radiation discussed in the previous section.

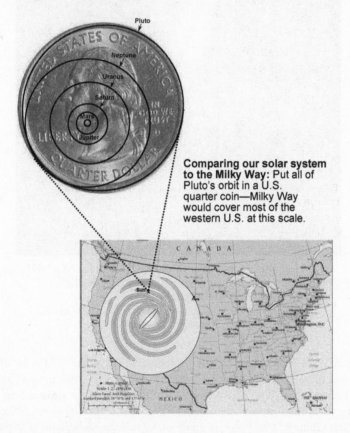

Comparing our solar system to the Milky Way: Put all of Pluto's orbit in a U.S. quarter coin—Milky Way would cover most of the western U.S. at this scale.

Our galaxy, the **Milky Way,** is disk-shaped with spiral arms in the disk. It has an elliptical bulge in the center with a bar-shaped distribution of gas/dust/stars going through the middle out of which the spiral arms extend and a spherical halo of stars that is denser closer to the Galaxy center. The disk of stars is about 100,000 light years across but only about 1000 light years thick (the dust layer is

Milky Way

even thinner). The bar going through the middle of the bulge is about 25,000 by 4000 light years in dimension. Our solar system is about two-thirds of the way out from the center in a spur off one of the major spiral arms. For comparison, our solar system including the Oort Cloud is only about one light year across. If Pluto's orbit were fit inside a U.S. quarter coin (so 80 AUs scaled to 24.26 mm), the Oort Cloud would be about 19 meters across, the next star system (Rigel Kentaurus & companions) would be about 84 meters away and the Galaxy would be about 1920 *kilo*meters across.

Two views of the Galaxy are shown on the next page (our solar system's position is marked). From the side the Galaxy would look very flat because most of the stars are in the disk.

Edgewise, our galaxy probably closely resembles NGC 891. Note the prominent dust lanes going through the disk mid-plane and how flat the galaxy is.
Image courtesy of David Malin/Institute de Astrofisicas de Canarias/ Royal Greenwich Observatory

finding the number of stars

You can make a *rough* guess of the number of stars in our galaxy by dividing the Galaxy's total mass by the mass of a typical star (e.g., 1 solar mass). The result is about 200 billion stars! The actual number of stars could be several tens of billions less or more than this approximate value. The disk contains over 98% of the dust and gas in the Galaxy. The bulge is made of a few tens of *billions* of stars while the stellar halo that extends out from it contains several hundreds of *millions* of stars. Most of the globular clusters (section 14.2.2) are in the stellar halo and, like the halo stars, the number of them increases toward the galactic center. Astronomers have discovered that most of the mass of the Galaxy (and other galaxies) is not in the form of stars, gas, or dust. It is made of some other material, as yet unknown,

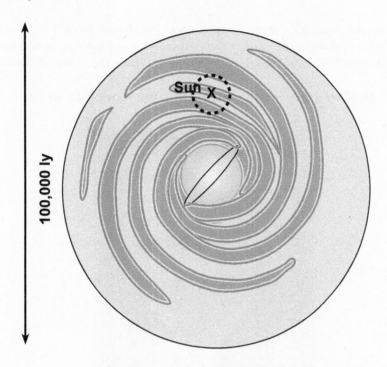

Top View of the Milky Way Galaxy

Hot, blue stars delineate spiral structure. Since hot stars are so luminous, they make the spiral arms stand out. Cool, orange and red stars are found in and between the spiral arms. The Sun's location in the Galaxy is marked with the "X". We are not at the center! Interstellar dust limits our view in visible light to roughly the area within the dashed circle around the Sun.

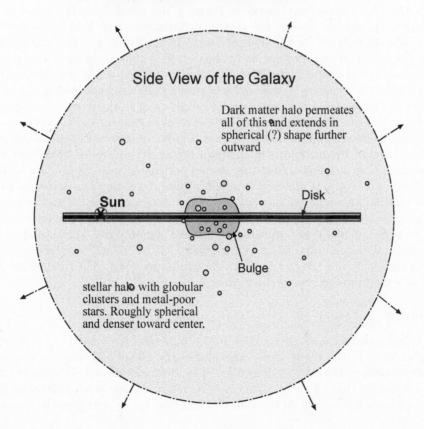

Side View of the Galaxy

Dark matter halo permeates all of this and extends in spherical (?) shape further outward

Disk

Sun

Bulge

stellar halo with globular clusters and metal-poor stars. Roughly spherical and denser toward center.

and is given the descriptive name "dark matter". Note that this affects your guess of the number of stars in the galaxy! (Does it increase the number or decrease it?) The dark matter halo may extend out two or three times the extent of the stars.

14.2.1   Period-Luminosity Relation for Variable Stars

Harlow Shapley (lived 1885–1972)
Image courtesy of The American Institute of Physics

Copernican extension
Shapley

In the 1540's Nicolaus Copernicus removed the Earth from the center of the universe. He put the Sun at the center. Copernicus' view held up against the observational evidence for hundreds of years. In the 1910's the Sun was removed from the center of the universe and relegated to a typical patch in the galactic disk far from the center of the Galaxy. *Harlow Shapley* made this discovery by determining the distances to very old star clusters. He used the inverse square law of light brightness on a particular type of variable star in those old star clusters.

standard candle

Some stars are very useful for finding distances to clusters and to other galaxies because they have a known luminosity that is large, so they can be seen from great distances away. Bright objects of a known luminosity are called **standard candles** (though, in our modern day they should perhaps be called "standard bulbs"). Standard candle objects are used to measure large distances. The particular **standard candle** stars Shapley used are in the last stages of their life and pulsate by changing size. They are trying to re-establish hydrostatic equilibrium but the thermal pressure is out of sync with the gravitational compression. The expanding star overshoots the equilibrium point. Then gravity catches up and contracts the star. But gravity contracts the star beyond the equilibrium point. The thermal pressure increases too much and the cycle continues.

Cepheids

Leavitt

In 1912 *Henrietta Leavitt* (lived 1868–1921) published the results of her study of variable stars in the Large and Small Magellanic Clouds. These are two small satellite galaxies orbiting the Milky Way. The linear size of each Magellanic Cloud is much smaller than its distance from us. Therefore, to a good approximation all of the stars in each galaxy are at the same distance from us. Leavitt found a very useful

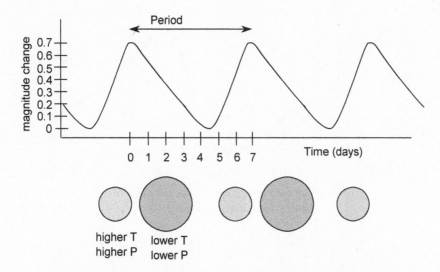

Cepheid variables: outward pressure (P) and inward gravity compression are out of sync, so star changes size and temperature: it **pulsates**. *RR-Lyrae* variables are smaller and have pulsation periods of less than 24 hours. Also, their light curve looks different from the Cepheid light curve.

relationship for a certain type of variable star called a **Cepheid** variable (after the prototype in the constellation Cepheus, see stage 6 of section 13.1.2). The fainter Cepheids in the Magellanic Clouds have shorter periods. Because all of the Cepheids in a Magellanic Cloud are at the same distance from us, Leavitt reasoned that the more *luminous* Cepheids pulsated more slowly. This is the **period-luminosity relation.** Leavitt did not know the distances to the Magellanic Clouds, so she could not tell what the actual value of the luminosity part of the relation was.

Astronomers had to wait a few years for Harlow Shapley to *calibrate* Leavitt's relation using Cepheids in our galaxy for which the distances could be determined. In the *calibration* process Shapley put actual values to the luminosity part of the period-luminosity relation. With a calibrated period-luminosity relation, astronomers could use Cepheid variables as standard candles to determine the distances to distant clusters and even other galaxies.

Cepheids have pulsation periods of 1 to 50 days. In the 1950's astronomers found that there are two types of Cepheids:

- Type I: *classical Cepheids* are from young "high-metallicity" stars (made of gas with significant amounts of processed materials from previous generations of stars) and are about 4 times more luminous than Type II Cepheids. Below is the *light curve* (the plot of brightness vs. time) of a classical Cepheid from the Hipparcos database of variable stars.

- Type II: *W Virginis Cepheids* are from older "low-metallicity" stars (made of less polluted, more primordial gas) and are about 4 times less luminous than Type I. Below is the light curve of a W Virginis Cepheid from the Hipparcos database of variable stars. Note the differences in the shape of the light curve. The two types of Cepheids are distinguished from each other by the *shape* of the light curve profile. In order to compare the shapes without having to worry about the pulsation periods, the time axis is divided by the total pulation period to get the "phase": one pulsation period = one "phase".

Because the luminosity of Cepheids can be easily found from the pulsation period, they are very useful in finding distances to the star clusters or galaxies in which they

Cepheid

period-luminosity relation

calibration of Cepheid relation

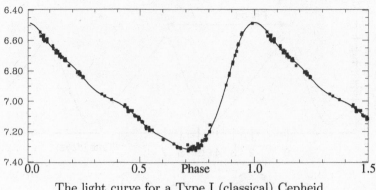

The light curve for a Type I (classical) Cepheid
Plot courtesy of Hipparcos/ESA

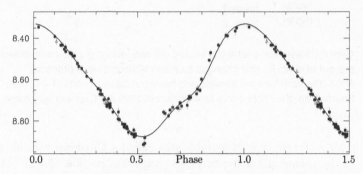

The light curve for a Type II (W Virginis) Cepheid
Plot courtesy of Hipparcos/ESA

importance of Cepheids

determining the distance

reside. By comparing a Cepheid's apparent brightness with its luminosity, you can determine the star's distance from the inverse square law of light brightness (see chapter 11 for further explanation). The inverse square law of light brightness says the distance to the Cepheid = (calibration distance) $\times \sqrt{(\text{calibration brightness})/(\text{apparent brightness})}$. Recall that brightnesses are specified in the magnitude system, so the calibration brightness (absolute magnitude) is the brightness you would measure if the Cepheid was at the calibration distance of 10 parsecs (33 light years). In some cases the calibration distance may be the already-known distance to another Cepheid with the same period you are interested in. As described below, Cepheid variable stars are a crucial link in setting the scale of the universe.

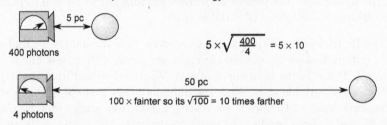

The distance is inversely proportional to
the *square root* of the energy we receive.

Early measurements of the distances to galaxies did not take into account the two types of Cepheids and astronomers underestimated the distances to the galaxies. Edwin Hubble measured the distance to the Andromeda Galaxy in 1923 using the period-luminosity relation for Type II Cepheids. He found it was about 900,000 light years away. However, the Cepheids he observed were Type I (classical) Cepheids that are about four times more luminous. Later, when the distinction was made between the two types, the distance to the Andromeda Galaxy was increased by about *two* times to about 2.3 million light years. Recent studies using various types of objects and techniques have given a larger distance of between 2.5 to 3 million light years to the Andromeda Galaxy.

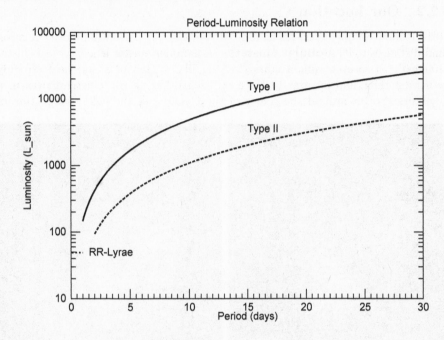

RR Lyrae

Another type of pulsating star similar to the Cepheids are the **RR Lyrae** variable stars (named after the prototype star RR Lyrae). They are smaller than Cepheids and, therefore, have shorter periods and lower luminosities. They pulsate with a period between 5 and 15 hours (Cepheid pulsation periods are greater than 24 hours). Low-mass stars will go through a RR Lyrae pulsation stage while the high-mass stars will go through a Cepheid stage. Because low-mass stars live longer than high-mass stars, the Cepheid stars as a group are younger than the RR Lyrae stars.

RR Lyrae are found in old star clusters called globular clusters and in the stellar halo part of our galaxy. All of the RR Lyrae stars in a cluster have the same *average* apparent magnitude. In different clusters, the average apparent magnitude was different. This is because all RR Lyrae have about the same average *absolute* magnitude (= +0.6, or 49 solar luminosities). If the cluster is more distant from us, the RR Lyrae in it will have greater apparent magnitudes (remember fainter objects have *greater* magnitudes!).

RR Lyrae stars can be used as standard candles to measure distances out to about 760,000 parsecs (about 2.5 million light years). The more luminous Cepheid variables can be used to measure distances out to 40 million parsecs (about 130 million light years). These distances are many thousands of times greater than the distances to the nearest stars found with the trigonometric parallax method. The method of standard candles (inverse square law) provides a crucial link between the geometric methods of trigonometric parallax and the method of the Hubble-Lemaître Law for very far away galaxies. (The Hubble-Lemaître Law is discussed in the next chapter.) In fact, this link between the parallax and the Hubble-Lemaître Law was so crucial that the diameter of the Hubble Space Telescope's mirror was

RR Lyrae

same luminosity

RR-Lyrae for local galaxies, Cepheids for nearby galaxy clusters

standard candles link trig parallax to Hubble-Lemaître Law

why Cepheids are so im-
portant

primarily determined by how large a mirror (its resolving power and light gathering power) would be needed to pick out Cepheids in the other galaxies and the Cepheid distance measurement of 18 galaxies was one of the three Key Projects for the Hubble Space Telescope during its first decade of operation. All of the pretty pictures of other objects during that time were just an extra bonus.

14.2.2 Our Location

globular cluster

In 1918 Harlow Shapley used his calibrated variable star period-luminosity relation to find distances to 93 **globular clusters**. A globular cluster is a spherical cluster of 100,000's to several million stars (looking like a glob of stars) held strongly together by their mutual gravity force on each other as the cluster moves in a very elliptical orbit around the center of the Galaxy. In the side view picture of

Two globular clusters: M5 (left) and 47 Tucanae.
Images courtesy of David Malin/Anglo-Australian Observatory

the Galaxy at the beginning of this section and on the next page, the globular clusters are represented by the small circles congregating around the bulge of the Galaxy (they have been enlarged over a 100 times to make them visible). Shapley found a strong concentration of globular clusters in the direction of the constellation Sagittarius. In a continuation of the process started by Copernicus almost 500 years before, Shapley announced that our solar system is not at the center of the Galaxy!

Copernican extension

how we know we're not at the center

If we were at the center of the Galaxy, the globular clusters would be distributed equally all around us. Instead, they congregate around some other point that Shapley calculated to be 32,600 light years from our solar system. He did not know about the dust in the interstellar medium. That discovery was made about a decade later. Taking into account the effects of dust extinction on the brightnesses of stars and also that there are different types of Cepheids, astronomers reduced the solar system's distance to the center of the Galaxy to about 26,000 light years. Trigonometric parallax measurements of star formation regions in 2009 and 2014 using VLBI measurements have fine-tuned that to about 27,000 light years. Our solar system's position is marked with a cross in the pictures of the Galaxy at the beginning of this section.

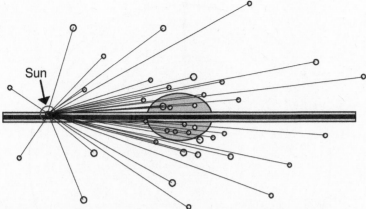

Find the distance and direction to each globular cluster to find the direction to the center of the Galaxy and how far away the center is from us.

14.2.3 Our Motion

Further evidence of Shapley's discovery is seen in the motion of the Sun about the center. Globular clusters on one side of the celestial sphere have redshifts and globular clusters on the other side of the celestial sphere have blueshifts. Stars and H II regions near the Sun have small doppler shifts. From this you can conclude that the galactic disk is rotating in an organized fashion but the globular clusters are not. The 21-cm line emission from neutral atomic hydrogen is now used to map the motion of the disk. Objects in the disk orbit about a common center that is 27,000 light years away in the direction of Sagittarius.

14.2.4 Deriving the Galactic Mass from the Rotation Curve

Recall from chapter 5 that if you know the size of an object's orbit and how quickly it is moving in its orbit, you can find the mass of the central object, or the mass of the two object's orbiting around a common point. The same principle can be used to calculate the mass of the Galaxy! (Isn't gravity wonderful?) In this case, the two masses involved are the mass of a star and the mass of the part of the Galaxy that is *inside* the star's orbit. For most orbits the Galaxy mass inside the orbit is MUCH larger than any star's mass, so it is safe to ignore the star's mass.

    mass inside the orbit

    The gravity from the part of the Galaxy inside a star's orbit accelerates the star so it moves in an orbit. The greater the gravity pulling on a star, the faster the star will move. Applying the mass and orbit speed relations of chapter 5, the enclosed mass = (orbital speed)$^2 \times$ (star's distance to the galactic center)$/G$, where G is the gravity constant. The Galaxy's mass is found from measuring the orbital speed of stars (or gas clouds) and their distance from the center.

    From measurements of stars and hydrogen clouds in the galactic disk, astronomers construct a **rotation curve** for the Galaxy. This is a plot of the orbital speed of stars (or gas clouds) vs. their distance from the center of the Galaxy (see an example plot on the next page). The "rotation" part of the term refers to the motion of the disk as a whole. As a whole the disk seems to be rotating (spinning) even though it is really the individual stars and clouds that are orbiting around the center. The rotation curve tells you the amount of mass inside a given distance from the center. You find how the mass is distributed in the Galaxy by looking at how the amount of enclosed mass changes with the size of the orbits.

    rotation curve

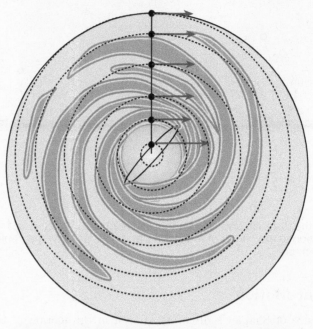

The mass inside an orbit can be found using the size of the orbit and the orbital speed. The arrows show the speeds for certain points on the **rotation curve** for this galaxy.

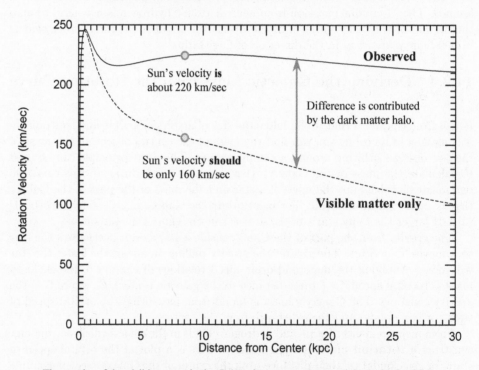

The gravity of the visible matter in the Galaxy is not enough to explain the high orbital speeds of stars in the Galaxy. For example, the Sun is moving about 60 km/sec too fast. The part of the rotation curve contributed by the visible matter only is the bottom curve. The discrepancy between the two curves is evidence for a **dark matter halo.**

A rigid body rotation is seen close to the center (as if the part close to the center was rotating as one single object even though it is made of stars and gas), then the curve drops off, then rises, and eventually flattens out as far out as can be seen. Because gravity becomes weaker with larger (increasing) distance, the stars on the outskirts of the visible galaxy should be moving slower than those closer to where most of the visible mass resides. Instead, they are moving at about the same speed even though they are *farther* from most of the visible mass! There must be extra mass in the Galaxy we cannot see to create the extra amount of gravity force. The Galaxy is spinning too quickly—the visible matter does not have enough mass to keep the Galaxy together! [Recent measurements on the size of the Milky Way using the VLBA have scaled the distances and speeds up—the Sun's distance from the center is 8.34 kpc and the Sun's speed is 240 km/sec—but how the speeds change with distance, the shape of the rotation curve, is still as described here.]

flat rotation curve

detecting dark matter

The observed rotation curve can be decomposed into the individual parts contributed by each component of the Galaxy: the disk, bulge + stellar halo, and the rest of total mass is what is called **dark matter**—material that does not emit any light (a small fraction of it is ordinary matter that is too faint to be detected yet) but has a significant amount of gravitational influence. The highest solid line in the left plot below is for all of the galactic components combined. The other curves (dashed, dotted, and solid) are the contributions of the individual galactic components (the bulge + stellar halo = "bulge", disk, and the dark matter halo) to the rotational velocity.

dark matter

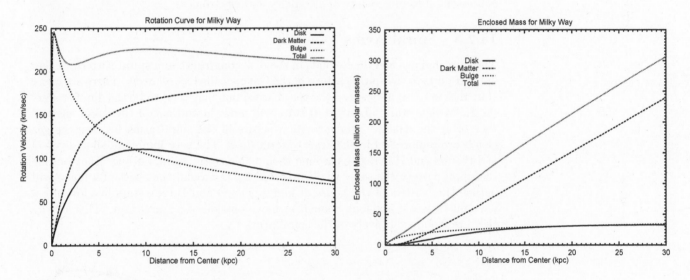

The plot on the right shows the *enclosed* mass inside a given distance. If you reach the point where the enclosed mass does NOT increase with distance, then you will have found the edge of the Galaxy's mass. *Beyond* the edge of the Galaxy, the rotational velocity will decrease as the distance from the center increases. Both plots show that the end of the Galaxy's mass has not yet been found but measurements of very distant globular clusters by Gaia and the Hubble Space Telescope in 2019 seem to indicate a total galactic mass of 1.5 trillion solar masses within a distance of 129,000 light years from the galactic center. The stars, dust, and gas in the disk and stellar halo do not explain all the mass. The part of the Galaxy that fills up the remainder of mass is the dark matter halo. Ninety percent of the Galaxy's mass is in the form of this dark matter! Unfortunately, because gravity depends only on the distance and mass and not the composition, astronomers are not certain what the dark matter is composed of. It could be in the form of planets, brown dwarfs (stars too small to shine from nuclear fusion), white dwarfs, black holes, neutrinos with mass, or other exotic particles that have not been discovered in the laboratory yet. For reasons to be explained in the next two chapters, astronomers have figured out that the dark matter is a combination of all those things but the exotic particles must make up the vast majority of the dark matter. In fact, of the total matter in the universe, the overall mass of the exotic particles is five times the overall mass of the "ordinary matter" we are more familiar with (matter made of protons, neutrons, electrons, neutrinos, etc.).

Is dark matter real?   You may be a bit skeptical about the existence of all this dark matter. Are not astronomers going "too far" with their speculations? Scientists, by nature, are skeptical themselves of any radical change in our understanding of the universe. However, nature and careful observations are the sole judge of scientific truth and even the smartest scientist must yield to what nature is telling us. The conclusion that dark matter exists has come from using the standard scientific method of observation, interpretation, and testing of the explanation. Looking back in history, the detection of dark matter is just another application of Newton's law of gravity. Until Neptune was directly observed, its presence was known from its gravitational effect on Uranus (Neptune was "dark matter"). Astronomers have used the orbits and wobbling of stars to detect the presence of as yet, unseen companions around them (i.e., exoplanets and black holes). The exoplanets and black holes are technically, dark matter too. They may be faint or invisible themselves, but they produce definite gravitational effects on nearby visible objects. At the other end of the scale, no one has ever directly seen an electron, but you know such a particle exists and it is essential to our society of electricity and electronics.

14.2.5 Spiral Arms

The stars and gas and dust clouds in the disk congregate in a spiral pattern. There are four parts to the spiral pattern in the Galaxy called *spiral arms*. There are many stars that are also in-between the spiral arms, but they tend to be the dimmer stars (G, K, M-type stars). Long-lived stars will move in and out of the spiral arms as they orbit the galaxy. Star formation occurs in the spiral arms because the gas clouds are compressed in the arms to form stars. The very luminous, short-lived O and B-stars and H II regions around them enhance the spiral outline. They outline the spiral pattern the same way Christmas lights around the edges of a house will outline the borders of the house at night. The O and B-type stars live for only a few million years, not long enough to move outside of a spiral arm. That is why they are found exclusively in the spiral arms.

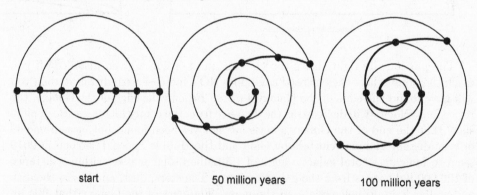

start   50 million years   100 million years

Differential rotation: stars near the center take less time to orbit the center than those farther from the center. Differential rotation can create a spiral pattern in the disk in a short time.

differential rotation   Differential rotation provides an easy way to produce a spiral pattern in the disk. **Differential rotation** is the difference in the *angular* speeds of different

parts of the galactic disk so stars closer to the center complete a greater fraction of
their orbit in a given time. But differential rotation is too efficient in making the
spiral arms. After only 500 million years, the arms should be so wound up that the
structure disappears. Also, the spiral pattern should occupy only a small part of the
disk. The observations of other galaxies contradicts this: the spiral arms in spiral
galaxies rarely have more than two turns. Galaxies are billions of years old so the
spiral pattern must be a long-lasting feature. What maintains the spiral pattern?

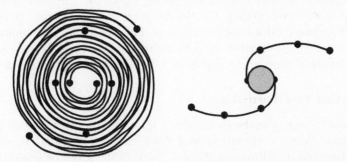

Prediction: 500 million years   **Observation**: 15,000 million years

The "winding problem": because of differential rotation, the spiral arms
should be so wound up after a short time that the spiral structure has
disappeared. Observation contradicts the prediction. What keeps the
spirals loose?

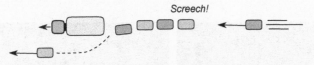

individual cars move through the traffic jam

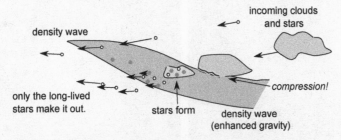

Spiral density waves are like traffic jams. Clouds and stars speed
up to the density wave (are accelerated toward it) and are tugged
backward as they leave, so they accumulate in the density wave
(like cars bunching up behind a slower-moving vehicle). Clouds
compress and form stars in the density wave, but only the fainter
stars live long enough to make it out of the wave.

Density Wave Theory

One popular theory says that the spiral structure is a wave that moves through
the disk causing the stars and gas to clump up along the wave—a density wave.
The spiral arms are where the stars pile up as they orbit the center. They are like
the entrance ramps onto a busy highway during rush hour: when a car comes to
the point where many other cars are merging, it slows down and cars jam up. But

stellar traffic jam

eventually, the car moves past the ramp and speeds up. A person in a helicopter above the traffic giving reports for the local radio station sees a traffic jam at the entrance ramp even though individual cars are moving through it. Another clump moving down the highway may be seen as cars pile up behind a slow-moving truck.

In a galaxy the spiral region of greater gravity concentrates the stars and gas. The spiral regions rotate about as half as fast as the stars move. Stars behind the region of greater gravity are pulled forward into the region and speed up. Stars leaving the region of greater gravity are pulled backward and slow down. Gas entering spiral wave is compressed. On the downstream side of wave, there should be lots of H II regions (star formation regions). This is seen in some galaxies with prominent two-armed spiral patterns. But there are some unanswered questions. What forms the spiral wave in the first place? What maintains the wave?

Self-propagating Star Formation

Another popular theory uses the shock waves from supernova explosions to shape the spiral pattern. When a supernova shock wave reaches a gas cloud, it compresses the cloud to stimulate the formation of stars. Some of them will be massive enough to produce their own supernova explosions to keep the cycle going. Coupled with the differential rotation of the disk, the shock waves will keep the spiral arms visible.

Computer simulations of galaxy disks with a series of supernova explosions do produce spiral arms but they are ragged and not as symmetrical and full as seen in so-called "grand-design" spirals that have two arms. There are spiral galaxies with numerous, ragged spiral arms in their disks (called "flocculent" spirals), so perhaps the self-propagating star formation mechanism is responsible for the flocculent spirals.

NGC 2997 (left): a "grand design" spiral galaxy.
M 33 (right): a "flocculent" spiral galaxy.

NGC 2997 courtesy of David Malin/Anglo-Australian Observatory
M 33 courtesy of David Malin/Institute de Astrofisicas de Canarias/
     Royal Greenwich Observatory

Transient Spirals

In this scenario the spiral arms come and go. This behavior is seen in computer simulations of galactic disks. It is possible that all three theories may be correct. Some galaxies (particularly the grand-design spirals) use the density wave mechanism and others use the self-propagating star formation or transient spiral mechanisms. Our galaxy may be an example of a spiral that uses more than one. The spiral density waves could establish the overall pattern in the disk and the supernova explosions could modify the design somewhat.

14.2.6 Populations of Stars

The astronomer *Walter Baade* (lived 1893–1960) working at Mount Wilson Observatory outside of Los Angeles was forbidden to work in the United States' military research during World War II because of his German birth. Being a good astronomer, he took advantage of the dark skies from the frequent blackouts of Los Angeles during the war. He also had plenty of time at the telescope because the other astronomers were engaged in the war effort. In 1944 he discovered that the stars in the Galaxy can be divided into two basic groups: **Population I** and **Population II**.

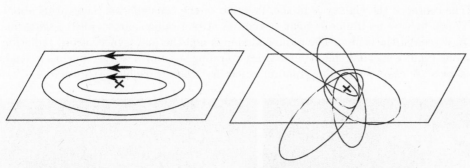

Population I stars: ordered motion. Circular orbits in the disk plane; younger, more metal-rich.

Population II stars: random motion. Eccentric orbits passing through disk plane; older, more metal-poor.

The **Population I** stars are in the *disk* component of the Galaxy. They have a wide range of ages, from 0 to 10 billion years old. The youngest ones are in the spiral arms. Population I star orbits are orderly: roughly circular orbits close to the mid-plane of the galactic disk. Young star clusters made of Population I stars are called *open clusters* because the stars are loosely bound together, in contrast to the old, concentrated globular clusters. Population I stars have a greater abundance of elements heavier than helium than the Population II stars. Elements heavier than helium are often called *metals* in astronomy even though many of them are not the shiny conductors called metals in popular usage. The Population I are said to be "metal-rich" in comparison to the Population II stars.

There is a continuum of the metal abundance and orbit shapes. The oldest Population I stars have 0.1 times the metal abundance of the Sun and have slightly elliptical orbits that can take them up to 3000 light years from the disk plane. The middle-aged stars like the Sun have metal abundances of 0.5 to 1 times solar abundance and can be found at heights up to 1100 light years from the disk plane. The young stars have metal abundances of 1 to 2 times the Sun's abundance and stay within 650 light years of the disk plane. Stars less than 100 million years old are found in the spiral arms within 400 light years of the disk plane. They have circular orbits and metal abundances of 1 to 2.5 times solar abundance.

The **Population II** stars inhabit the *spheroidal* component (the stellar halo and bulge). They are old: ages range from 10 to 13 billion years old, so they have masses less than or equal to 0.8 solar masses. Their orbits are much more randomly oriented than the Population I orbits and are highly elliptical. The combination of

Baade

Population I
younger, disk stars

"metal"= heavier than helium

metal-rich

Population II
older, halo+bulge

all of the elliptical orbits randomly aligned produces the spherical distribution seen. As a unit the spheroidal component has little overall rotation. *Globular clusters* are made of Population II stars. Because they swarm around the center like bees around a hive, the globular clusters were used to locate the center of the Galaxy as described in section 14.2.2.

metal-poor halo

metal-rich bulge

The halo stars are metal-poor (0.001 to 0.03 times solar abundance), but the abundance increases inward toward the center. The bulge stars have metal abundances of 1 to 3 times that of the Sun. Early in the history of the Galaxy, there was probably a lot of star formation and death in the bulge component, so the metal content rose quickly. The star formation rate in the disk has been more steady, so it is slowly catching up to the bulge's metal abundance. Star formation now occurs in just the disk. Eventually, the new disk stars will be born with greater metal abundance than the metal-richest bulge stars.

14.2.7 Galactic Center

The center of the Galaxy is in the direction of the constellation Sagittarius about 27,000 light years from our solar system. A strong radio source, called Sagittarius A, is seen at the center. The radio emission is non-thermal (synchrotron) radiation from rapidly moving charged particles spiraling around a strong magnetic field. X-rays are also seen coming from an object less than three light years across.

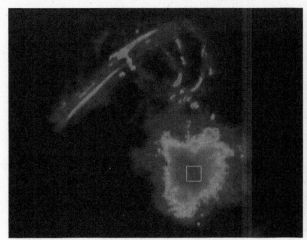 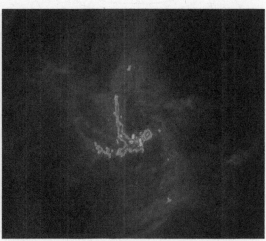

Central 25 arc minutes (58 pc) of galaxy center at a wavelength of 20 cm. Plane of galaxy runs upper left to lower right. Parallel filaments areperpendicular to galactic plane. Box is area of right image.

Central 3 arc minutes (7 pc) of galaxy center at a wavelength of 6 cm. Matter is spiralling into an object at the center, probably a supermassive black hole.

Images courtesy of National Radio Astronomy Observatory/Associated Universities, Inc.

Stellar velocities found from the doppler shifts of the spectral lines from the stars' near the center indicate the presence of a large, compact mass at the center with at least 1 million solar masses. It is probably a massive black hole formed by mergers of stars and stellar remnants. As you look closer to a supermassive black hole, you should see the stars nearer the black hole moving faster than the ones farther out. Stars nearer the supermassive black hole move fast enough to balance the stronger gravity closer to the black hole.

supermassive black hole

High-resolution infrared measurements of the *orbits* of the stars at the center show that a very compact mass—a supermassive black hole—with about 4.5 million solar masses lies at the center (if use our distance to the center as 8.4 kpc). The picture on the next page shows the orbits of the stars around the black hole from the years 1995 to 2018. At a distance of 8.4 kpc for the Sun, the 0.2 arc second scale bar in the figure corresponds to about 0.027 light years or 1680 AU. The object is too compact to be a dense cluster of stars—the Chandra X-ray Observatory's observations of X-ray bursts from the object place an upper limit of the diameter of the object of the size of the Earth's orbit. An expanding ring is also seen about 9000 light years from the center. Other galaxy cores have supermassive compact objects (the Andromeda Galaxy, M32, Sombrero Galaxy, M87, and many others).

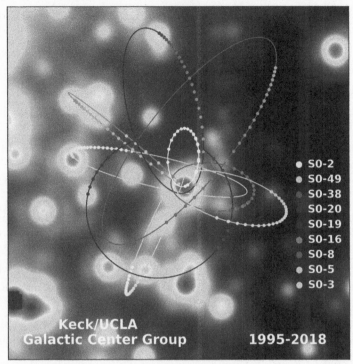

Image created by Andrea Ghez and her research team at UCLA and are from data sets obtained with the W.M. Keck Telescopes.

Just because there is a large black hole at the center, does not mean that the stars in the Galaxy are all orbiting around it like the planets orbit the Sun. Even if the supermassive black hole was not there, the stars would still orbit pretty much as they do now because of their mutual gravity. If you compare the enclosed mass inside the Sun's orbit (see the enclosed mass figure of section 14.2.4) with the 4.5 million solar masses of the black hole, you will see that the central black hole's mass is insignificant compared to the entire Galaxy.

Vocabulary

Cepheid	dark matter	differential rotation
galaxy	globular clusters	Milky Way
period-luminosity relation	Population I	Population II
rotation curve	RR Lyrae	standard candle

Formulae

- *Inverse square law* (standard candle): distance to the standard candle = (calibration distance) $\times \sqrt{\text{(calibration brightness)}/\text{(apparent brightness)}}$. Calibration distance is either 10 parsecs or it is the distance to a similar object at a known distance.

- *Orbital speed* $= \sqrt{(G \times \text{(enclosed mass)})/\text{(star's distance from the galactic center)}}$, where the enclosed mass is the mass of the galaxy *inside* the star's orbit, and G is the gravity constant.

- *Enclosed mass* = (orbital speed)^2 × (star's distance from the galactic center) / G, where G is the gravity constant.

Review Questions

1. What is the name for our galaxy and what kind of galaxy is it?

2. How big is our galaxy? How many stars are in it and how do you know?

3. How are **Cepheids** and **RR-Lyrae** stars considered to be standard candles? How can you find their luminosity?

4. How can you use the **period-luminosity relation** to find distances?

5. Why do variable stars like Cepheids, RR-Lyrae stars, and Mira variables vary in brightness?

6. Where are we in the Galaxy and how do you know? How can the distribution of globular clusters tell you about our place in the Galaxy?

7. What are the four basic components of our galaxy? Where would old stars be found? Where would stars with very small amounts of "metals" (elements heavier than helium) be found? Where are new stars being formed? Where would stars enriched with "metals" be found?

8. If you could analyze the spectra of 10 stars *every second,* how many *years* would it take you to check every star *inside the Sun's orbit that is in our half of the Galaxy?* [Hint: used the "enclosed mass" graph, divide by 2, and the Sun's distance from the center = 27,000 light years (8,400 parsecs).]

9. What are the theories for how spiral arms are formed and maintained? What are the verifiable predictions made by these theories?

10. How does the density wave theory explain why stars form in the spiral arms? Also, contrast it with the explanation given by the self-propagating star formation theory.

11. How do astronomers know the **dark matter** halo exists if it does not radiate anything telescopes can detect?

12. Scientists are advocating a focused search for extra-terrestrial intelligence that looks at stars relatively abundant in elements heavier than helium because those are the elements from which life could possibly form. What part(s) of the Galaxy would such stars be found and what are the distinguishing orbital characteristics of such stars?

13. If very old stars tend to be metal-poor, how could you explain the presence of recently-formed stars that are metal-poor?

14. How do astronomers know that there is a very massive black hole at the center of the Galaxy?

15. If there was no black hole in the center of the Galaxy, how would the orbits of the stars near the Sun be affected? (Hint: compare the mass of the black hole to the total mass inside the Sun's orbit [black hole mass/total enclosed mass]—would the gravity change significantly?)

Chapter 15

Other Galaxies and Active Galaxies

Using large telescopes you can see clouds of dust and gas inside the Galaxy. You can also see other peculiar milky nebulae scattered among the stars. Some of these milky nebulae have spiral shapes to them and others look like squashed spheres or tortured messes of material. Three of the milky nebulae are visible as fuzzy patches to the naked eye: one is in the constellation Andromeda and two others (called the Large and Small Magellanic Clouds after the first European explorer to see them, Ferdinand Magellan) are in the southern sky in the constellations Mensa and Hydrus.

Edwin Hubble (lived 1889–1953)
Image courtesy of The Observatories of the
Carnegie Institution of Washington

Milton Humason (lived 1891–1972)
Image courtesy of The Observatories of the
Carnegie Institution of Washington

Work by *Edwin Hubble* and *Milton Humason* in the 1920s established that each of the spiral nebulae was another huge star system, called a galaxy (from the Greek "galactos", meaning "milk"), outside our own galaxy. Telescopes of sufficient size to have the needed resolution to see individual stars in the other galaxies were used by Hubble and Humason to measure the distances to the galaxies. This chapter

Hubble and Humason

covers the galactic systems outside our own and a peculiar group of galaxies that produce a large amount of energy in their centers. The vocabulary terms are in boldface.

15.1   Other Galaxies

galaxy definition

counting stars in a galaxy

Galaxies are organized systems thousands to hundreds of thousands of light years across made of tens of millions to trillions of stars sometimes mixed with gas and dust all held together by their mutual gravity and the gravity of dark matter. There is not some unfortunate astronomer counting up all the stars in the galaxies. You can quickly get an estimate of the number of stars in a galaxy by dividing the total luminosity of the galaxy by a typical star's luminosity. A more accurate value would result if you use the galaxy's *luminosity function* (a table of the proportion of stars of a given luminosity). Or you could divide the total mass of the galaxy by a typical star's mass (or use the *mass function* to get the proportions right) but one must also consider the dark matter that makes up at least 90% of the mass of most galaxies (section 15.1.5).

Shapley-Curtis Debate

Curtis

The distances between galaxies are large and are often measured in *megaparsecs*. A megaparsec is one million parsecs (or about 3.3 million light years). For instance, the distance between the Milky Way and the closest large galaxy, the Andromeda Galaxy, is about 0.899 megaparsecs. There was a big controversy in the 1910s and early 1920s over whether the nebulae called galaxies were outside the Milky Way or were part of it. There was so much controversy that the National Academy of Sciences held a debate between the opposing sides in 1920. Those favoring a large Milky Way with the spiral nebulae inside it were represented by Harlow Shapley. Those favoring the spiral nebulae as separate groups of stars outside the Milky Way were represented by *Heber Curtis* (lived 1872–1942). The *Shapley-Curtis* debate did not decide much beyond the fact that both sides had powerful evidence for their views.

Cepheids discovered

Edwin Hubble and Milton Humason set out to resolve the debate by using the largest telescope at the time, the 100-inch telescope on Mount Wilson, to study the large spiral nebula in the Andromeda constellation. Because of its large mirror, the telescope had sufficient resolving power and light-gathering power to spot individual stars in the Andromeda Galaxy. In the mid-1920s they discovered Cepheid variables in the galaxy and used the period-luminosity relation to find that the distance to the galaxy was very much greater than even the largest estimates for the size of the Milky Way. Galaxies are definitely outside the Milky Way and our galaxy is just one of billions of galaxies in the universe.

Copernican extension

Their discovery continued the process started by Copernicus long ago of moving us from the center of the universe. It is ironic that the person who moved the Sun from the center, Harlow Shapley, would be the one to hold fast to our galaxy being the center of the universe. Scientists are humans with all of the greatness and foibles that comes with being human. Despite our prejudices, nature and experiments will always ultimately show us the truth about the physical universe.

15.1.1   Types of Galaxies

Edwin Hubble divided the galaxies into three basic groups based on their appearance: ellipticals, spirals, and irregulars. The ellipticals are smooth and round or elliptical, the spirals are flat with a spiral pattern in their disk, and the irregulars have stars and gas in random patches. Most galaxies are small and faint so only the luminous galaxies are seen at great distances. These spectacular galaxies tend to be either the elliptical or spiral type, so they are the ones often displayed in astronomy textbooks.

In 1936 Hubble put these groups onto a two-pronged sequence that looks like a tuning fork because he thought that the galaxies started out as ellipticals, then changed to spirals and then to irregulars. In this scenario, a galaxy could take one of two paths. It could take the top prong and be a regular spiral where the arms come right out of the galaxy center, or it could take the bottom prong and be a *barred* spiral with the arms starting from the ends of a bar of gas and stars going through the center. The ellipticals are sub-divided by how round they are and the spirals are sub-divided by how loose their arms are and how big their nucleus is.

The Hubble "tuning fork" Sequence of galaxy classification. Galaxies are classified by shape. The **elliptical** galaxies go from circular (E0) to significantly flattened (E7). The spirals are sub-divided into **regular spirals** and **barred spirals.** Each of them is further sub-divided into groups depending on the size of the central bulge and how tightly the arms are wound around the center. The **irregular** galaxies have no definite structure. This is **not** an evolutionary sequence!

Astronomers now know that it is NOT an evolutionary sequence because each type of galaxy has very old stars.   The oldest stars in any galaxy all have about the same age of around 13 billion years. This means that spirals form as spirals, ellipticals form as ellipticals, and irregulars form as irregulars. However, the "tuning fork" diagram is still used to classify galaxies because of its convenience.

age of all galaxies

The next six pages will have a description of each basic type of galaxy on the left page and examples of each type on the right page. The textbook's website has color versions of the pictures.

Ellipticals

elliptical galaxy

Elliptical galaxies are smooth and elliptical in appearance. There are four distinguishing characteristics of the ellipticals: (a) they have much more *random* star motion than orderly rotational motion (star orbits are aligned in a wide range of angles and have a wide range of eccentricities); (b) they have very little dust and gas left between the stars; (c) this means that they have no new star formation occurring now and no hot, bright, massive stars in them (those stars are too short-lived); and (d) they have no spiral structure.

Elliptical galaxies are sub-classified according to how flat they are. The number next to the "E" in the tuning fork diagram = 10×(largest diameter − smallest diameter) / (largest diameter), so an E7 galaxy is flatter than an E0 galaxy. The flattened shape is not due to rotational flattening but to how the orbits are oriented and the distribution of the star velocities. Most ellipticals are small and faint. The dwarf ellipticals may be the most common type of galaxy in the universe (or maybe the dwarf irregulars are). Examples of elliptical galaxies are M32 (an E2 dwarf elliptical next to the Andromeda Galaxy) and M87 (a huge elliptical at the center of the Virgo cluster).

M 32: a dwarf elliptical (E2) satellite galaxy of the Andromeda Galaxy.

Image courtesy of AURA/NOAO/NSF

M 110: a dwarf elliptical (E6) satellite galaxy of the Andromeda Galaxy.

Image courtesy of Bill Schoening, Vanessa Harvey/ REU program/AURA/NOAO/NSF

Leo I: a dwarf elliptical (E3) in the Local Group.
Image courtesy of David Malin/Anglo-Australian Observatory

M 87: a giant elliptical (E1) at the Virgo Cluster's core. It has grown very large by "eating" other galaxies.
Image courtesy of David Malin/Anglo-Australian Observatory

Spirals

spiral galaxy

Spiral galaxies have flattened disks with a spiral pattern in the disk. The spiral arms can go all of the way into the bulge or be attached to the ends of a long bar of gas and dust that bisects the bulge. The four distinguishing characteristics of the spirals are: (a) they have more orderly, rotational motion than random motion (the rotation refers to the disk as a whole and means that the star orbits are closely confined to a narrow range of angles and are fairly circular); (b) they have some or a lot of gas and dust between the stars; (c) this means they can have new star formation occurring in the disk, particularly in the spiral arms; and (d) they have a spiral structure.

Spiral galaxies are sub-classified into "a", "b", "c", and "d" groups according to how loose their spiral arms are and how big the nucleus is. The "a" group spirals have large bulges and very tightly wound spiral arms and the "d" group spirals have almost no bulge and very loose arms. The Milky Way is between the "b" and "c"

Milky Way type

groups with a bar, so it is an SBbc-type spiral galaxy. Most spirals are luminous. Some other examples of spiral galaxies are M31 (the Andromeda Galaxy) and M33 (a small spiral in the Local Group).

Some disk galaxies have no spiral arms and are called "S0" ("SB0" if there is a bar) or lenticular galaxies. They are placed at the point in the tuning fork diagram where it branches off to the regular spiral or barred spiral pattern prong. Their gas and dust may been blown away by the galaxy moving quickly through the low-density intergalactic medium (hot, very thin gas between the galaxies) or used up in a rapid burst of star formation.

The Andromeda Galaxy (=M 31): a large spiral galaxy (Sb) near the Milky Way. Note M 32 just above it and M 110 below it.

Image courtesy of Jason Ware

The Triangulum Galaxy (=M 33): a small spiral galaxy (Scd) in the Local Group.

Image courtesy of David Malin/Institute de Astrofisicas de Canarias/Royal Greenwich Observatory

M 81: a large spiral galaxy (Sb).

Image courtesy of AURA/NOAO/NSF

NGC 2997: a large face-on spiral galaxy (Sc).

Image courtesy of David Malin/Anglo-Australian Observatory

NGC 1365: a barred spiral galaxy (SBbc)

Image courtesy of David Malin/Anglo-Australian Observatory

NGC 3351 (=M 95): a barred spiral galaxy (SBb)

Image courtesy of David Malin/Anglo-Australian Observatory

Irregulars

irregular galaxy

Irregular galaxies have no definite structure. The stars are bunched up but the patches are randomly distributed throughout the galaxy. Some irregulars have a lot of dust and gas so star formation is possible. Some are undergoing a burst of star formation now, so many H II regions are seen in them. Others have very little star formation going on in them (even some of those with a lot of gas and dust still in them).

Most irregulars are small and faint. The dwarf irregulars may be the most common type of galaxy in the universe (or maybe the dwarf ellipticals are). The estimates of the number of dwarf irregulars and dwarf ellipticals are based on the proportions of these types of galaxies in nearby groups. The dwarf galaxies far away are too faint to be seen and are, therefore, overlooked in surveys of the sky. Perhaps if the dwarf galaxies were brighter, Hubble would have arranged the galaxies in a different sequence instead of the two-pronged sequence. Examples of irregular galaxies are the Large and Small Magellanic Clouds (two small irregulars that orbit the Milky Way).

15.1.2   Positions on The Sky

dust blocks view

Galaxies are distributed fairly uniformly across the sky. Approximately the same number of galaxies are seen in every direction you look except for a narrow 5 to 10 degree band along the Milky Way's mid-plane. That narrow band, called the "zone of avoidance", is created by the dust in the disk (see the first figure in the previous chapter). The galaxies along that line-of-sight would be visible if the dust were not there. Radio waves are not affected by the dust and radio surveys show that there are, in fact, galaxies in the direction of the Milky Way's mid-plane.

galaxies clump together

The distribution of galaxies is not perfectly smooth. They clump together into loose groups. If you focus on just the galaxy positions on the sky, you get just a two-dimensional picture. Finding the distances to the galaxies allows you to get a three-dimensional view of the galaxy positions. Three-dimensional maps of the universe have revealed surprisingly large structures in the universe. Galaxies like to group together and those groups, in turn, congregate together.

Vocabulary

elliptical galaxy	irregular galaxy	spiral galaxy

Review Questions

1. What is a typical size of a **galaxy**? What is a typical number of stars in a galaxy? How do you know? What holds them all together?

2. What separates a cluster of stars from a galaxy?

3. What are four basic distinguishing characteristics between a **spiral galaxy** and an **elliptical galaxy**? What kind of galaxy do we live in?

4. What is the most common type of galaxy? How does their proportion in the universe compare with the proportion of them shown in astronomy books? Explain any differences there may be.

5. Why are **irregular galaxies** called irregulars?

6. Why do you see more galaxies when you look in a direction perpendicular to the Galactic plane than when you look along Galactic plane?

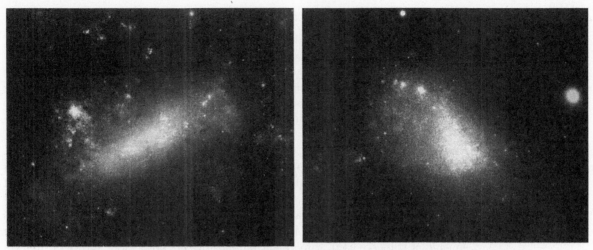

The Large Magellanic Cloud (left) and the Small Magellanic Cloud (right) are dwarf irregular galaxies and are satellites of the Milky Way.

Images courtesy of David Malin/Anglo-Australian Observatory/Royal Observatory, Edinburgh

NGC 6822 (left) and IC 5152 (right) are dwarf irregular galaxies in the Local Group.

Images courtesy of David Malin/Anglo-Australian Observatory

NGC 1313: a starburst galaxy also called a barred spiral galaxy (SBc).

Image courtesy of David Malin/Anglo-Australian Observatory

M 82: a starburst galaxy.

Image courtesy of NASA/ESA/Hubble Heritage Team (STScI/AURA)

15.1.3   Distances to Galaxies

Just like you found for the determination of stellar properties, finding the distance to the galaxies is essential for comparing the galaxies against each other. In order to determine the luminosities and masses of the galaxies and the distribution of the mass inside the galaxies, you must first know the distances to them. Is that galaxy in your telescope bright because it is producing a lot of energy or because it is close to us? Are the stars moving quickly in a galaxy because the combined mass is large or because the distances inside the galaxy are small? You need to find the distance to the galaxy to be sure.

standard candle method

One method of determining the distance uses the period-luminosity relation of Cepheid variable stars to derive the distance from the apparent brightness of the Cepheids (section 14.2.1). This works for the nearby galaxies. To find the distance to galaxies farther away, other *standard candle* techniques involving objects more luminous than Cepheids like Type Ia supernova explosions (section 13.3.3) or supergiant stars are used. Supergiant luminosities are not as well known or uniform as the Type Ia supernova, so astronomers prefer to use the Type Ia supernova to derive the distances to the very distant galaxies.

spectral line width method

Another method uses the width of a galaxy's spectral lines. The width of the absorption lines from the stars or the radio emission lines from the gas in a galaxy depend on the amount of stellar motion in the galaxy. Most galaxies are too far away for us to resolve the fine-scale details of the internal motions in the galaxies. The spectrum of far away galaxies is from the *combined* motions of all of the material in them.

Blue-shifted and red-shifted lines from individual stars in the galaxy blend together to form broadened absorption lines in the galaxy's spectrum.

If the spread in velocities is greater, the blended absorption lines are fatter. This happens for the more massive and luminous galaxies.

Some stars in a far away galaxy are moving toward us, so their absorption lines will be blueshifted. Other stars will have redshifted lines because they are moving away from us. The resulting spectral lines from the entire galaxy blend together to form a FAT line. The same effect is seen with the gas motions (caused by heat and rotation) inside a single star or gas cloud in our galaxy. The more random motion there is in an elliptical galaxy, the greater the spread in the distribution of velocities and the fatter the resulting galaxy spectral lines will be. More massive galaxies have more gravity so their stars are accelerated to faster orbital speeds. The more massive galaxies should have broader lines and if the luminosity correlates with the mass, the more massive galaxies should have greater luminosity.

Sandra Faber and Robert Jackson discovered in 1976 a simple relation between the spread of velocities (called the **velocity dispersion**) and the luminosity of elliptical galaxies. For the inner few kiloparsecs of the elliptical galaxies, the velocity dispersion $= 220 \times (L/L_*)^{0.25}$, where L_* is a characteristic galaxy luminosity (around 10 billion solar luminosities). This is known as the *Faber-Jackson relation.* An elliptical galaxy's luminosity can be found from the velocity dispersion of the stars in the central few kiloparsecs of the galaxy.

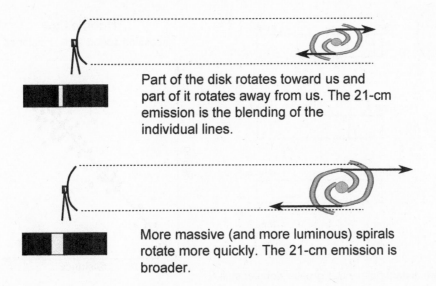

Part of the disk rotates toward us and part of it rotates away from us. The 21-cm emission is the blending of the individual lines.

More massive (and more luminous) spirals rotate more quickly. The 21-cm emission is broader.

In 1977 Brent Tully and Richard Fisher discovered a similar relation between the rotational velocity of the disk and the luminosity of a spiral galaxy. The rotational velocity is found from the 21-cm emission of the neutral atomic hydrogen gas in the outer parts of the disk. The rotation curve is flat in the outer parts of most galactic disks (dark matter!). The part of a spiral galaxy's disk that is rotating toward us will have its lines blueshifted. The part of the disk rotating away from us will have its lines redshifted. The 21-cm emission from a galaxy of small angular size will be the blended result of the emission from all parts of the disk. The faster the disk rotates, the broader the 21-cm emission line will be. The *Tully-Fisher relation* for the *infrared* luminosity is: circular velocity $= 220 \times (L/L_*)^{0.22}$. Infrared is used to lessen the effect of the dust in our galaxy and in the other spiral galaxy. The luminosity of the galaxy is found from the width of the 21-cm emission line and the distance is then derived using the apparent brightness and the inverse square law. The methods of determining the distances to the galaxies are summarized in the "Steps to the Hubble Constant" section.

15.1.4 Hubble-Lemaître Law

In 1914 *Vesto Slipher* (lived 1870–1963) announced his results from the spectra of over 40 spiral galaxies (at his time people thought the "spiral nebulae" were inside the Milky Way). He found that over 90% of the spectra showed redshifts which meant that they were moving away from us. Edwin Hubble and Milton Humason found distances to the spiral nebulae. When Hubble plotted the redshift vs. the distance of the galaxies, he found a surprising relation: *more distant galaxies are moving faster away from us.* Hubble first announced his findings at the National Academy of Sciences in 1929 and then Hubble and Humason followed up with a peer-reviewed article in the widely-read *Astrophysical Journal* in 1931: the recession speed $= H \times$ distance, where H is a number now called the *Hubble constant*. As described in chapter 16, Georges Lemaître explained how this arose from Einstein's

General Relativity, so this relation is called the **Hubble-Lemaître Law** and the *Hubble constant* is the slope of the line. The line goes through the origin (0,0) because that represents our home position (zero distance) and we are not moving away from ourselves (zero speed). Hubble and Humason's work provided convincing observational confirmation of the expansion of the universe discussed further in the next chapter.

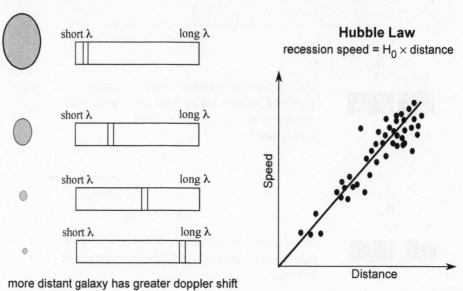

Hubble Law
recession speed = H_0 × distance

Speed

Distance

more distant galaxy has greater doppler shift

H is the Hubble constant

how to use Hubble-Lemaître Law to get distances

If the distance is measured in units of megaparsecs (Mpc) and the recession speed is in kilometers/second (km/sec), the *Hubble constant* (the slope of the line) is between 70 and 80 km/sec/Mpc. This value is found by using the galaxies that have accurate distances measured (Cepheids, etc.) and dividing their recession speeds by their distances. It is easy to find the recession speeds of galaxies from their redshifts. The Hubble-Lemaître Law provides an easy way to measure the distances to even the farthest galaxies from the (recession speed/H). For example, if a galaxy has a redshift of 20,000 kilometers/second and H is set to 70 km/sec/Mpc, then the galaxy's distance = (20,000 km/sec)/(70 km/sec/Mpc) = 20,000/70 × [(km/sec)/(km/sec)] Mpc = 286 megaparsecs.

At first glance it looks like the Milky Way is at the center of the universe and it committed some galactic social blunder because all of the other galaxies are rushing away from it (there are a few true galactic friends like the Andromeda Galaxy that are approaching it). The Hubble-Lemaître Law shows that there is actually not a violation of the Copernican principle. Because the more distant galaxies move faster, this means that the galaxies (or galaxy clusters) are all moving away from each other—the universe is expanding uniformly. Every other galaxy or galaxy cluster is moving away from everyone else. Every galaxy would see the same Hubble-Lemaître Law.

uniform expansion

In the next chapter you will see that the expansion of the universe is the expansion of space itself—the galaxies are not moving through space, but, rather, they are being carried along with the expansion of space. For now, use the figure on the next page to see how a uniform expansion gives the Hubble-Lemaître Law. Since space itself expands, all distances will increase by the same *factor* in the same amount of time. Galaxy (a) is 10 megaparsecs from galaxy (b) and galaxy (c) is 10 megaparsecs from galaxy (b). If the Hubble constant this time is 77 km/sec/Mpc, then galaxy (a) sees galaxy (b) moving at 770 kilometers/second away from it and galaxy (c) is moving away from galaxy (b) at 770 kilometers/second. Astronomers on galaxy (a) will see the galaxy (c) moving away at (770 + 770) kilometers/second

how everyone gets the same Hubble-Lemaître Law

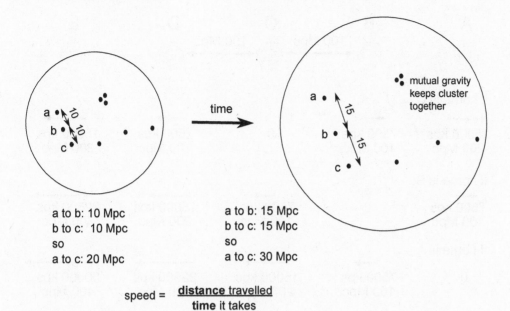

a to b: 10 Mpc
b to c: 10 Mpc
so
a to c: 20 Mpc

a to b: 15 Mpc
b to c: 15 Mpc
so
a to c: 30 Mpc

$$\text{speed} = \frac{\text{\underline{distance} travelled}}{\text{\textbf{time} it takes}}$$

Expansion of **space between** galaxies (or galaxy clusters) moves galaxies away from each other. If the time interval for the situation above is 6.5 billion years, then galaxy (b) appears to be moving at a speed of 5 Mpc/(6.5 billion yr) = 0.77 Mpc/by (= 770 km/sec) from galaxy (a). Galaxy (c) is **twice as far** and appears to be moving **twice as fast**: 10 Mpc/(6.5 billion yr) = 1.54 Mpc/by (= 1,540 km/sec).

= 1,540 kilometers/second twice as fast as galaxy (b), because galaxy (c) is at a distance of (10 + 10) megaparsecs from galaxy (a), twice as far as galaxy (b).

The galaxy (a) astronomers see the other galaxies moving away from them and their home galaxy appears to be at rest. Now jump to galaxy (c). To the astronomers on galaxy (c), galaxy (a) is moving away at 1,540 kilometers/second and galaxy (b) is moving away at 770 kilometers/second. Their home galaxy (c) appears to be at rest. You can use similar reasoning to show that everybody will also get the same *numerical* value for the Hubble constant. The figure above also illustrates another point about the expansion. Notice that the sizes of the dots and the size of the threesome group at center-top do not change. The galaxies themselves do not expand and the galaxies inside a cluster do not expand away from each other. On small size scales, the internal gravity of a galaxy or galaxy cluster prevents the expansion inside the galaxy or galaxy cluster. *The Hubble-Lemaître Law applies for only the very large distances.*

gravity keeps a galaxy & galaxy cluster from expanding internally— Hubble-Lemaître Law only for very large distances

Another example of how everyone will see the same Hubble-Lemaître Law is given in the figure at the top of the next page. Each of the galaxies in the figure is 100 million parsecs (about 300 million light years) apart from each other and the Hubble constant is set to 75 km/sec/Mpc here. If you choose galaxy C to be your home galaxy, then you will see galaxies B and D moving at 7,500 kilometers/second away from you because they are at a distance of 100 megaparsecs from you. Galaxies A and E are 100 megaparsecs from their closest neighbors, so they are moving away from them at 7,500 kilometers/second and 15,000 kilometers/second from galaxy C since they are each 200 megaparsecs from galaxy C. What would the galaxy speeds be if you chose galaxy D or galaxy E as your home galaxy?

A	B	C	D	E

| | | 100 Mpc | 100 Mpc | |

If home is C:

←	←		→	→
15000 kps	7500 kps	0	7500 kps	15000 kps
200 Mpc	100 Mpc		100 Mpc	200 Mpc

If home is B:

←		→	→	→
7500 kps	0	7500 kps	15000 kps	22500 kps
100 Mpc		100 Mpc	200 Mpc	300 Mpc

If home is A:

	→	→	→	→
0	7500 kps	15000 kps	22500 kps	30000 kps
	100 Mpc	200 Mpc	300 Mpc	400 Mpc

Uniform expansion—every distance expands by the same *factor*. Everybody sees the same Hubble Law at the same time interval after the expansion start.

15.1.5 Masses of Galaxies

The masses of galaxies are found from the orbital motion of their stars. Stars in a more massive galaxy will orbit faster than those in a lower mass galaxy because the greater gravity force of the massive galaxy will cause larger accelerations of its stars. By measuring the star speeds, you find out how much gravity there is in the galaxy. Since gravity depends on mass and distance, knowing the size of the star orbits enables you to derive the galaxy's mass.

rotation curve   For spiral galaxies the **rotation curve** is used to measure their masses like is done to find the mass of the Milky Way. The rotation curve shows how orbital speeds in a galaxy depend on their distance from the galaxy's center. The mass inside a given distance from the center = (orbital speed)^2×(distance from the center)$/G$. The orbital speed is found from the doppler shifts of the 21-cm line radiation from the atomic hydrogen gas. The *angular* distance of the piece of the disk from the center is measured, but to use the enclosed mass formula, the piece of the disk's actual *linear* distance from the center must be found.

why galaxy distance must be known to get galaxy mass   Remember way back in section 9.1.3 that the linear distance can be found from the angular distance if you know the distance *to* the object? The linear distance from the galaxy center = [2π×(distance *to* the galaxy)×(angular distance in degrees)]/360°. This is why you must first know the distance to a galaxy if you want to measure its mass.

For elliptical galaxies the width of the absorption lines from all of the stars blended together is used to measure the mass of elliptical galaxies. The width of the absorption lines depends on the spread of the distribution of the velocities—the **velocity dispersion**   **velocity dispersion**. The elliptical galaxy's mass = k×(velocity dispersion)^2×(the distance the stars are from the galaxy center)$/G$, where k is a factor that depends on the shape of the galaxy and the angle the galaxy is from Earth.

The stars and gas in almost all galaxies move much quicker than expected from the luminosity of the galaxies. In spiral galaxies, the rotation curve remains at about the same value at great distances from the center (it is said to be "flat").

This means that the enclosed mass continues to increase even though the amount of visible, luminous matter falls off at large distances from the center. In elliptical galaxies, the gravity of the visible matter is not strong enough to accelerate the stars as much as they are. Something else must be adding to the gravity of the galaxies without shining.

That something else is called **dark matter**—material that does not produce detectable amounts of light but does have a noticeable gravitational effect. Astronomers are not sure what the dark matter is. Possibilities range from large things like planets, brown dwarfs, white dwarfs, black holes to huge numbers of small things like neutrinos or other particles that have not been seen in our laboratories yet. For reasons to be explained in the next section and in the cosmology chapter, astronomers have figured out that the dark matter is a combination of all those things but the exotic particles must make up the vast majority of the dark matter. In fact, of the total matter in the universe, the overall mass of the exotic particles is five times the overall mass of the "ordinary matter" we are more familiar with (matter made of protons, neutrons, electrons, neutrinos, etc.). The nature of dark matter is one of the central problems in astronomy today. Although its nature is unknown, dark matter appears to be such an integral part of galaxies that the presence of dark matter is used to distinguish a small galaxy from a large globular cluster, both of which may have the same number of stars.

The possible discovery in 2018 that the small ultra diffuse galaxy (one with a very small number of stars per volume) 65 million light years from us called NGC 1052-DF2 has little to no dark matter was quite surprising. Perhaps it is "the exception that proves the rule" but the search is on for other small galaxies without dark matter. However, it is also possible that the lack of dark matter conclusion for NGC 1052-DF2 is incorrect because the motions of only ten globular clusters in the small galaxy were used to measure its mass. More objects are needed to make a more certain measurement of the galaxy's mass, so it is possible that the mass measurement was too low and that there is actually a significant amount of dark matter. Another independent method of measuring the galaxy's mass supports the view that this galaxy has little to no dark matter. Furthermore, using seven clusters in another galaxy, NGC 1052-DF4, the research team who made the NGC 1052-DF2 discovery found that NGC 1052-DF4 also appears to have no dark matter. The discovery of two galaxies without dark matter shows that dark matter can be found separately from ordinary matter and that fact argues against the view that dark matter is actually just a misunderstanding of how gravity works for ordinary matter on large scales. Another possibility is that the distances to the two small galaxies have not been measured correctly. If the two galaxies are actually closer to us, then their derived mass to luminosity ratio will be larger and dark matter will need to be present. More observations are needed!

15.1.6 Clusters of Galaxies

Galaxies love to cluster together! Their mutual gravity can draw galaxies together into a cluster that is several millions of light years across. Some clusters have only a handful of galaxies and are called **poor clusters**. Other clusters with hundreds to thousands of galaxies are called **rich clusters**. The low mass of a poor cluster prevents the cluster from holding onto its members tightly. The poor cluster tends to be a bit more irregular in shape than a rich cluster.

The Milky Way is part of a poor cluster called the *Local Group* (an imaginative name, yes?). The Local Group has two large spirals, one small spiral, two ellipticals, at least 19 irregulars, at least 17 dwarf ellipticals and at least 5 dwarf spheroidals (have lower luminosity than dwarf ellipticals and are spheroidal in shape; some lists will have some of the dwarf ellipticals listed as dwarf spheroidals). There may be

dark matter

small galaxy vs. large cluster of stars

two galaxies without dark matter?

poor cluster
rich cluster

Local Group

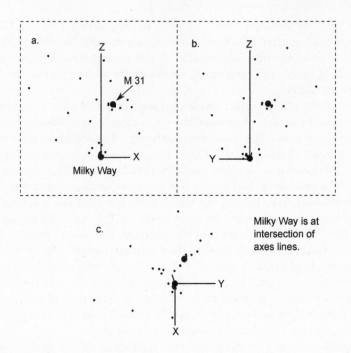

over 70 additional irregular and dwarf galaxies in the Local Group. The distribution of most of the confirmed Local Group galaxies is shown in the figure below. The Local Group is about 3 million light years across with the two large spirals, the Milky Way and Andromeda Galaxy, dominating the two ends. Each large spiral has several smaller galaxies orbiting them. The proportions of the different types of galaxies in the Local Group probably represents the number of the different types of galaxies in the rest of the universe. The small galaxies can be seen in the Local Group because they are close enough to us but the dwarf galaxies are hard to see in far away clusters. See the textbook's website for a link to a better looking map of the Local Group.

Virgo Cluster

The closest large cluster to us is the moderately-rich cluster called the *Virgo Cluster* because it is in the direction of the Virgo constellation. It has many hundreds of galaxies (mostly spirals and irregulars) distributed into an irregular shape about 10 million light years across. It is about 49 to 59 million light years from us. Some ellipticals are present in the central part of the cluster including a giant elliptical at the center (M87) that has become so large by gobbling up nearby galaxies that were attracted by its enormous gravity. The total mass of the Virgo cluster is large enough that its gravity pulls nearby groups of galaxies (including the Local Group) toward it.

Coma Cluster

A rich cluster is seen in the Coma constellation—the *Coma Cluster*. It has thousands of galaxies (mostly ellipticals and S0 spirals) in a large, spherically-shaped cluster about 300 million light years from us. It is at least ten million light years across. The elliptical galaxies congregate toward the central regions while the few spirals present in the cluster are found on the outskirts. Two giant ellipticals (NGC 4874 & NGC 4889) occupy the central part of the cluster. Like M87 in the Virgo Cluster, they have grown very large from pulling in galaxies that were unfortunate to have strayed too close to escape the giant ellipticals' gravity. Other rich clusters show the same segregation of the spirals from the ellipticals as the Coma Cluster. Ellipticals gather together in the center of clusters while spirals prefer to stay close to the periphery.

The center of the Virgo cluster has three giant ellipticals,
M 87 (bottom left corner) and M 84, M 86 (center right).
M 86 may be a lenticular S0 type instead.

Image courtesy of David Malin/Anglo-Australian Observatory/
Royal Observatory, Edinburgh

The Coma cluster is a rich galaxy cluster with
thousands of galaxies.

Image courtesy of AURA/NOAO/NSF

The Hercules cluster is a poor galaxy cluster with
less than a hundred galaxies.

Image courtesy of AURA/NOAO/NSF

15.1.7   Dark Matter in Galaxy Clusters

Galaxy clusters provide another probe of dark matter. Much like is done in measuring the masses of galaxies from the motions of the stars and gas clouds in them, you can use the motions of the galaxies in the clusters to measure the masses of the galaxy clusters. What you find is galaxy cluster members are moving too fast to be gravitationally bound unless there is unseen mass. The reasonable assumption is that we do not live at a special time, so the galaxies in the cluster must have always been close to each other. The large velocities of the galaxies in the clusters are produced by more gravity force than can be explained with the gravity of the visible (either shining or blocking light) matter in the galaxies. The extra gravity is supplied by the dark matter.

Astronomers have found that galaxy clusters have a lot of very hot gas (i.e., gas made of very fast moving particles) in them with about two-thirds of it in between the galaxy members of the cluster. This gas is so hot that it emits in the X-ray band. The gravity of the galaxy clusters also gathers up gas and the gas heats up from the friction of the intergalactic gas particles bumping into each other. Again, we assume that we do not live at a special time, so to have kept the very fast moving particles around, there needs to be extra gravity supplied by the dark matter.

An independent way of measuring the mass of individual galaxies and galaxy clusters uses the gravitational lensing effect described in chapter 6. The matter in a nearby object stretches the spacetime around the object so as light from a distant object passes through that stretched spacetime, it follows a curved path. The more mass there is, the greater is the stretching of spacetime. If the lensing effect is strong, then multiple images of a distant galaxy will be produced and the separation angle between the multiple images gives us the mass of the lensing object (in this case, the closer galaxy or galaxy cluster). If the lensing is weaker, multiple images of the distant galaxy will not be seen so the mass of an individual nearby lensing object (a galaxy) cannot be easily measured. However, if the light from many distant galaxies passes through the stretched spacetime of a nearby galaxy cluster, then the mass of the galaxy cluster can be derived from a careful analysis of the ensemble of warped shapes and their orientations. One example cluster is Abell 1689 shown on the next page. The gravitational lensing can also sometimes magnify the light of an otherwise too-faint, very distant galaxy enough for us to see it—a bonus natural telescope! The cluster Abell 1689 magnified the infrared light of an infant galaxy from 12.8 billion years in the past enough to just barely be detected by the infrared camera on the Hubble Space Telescope and by the Spitzer Space Telescope. More recent lensing discoveries have found lensed infant galaxies from even further in the past.

Gravitational lensing of the light from distant galaxies and quasars by closer galaxies or galaxy clusters enables us to calculate the amount of mass in the closer galaxy or galaxy cluster from the amount of bending of the light. The derived mass is greater than the amount of mass in the visible matter. Inventorying all of the ordinary matter in the lensing galaxy clusters (those that lens the light from distant galaxies) and comparing it to the total mass of the galaxy clusters gives a five-to-one ratio of dark matter to ordinary matter. An added feature of gravitational lensing is that it reveals dark matter even where there is no ordinary matter present so gravitational lensing can be used to map the distribution of dark matter within AND beyond the extent of the glowing, ordinary matter.

When we do a careful accounting of all of the ordinary matter that can respond to electromagnetism (matter made of protons, neutrons, electrons, etc. either making light or blocking it), we find that the ordinary matter makes up less than 20% of the gravity of the overall matter and the remaining gravity seems to be from exotic particles predicted by particle theory but not yet discovered in our particle

The very massive galaxy cluster Abell 1689 with a number of curved blue and red streaks caused by the gravitational lensing of the light from distant galaxies behind the cluster. The amount of lensing depends on the total mass of the foreground cluster (ordinary matter + dark matter). The light from distant galaxies can be magnified enough to make otherwise too faint galaxies become visible—a bonus natural telescope! Abell 1689 is 2.2 billion light years away.

Image taken with the Advanced Camera for Surveys on the Hubble Space Telescope. Courtesy of NASA, N. Benitez (JHU), T. Broadhurst (Racah Institute of Physics/The Hebrew University), H. Ford (JHU), M. Clampin (STScI), G. Hartig (STScI), G. Illingworth (UCO/Lick Observatory), the ACS Science Team and ESA. STScI-PRC03-01a

experiments such as at Fermilab and the Large Hadron Collider. The mass ratio of exotic particles to ordinary matter is five to one. Stronger evidence for the five-to-one mass ratio comes from looking at relics of the early universe as explained in the cosmology chapter.

15.1.8 Superclusters

The clustering phenomenon does not stop with galaxies. Galaxy clusters attract each other to produce **superclusters** of tens to hundreds of clusters. Their mutual gravity binds them together into long filaments (thin, stringlike structures) 300 to 900 million light years long, 150 to 300 million light years wide, and 15 to 30 million light years thick on average. The discovery of these huge structures was made recently from years of taking doppler shifts of thousands of galaxies. The doppler

supercluster

voids shifts of the galaxies were converted to distances using the Hubble Law. Between the filamentary superclusters are HUGE voids with very few (if any) galaxies. The voids are typically 150 million light years across.

Two pioneers in the mapping of the structure of the universe are Margaret Geller and *John Huchra* (lived 1948–2010). They and their students took thousands of spectra of galaxies along thin pie-shaped slices of the sky over 15 years to produce a map with 2 slices extending out about 400 million light years. It would take much too long to take spectra of galaxies in every direction in space, so astronomers map the universe in slices. In 2003, the Anglo-Australian Observatory released a much larger survey ("2dF survey") of over 221,000 galaxies in two slices that extend over 1.5 billion light years in a two-degree field of the sky. The 2dF survey system could

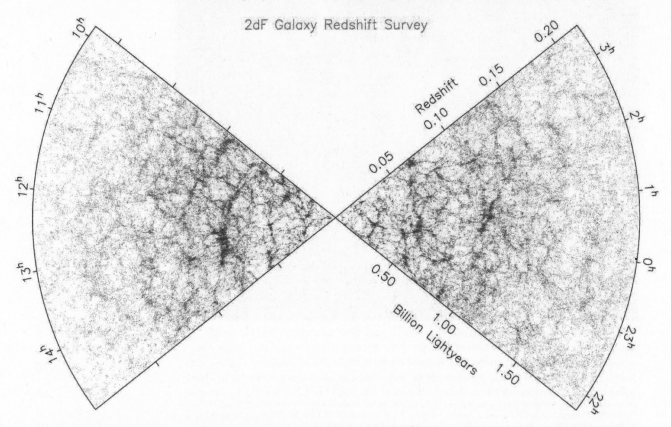

Two 3D "slices" of the nearby part of the universe from the 2dF Galaxy Redshift Survey. The distribution of galaxies is not random or uniform: galaxies cluster together and galaxy clusters are close to other galaxy clusters—superclusters. Galaxy superclusters form long, narrow bands with large voids between them. Each dot is a galaxy. There are over 221,000 galaxies! Image courtesy of 2dF survey team at the Anglo-Australian Observatory.

sudsy, lacy structure take the spectra of 400 objects simultaneously so it took them "only" 5 years to complete the survey. The arrangement of the superclusters and voids looks like a bunch of soap bubbles or swiss cheese with the galaxies on the borders of the huge holes. Although the picture above is only a two-dimensional version of the three-dimensional map, you can still see the lacy, foamy structure. In 2009, AAO completed a six-degree field galaxy survey called 6dF Galaxy Survey that did not go quite as deep but gave greater detail of the local structure. See the textbook's website for the link to the 6DFGS Gallery for their slice maps.

SDSS The Sloan Digital Sky Survey (SDSS) greatly expanded the volume to a million galaxies in one-quarter of the entire sky. SDSS measured spectra of more than 930,000 galaxies and 120,000 quasars as well as mapping the structure of the Milky Way by taking spectra of 240,000 stars and finding Type Ia supernovae to help us measure the history of the expansion of the universe. The SDSS galaxy surveys also showed the same sort of lacy, foamy large-scale structure—see one of the slice maps below. The current SDSS-IV project is focusing on three areas: measuring the expansion history of the Universe through 80% of its history to improve constraints on dark energy (section 16.3.2); measuring the structure, dynamics, and chemical evolution of the Milky Way; and making spectral measurements across the face of 10,000 nearby galaxies. The fourth phase finished in 2020.

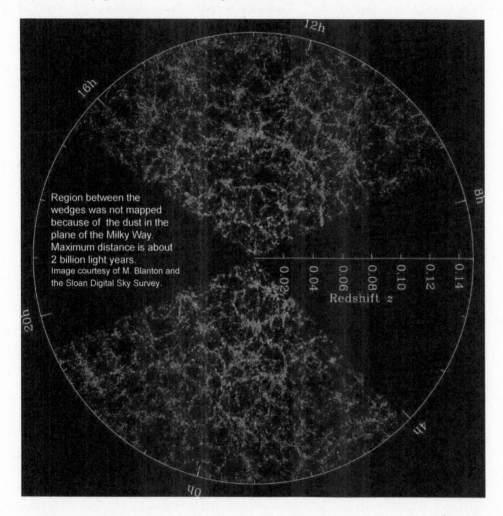

Region between the wedges was not mapped because of the dust in the plane of the Milky Way. Maximum distance is about 2 billion light years. Image courtesy of M. Blanton and the Sloan Digital Sky Survey.

What produces the long thin strands of clusters around the huge bubbles of empty space? Obviously, gravity is the force at work, but how has it worked to produce these structures? Dark matter must play a significant role but how it does that is not completely known. Astronomers are using powerful supercomputers to simulate the gravitational interactions of hundreds of millions of particles and they program guesses of the behavior of dark matter into the simulation code. The simulations are able to produce the filamentary structure and voids (see the textbook's website for pictures). The dark matter forms a web structure and the galaxies made of ordinary visible matter are found where the dark matter is densest.

The dark matter behavior that fits the observed galaxy clustering best comes from dark matter made of particles that are massive and weakly interacting, meaning that they do not feel the stronger forces like electromagnetism or the nuclear forces and respond only to gravity. Because ordinary matter can radiate its energy away, ordinary matter is able to form more concentrated clumps than dark matter can, so galaxies and galaxy clusters are embedded within larger dark matter clumps.

cold dark matter

WIMPs

Recall that the speed of the particles in an object slows down as the object's temperature decreases—as the object cools down. Since massive particles will move relatively slowly, the massive dark matter particle is called "cold dark matter" and creative astronomers who like acronyms have coined the term "WIMPs" for these particles which means "weakly- interacting massive particles". Neutrinos have such a small mass that they move too quickly to form the galaxy cluster and supercluster structures we see (... their masses are too wimpy to be WIMPs). Neutrinos would be a form of "hot dark matter". There are no particles in the Standard Model of Particle Physics that are WIMPs, so the nature of dark matter has been one major problem pushing physicists to explore extensions of the Standard Model.

15.1.9 Galaxy Origins

"top-down" model

All galaxies began forming at about the same time approximately 13 billion years ago. The origin of galaxies and how they changed over billions of years is an active field of research in astronomy today. Models for galaxy formation have been of two basic types: "top-down" and "bottom-up". The "top-down" model on the origin of the galaxies says that they formed from huge gas clouds larger than the resulting galaxy. The clouds began collapsing because their internal gravity was strong enough to overcome the pressure in the cloud. If the gas cloud was slowly rotating, then the collapsing gas cloud formed most of its stars before the cloud could flatten into a disk. The result was an elliptical galaxy. If the gas cloud was rotating faster, then the collapsing gas cloud formed a disk before most of the stars were made. The result was a spiral galaxy. The rate of star formation *may* be the determining factor in what type of galaxy will form. But, perhaps the situation is reversed: the type of galaxy determines the rate of star formation. Which is the "cause" and which is the "effect"?

A more recent variation of the "top-down" model says that there were extremely large gas clouds that fragmented into smaller clouds. Each of the smaller clouds then formed a galaxy. This explains why galaxies are grouped in clusters and even clusters of galaxy clusters (superclusters). However, the model predicts a very long time for the collapse of the super-large clouds and fragmentation into individual galaxy clouds. There should still be galaxies forming today. Astronomers looking for these nearby young galaxies focus their attention on the galaxies with very small amounts of "metals" (elements heavier than helium), particularly those with low percentages of oxygen. Recall from section 13.1.3 that the metals are made from the stars and oxygen is the third most abundant element in the universe. Younger galaxies with younger generations of stars will have less pollution of metals in them.

The first nearby oxygen-poor galaxy discovered is "I Zwicky 18", just 60 million light years away. It has just 2.6% the amount of oxygen as the Milky Way and appears to have begun forming stars only 500 million years ago. However, further observations have revealed it does have much older stars as well and we're seeing it undergo a burst of star formation now. Its oxygen-poor composition may be due to unpolluted gas falling into the galaxy.

Another even nearer oxygen-poor galaxy, Leo P, is just 5 million light years away and has a very low star formation rate, just 1/50,000 the rate of the Milky Way. Like I Zwicky 18, Leo P also contains very old stars as well. Due to its small mass, Leo P wasn't able to hold on to its metals as supernovae blasted the metals away. It still has gas in it to make stars because it hasn't passed close to a large galaxy and had the gas stolen yet. The current record-holder for lack of oxygen is J0811+4730 with just 1.7% the amount of oxygen as the Milky Way. It is 620 million light years away and it is undergoing a burst of star formation now. Rather than being truly young galaxies, these and other oxygen-poor galaxies have kept low levels of metals because of their environment and small mass. Astronomers are now using these oxygen-poor galaxies to better understand how the universe's first galaxies formed stars billions of years ago. Observations and computer simulations show that the "bottom-up" model is how galaxies developed.

The "bottom-up" model builds galaxies from the merging of smaller clumps about the size of a million solar masses (the sizes of the globular clusters). These clumps would have been able to start collapsing when the universe was still very young. Then galaxies would be drawn into clusters and clusters into superclusters by their mutual gravity. This model predicts that there should be many more small galaxies than large galaxies—that is observed to be true. The dwarf irregular galaxies may be from cloud fragments that did not get incorporated into larger galaxies. Also, the galaxy clusters and superclusters should still be in the process of forming—observations suggest this to be true, as well.

"bottom-up"

hierarchical clustering

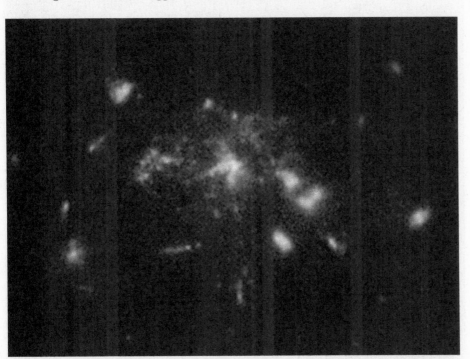

The large "Spiderweb Galaxy" under assembly by the merging of smaller galaxies. We see it as it was only 3 billion years after the beginning of the universe. Note the small "tadpole" and "chain" galaxies that are merging together as the "bottom-up" model predicts. Courtesy of NASA, ESA, G. Miley & R. Overzier (Leiden Observatory), and the ACS Science Team

Astronomers are now exploring formation models with supercomputer simulations that incorporate the dark matter which makes up most of the matter in the universe. Huge dark matter clumps the size of superclusters gather together under the action of gravity into a network of filaments to make the "cosmic web" described in the previous section. Where the dark matter filaments intersect, regular matter concentrates into galaxies and galaxy clusters. The densest places with many intersecting filaments would have had more rapid star formation to make the elliptical galaxies while the lower density concentrations along more isolated filaments would have made the spiral galaxies and dwarf galaxies. In such a model, the visible galaxies ablaze in starlight are like the tip of an iceberg—the visible matter is at the very densest part of much larger dark matter chunks. Some dark matter clumps may have cold hydrogen and helium gas making "dark galaxies" that haven't become concentrated enough to start star formation.

A dark matter map was published at the beginning of 2007 that probed the dark matter distribution over a large expanse of sky and depth (distance—see the

"Distribution of Dark Matter" figure below). The map is large enough and has high enough resolution to show the dark matter becoming more concentrated with time. The map stretches halfway back to the beginning of the universe. It also shows the visible matter clumping at the densest areas of the dark matter filaments (see the "Distribution of Visible and Dark Matter" figure on the next page). The dark matter distribution was measured by the weak gravitational lensing of the light from visible galaxies by the dark matter (see chapter 6).

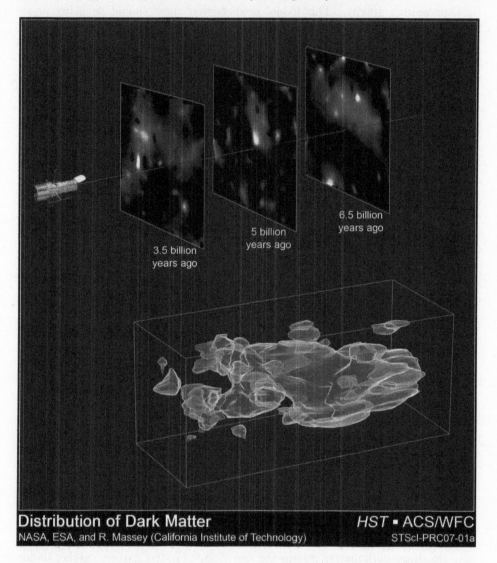

Distribution of Dark Matter
NASA, ESA, and R. Massey (California Institute of Technology)
HST • ACS/WFC
STScI-PRC07-01a

Galaxy Collisions and Mergers

Modern research into galaxy formation is also exploring the role that mergers and collisions of galaxies plays in the structure of galaxies. The distances between galaxies is large, but compared to the size of the galaxies, the distances are not extremely large. Stars inside a galaxy do not collide because the distances between them are hundreds of thousands to millions of times larger than the sizes of the stars (recall the solar system as a quarter coin scale model from the previous chapter). The distances between galaxies are only a few tens of times bigger than the galaxy sizes. The Milky Way has several small galaxies orbiting it that are one to two Milky Way diameters away. The closest large galaxy, the Andromeda Galaxy, is

Distribution of Visible and Dark Matter · Cosmic Evolution Survey
Hubble Space Telescope · Advanced Camera for Surveys

Visible (Baryonic) Matter

Dark Matter

NASA, ESA, and R. Massey (California Institute of Technology)   STScI-PRC07-01b

only about 30 Milky Way diameters away. Galaxies in rich clusters are closer to each other than that.

Collisions take place over very long timescales compared to the length of our lifetime—several tens of millions of years. In order to study the collisions, astronomers use powerful computers to simulate the gravitational interactions between galaxies. The computer can run through a simulation in several hours to a few days depending on the computer hardware and the number of interacting points. The results are checked with observations of galaxies in different stages of interaction. Note that this is the same process used to study the evolution of stars. The physics of stellar interiors are input into the computer model and the entire star's life cycle is simulated in a short time. Then the results are checked with observations of stars in different stages of their life. *use computer simulations*

In the past, computer simulations used several million points to represent a galaxy to save on computer processing time. A simulation of several million points could take many weeks to process. However, galaxies are made of billions to trillions of stars, so each point in the simulation actually represented large clusters of stars. The simulations were said to be of "low resolution" because many individual stars were smeared together to make one mass point in the simulation. The resolution of a computer simulation does affect the result, but it is not known how much of the result is influenced by the resolution of the simulation and how much the ignorance of the physics plays a role. Computer hardware speeds and the programming techniques have greatly improved, so astronomers are now getting to the point where they can run simulations with several billion mass points in a few weeks time. The computer simulations are also now incorporating more physical effects than just gravity and simplified hydrodynamics (gas motion) such as star formation, supernovae, formation of very large black holes at the centers of galaxies, electromagnetic fields, and other processes associated with ordinary matter. While dark matter makes up most of the matter in the universe and acts by the force of gravity alone, it turns out that smaller-scale effects from ordinary matter can make a significant impact on the structure and evolution of galaxies and clusters, much like differences in seasonings and leavening can greatly change the taste and texture of a baked clump of flour. *resolution of simulations*

When two galaxies collide the stars will pass right on by each other without colliding. The distances between stars is so large compared to the sizes of the stars *stars do not hit each other*

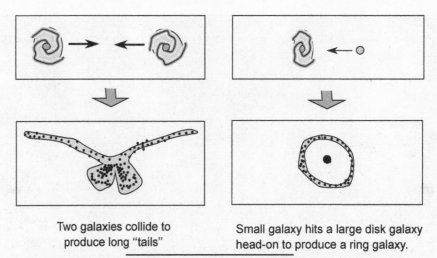

Two galaxies collide to produce long "tails"

Small galaxy hits a large disk galaxy head-on to produce a ring galaxy.

Galaxies collide, but stars do not. Their **gravity** radically changes the star orbits. Gas clouds do collide, so rapid burst of star formation results (***starburst galaxies***).

that star-star collisions are very rare when the galaxies collide. The orbits of the stars can be radically changed, though. Gravity is a long-range force and is the primary agent of the radical changes in a galaxy's structure when another galaxy comes close to it. Computer simulations show that a small galaxy passing close to a disk galaxy can trigger the formation of spiral arms in the disk galaxy. Alas! The simulations show that spiral arms formed this way do not last long. Part of the reason *may* be in the low resolution of the simulations.

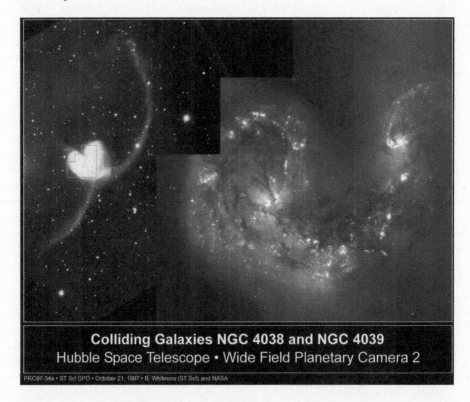

Colliding Galaxies NGC 4038 and NGC 4039
Hubble Space Telescope • Wide Field Planetary Camera 2

PRC97-34a • ST ScI OPO • October 21, 1997 • B. Whitmore (ST ScI) and NASA

The stars may be flung out from the colliding galaxies to form long arcs. Several examples of very distorted galaxies are seen with long antenna-like arcs. Above is a picture of the Antennae Galaxies (NGC 4038 & NGC 4039) as viewed from the ground (left) and from the Hubble Space Telescope (right). A large number of H II regions have been produced from the collision. The text website has a movie of a computer simulation showing two galaxies colliding to produce long antenna-like arcs. In some collisions a small galaxy will collide head-on with a large galaxy and punch a hole in the large galaxy. The stars are not destroyed. The star orbits in the large galaxy are shifted to produce a ring around a compact core. Below is a picture of the Cartwheel Galaxy as viewed with the Hubble Space Telescope. A large spiral was hit face-on by one of the two galaxies to the right of the ring. The insets on the left show details of the clumpy ring structure and the core of the Cartwheel.

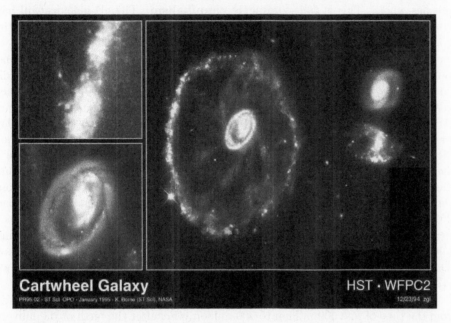

Cartwheel Galaxy HST · WFPC2
PR95-02 · ST ScI OPO · January 1996 · K. Borne (ST ScI), NASA   12/23/94 zg

The gas clouds in galaxies are much larger than the stars, so they will very likely hit the clouds in another galaxy when the galaxies collide. When the clouds hit each other, they compress and collapse to form a lot of stars in a short time. Galaxies undergoing such a burst of star formation are called **starburst galaxies** and they can be the among the most luminous of galaxies.

gas clouds hit each other

starburst galaxy

Though typical galaxy collisions take place over what seems a long timescale to us, they are short compared to the lifetimes of galaxies. Some collisions are gentler and longer-lasting. In such collisions the galaxies can merge. Computer simulations show that the big elliptical galaxies can form from the collisions of galaxies, including spiral galaxies. Elliptical galaxies formed in this way have faint shells of stars or dense clumps of stars that are probably debris left from the merging process. Mergers of galaxies to form ellipticals is probably why ellipticals are common in the central parts of rich clusters. The spirals in the outer regions of the clusters have not undergone any major interactions yet and so retain their original shape. Large spirals can merge with small galaxies and retain a spiral structure.

mergers

Some satellite galaxies of the Milky Way are in the process of merging with our galaxy. The dwarf elliptical galaxy SagDEG in the direction of the Milky Way's center is stretched and distorted from the tidal effects of the Milky Way's strong gravity. The Canis Major Dwarf galaxy about 25,000 light years from us is in a more advanced stage of "digestion" by the Milky Way—just the nucleus of a former galaxy is all that is left. A narrow band of neutral hydrogen from other satellite galaxies, the Magellanic Clouds, appears to be trailing behind those galaxies as they orbit the Milky Way. The band of hydrogen gas, called the "Magellanic Stream", extends almost 90° across the sky away from the Magellanic Clouds and may be the result of an encounter they experienced with the Milky Way about 200 million years ago. At least eight other streams in the Milky Way from other dwarf galaxies have been found. The Andromeda Galaxy and the Milky Way will collide with each other 4.5 billion years from now and over the following two billion years after that initial encounter, they will merge to form an elliptical galaxy. The smaller spiral galaxy of the Local Group, the Triangulum Galaxy (M33) will also probably merge with us after that.

galactic cannibalism

The giant ellipticals (called "cD galaxies") found close to the centers of galaxy clusters, like M 87 in the Virgo Cluster, were formed from the collision and merging of galaxies. When the giant elliptical gets large enough, it can gobble up nearby galaxies whole. This is called **galactic cannibalism**. The cD galaxies will have several bright concentrations in them instead of just one at the center. The other bright points are the cores of other galaxies that have been gobbled up.

more collisions in early universe

early galaxies different than modern galaxies: universe has changed!

If collisions and mergers do happen, then more interactions should be seen when looking at regions of space at very great distances. When you look out to great distances, you see the universe as it was long ago because the light from those places takes such a long time to reach us over the billions of light years of intervening space. Edwin Hubble's discovery of the expansion of the universe means that the galaxies were once much closer together, so collisions should have been more common. Pictures from the Hubble Space Telescope of very distant galaxies (seeing them as they were long ago) show more distorted shapes, bent spiral arms, and irregular fragments than in nearby galaxies (seen in a more recent stage of their evolution). On the next page is the "Hubble Ultra Deep Field" (HUDF)—a narrow look back through time past many intervening galaxies to the universe as it looked billions of years ago near the start of the expansion. There were more distorted (interacting) galaxies back then! The larger fuzzy patches in the picture are closer galaxies and the smallest bright points are very distant galaxies. It is a 278-hour exposure (over 412 orbits) of a single piece of sky in the Fornax constellation.

In early 2010, astronomers announced that they were able to detect galaxies from the time of just 600 million to 800 million years after the birth of the universe (the Big Bang) using the new camera on the Hubble Space Telescope. A later study in 2012 found a cluster of galaxies beginning to form 600 million years after the Big Bang. Another study in 2012 called the Extreme Deep Field honed in on the center of the HUDF and detected galaxies forming just 450 million years after the Big Bang. A very deep look with the Spitzer Space Telescope in 2019 at two other patches of sky near the HUDF patch was able to get spectra of the H II regions (emission nebulae) in 135 galaxies at a stage less than a billion years after the Big Bang. Although these nebulae glow in the visible band, the light has been greatly redshifted into the infrared by the expansion of the universe to be detectable by Spitzer. It found that the early galaxies produced much more ionizing radiation that do modern galaxies. A detailed analysis of these early galaxies to figure out why they are so different than modern galaxies will have to wait until the much larger James Webb Space Telescope is trained on them.

The formation of galaxies is one major field of current research in astronomy. Astronomers are close to solving the engineering problem of computer hardware speeds and simulation techniques so that they can focus on the physical principles of galaxy formation. One major roadblock in their progress is the lack of understanding of the role that dark matter plays in the formation and interaction of galaxies. Since the dark matter's composition and how far out it extends in the galaxies and galaxy clusters is only beginning to be mapped, it is not known how to best incorporate it into the computer simulations. Faced with such ignorance of the nature of dark matter, astronomers try inputting different models of the dark matter into the simulations and see if the results match the observations. As mentioned in the previous section, models that use "cold dark matter" of "WIMPs" provide the

Hubble Ultra Deep Field
Hubble Space Telescope • Advanced Camera for Surveys

NASA, ESA, S. Beckwith (STScI) and the HUDF Team   STScI-PRC04-07a

best fit to the observed structures. The recent discovery of "dark energy" (see chapter 16) is another major unknown in galaxy evolution models though its effects may be more important to the future of the universe than to the origin and early history of the galaxies in which gravity and gas dynamics played the significant role. On the observational side, the earliest stages of galaxy formation can be studied spectroscopically only in the infrared due to the expansion of the universe, so large infrared space telescopes like Webb (launch date in early 2021) or the Wide Field Infrared Survey Telescope (launch date in 2025) are required to test the computer models.

There will be many new fundamental discoveries made in the coming years, so this section of the textbook will surely undergo major revisions of the content. Although the content of the knowledge will be changed and expanded, the process of figuring out how things work will be the same. Theories and models will be created from the past observations and the fundamental physical laws and principles. Predictions will be made and then tested against new observations. Nature will

facts always updated but science process remains the same

veto our ideas or say that we are on the right track. Theories will be dropped, modified, or broadened. Having to reject a favorite theory can be frustrating but the excitement of meeting the challenge of the mystery and occasionally making a breakthrough in our understanding motivates astronomers and other scientists to keep exploring.

Vocabulary

dark matter	galactic cannibalism	Hubble-Lemaître Law
poor cluster	rich cluster	rotation curve
starburst galaxy	supercluster	velocity dispersion

Review Questions

1. Why must the distance to a galaxy be known first before you can measure basic properties of the galaxy such as its luminosity, mass, and size?

2. What are the various ways you can find distances to the galaxies?

3. What do you find when you plot the redshifts of the galaxies vs. their distance from us? How does the speed of most galaxies vary with increasing distance from our galaxy?

4. How does the **Hubble-Lemaître Law** show that the universe is expanding?

5. How does the **Hubble-Lemaître Law** show that all of the galaxies are moving away from each other and that astronomers in every galaxy will see the same Hubble law?

6. How can you measure the masses of galaxies?

7. What is it about the motions of the stars in galaxies that indicates a large amount of **dark matter** is present?

8. What is a cluster of galaxies? Are we in one? What is the nearest large cluster of galaxies to us?

9. Why are collisions of galaxies much more common than collisions of stars?

10. How are spiral galaxies formed?

11. What two ways are there to create an elliptical galaxy?

12. What kind of galaxy is typically found near the center of a large cluster of galaxies? Why is that kind of galaxy so big?

13. Why is the spatial distribution of clusters of galaxies sometimes described as a foamy structure or like edges of soap bubbles? How do we know that the clusters have this spatial distribution?

15.2   Active Galaxies

When the universe was younger, some galaxies produced a lot more radiation than galaxies do today. A *typical* galaxy shines with the energy from billions of stars and is tens of thousands of light years (or more) across. A peculiar group of galaxies are extremely luminous but very compact. The light from these *active galaxies* is produced by a strange process in the centers of the galaxies. Sometimes starburst galaxies are grouped with these peculiar galaxies, but here I will consider an "active galaxy" to be a galaxy with a very luminous nucleus. The great luminosity of starburst galaxies is not confined to their nucleus.

15.2.1   Quasars

The two basic things used for studying the far away galaxies are (1) the *data* encoded in the light received; and (2) our creative minds to interpret what is seen using the *laws of physics*. Some blue star-like objects appeared to violate those rules. Stars do not produce much energy in the radio band, so when strong radio emission coming from some blue stars was spotted in 1960, astronomers quickly took spectra of the stars in the visible (optical) band to find out the conditions in these strange objects. However, the pattern of lines did not match any of the lines seen in thousands of stellar spectra gathered over a hundred years. Furthermore, the spectra of the blue radio sources did not have absorption lines, but broad emission lines! What a mystery!

Which is the quasar and which is an ordinary star in our galaxy?
(The quasar is the bright one on the left.)
Image courtesy of C. Steidel (Cal Tech) and STScI/AURA/NASA

Maarten Schmidt solved the mystery in 1963. In order to figure out the structure of the atoms producing the bizarre spectra, he set out to construct an energy level diagram from the pattern of the emission lines. He made some mistakes in his calculations because his calculations were not showing the regularity he could clearly see in the spectrum of a radio source called 3C 273 (the 273rd object in the third Cambridge catalog of radio sources). As a test of the regularity he compared the spectrum of 3C 273 with the spectrum of hydrogen. He was shocked because the pattern was the same but greatly redshifted! 3C 273 is moving at a speed of 47,400 kilometers/second (almost 16% the speed of light!). The Hubble-Lemaître Law says that this blue radio object is far outside the Galaxy. The other radio "stars" are also at great distances from us. They are called *quasi-stellar radio sources* or **quasars** for short. Later, some other blue star-like objects at large redshifts were discovered to have no radio emission, but they are still called **quasars.** *large redshifts*

quasar

What is strange about the quasars is not their great distance, but, rather, their incredible luminosities. They are hundreds to thousands of times more luminous than ordinary galaxies. Yet, all of this energy is being produced in a small volume of space. Their luminosity varies on time scales of a few months to as short as a few days. Remember from the discussion of pulsars and black holes in chapter 13 *ultra-luminous but very compact* that the light fluctuation time scale from any object gives you an estimate of the *maximum* possible size of the object. The maximum size = (speed of light)×(light fluctuation time interval). The quasars that vary their light output over a few months are about the size of our solar system. This is tens of thousands of times smaller than a typical galaxy!

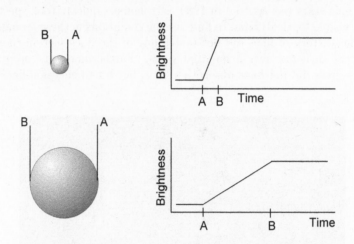

The light from side A reaches us before the light from side B so even if the object could brighten everywhere simultaneously, there is still a delay in brightening observed by us.

The shape of the continuous part of a quasar spectrum is also quite unusual (see figure below). Stars are luminous in primarily the visible (optical) band of the electromagnetic spectrum. The hottest stars also emit a significant fraction of their light in the ultraviolet band and the coolest stars emit a significant fraction of their light in the infrared band. Regardless of the star, though, the spectrum of a star, *and, hence, the spectrum of a normal galaxy*, rises to a peak at some wavelength determined by the temperature (remember Wien's law?) and drops off at wavelengths shorter or longer than the peak wavelength. Such a spectrum is called a *thermal spectrum* because it depends on just the temperature.

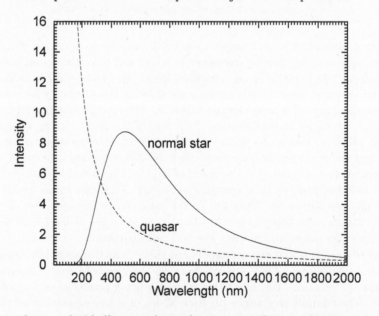

non-thermal spectrum   Quasars have a decidedly *non-thermal spectrum*: they are luminous in the X-rays, ultraviolet, visible, infrared, and radio bands. They have about the same power at all of the wavelengths down to the microwave wavelengths (shortwave radio wavelengths). The spectrum looks like the synchrotron radiation from charged particles spiraling around magnetic field lines at nearly the speed of light (remember the emission from pulsars?).

Perhaps the quasars are not as far away as the Hubble-Lemaître Law says from their redshifts. If their large redshifts are due to some powerful explosive event that shot the quasars out at some tremendous speed, then you would not have to worry about the tremendous luminosities. That would be nice, but unfortunately, (or fortunately, if you like a good mystery) that does not appear to be the case. Quasars are found in clusters of galaxies. The galaxies are much fainter than the quasars so only the largest telescopes can gather enough light to create a spectrum for those far away galaxies. Their spectra also have the same large redshift of the quasars in the cluster. Also, some quasars are close enough to us that some fuzz is seen around them. The color of the fuzz is like that of normal galaxies. The spectra of the fuzzy patches around the bright quasar shows that the light from the fuzz is from stars.

how we know quasars are very far away

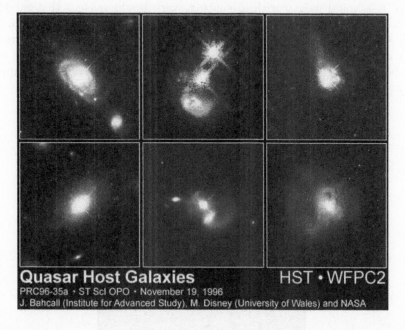

Quasar Host Galaxies   HST • WFPC2
PRC96-35a • ST ScI OPO • November 19, 1996
J. Bahcall (Institute for Advanced Study), M. Disney (University of Wales) and NASA

The superior resolution of the Hubble Space Telescope now clearly shows the galaxy hosts of the quasars. The picture above shows that quasars can be in any type of galaxy's nucleus: top left: core of a normal spiral, bottom left: core of a normal elliptical, top center: a spiral galaxy hit face-on to make a quasar+starburst galaxy, bottom center: a quasar merging with a bright galaxy and maybe another one, top right: a tail of dust and gas shows that the host galaxy collided with another one, bottom right: merging galaxies create a quasar in their combined nucleus.

In addition, the gravitational lensing of quasars by distant galaxies is only possible if the lensed quasars are farther away than the galaxy bending the quasar's light. Quasars are the exceptionally bright nuclei of galaxies!

15.2.2   Active Galaxies

Not all active galaxies blaze with the strength of a quasar. They do exhibit a non-thermal spectrum that has no peak and does not depend on the temperature. Also, their energy is generated in the nuclei of galaxies. The **active galaxies** are less

active galaxy

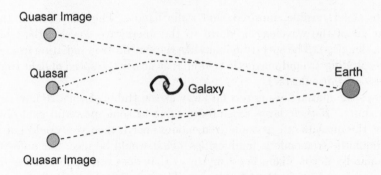

energetic cousins of the quasars. Their luminosity is between the luminosities of typical galaxies and the powerful quasars. Whatever is going on in quasars, is going on in active galaxies to a lesser extent.

One type of active galaxy is the **Seyfert galaxy**, named after Carl Seyfert who was the first to discover the peculiar spectra of these types of galaxies. A **Seyfert galaxy** is a spiral galaxy with a compact, very bright nucleus that produces a non-thermal continuous spectrum with broad (fat) *emission lines* on top. Some of the emission lines are produced by atoms that have several electrons removed from them. Such *highly ionized* atoms are found only in regions of intense energy. Many Seyfert nuclei are in disk galaxies with distorted spiral arms and a companion galaxy nearby that is probably gravitationally interacting with the galaxy.

Seyfert galaxy

NGC 1566 is a Seyfert galaxy (a spiral
galaxy with an active nucleus).
Image courtesy of David Malin/Anglo-Australian Observatory

The energy of Seyfert galaxy nuclei fluctuates quickly like the quasar fluctuations, so the energy generator must be quite small. The broad emission lines are produced by gas clouds moving at about 10,000 kilometers/second. The doppler shifts of the gas moving around the core widens the emission lines. Some Seyfert galaxies have narrow emission lines instead of broad emission lines and are bright at infrared wavelengths. These are called "Type 2" Seyferts to distinguish them from the classical "Type 1" Seyferts with the broad emission lines.

radio galaxy

Another type of active galaxy is the **radio galaxy**, which emits huge amounts of radio energy. The radio emission comes from the core AND from very large regions on either side of the optical part of the galaxy called "radio lobes". The radio lobes can extend for millions of light years from the center of the galaxy. The radio emission from normal galaxies is thousands to millions of times less intense and is from the gas between the stars. Most radio galaxies are elliptical galaxies. The spectrum of the radio emission has the same non-thermal (synchrotron) shape as the quasars and Seyferts. The radio lobes are produced from electrons shot out from the nucleus in narrow beams called *jets*. When the electrons in the beam hit the gas surrounding the galaxy, the beam spreads out to form the lobes.

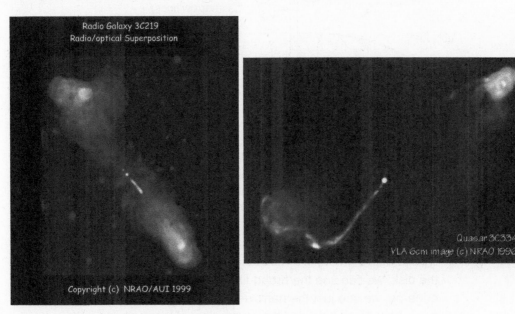

Some lobes are swept out into arcs behind the galaxy. This is probably caused by the galaxy moving through the gas around the galaxy. A third type of active galaxy called *BL Lacertae objects* (BL Lac objects for short) are probably radio galaxies with their jets pointed right at us. The energy from BL Lac objects varies very quickly and erratically.

15.2.3 Power Source for Active Galaxies and Quasars

So here's the problem: how does nature produce objects that are luminous over such a large range of wavelengths and generate the energy in a very small volume? The number of stars needed to produce the tremendous luminosity could not be packed into the small region and neither would they produce the peculiar non-thermal radiation. One mechanism you have already learned about in chapter 13 is the intense radiation produced by hot gas in an accretion disk around a black hole.

accretion disk around su-permassive black hole

In order to produce the enormous amount of energy seen in active galaxies and quasars, the black hole must be supermassive. The intense radiation from the disk would drive the gas outward if the black hole did not have enough gravity to keep the gas falling onto the black hole. In order to keep the gas spiraling in and heating up, the mass of the black hole must be hundreds of millions to several billion solar masses. The accretion disk is a few trillion kilometers across (a few light *months* across) but most of the intense radiation is produced within a couple of hundred billion kilometers from the black hole.

The gas in the disk is heated by the friction it experiences rubbing against other gas in the disk and also by the release of gravitational potential energy as it falls inward onto the black hole. If you have dropped down from a large height

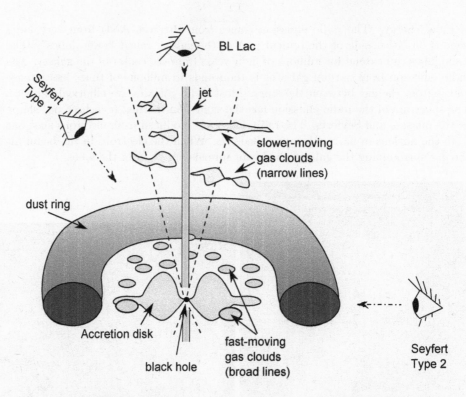

Viewing angle of the accretion disk and dust ring determines the type of active galaxy we will see. For example: 30–60° above the disk, we can see the broad-line region: a Type 1 Seyfert, but edge-on, we see just the narrow-line region from clouds further away from black hole and the warm glow of the dust ring in the infrared: a Type 2 Seyfert.

(from a tree or ladder?) you know that your feet absorb a lot more energy than if you dropped from a small height (you did land on your feet, hopefully). The gravitational potential energy you had above the ground was converted to kinetic energy (energy of motion) as you fell. If you dropped to the ground from a very high height (great gravitational potential energy), you know that you would hit the ground with a great amount of energy. The situation would be worse on an object with stronger gravity. The process of converting mass to energy from falling onto a black hole has an efficiency that is over ten times as large as the efficiency of nuclear fusion. The amount of mass needed to power the nuclei in active galaxies is from one to ten solar masses per year.

how the jets are produced   If there is a strong magnetic field in the accretion disk, the magnetic field lines can be distorted into a tangled, narrow mess of magnetic field lines that run toward the poles perpendicular to the accretion disk. Gas escaping along the magnetic field would produce the beams of electrons and gas seen in the jets to make the radio lobes of radio galaxies. Also, the shape of the accretion disk may play a role in directing the gas into the jets. The outer parts of the disk can be thick, but they will narrow down to a very thin layer just outside of the black hole. A thick accretion disk that narrows down only very close to the black hole could pinch the outflowing gas into a narrow beam.

Around the accretion disk are relatively dense clouds of hot gas that could be responsible for the broad emission lines seen in Type 1 Seyferts. Further out is a thick dusty molecular doughnut-shaped ring with a diameter of ten to several hundred light years. The particular type of active galaxy seen then simply depends on the angle the accretion disk and dust ring are to the line of sight (see figure previous page).

If the accretion disk is tipped enough, the fast-moving hot clouds that produce the broad emission lines of Type 1 Seyferts are visible. If the dust ring hides the accretion disk, then only the slower-moving hot clouds that are farther from the black hole are visible. The result is the narrow emission lines and the dust ring glowing in the infrared of a Type 2 Seyfert. If the disk is face-on and a beam of radiation is being produced, then the active galaxy is a BL Lac object.

The Hubble Space Telescope has imaged the nuclei of several active galaxies. Around the core of the radio galaxy NGC 4261 is a ring of dust and gas about 400 light years in diameter and the jets emerge perpendicular to the plane of the dust/gas ring. The black event horizon of the supermassive black hole is too small to be resolved from our distance.

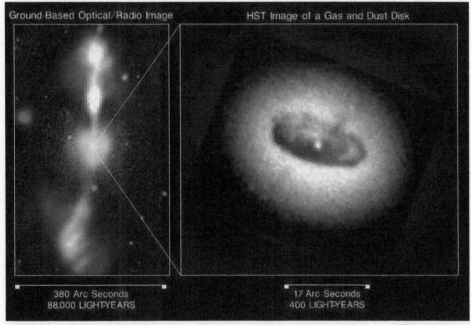

The core of the radio galaxy NGC 4261 as seen through the Hubble Space Telescope.
Image courtesy of H. Ford and L. Ferrares (JHU) and STScI/AURA/NASA

The core of the active galaxy M87 is seen to have a disk of hot gas moving very quickly around the center (see the figure on the next page). Doppler shifts of the disk material close to the center show that the gas is moving at speeds of hundreds of kilometers per *second*. Blueshifted lines are produced from one part of the disk and redshifted lines are produced from the opposite part of the disk. This is clear proof that the disk is rotating. The speed and distance the gas from the center show that the central object must have a mass of at least 2.5 billion solar masses. Only a black hole could be this massive and compact. The jet coming from the nucleus is also seen to be perpendicular to the plane of the disk.

The Hubble Space Telescope's resolution is much too poor to image the black hole itself. To do that requires an array of telescopes the size of Earth. The best view yet of a supermassive black hole came with the Event Horizon Telescope's image of M87's center announced on April 10, 2019. The Event Horizon Telescope uses observations from eight radio telescopes in six locations: Hawaii, Arizona, Mexico, Spain, Chile, and the South Pole.

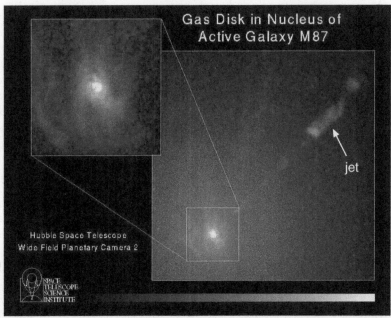

Doppler shifts of spectral lines from material on opposite sides of the disk show that the disk is rotating as an accretion disk would. The mass of the central object derived from the disk's high orbital speeds is 2.5 billion solar masses! Note that the jet of electrons is perpendicular to the disk.

Image courtesy of H. Ford et al. and STScI/AURA/NASA

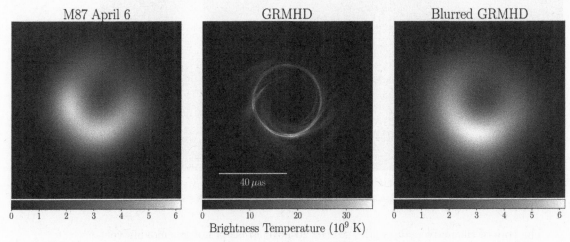

(Far left) Event Horizon Telescope image from its April 6, 2017 observation run.
(Middle) Simulated image based on a general relativistic magnetohydrodynamic model.
(Far right) Model image blurred to the same resolution as the EHT.
Image courtesy of the EHT Collaboration and the American Astronomical Society.

The dark hole in the ring of light (the "lensed photon ring") in the image is similar to a shadow, caused by the gravitational bending and capture of light by the event horizon around the black hole now known to be of mass 6.5 billion solar masses. The shadow of the black hole is the closest we can come to an image of the black hole itself. The event horizon is about 2.5 times smaller than the shadow it casts and measures just under 40 billion kilometers across (about three times the diameter of Plutos orbit). The images released in 2019 were from observing runs two years earlier in 2017. The EHT team was still working on data from

observing the supermassive black hole at the center of our galaxy, Sagittarius A*
(Sgr A* for short). Because the event horizon of Sgr A* is about a thousand times
smaller in diameter than M87's black hole, there are faster changes in the light from
the swirling gas in the accretion disk around Sgr A*. All that turbulence makes
discerning the shadow signature harder to do. See the textbook's website for links
to more information about the EHT imaging of supermassive black holes.

15.2.4 The Short Life of an Active Galaxy

Galaxy nuclei do not remain active for billions of years. Eventually, the gas fuel
runs out in the accretion disk. The disk's gas can be replenished if some stars in
the galaxy wander too close to the central black hole and get stretched apart by
the black hole's strong gravity. Also, galaxy mergers and collisions will keep the
gas and stars in the central part of active galaxies sufficiently stirred up so some of
that material will become part of the accretion disk. The expansion of the universe
decreases the rate at which interactions will happen. Because the frequency of
galaxy close encounters decreases over time as the universe expands, the quasars
and active galaxies can last for only a few billion years at most.

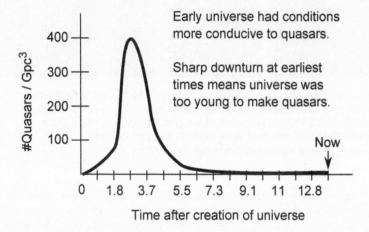

Quasars tend to be found at great distances from us; there are no nearby quasars.
When we look at quasars, we see them as they were billions of years ago. The
number of them increases at greater distances, so that must mean they were more
common long ago. The number of quasars peaks at a time when the universe was
about 20% of its current age. Back then the galaxies were closer together and *quasar number peak*
collisions were more common than today. Also, the galaxies had more gas that had
not been incorporated into stars yet. The number of quasars was hundreds of times
greater than the time closer to the present. At very great distances the number of
quasars drops off. The light from the most distant quasars are from a time in the *need time for galaxies to*
universe before most of the galaxies had formed, so fewer quasars could be created. *form*

This model predicts that there should be many dead quasars (supermassive
black holes without accretion disks) lurking at the cores of galaxies. Astronomers
are beginning to find the inactive supermassive black holes in some galaxies. In
most galaxies the central black hole would have been smaller than the billions of
solar mass black holes for quasars. This is why the less energetic active galaxies are
more common than quasars. Our galaxy harbors a supermassive black hole in its
core that has a mass of "only" 4.5 million solar masses. Astronomers are studying
the cores of other normal galaxies to see if there are any signs of supermassive black
holes that are now "dead".

An important implication of the fact that there were more quasars billions of
years ago than there are now, is that the *universe changes over time*. The conditions

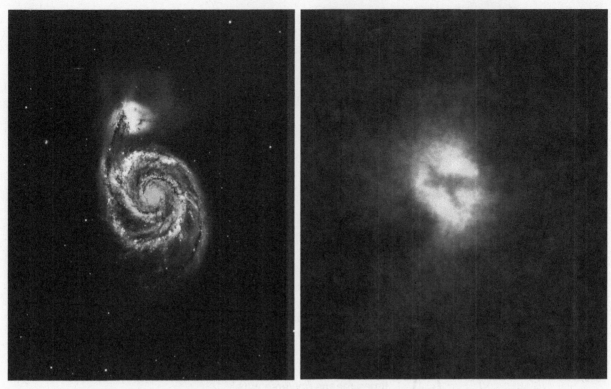

X marks the spot of the core of the beautiful Whirlpool Galaxy (=M 51, left frame)! The darker bar may be the dust ring surrounding the million solar-mass black hole seen edgeways. A jet seen in wider fields of view is perpendicular to the darker bar. The lighter bar may be another another dust disk oriented at an angle to our line of sight.

Images courtesy of NOAO/AURA/NSF and STScI/AURA

changing universe

long ago were more conducive to quasar activity than they are today. In the next chapter you will explore the overall evolution of the universe. You will need to remember this point about a changing universe when you consider ideas for how the universe formed and grew. Also, the sharp drop in the quasar number for the earliest times is evidence for a beginning to the universe.

Vocabulary

active galaxy   quasar   radio galaxy
Seyfert galaxy

Review Questions

1. Compare the luminosity and size of the power source for quasars to that of a normal galaxy.

2. Contrast the shape of the spectrum and the relative power at different wavelength bands (X-ray, ultraviolet, visible, infrared, radio) for the energy coming from quasars (and active galaxies) to that from normal galaxies (and stars).

3. What produces the huge power output in quasars and active galaxies?

4. What could cause the power generation to "turn off" and later turn back on?

5. What determines the type of active galaxy (i.e., Seyfert 1 or 2, radio galaxy, BL Lac, etc.) you will see?

6. What is the broad-line emission region and what must the orientation of the disk and dust ring be to see the broad-line emission region?

7. What are the jets in active galaxies and how are they produced?

8. Why are there many more quasars billions of light years away than nearby? Include in your explanation a contrast of the conditions of the universe billions of years ago to the current conditions.

9. What does the changing number of quasars with increasing distances tell us about the character of the universe?

15.3 Steps to the Hubble Constant

This section is a short essay that summarizes the ways astronomers find distances to various objects in the universe.

Why do we care so much about finding distances in astronomy? If you know the distance to a star, you can determine its luminosity and mass. You can then discover a correlation between luminosity, mass, and temperature for main sequence stars that your physical theories must account for. Finding distances to stellar explosions like planetary nebulae and supernovae enables you to determine the power needed to make the gaseous shells visible and how much was needed to eject them at their measured speeds. Stellar distances and distances to other gaseous nebulae are necessary for determining the mass distribution of our galaxy. Astronomers have then been able to discover that most of the mass in the Galaxy is not producing light of any kind and is in a dark halo around the visible parts of the Galaxy.

Finding distances to other galaxies enables you to find their mass, luminosity, and star formation history among other things. You are better able to hone in on what is going on in some very active galactic cores and also how much dark matter is distributed among and between galaxy cluster members. From galaxy distances, you are also able to answer some cosmological questions like the large-scale geometry of space, the density of the universe needed to stop the expansion, age of the universe, and whether or not the universe will keep expanding. The cosmological questions will be discussed fully in the next chapter on cosmology. This is only a quick overview of the reasons for distance measurements and is by *no* means an exhaustive list of reasons why distance measurements are so important.

Now let's take a look at the distance scale ladder. The bottom foundational rung of the ladder is the most accurate and the most certain of all the distance determination methods. Each rung depends on the rung below and it is less certain than the previous one.

15.3.1 Rung 1: The Astronomical Unit

The Earth and Distance to the Sun. Radar reflections from Venus and its angular separation from the Sun are used to calculate the numerical value of the Astronomical Unit (A.U.). You can use radar to measure distances out to 50 A.U.

15.3.2 Rung 2: Geometric Methods

On the next rung of the distance scale ladder, you can convert trigonometric parallax measurements into distances to the nearby stars using their angular shift throughout the year and the numerical value of the Astronomical Unit. Distances to nearby clusters like the Hyades or the Pleiades are found via trigonometric parallax or the moving clusters method (another geometric method). The cluster's main sequence is calibrated in terms of absolute magnitude (luminosity). Geometric methods are used to find distances out to about 100 parsecs (or several hundred parsecs with Hipparcos' data and about 40,000 parsecs with Gaia data).

15.3.3   Rung 3: Main Sequence Fitting and Spectroscopic Parallax

On the next rung outward the spectral type of a star is determined from its spectral lines and the apparent brightness of the star is measured. The calibrated color-magnitude diagram is used to get its luminosity and then its distance from the inverse square law of light brightness.

The entire main sequence of a cluster is used in the same way to find the distance to the cluster. You first plot the cluster's main-sequence on a color-magnitude diagram with apparent magnitudes, not absolute magnitude. You find how far the unknown main sequence needs to be shifted vertically along the magnitude axis to match the calibrated main sequence. The amount of the shift depends on the distance.

The age of the cluster affects the main sequence. An older cluster has only fainter stars left on the main sequence. Also, stars on the main sequence brighten slightly at a constant temperature as they age so they move slightly vertically on the main sequence. You must model the main sequence evolution to get back to the Zero-Age Main Sequence. This method assumes that all Zero-Age main sequence stars of a given temperature (and, hence, mass) start at the same luminosity. These methods can be used to find distances out to 50 kiloparsecs.

15.3.4   Rung 4: Period-Luminosity Relation for Variable Stars

Continuing outward you find Cepheids and/or RR-Lyrae in stars clusters with a distance known through main sequence fitting. Or you can employ the more direct "Baade-Wesselink method" that uses the observed expansion speed of the variable star along the line of sight from the doppler shifts in conjunction with the observed angular expansion rate perpendicular to the line of sight. Since the linear expansion rate depends on the angular expansion rate and the distance of the star, the measurement of the linear expansion rate and angular expansion rate will give you the distance of the variable star.

RR-Lyrae have the same time-averaged luminosity (about 49 $L_\odot$ or an absolute magnitude $M_V = +0.6$). They pulsate with periods < 1 day. Cepheids pulsate with periods > 1 day. The longer the pulsation, the more luminous they are. There are two types of Cepheids: classical (brighter, type I) and W Virginis (fainter, type II). They have different light curve shapes. The period-luminosity relation enables the determination of distances out to 4 megaparsecs (40 megaparsecs with the Hubble Space Telescope).

15.3.5   Rung 5a: Galaxy Luminosity vs. Other Bright Feature

The periods and apparent brightnesses of Cepheids in other nearby galaxies are measured to get their distances. Then the galactic flux and the inverse square law of brightness are used to get the galactic luminosity. You can find the geometric sizes of H-II regions in spiral and irregular galaxies. From this you can calibrate the possible H-II region size–galactic luminosity relation. Or you can calibrate the correlation between the width of the 21-cm line (neutral hydrogen emission line) and the spiral galaxy luminosity. The width of the 21-cm line is due to rotation of the galaxy. This correlation is called the *Tully-Fisher relation*: infrared luminosity $= 220 \times V_{rot}^4$ solar luminosities if V_{rot} is given in units of km/sec. Elliptical galaxies have a correlation between their luminosity and their velocity dispersion, v_{disp}, within the inner few kpc called the *Faber-Jackson law*: $v_{disp} \approx 220 \times (L/L_*)^{1/4}$ km/sec, where $L_* = 1.0 \times 10^{10} \times (H_0/100)^{-2}$ solar luminosities in the visual band, and the Hubble constant $H_0 = 60$ to 70 km/sec/Mpc.

15.3.6   Rung 5b: Luminosity or Size of Bright Feature

Cepheids are found in other nearby galaxies to get their distance. Then the luminosities of several things are calibrated: (a) supernova type 1a maximum luminosity in any type of galaxy; (b) globular cluster luminosity function in elliptical galaxies; (c) blue or red supergiant stars relation in spirals and irregulars; (d) maximum luminosity–rate of decline relation of novae in ellipticals and bulges of spirals; & (e) planetary nebula luminosity function in any type of galaxy.

The Rung 5 methods can measure distances out to 50 to 150 megaparsecs.

15.3.7   Rung 6: Galaxy Luminosity and Inverse Square Law

The Hubble-Lemaître Law is calibrated using rung 4 methods for nearby galaxy distances and rung 5 methods for larger galaxy distances. If those rung 5 galaxies are like the nearby ones (or have changed luminosity in a known way), then by measuring their apparent brightness and estimating their luminosity OR by measuring their angular size and estimating their linear size, you can find their distance. You need to take care of the effect on the measured velocities caused by the Milky Way falling into the Virgo Cluster. You can also calibrate the galaxy cluster luminosity function.

The **Hubble-Lemaître Law** relates a galaxy's recession (expansion) speed with its distance: speed = $H_0 \times$ distance. Measuring the speed from the redshift is easy, but measuring the distance is not. You can calibrate the Hubble-Lemaître Law using galaxies out to 500 megaparsecs.

Hubble-Lemaître Law

15.3.8   Rung 7: Hubble-Lemaître Law

This is the final rung in the distance scale ladder. You use the Hubble-Lemaître Law for all far away galaxies. You can make maps of the large-scale structure of the universe. The Hubble-Lemaître Law is also used to determine the overall geometry of the universe (how the gravity of the universe as a whole has warped it). You will see in the next chapter that the geometry of the universe determines the fate of the universe.

Rung 4 is a critical one for the distance scale ladder. With the Hubble Space Telescope, astronomers were able to use the Cepheid period-luminosity relation out to distances ten times further than what could be done on the ground. Previous ground measurements of the Hubble constant were 50 to 100 km/sec/Mpc. Using the Hubble Space Telescope, astronomers constrained its value to between 64 and 80 km/sec/Mpc with a best value of 72 km/sec/Mpc. More recently, the Hubble Constant has been narrowed even further to between 70.6 and 77.8 with a best value of 74.2 km/sec/Mpc by using Cepheid period-luminosity relation in the near-infrared. The earlier measurement of 72 km/sec/Mpc had an uncertainty (error margin) of +/- 8 km/sec/Mpc and the newer near-infrared work reduces the uncertainty by more than two times to +/- 3.6 km/sec/Mpc.. The value of $1/H_0$ is a rough upper limit on the age of the universe (assuming constant recession speeds!), so the new measurements imply an universe age of about 14 billion years. The favorite model for how the recession speeds have changed over the history of the universe gives an age of about 13.8 billion years with this value for the Hubble constant. This agrees with the ages derived for the oldest stars (found in globular clusters) of about 12 to 13 billion years. Also, the greater precision of the newer measurement of the Hubble Constant provides increased constraints on the nature of the "dark energy" discussed in the next chapter.

An entirely independent way of determining the Hubble Constant (Ho) of the Hubble-Lemaître Law was made possible when we detected in mid-August 2017 the gravitational waves coming from the merger of two neutron stars in an elliptical galaxy NGC 4993, 130 million light years away (see section 6.2). The amplitude of the gravitational waves enables us to determine the distance of the source independent of the distance scale ladder. The merger of the neutron stars created an explosion that could be seen with ground and space-based telescopes from gamma rays to radio waves. The telescope data give us the redshift due to the Hubble expansion that when coupled with the direct distance measurement from the gravitational wave data gives us a Hubble Constant value of 70 km/sec/Mpc (with an uncertainty of +12 and −8 km/sec/Mpc).

Review Questions

1. Why is finding accurate extragalactic distances so important?

2. What are the more accurate or more certain ways to measure distances? What are the less accurate (less certain) ways to measure distances? What assumptions are made when using the less certain techniques?

3. What is the **Hubble-Lemaître Law**? What two things does it relate? Why is it important?

15.4   A Final Word

The Sombrero Galaxy is one of the most photographed galaxies and this exquisitely beautiful picture from the Hubble Space Telescope shows why. There are number of beautiful objects that draw people to take up astronomy as a profession or a life-long hobby and the Sombrero Galaxy is one of them. Seeking to understand what these objects are made of, how they behave, and how they formed gives us a greater appreciation for the art that surrounds us. Visible in even small telescopes at the southern edge of the Virgo cluster of galaxies, the Sombrero Galaxy is a spiral galaxy more massive than the Milky Way seen nearly edge-on from a distance of about 28 million light years away.

This image also provides a nice illustration of the parts of a spiral galaxy and its history. The oldest stars are in the spherical bulge & stellar halo retaining their randomly-oriented eccentric orbits of the original gas cloud from which the galaxy formed about 13 billion years ago. The stellar halo also sports almost 2000 globular clusters (the Milky Way has only about 150 globular clusters). The more massive stars in the spherical component added heavier elements (dust) to the newly-formed disk in which younger generations of stars are still forming. These younger stars have added to the dust layer that now outlines the disk and spiral arms. The fortunate slight tilt of the disk to our line of sight allows us to easily distinguish the near side of the disk from the far side. The disk star orbits are closely aligned to each other to make the very thin disk characteristic of spiral galaxies. A billion solar-mass black hole lies at the heart of the bright core. This beautiful image is courtesy of the Hubble Heritage Team and NASA.

Chapter 16

Cosmology

This chapter gives you the Big Picture called cosmology. **Cosmology** is the study of the nature, origin, and evolution of the universe as a whole. The observational aspect of cosmology deals with finding distances to galaxies which is necessary for determining the geometry of the universe. This was covered in the last chapter. Vocabulary terms in the text are in boldface.

cosmology

16.1   Observations and Some Implications

At first you might think that in order to understand the structure of something as large as the universe, which by definition contains everything there is, you would need some very powerful telescope to see to the farthest reaches of space and a complex theoretical model. Actually, there are some powerful conclusions you can draw from observations with the naked eye. You will explore that first and then move on to conclusions you can draw from extending your eyesight. You will explore the basic questions that human beings have been asking themselves ever since we have walked the Earth: where did we come from and where are we going?

16.1.1   Universe Contains Mass—Why Has the Universe Not Collapsed?

The universe is not empty. There is matter with mass, so the attraction of gravity is present. Newton knew that if the universe has existed forever and is static, that is, it has no net pattern of motion, then there must be enough time for gravity to collapse the universe, but this has clearly not happened! He knew of three ways to resolve this paradox. Either the universe is infinite in volume and mass or it is expanding fast enough to overcome the gravitational attraction or the universe has a beginning and/or an end. The last two ways violate the assumptions of an eternal and static universe, of course. So Newton chose the infinite universe option. Notice that you are able to arrive at the conclusion of an infinite universe from just one observation: the universe is not empty. No telescopes are needed, just the ability to follow a train of logical thought to its conclusion.

16.1.2   Olbers' Paradox and the Dark Night Sky

Another simple observation is that the visible night sky is dark. *IF* the universe is infinite, eternal, and static, then the sky should be as bright as the surface of the Sun all of the time! *Heinrich Olbers* (lived 1758–1840) popularized this paradox in 1826, but he was not the first to come up with this conclusion. Thomas Digges wrote about it in 1576, Kepler stated it in 1610, and Edmund Halley and Jean Philippe

Olbers' Paradox

de Cheseaux talked about it in the 1720's, but Olbers stated it very clearly, so he was given credit for it. This problem is called **Olbers' Paradox**.

If the universe is uniformly filled with stars, then no matter which direction you look, your line of sight will eventually intersect a star (or other bright thing). Now it is known that stars are grouped into galaxies, but the paradox remains: your line of sight will eventually intersect a galaxy. The brightnesses of stars does decrease

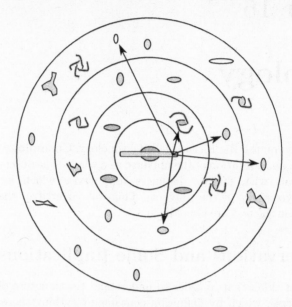

Olbers' Paradox: No matter what direction you look, you will eventually see a bright object. Farther away objects are fainter, but there are more of them. So each shell has the **same** overall brightness. The night sky should be bright!

with greater distance (remember the inverse square law) BUT there are more stars further out. The number of stars within a spherical shell around us will increase by the same amount as their brightness decreases. Therefore, each shell of stars will have the same overall luminosity and because there are a lot of ever bigger shells in an infinite universe, there is going to be a lot of light!

Any intervening material absorbing the starlight would eventually heat up and radiate as much energy as it absorbed, so the problem remains even if you try these "shields". Of course, stars are not points. They do have a definite size, so they can block light from other stars. The total brightness of the universe will not be infinite, but only as bright as the surface of a star (!). You can substitute "galaxy" for "star" in the preceding paragraphs if you want to update Olbers' Paradox for modern times. The way to resolve a paradox like this is to look at the assumptions that are used (the "if" statements) and determine whether or not they are valid.

16.1.3   Universe Is Expanding

In 1915 Albert Einstein published his Theory of General Relativity that described gravity as a curvature of spacetime (see chapter 6). In 1917 Einstein applied General Relativity to the universe as a whole and showed that the universe must either expand or contract. Since there was no evidence of such large-scale motion, he added a term to the equations called the "cosmological constant" (see section 16.3) to keep the universe static. *Alexander Friedman* (lived 1888–1925) in 1922 and then the Belgian priest/astrophysicist *Georges Lemaître* (lived 1894–1966) in 1927 (independent of Friedman) used General Relativity to show that the universe must be expanding. In his 1927 paper Lemaître suggested a relation between the galaxy speeds and distances like what Edwin Hubble would later observe. Einstein disagreed with Lemaître but Lemaître persevered. Einstein would later come to agree with Lemaître on the expansion of the universe arising from General Relativity after Edwin Hubble announced his observations in 1929 that the universe is not static—it is expanding. In later papers and conferences Lemaître argued for a beginning to the universe that would later become the Big Bang Theory described more fully later in this chapter. In 1933 Einstein agreed that Lemaître was correct. [There is now evidence that Lemaître actually derived a value for the Hubble constant using some early distance measurements of Hubble and Slipher's redshifts in his 1927 paper but his work is less well-known than Hubble's because the paper was published in an obscure journal (Annales de la Societe scientifique de Bruxelles) written in French while Hubble's paper (with Milton Humason) in 1931 with better distance data laying out the case for the galaxy motions first announced in 1929 appeared in the more widely-read Astrophysical Journal and the English translation of Lemaître's paper in a 1931 issue of Monthly Notices of the Royal Academy of Sciences did not have that derivation of the Hubble constant. It was probably the more convincing observational evidence laid out in the Hubble & Humason paper that led Einstein to admit that Lemaître was correct all along.]

The expansion of the universe is enough to resolve the paradox. As the universe expands, the light waves are stretched out and the energy is reduced. Also, the time to receive the light is also lengthened over the time it took to emit the photon. Because the luminosity = the energy/time, the apparent brightness will be reduced enough by the expansion to make the sky dark.

Lemaître

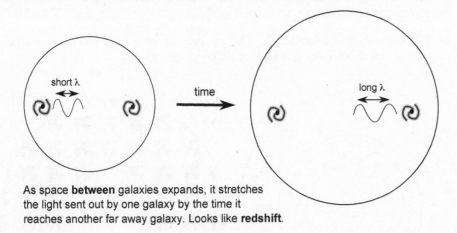

As space **between** galaxies expands, it stretches the light sent out by one galaxy by the time it reaches another far away galaxy. Looks like **redshift**.

The stretching of the light waves makes the light from galaxies appear redshifted, mimicking a redshift from the doppler effect as if the galaxies were moving *through* space away from us. However, the galaxies are simply being carried along with the expansion of the space between them—the whole coordinate system is expanding. The expansion of the universe means that galaxies were much closer together long ago. This implies that there is a finite age to the universe, it is not eternal. Even if the universe is infinite, the light from places *very* far away will not have had enough time to reach us. This will make the sky dark.

The **Hubble-Lemaître Law,** speed = $H_o \times$ distance, says the expansion is uniform. The **Hubble constant,** H_o, is the slope of the line relating the speed of the galaxies away from each other and their distance apart from each other. It indicates the rate of the expansion. If the slope is steep (large H_o), then the

finite age means a "time horizon"

Hubble-Lemaître Law
Hubble constant

expansion rate is large and the galaxies did not need much time to get to where they are now. If the slope is shallow (small H_o), then the galaxies need a lot of time to get to where they are now.

The age of the universe can be easily estimated from the simple relation of *time = distance/speed*. The Hubble-Lemaître Law can be rewritten $1/H_o$ = distance/speed. Notice that the expansion time interval = $1/H_o$. The Hubble constant tells you the age of the universe, i.e., how long the galaxies have been expanding away from each other: Age = $1/H_o$. This value for the age is an upper limit since the expansion has been slowing down due to gravity. That means that the Hubble "constant" actually was larger in the past. Taking the expansion slowdown into account, you get an age closer to $2/(3H_o)$. Still, the age looks like a number$\times(1/H_o)$, so if the Hubble constant is *large*, the derived age of the universe will be *small*.

larger Hubble constant, smaller age

16.1.4   Universe Is Uniform on Large Scales

On size scales of billions of light years, the universe is assumed to be uniform. This makes the universe models simpler and "more reasonable"—if we lived in an unusual part of the universe, then it would be almost impossible to understand the universe as a whole from observing our surroundings. The discovery of the long superclusters may seem to endanger this assumption. On large enough scales though, the universe has many superclusters in all directions. It is like a large bowl of tapioca pudding, one spoonful of pudding looks like any other spoonful, even though, there are the small tapioca pieces.

cosmological principle

The idea of a uniform universe is called the **cosmological principle**. There are two aspects of the cosmological principle:

homogeneous

- The universe is **homogeneous**. This means there is no preferred observing position in the universe.

isotropic

- The universe is also **isotropic**. This means you see no difference in the structure of the universe as you look in different directions.

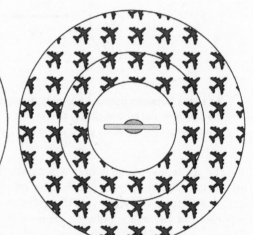

Is this *homogeneous* and *isotropic*? Which aspect is it not?

Outside the central sphere, is this universe *homogeneous* and *isotropic*? Which aspect is it not?

Copernican principle

The cosmological principle is a Copernican idea. It means we are not in a special place. Every observer at a given *cosmological time* will see the same thing, such as the same Hubble-Lemaître Law. "Cosmological time" in this context means the time measured from some common event like the creation of the universe. Everyone at the same cosmological time will measure the same age of the universe. The cosmological principle allows the universe to change, or evolve, throughout time.

An extension of the cosmological principle called the **perfect cosmological principle** says that the universe also does not change with time; there is no evolution. Therefore, in an expanding universe, *new* matter must be continually created. This violates a central rule of nature known as the *law of the conservation of mass*. This law says that the total amount of mass does not change—mass is not created from nothing or destroyed. However, the amount of new matter that would need to be created for the perfect cosmological principle to be true is quite small—only one hydrogen atom per cubic centimeter every 10^{15} years. This is approximately one hydrogen atom/Houston Astrodome every year—a very small amount!

perfect cosmological principle

16.1.5   No Center to the Expansion in 3-D Space

General Relativity describes gravity as a warping or distortion of space and time near a massive object. In General Relativity, four-dimensional spacetime is curved. You may want to refresh your memory of these concepts by reading chapter 6 again.

To help you understand what curved spacetime means, let's use the analogy of a two-dimensional world curving into the third dimension. Pretend you are confined to the surface of a balloon and you only know about "front", "back", "left", and "right", but not "up" and "down". In your 2D universe you cannot see the third dimension. Your universe appears flat. Yet you know that your 2D universe must be curved because if you walk in a straight line, you eventually arrive back at where you started! The balloon universe has a finite size but *no edge*. You also know that the angles of large triangles add up to a number larger than 180°! For example, on the balloon the lines of longitude running north-south intercept the equator at a 90° angle and converge at the poles. So a triangle made of one point on the equator + the north pole + another point on the equator will have the angles add up to *more* than 180°. In a truly flat universe, the angles would add up to exactly 180°. You would be able to deduce that your universe is *positively* curved.

figuring out your universe is curved

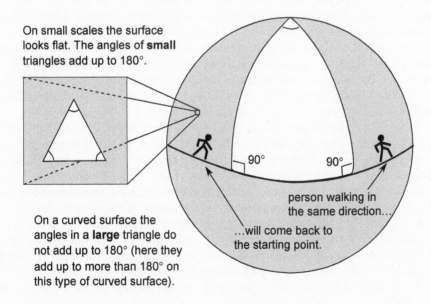

On small scales the surface looks flat. The angles of **small** triangles add up to 180°.

On a curved surface the angles in a **large** triangle do not add up to 180° (here they add up to more than 180° on this type of curved surface).

90°   90°

person walking in the same direction...

...will come back to the starting point.

On sufficiently small scales the surface looks flat so the regular geometry rules apply. The angles in a small triangle add up to 180°. Here on the surface of the Earth, the Earth looks flat to us because the curvature of the Earth is so much larger than we are. The universe does not have to curve back on itself as shown in the illustrations above. This type of *positively-curved* universe is usually easier to picture, but the curvature could be the opposite. In a *negatively-curved* universe, the universe curves away from itself. A two-dimensional analogy would look like a saddle. The angles in large triangles would add up to less than 180°. Like the positively-curved universe, there would be no center on the surface and *no edge*.

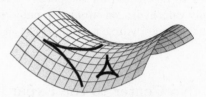

Universe with *positive* curvature. Diverging line converge at great distances. Triangle angles add to more than 180°.

Universe with *negative* curvature. Lines diverge at ever increasing angles. Triangle angles add to less than 180°.

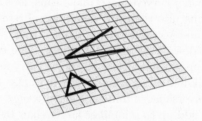

Universe with no curvature. Lines diverge at constant angle. Triangle angles add to 180°.

Rather than setting up BIG triangles in the universe, astronomers can use how the number of galaxies increases with increasing distance. If the universe has zero curvature and the galaxies are spread roughly uniformly in the universe, then the number of galaxies should increase linearly with ever greater volume. Lines defining an angle spread out in straight lines. If the universe has positive curvature, then the number of galaxies increases with greater volume then decreases with very large volumes. Lines defining an angle spread out at first and then converge at great distances. If the universe has negative curvature, then the number of galaxies increases more rapidly with ever greater volume than a flat universe. Lines defining an angle diverge at increasing angles as the lines curve away from each other.

The idea of a curved surface also explains why astronomers in every galaxy will see the other galaxies moving away from it and, therefore, they will derive the same Hubble-Lemaître Law. Go back to the balloon analogy and imagine that there are flat houses on it. As the balloon expands, the elastic material moves the houses apart from each other. A person sitting on the front porch sees everybody else moving away from her and she appears to be the center of the expansion.

Now add another dimension and you have our situation. Just like there is not new balloon material being created in the 2D analogy, new three-dimensional space is not being created in the expansion. Like any analogy, though, the balloon analogy has its limits. In the analogy, the balloon expands into the region around it—there is space beyond the balloon. However, with the expanding universe, space *itself*

limit of analogy

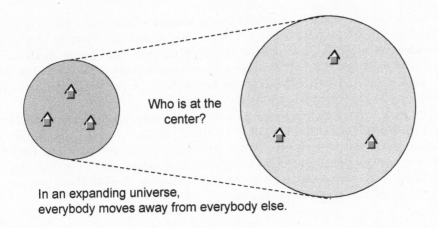

Who is at the center?

In an expanding universe, everybody moves away from everybody else.

is expanding in three dimensions—the whole coordinate system is expanding. *Our universe is NOT expanding "into" anything "beyond".*

Vocabulary

cosmological principle	cosmology	homogeneous
Hubble constant	Hubble-Lemaître Law	isotropic
Olbers' Paradox	perfect cosmological principle	

Review Questions

1. What are the assumptions that **Olber's Paradox** is based on?

2. Why is the night sky dark? What important conclusions can you draw from the simple observation that the night sky is dark?

3. Will an object with a large redshift be far away or close?

4. What can the **Hubble constant** constant (H_o) tell you about the age of the universe? How would the derived age of the universe change if H_o was 50 km/sec Mpc^{-1} instead of 100 km/sec Mpc^{-1}?

5. Is the Hubble constant actually constant throughout time? Why or why not?

6. What would the relation between the radial velocity and distance be if there was *no* expansion? What would the relation be if the universe was contracting?

7. Is there a center to the expansion in normal three-dimensional space? Why or why not?

8. Why is an analogy like flat houses on an expanding balloon used to try to picture the expansion?

9. Is the space between stars *inside* a galaxy expanding? Why or why not? Is the space between the molecules in your body expanding with the universe? Why or why not?

10. How is looking at faraway objects equivalent to looking back in time?

11. What is the **cosmological principle**? What is the **perfect cosmological principle**? Which one can an evolving universe fit in? Why?

16.1.6 Cosmic Microwave Background Radiation

George Gamov (lived 1904–1968) predicted in 1948 that there should be a faint glow left over from when the universe was much hotter and denser. Since the universe is observed to be expanding, it means that the galaxies were originally right on top of each other. Also, the energy of the universe was concentrated in a smaller volume.

Gamov

early hot universe as it expands

The entire universe would have glowed first in the gamma ray band, then the X-ray band, then to less energetic bands as the universe expanded. By now, 13.8 billion years after the start of the expansion, the cold universe should glow in the radio band. The expansion rate has slowed down over time because of the force of gravity. This means that the early expansion was faster than it is now. At the start of the expansion, the expansion rate was extremely rapid.

Big Bang

The early large expansion rate and very hot temperatures made *Fred Hoyle* (lived 1915–2001) call this theory of the birth of the universe, the **Big Bang.** At the time he coined the term, Hoyle was advocating another theory that used the perfect cosmological principle called the *Steady State* theory. So at the time, Hoyle's "Big Bang" term was made in joking disdain. However, the Big Bang proponents liked the term and used it from then on.

Observation

cosmic microwave background radiation

Arno Penzias and Robert Wilson observed in 1965 a radio background source that was spread all over the universe—the **cosmic microwave background radiation.** The radiation has the same intensity and spectral character as a thermal continuous source at 3 K (more precisely, 2.728 ± 0.004 K) as measured by the COBE satellite in every direction observed. To a high degree of precision the sky is *uniformly* bright in radio. The uniformity of the background radiation is evidence for the cosmological principle. The error bars in the figure below are too small to be seen.

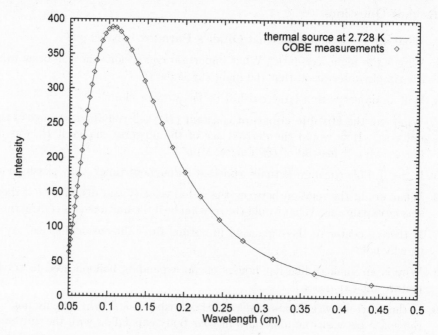

Interpretation

highly redshifted energy from warm universe few 100,000 years after Big Bang

This background radiation is interpreted to be the relic of the early universe. If this is correct, then the early universe was very uniform. Since the further out in space you look means the further back in time you look, the microwave radiation is coming from the universe as it was a few hundred thousand years after the Big Bang when the universe was much hotter. The glow from the early hot universe has been redshifted by 1000 times! Hoyle's Steady State theory could not adequately explain the presence of the background radiation and so was abandoned by most astronomers.

Let's take a closer look at what was happening in the universe when it produced the background radiation. The early universe (both the matter and the radiation) was much more compact. The radiation density was so great that it dominated the expansion rate and the conditions of the universe for the first 10,000 years. Remember Einstein's equation relating energy and mass? The energy $E=mc^2$ so the radiation energy had a definite gravitational effect!

The early universe was hot and *opaque* (photons could not move very far before being absorbed). The freely-moving electrons, protons, and neutrons scattered the photons all about making the dense gas opaque. Dense hot gases will produce a continuous spectrum that depends only on the temperature (a *thermal spectrum*). The universe cooled off as it expanded. Eventually, the early universe cooled to about 3000 K so that the electrons and protons could combine to form neutral hydrogen atoms and not be blown apart by energetic photons. The process of the electrons becoming bound to the protons to make atoms is called **recombination**. Okay, "recombination" is not really correct since this was the *first* time that the electrons combined with the protons, but it also describes processes that occur today. Extrapolating the expansion rate and the temperature of the universe backward in

early universe was opaque

atoms form 380,000 years after Big Bang

recombination

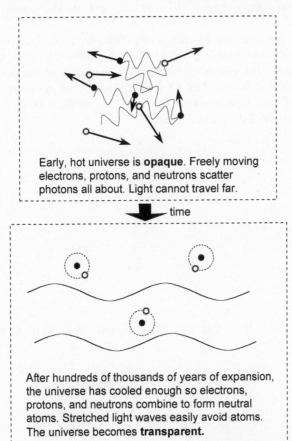

Early, hot universe is **opaque**. Freely moving electrons, protons, and neutrons scatter photons all about. Light cannot travel far.

time

After hundreds of thousands of years of expansion, the universe has cooled enough so electrons, protons, and neutrons combine to form neutral atoms. Stretched light waves easily avoid atoms. The universe becomes **transparent.**

time, one finds that at the temperature of 3000 K, the universe was about 380,000 years old.

At the time of recombination, the number of unit particles was cut at least in half (one electron + one proton become a single atom; the neutrons also were incorporated into the atoms). That meant the photons could travel further without hitting some kind of unit particle. Also, the expansion of the universe spread the matter out. In addition, the coolness of the universe (only 3000 K at the time of recombination) meant that longer wavelengths of light were present. Instead of the gamma rays and X-rays of earlier times, the predominant form of radiation was the longer wavelength visible light and infrared. Longer wavelengths of light are able to more easily to pass through gas. For all of these reasons the photons could then travel long distances without running into some particle. The universe became *transparent* when the universe was glowing at the temperature of the surface of a cool star. The photons from this time are just now reaching our radio telescopes. They are by far the oldest radiation that can be detected.

The universe could not have been perfectly uniform, though. The universe must have been slightly lumpy to form galaxies and people later on from the internal gravity of the lumps. Gravity is symmetrical so it needed some initial density variations to provide some direction to where surrounding matter could be attracted. The COBE satellite found *slight variations* in the brightness of the background radiation of about 1 part in 100,000. The slight variations exist because some parts of the universe were *slightly* denser than other parts. The slightly denser regions had more gravity and attracted more material to them while the expansion occurred. Over time, the denser regions got even denser and eventually formed galaxies about 1 billion years after the Big Bang. The slightly less dense places got even emptier as gravity increased the contrast between the denser places and less dense places.

What follows is a sequence of microwave all-sky from the Differential Microwave Radiometer (DMR) instrument on the COBE satellite. The galactic equator runs horizontally through the center of each map. The range of temperatures for each map is given in the caption. The COBE datasets were developed by the NASA Goddard Space Flight Center under the guidance of the COBE Science Working Group and were provided by the NSSDC.

Temperature range from 0 to 4 K. The background looks perfectly uniform at a temperature of 2.728 K.

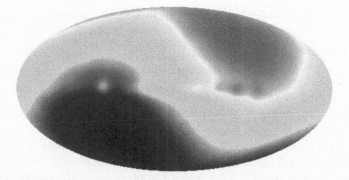

The intensity levels for the temperatures range from 2.724 to 2.732 K. The double-lobe pattern shows the doppler effect from the motion of the Sun with respect to the background radiation. You see our motion with respect to the rest frame of the microwave background. The background appears about 1/1000 times hotter in the direction the Sun is moving toward (upper right) and about 1/1000 times cooler in the direction the Sun is moving away from (lower left).

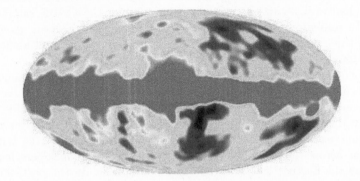

The intensity levels for the temperatures range from 2.7279 to 2.7281 K. The effect of the Sun's motion has been subtracted out leaving fluctuations that are thirty times smaller than the previous map. The faint microwave contribution of the Milky Way is clearly seen along the center. The Cygnus constellation is at left center, the Sagittarius constellation is at the center, and the Orion constellation is at right center.

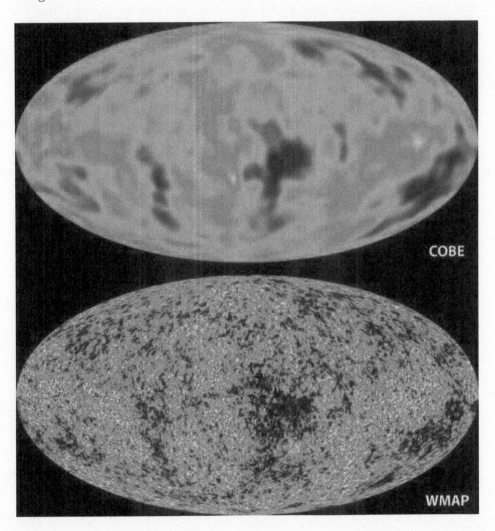

WMAP higher resolution than COBE

On the previous page is a picture of the fluctuations in the background radiation when the Milky Way's contribution is subtracted out. It shows a comparison of the coarse resolution of COBE with the finer resolution of the Wilkinson Microwave Anisotropy Probe (WMAP, image courtesy of the NASA/WMAP Science Team).

WMAP had over 30 times greater resolution than the COBE satellite. With that greater resolution, WMAP enabled us to learn the composition, geometry, and history of the universe, amount of matter in the universe, as well as, it provided much tighter constraints on the models.

Planck mission

The follow-up to WMAP is the Planck mission with over 2.5 times greater resolution than WMAP. The first data release in early 2013 confirmed the standard cosmology model derived from the COBE and WMAP missions but it did show some surprises at the really large scales (6 to 90 degrees across) with slightly weaker than expected fluctuations at those scales and also an asymmetry in the temperature fluctuations across the two halves of the sky, where one hemisphere has a wider variation in the fluctuations than the other hemisphere. In the past, advances in technology led to breakthroughs in our understanding of the nature of the universe and the high-precision measurements of Planck may be indicating a need to modify the standard cosmology model.

The time period between when the universe became transparent about 380,000 years after the Big Bang and formation of the first stars in the galaxies and the large black holes in the quasars began flooding the universe with powerful ultraviolet is called the "Dark Ages" or "Dark Era" in cosmological models. The ultraviolet light re-ionized the gas, freeing a lot of electrons. The transition period from the Dark Ages to the modern universe is called the "Epoch of Reionization". The light from the cosmic background would scatter off these newly freed electrons and become "polarized" so that the light waves tend to oscillate in a particular direction. How the light is polarized can tell you when the electrons were being freed again, i.e., when the stars first began to shine.

Dark Ages

Epoch of Reionization

WMAP has detected the polarization of the microwave background and derived a time of about 400 million years after the Big Bang for the first stars but the higher resolution data of Planck puts the time at about 560 million years after the Big Bang. The Epoch of Reionization is thought to take place between about 560 million years to about 1 billion years after the Big Bang. The visible light from these first stars will now have been redshifted into the infrared.

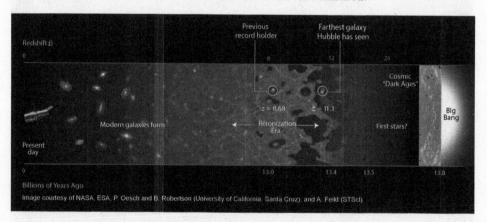

The Hubble Space Telescope has detected near-infrared light from galaxies shining about 750 million years after the Big Bang in the "Hubble Ultra Deep Field" (and even further back—400 million years after the Big Bang with the new WFPC3 camera; section 15.1.9) and the Spitzer Space Telescope may have spotted infrared light from early galaxies of about that time in other areas of the sky. One galaxy whose light was magnified by gravitational lensing by a foreground galaxy cluster appears to have formed a mere 200 million years after the Big Bang. A 2019 study using Spitzer found that the earliest galaxies near the end of the Epoch of Reionization produced much more ionizing radiation than do modern galaxies for some unknown reason. However, it will take the much larger light-gathering power and resolution of the infrared James Webb Space Telescope to study these objects in detail and figure out why.

16.1.7 Matter to Energy to Matter Conversion

Einstein's equation $E = mc^2$ says that mass can be converted to energy *and vice versa*. If you extrapolate the expansion rate and temperature of the universe back to much closer to the Big Bang than when the cosmic microwave background was produced, you find that within the first few seconds, the energy of the photons was great enough to create particles like electrons and protons. But along with the ordinary particles, the photons also created the *antimatter* counterparts to the particles, e.g., anti-electrons (called positrons) and anti-protons. Antimatter is briefly discussed in the context of nuclear fusion and the neutrino in section 12.3.

energy to matter to energy to...

The antimatter counterpart of an ordinary particle has the same mass and opposite charge of the ordinary particle (if it is not neutral). When an ordinary particle and its antimatter counterpart collide, they completely annihilate each other to create photons. The process can be reversed if the photons have enough energy (i.e., are high-energy gamma ray photons). Within the first microsecond (10^{-6} second), the universe was hot enough for the photon radiation to undergo this matter-antimatter particle transformation using massive particles like protons and neutrons. When the temperature dropped to about 10^{13} K at one microsecond after the Big Bang, this process stopped for the protons but it continued for the less massive particles like the electrons. Neutrons were not created in the energy-matter conversion process but some were created when protons and electrons fused together.

all protons made in first microsecond

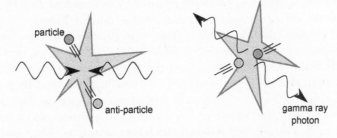

particle

anti-particle

gamma ray photon

In the first few seconds, photons convert to matter-antimatter and matter-antimatter convert to photons (Energy = mass × c²).
Process stops for **protons** after 10^{-6} seconds when temperature drops to about 10^{13} K.
Process stops for **electrons** after a few seconds when temperature drops to about 6×10^9 K.

When the universe had expanded for another few seconds, it cooled to a temperature of "only" 6×10^9 K and the electron-positron production and annihilation process ceased. This is also the time when the number of neutrons stopped increasing from the proton-electron fusion process. The number of neutrons was fixed at a ratio of 1 neutron for every 5 protons. For reasons not completely understood, there was a very slight excess of ordinary matter over antimatter (by about 1 part in 10^9). This is why there was still some ordinary matter left over when all the antimatter had been annihilated. (This must be the case, otherwise you would not be here!) *All of the protons, neutrons, and electrons in matter today were created in the first few seconds after the Big Bang.*

all electrons made in first few seconds

The extreme conditions described above have been reproduced in high-energy particle accelerators on Earth and the experiments have confirmed this description. For times much closer to the moment of the Big Bang we need to extend the theory beyond direct experimental bounds to much higher energies and temperatures. At a time of 10^{-38} to 10^{-36} second after the Big Bang, most early universe models say there was an ultra-fast expansion called "inflation". This will be discussed below in section 16.3.

16.1.8   Cosmic Abundance of Helium and Hydrogen

deuterium

The Big Bang theory provides a natural way to explain the present abundance of the elements. At about 2 to 3 minutes after the Big Bang, the expanding universe had cooled to below about 10^9 K so that protons and neutrons could fuse to make stable **deuterium** nuclei (a hydrogen isotope with one proton and one neutron) that would not be torn apart by energetic photons. Recall from chapter 12 that deuterium is one part of the fusion chain process used by nature to fuse hydrogen nuclei to make a helium nucleus. The fusion chain process in the early universe was slightly different than what occurs in stars because of the abundant free neutrons in the early universe. However, the general process is the same: protons react to produce deuterium, deuterium nuclei react to make Helium-3 nuclei, and Helium-3 nuclei react to make the stable Helium-4 nucleus.

fusion reactions in first several minutes create helium

The deuterium nucleus is the weak link of the chain process, so the fusion chain reactions could not take place until the universe had cooled enough. The exact temperature depends sensitively on the density of the protons and neutrons at that time. Extremely small amounts of Lithium-7 were also produced during the early universe nucleosynthesis process. After about 15 minutes from the Big Bang, the universe had expanded and cooled so much that fusion was no longer possible. The composition of the universe was 10% helium and 90% hydrogen (or if you use the proportions by *mass*, then the proportions are 25% helium and 75% hydrogen).

Except for the extremely small amounts of the Lithium-7 produced in the early universe, the elements heavier than helium were produced in the cores of stars. Stars do produce some of the helium visible today, but not most of it. If all the helium present today was from stars, then the nuclear reaction rates would have to be extremely high and the galaxies should be much brighter than they are.

importance of deuterium

The deuterium nucleus is a nucleus of special importance because of the sensitivity of its creation to the density of the protons and neutrons and temperature in the early universe. The number of deuterium nuclei that do not later undergo fusion reactions to make Helium-3 nuclei also depends sensitively on the temperature and density of the protons and neutrons. A denser universe would have had more deuterium fused to form helium. A less dense universe would have had more deuterium remaining. The amount of the final Helium-4 product is not as sensitive to the density of the early universe, so the amount of the remaining deuterium seen *today* is used as a probe of the *early density*. Therefore, measurement of the primordial deuterium can show if there is enough matter to make the universe positively-curved and eventually stop the expansion (section 16.2). Current measurements of the primordial deuterium show that the density of ordinary matter is about only 5% of the *critical density*—the boundary between having too little to stop the expansion and enough to eventually stop the expansion.

early density determines universe fate

primordial abundances test Big Bang theory

Measuring the abundances of the primordial material and comparing it with what is predicted in the Big Bang theory provides a crucial test of the theory. Astronomers have measured the abundances of primordial material in unprocessed gas in parts of the universe where there are no stars around to contaminate the gas when the stars die. The observed abundances match the predicted abundances very well.

The Big Bang nucleosynthesis also turns out to place great constraints on the variation of G, the gravitational constant, because a different value of G in those first few minutes than what we see today would have significantly changed the expansion rate of the universe and that would have significantly (measurably) altered the relative abundances of the primordial elements. The gravitational constant G appears to truly be constant. The Big Bang nucleosynthesis also provides constraints in the number of types of neutrinos in the universe. It shows that there cannot be more than the three types of neutrinos already given by the Standard Model of Particle Physics. More than three families of particles would also have significantly changed the expansion rate of the early universe to produce abundances of the primordial elements much different than what we observe. This result also constrains the possibilities for the nature of dark matter. Measuring the masses of galaxies and galaxy clusters through several independent methods shows us that the overall density of matter in the universe is about 30% of the *critical density* but Big Bang nucleosynthesis shows us that the density of ordinary matter is just 5% of the *critical density*. The dark matter must be made of particles that are not the usual protons, neutrons, electrons, etc. of ordinary matter. In fact, the dark matter must be made of particles not within the three families of particles in the Standard Model.

testing variation of gravitational constant

16.1.9 Evidence Supporting the General Big Bang Scheme

The Big Bang Theory is a natural result of Einstein's Theory of General Relativity as Lemaître showed back in the 1930s. What evidence is there for thinking the Big Bang theory is correct? The Big Bang theory may be nice but it has to pass the judgement of observation. Nature and experiments are the final judge of the correctness of scientific ideas. Though some details of the Big Bang still need to be perfected, the general scheme of an early hot universe with a definite beginning is accepted by most astronomers today. Even so, we have to be open to the possibility that future observations could show it to be wrong. The observations given below are sometimes said to be "proof" of the Big Bang theory. Actually, the observations are *consistent* with the Big Bang theory, but do not provide proof. Recall from the discussion in chapter 2 that scientific theories cannot be *proven* to be correct. As of now, the Big Bang theory is the only one that can explain all of these observations.

Big Bang vs. Steady State

1. The galaxies (or galaxy clusters) are systematically moving away from us such that the farther away galaxies are moving faster away from us. As a result of General Relativity this means that space itself is expanding carrying the galaxies with it. Both the Big Bang Theory and its major competitor, the Steady State Theory, could explain it. Recall that the Steady State Theory used the perfect cosmological principle while the Big Bang uses the cosmological principle.

2. The cosmic microwave background radiation can be explained only by the Big Bang theory. The background radiation is the relic of an early hot universe. The Steady State theory, could not explain the background radiation, and so fell into disfavor.

3. The amount of activity (active galaxies, quasars, collisions) was greater in the past than now. This shows that the universe does evolve (change) with time. The Steady State theory says that the universe should remain the same with time, so once again, it does not work.

4. The number of quasars drops off for very large redshifts (redshifts greater than about 50% of the speed of light). The Hubble-Lemaître Law says that

these are for large look-back times. This observation is taken to mean that the universe was not old enough to produce quasars at those large redshifts. The universe did have a beginning.

5. The observed abundance of hydrogen, helium, deuterium, lithium agrees with that predicted by the Big Bang theory. The abundances are checked from the spectra of the oldest stars and gas clouds which are made from unprocessed, primitive material. Even better observations are those made of light from very distant quasars that have passed through gas in regions of the universe where are no stars that could have contaminated the gas. The intervening intergalactic primordial gas imprints its signature on the quasar light giving us the composition of the primordial gas. All of those places have the predicted relative abundances.

Vocabulary

Big Bang   cosmic microwave background radiation   deuterium
recombination

Review Questions

1. What is the **cosmic microwave background radiation** a relic of?

2. What is the type of spectrum of the background radiation? What is the temperature of the Universe now?

3. What can the photons do when **recombination** occurs and why is that?

4. About when did the Big Bang supposedly occur?

5. What was the universe like for the first few million years after the Big Bang? How was the early universe like the cores of stars shining today?

6. Where did most of the hydrogen and helium in the universe come from? How about the deuterium? Why did the early universe not continue the nucleosynthesis process to heavier nuclei?

7. How does the present abundance of deuterium provide a good constraint on the early density of the universe?

8. What is the evidence for a Big Bang type of model for the universe and for a universe that has evolved over time?

16.2   Fate of the Universe

Now that you have explored the beginnings of the universe and have an answer to the question "where did we come from?", let's address the other question, "where are we going?" This final section will cover the fate of the universe. We observe that the universe is expanding and that gravity is slowing it down. Which of them will win?

16.2.1   Depends on Mass (Curvature of Space)

The more mass there is, the more gravity there is to slow down the expansion. Is there enough gravity to halt the expansion and recollapse the universe or not? If there is enough matter (gravity) to recollapse the universe, the universe is **"closed"**.
closed universe   In the examples of curved space above, a closed universe would be shaped like a four-dimensional sphere (finite, but unbounded). Space curves back on itself and time has a beginning and an end. If there is not enough matter, the universe will
open universe   keep expanding forever. Such a universe is **"open"**. In the examples of curved

space, an open universe would be shaped like a four-dimensional saddle (infinite and unbounded). Space curves away from itself and time has no end.

 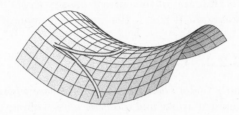

A *closed* universe curves "back on itself". Lines that were diverging apart come back together. Density > critical density.

An *open* universe curves "away from itself". Diverging lines curve at increasing angles away from each other. Density < critical density.

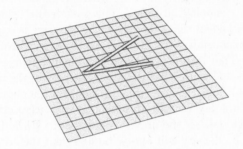

A *flat* universe has no curvature. Diverging lines remain at a constant angle with respect to each other. Density = critical density.

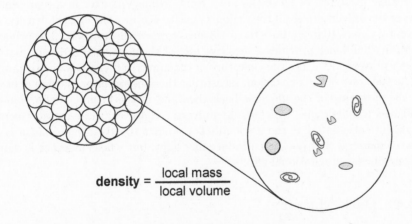

$$\textbf{density} = \frac{\text{local mass}}{\text{local volume}}$$

Find **density** of a representative volume of the universe.
Total mass = **density** × total volume.

Instead of trying to add up all of the mass in the universe, a more reasonable thing to do is to find the *density* of a representative region of the universe. The *density* = (mass in the region)/(volume of the region). If the region is truly representative, then the total mass of the universe = the *density* × the total volume of the universe. If the density is great enough, then the universe is closed. If the density is low enough, then the universe is open. In the popular astronomy magazines, you will probably see the mass density of the universe specified by the symbol Ω. It is the ratio of the current density to the "critical density" described in the next paragraph. If $\Omega < 1$, the universe is open; if $\Omega > 1$, the universe is closed.

Ω density parameter

16.2.2   Critical Density

critical density

The boundary density between the case where the universe has enough mass/volume to close universe and too little mass/volume to stop the expansion is called the **critical density.** The critical density = $3H^2/(8\pi G)$, where H is the Hubble constant *for a given cosmological time.*   Notice that the Hubble constant has appeared again! It measures the expansion rate, so it should be in the critical density relation. The *current* critical density is approximately 1.06×10^{-29} g/cm^3. This amounts to six hydrogen atoms per cubic *meter* on average overall.

flat universe

   A critical density universe has **"flat"** curvature.   The Ω density parameter equals exactly 1 in a **flat** universe. The Hubble "constant" is not really a constant—it is different at different cosmological times. The greater the value of the Hubble constant at a given cosmological time, the faster the universe is expanding at that time. Gravity slows the expansion of the universe, so the early universe was expanding faster than it is now. That means that the critical density was greater at earlier times. It changes by the same factor that the actual density of the universe changes throughout the expansion. So if the universe starts out with a density greater than the critical density, then its density will *always* be greater than critical density (a closed universe remains closed). If the universe starts out with a density less than the critical density, then its density will *always* be less than the critical density (an open universe remains open).

16.2.3   Is The Universe Open or Closed?

The curvature of the universe is determined by the density of the universe. You can do a cosmic inventory of all of the mass from ordinary matter in a representative region of the universe to see if the region's density is above the critical density. Such an inventory gives 10 to 20 times too little mass to close the universe. The primordial deuterium abundance provides a sensitive test of the density of ordinary matter in the *early* universe. Because the curvature of the universe (negative, positive, or flat) is set at the start of the expansion, measuring the amount of primordial deuterium gives the curvature of the universe back then and in the future. Again, you get 5 to 15 times too little mass to close the universe. However, these measurements do not take into account all of the **dark matter** known to exist. Dark matter is all of the extra material that does not produce any light, but whose presence is detected by its significant gravitational effects.

early density determines universe fate

dark matter

16.2.4   Dark Matter

There is much more dark matter mass than visible, glowing matter. Some of the dark matter is regular sort of matter (atoms) that is too faint for us to detect such as dead burned out stars, planets, brown dwarfs, gas and dust clouds, etc. The rest of the dark matter is made of material that is not made of atoms or their constituent parts. This strange material has a total mass about five times more than the total mass of the ordinary matter. Some evidence for the presence of dark matter has already been presented in the previous chapters. The list below summarizes the evidence for dark matter's existence.

1. Flat rotation curves of spirals even though the amount of the light-producing matter falls off as the distance from the galaxy center increases. Remember the enclosed mass = (orbital speed)$^2 \times$(orbit size)$/G$—see the previous chapters for more details of this.

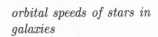

orbital speeds of stars in galaxies

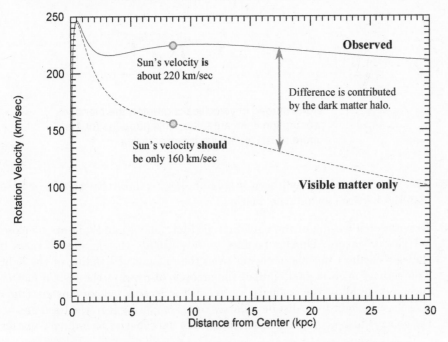

The gravity of the visible matter in the Galaxy is not enough to explain the high orbital speeds of stars in the Galaxy. For example, the Sun is moving about 60 km/sec too fast. The part of the rotation curve contributed by the visible matter only is the bottom curve. The discrepancy between the two curves is evidence for a **dark matter halo.**

Also, the orbital speeds of stars in elliptical galaxies are too high to be explained by the gravitational force of just the luminous matter in the galaxies. The extra gravitational force is supplied by the dark matter in the ellipticals.

2. Ellipticals have faint gas shells that need massive "dark" haloes to contain them. The gas particles are moving too quickly (they are too hot) for the gravity of the visible matter to hang onto it. However, the number of ellipticals with these faint gas shells is too large to be only a temporary feature of ellipticals. The dark haloes must extend out to 300,000 light years around each galaxy. The extent of this dark matter pushes Ω up to around 0.2. If the haloes are larger than originally thought, Ω be around 0.3.

faint gas shells around ellipticals

3. Galaxy cluster members are moving too fast to be gravitationally bound unless there is unseen mass. The reasonable assumption is that we do not live at a special time, so the galaxies in the cluster must have always been close to each other. The large velocities of the galaxies in the clusters are produced by more gravity force than can be explained with the gravity of the visible matter in the galaxies.

motion of galaxies in a cluster

4. The existence of HOT (i.e., fast moving) gas in galaxy clusters. To keep the gas bound to the cluster, there needs to be extra unseen mass.

hot gas in clusters

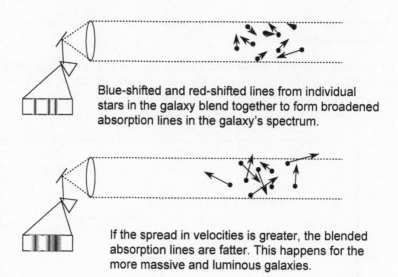

Blue-shifted and red-shifted lines from individual stars in the galaxy blend together to form broadened absorption lines in the galaxy's spectrum.

If the spread in velocities is greater, the blended absorption lines are fatter. This happens for the more massive and luminous galaxies.

quasar spectra

5. Absorption lines from hydrogen in quasar spectra show that there is a lot of material between us and the quasars.

gravitational lensing

6. Gravitational lensing of the light from distant galaxies and quasars by closer galaxies or galaxy clusters enables us to calculate the amount of mass in the closer galaxy or galaxy cluster from the amount of bending of the light. The derived mass is greater than the amount of mass in the visible matter. Inventorying all of the ordinary matter in the lensing galaxy clusters (those that lens the light from distant galaxies) and comparing it to the total mass of the galaxy clusters gives a five-to-one ratio of dark matter to ordinary matter.

separation of dark matter from ordinary matter in galaxy cluster collision

7. The collision of the galaxy cluster 1E 0657-56, called the "bullet cluster", with another galaxy cluster has produced a clear separation of the ordinary matter from the dark matter. The ordinary matter of one cluster is slowed by a drag force as it interacts with the gas (ordinary matter) of the other cluster. The dark matter is not slowed by the impact because it responds only to gravity and is not affected by gas pressure. See the textbook's website for a color picture highlighting the two forms of matter in the collision and more details. The more recent observation of the MACS J0025.4-1222 cluster collision has shown the same sort of separation of dark matter from ordinary matter.

Current tallies of the total mass of the universe (visible and dark matter) indicate that there is only 32% of the matter needed to halt the expansion—we live in an open universe. Ordinary matter amounts to almost 5% and dark matter makes up the other 27%. One possible dark matter candidate was the neutrino. There are a lot of them, they have neutral charge and photons do not bump into them. Unfortunately, their mass is too small and they move much too fast to create the clumpy structure we see of the dark matter and ordinary matter. The universe would not have been able to make the galaxies and galaxy clusters if the dark matter was neutrinos. To create the lumpy universe, astronomers are looking at possible massive neutral particles that move relatively slowly. Various candidates fall under the heading of "WIMPs"—weakly interacting massive particles (sometimes, astronomers and

WIMPs

physicists can be clever in their names). Another possible dark matter candidate was simply ordinary matter locked up in dim things like white dwarfs, brown dwarfs, neutron stars, or black holes in the halos of the galaxies. These massive compact

MACHOs

halo objects ("MACHOs") can be detected via microlensing like that used to detect exoplanets. Some MACHOs have been found but the number (and resulting total mass) of them appears to be much too small to account for the dark matter. Big Bang nucleosynthesis and the microwave background radiation (as described below) also provide a strict upper limit on the amount of ordinary matter that could produce the MACHOs in any case. As if the dark matter mystery were not enough, astronomers and physicists have now found that there is an additional form of energy not associated with ordinary or dark matter, called "dark energy", that has an even greater effect on the fate of the universe. This is discussed further in the last section of this chapter.

16.2.5 Deriving the Geometry of the Universe from the Background Radiation

An independent way to measure the overall geometry of the universe is to look at the fluctuations in the cosmic microwave background radiation. If the universe is open (saddle-shaped), then lines starting out parallel will diverge (bend) away from each other (see the first figure of section 16.2.1). This will make distant objects look smaller than they would otherwise, so the ripples in the microwave background will appear largest on the half-degree scale. If the universe is flat, then lines starting out parallel will remain parallel. The ripples in the microwave background will appear largest on the 1-degree scale. If the universe is closed, the lines starting out parallel will eventually converge toward each other and meet. This focusing effect will make distant objects look larger than they would otherwise, so the ripples in the microwave background will appear largest on scales larger than 1-degree. See the figure below (courtesy of the NASA/WMAP Science Team).

open: lumps look smaller

closed: lumps look larger

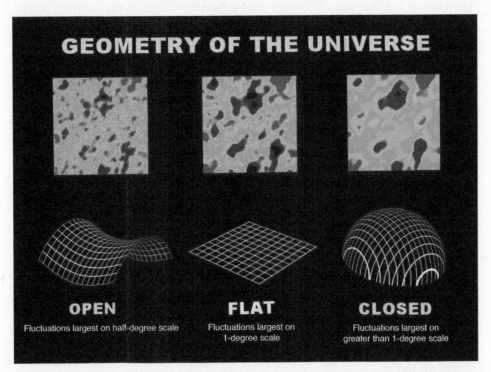

GEOMETRY OF THE UNIVERSE

OPEN
Fluctuations largest on half-degree scale

FLAT
Fluctuations largest on 1-degree scale

CLOSED
Fluctuations largest on greater than 1-degree scale

The resolution of the COBE satellite was about 7 degrees—not good enough to definitively measure the angular sizes of the fluctuations. After COBE, higher-resolution instruments were put up in high-altitude balloons and high mountains to observe the ripples in small patches of the sky. Those experiments indicated a flat geometry for the universe (to within 0.4% uncertainty). Cosmologists using the high resolution of the WMAP satellite to look at the distribution of sizes of the

COBE view too fuzzy

high-resolution view shows the universe is flat

ripples confirmed that conclusion using its all-sky map of microwave background at a resolution over 30 times better than COBE. WMAP also gave a much improved measurement of the ripples. The distribution of the ripples peaks at the one-degree scale—the universe is flat, a result confirmed by the even higher precision Planck satellite with over 2.5 times higher resolution than WMAP.

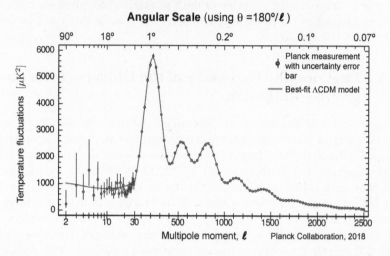

This result from the WMAP and Planck satellites and the too meager amount of matter in the universe to make the universe geometry flat along with the observed acceleration of the universe's expansion rate are forcing astronomers to conclude that there is another form of energy that makes up 68.5% of the universe (called "dark energy" for lack of anything better). The "dark energy" is probably the "cosmological constant" discussed in the last section of this chapter. Furthermore, the distribution of the sizes of the ripples shows that some sizes are preferred and other sizes are damped out as would be the case if the dark matter was different from ordinary matter. The size distribution, the spectrum of sizes, gives the ratio of dark matter to ordinary matter. Dark matter not made of atoms or other particles in the Standard Model makes up 26.5% of the universe, leaving just 5.0% of the universe with what the rest of the previous chapters of this textbook have been about (ordinary matter). That ratio matches up very nicely with the ratios found using the other independent methods of Big Bang nucleosynthesis and the motions of galaxies.

dark energy

In addition to the dark energy, dark matter, and ordinary matter terms, the model used to fit the observed spectrum of the sizes of the ripples and the polarization spectrum also includes terms for how far sound waves traveled when the microwave background photons were released, the scattering of the microwave background photons by high energy electrons in galaxy clusters, and a couple of terms for the density fluctuations at the end of the "inflation period" described in the last section of this chapter. The closest or best fit of the model to the ripple size and polarization spectra can be used to derive what the Hubble Constant should be for today. The result is 67.4 km/sec/Mpc with an uncertainty of just 0.5 km/sec/Mpc.

Hubble Constant derived from microwave background fluctuations

Vocabulary

closed universe   critical density   dark matter
flat universe   open universe

Review Questions

1. What is the overall curvature of space in a **closed** or **open** or **flat** universe? How does the expansion rate compare to the amount of gravity deceleration

in each of these cases?

2. Why is the universe's expansion rate slowing down?

3. Will it ever slow down completely? How can you find out?

4. What type of universe has a **critical density**? What would happen to the expansion if the current density < critical density? How about the case for the current density > critical density?

5. Would a universe starting out with a density > critical density ever expand enough so its density dropped below critical density? Explain why or why not!

6. What is all the fuss about **dark matter**? If it is not putting out any light for us to see, how is it known to exist? What are some examples of observations indicating its presence?

7. How can you use the cosmic microwave background (something from the far past) to determine the fate of the universe (something in the far future)?

16.3   Embellishments on the Big Bang

There are a couple of problems with the standard Big Bang model. The first is called the *flatness problem*—why is the universe density so nearly at the critical density or put another way, why is the universe so flat? Currently, the universe is so well-balanced between the positively-curved closed universe and the negatively-curved open universe that astronomers have a hard time figuring out which model to choose. Of all the possibilities from very positively-curved (very high density) to very negatively-curved (very low density), the current nearly flat condition is definitely a special case. The balance would need to have been even finer nearer the time of the Big Bang because any deviation from perfect balance gets magnified over time. For example, if the universe density was slightly greater than the critical density a billion years after the Big Bang, the universe would have re-collapsed by now.

flatness problem

universe should be either very obviously open or very obviously closed after 13.8 billion years

Consider the analogy of the difficulty of shooting an arrow at a small target from a distance away. If your angle of shooting is a little off, the arrow misses the target. The permitted range of deviation from the true direction gets narrower and narrower as you move farther and farther away from the target. The earlier in time the universe's curvature became fixed, the more finely tuned the density must have been to make the universe's current density be so near the critical density. If the curvature of the universe was just a few percent off from perfect flatness within a few seconds after the Big Bang, the universe would have either re-collapsed before fusion ever began or the universe would expanded so much that it would seem to be devoid of matter. It appears that the density/curvature was very finely tuned.

The second problem with the standard Big Bang model is the *horizon problem*— why does the universe, particularly the microwave background, look the same in all directions? The only way for two regions to have the same conditions (e.g., temperature), is that they are close enough to each other for information to be exchanged between them so that they can equilibrate to a common state. The fastest speed that information can travel is the speed of light. If two regions are far enough apart that light has not had enough time to travel between the regions, the regions are isolated from each other. The regions are said to be beyond their *horizons* because the regions cannot be in contact with each other (recall the term *event horizon* in the discussion about black holes).

horizon problem

universe is too uniform, too smooth

The photons from the microwave background have been traveling nearly the age of the universe to reach us right now. Those photons have certainly not had the time to travel across the entire universe to the regions in the opposite direction from which they came. Yet when astronomers look in the opposite directions, they see that the microwave background looks the same to very high precision. How can the regions be so precisely the same if they are beyond each other's horizons? Running the expansion backward, astronomers find that apart should be regions even a degree apart in angular separation on the sky would have been beyond each other's horizons at the time the microwave background was produced.

even neighboring patches of the sky should be very different from each other

16.3.1 Inflation

On theoretical grounds, astronomers think that the very early universe experienced a time of ultra-fast expansion (called **inflation**). The inflation probably took place from about 10^{-38} to 10^{-36} seconds after the Big Bang, but astronomers are not sure of the cause of inflation so they cannot pinpoint the time it would have occurred. The size of the fluctuations in the cosmic microwave background indicate that the inflation could not have occurred before 10^{-38} seconds after the Big Bang. The leading theory for the cause of the inflation says that it occurred when there was a break in the fundamental forces of nature. Before the time of 10^{-38} seconds after the Big Bang, the fundamental forces of the strong nuclear force, the weak nuclear force, and electromagnetic force behaved in the same way under the extreme temperatures. They were part of the same fundamental unified force. Theories that describe the conditions when the forces were unified are called *Grand Unified Theories* (GUTs for short). At about 10^{-38} seconds after the Big Bang, the universe had cooled down to "only" 10^{29} K and the strong nuclear force broke away from the weak nuclear and electromagnetic forces. This breaking apart of the forces from each other somehow produced the huge expansion that expanded the universe by about 10^{50} times in about 10^{-36} seconds.

inflation

GUTs

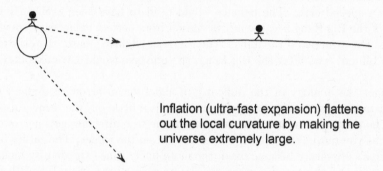

Inflation (ultra-fast expansion) flattens out the local curvature by making the universe extremely large.

flat universe

The inflation theory predicts that the ultra-fast inflation would have expanded away any large-scale curvature of the part of the universe we can detect. It is analogous to taking a small globe and expanding it to the size of the Earth. The globe is still curved but the local piece you would see would appear to be fairly flat. The small universe inflated by a *large* amount and the part of the universe you can observe appears to be nearly flat. That solves the flatness problem.

The horizon problem is solved by inflation because regions that appear to be isolated from each other were in contact with each other before the inflation period (see the figure on the next page). They came into equilibrium before inflation expanded them far away from each other. Another bonus is that the GUTs that predict inflation also predict an asymmetry between matter and antimatter, so that there should be an excess of matter over antimatter.

making   the   "galaxy seeds"

The inflation theory might also explain where the ripples in the microwave background (the "galaxy seeds") come from. Recall from section 16.1.7 that matter-antimatter can change to energy and energy can change back to matter-antimatter. The laws of physics that deal with the very small scales of atoms, sub-atomic parti-

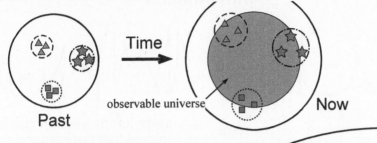

NO inflation: observable universe (shaded) includes parts that are different from each other

Past — Time → observable universe — Now

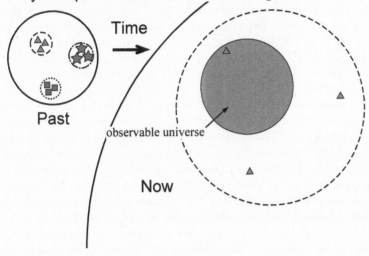

Inflation: observable universe (shaded) includes only one part that is the same throughout

Past — Time → observable universe — Now

cles, etc. (quantum mechanics) predict that the matter-energy fluctuations should be going on even today at every point in space. It turns out that these quantum fluctuations can occur if they happen quickly enough to not be noticed (the greater the energy-matter fluctuation, the quicker the fluctuation must occur). Therefore, even in perfectly empty space (complete vacuum), there is a seething froth of fluctuations at very tiny scales, a *vacuum energy*—matter-antimatter virtual particles spontaneously appearing and then annihilating each other too quickly for us to detect. Although virtual particles-quantum foam might seem a bit too fanciful (to put it kindly), these virtual particles do produce measurable effects such as:

vacuum energy

quantum   fluctuations proof

- In an atom, the appearance of electron-positron virtual particles will alter the orbit of the real electron orbiting the nucleus altering the energy levels which can be measured with very sensitive, precise equipment. The measured energy levels agree with those predicted by quantum if virtual particles are taken into account.

- Extra forces generated between close metal plates (the "Casimir Effect") can be explained by the presence of more virtual particles on either side of the plates than in the gap between the plates.

- Collisions of real particles and real antiparticles in high-energy particle accelerators can supply energy to the vacuum and cause other particle-antiparticles to appear.

Now back to inflation. The quantum fluctuations in the very early universe could have been the galaxy seeds, but they would have been much too small to be the

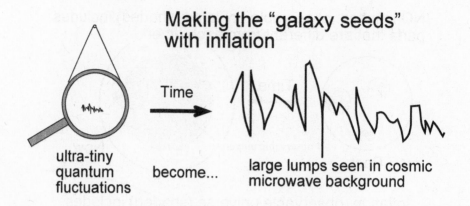

Making the "galaxy seeds" with inflation

Time

ultra-tiny quantum fluctuations

become...

large lumps seen in cosmic microwave background

ripples we see in the cosmic microwave background. Before inflation that is! The super-rapid growth of the universe during inflation would have stretched the fluctuations to much larger sizes—large enough to create the ripples in the microwave background that eventually became enhanced to form galaxies under the action of gravity over billions of years. Although the current versions of inflation theory cannot answer all of the questions about the large-scale structures of our universe, they do predict a particular distribution of the ripple sizes in the microwave background that is consistent with the results from the high-altitude balloon experiments, the WMAP mission, and the Planck mission. The distribution of the ripples peaks at an angular size of one degree on the sky and the temperature varies by about 1 part in 100,000 as predicted by inflation. As astronomers continue to analyze data from the Planck spacecraft, they will be looking at how the microwave background photons scattered off the electrons just before the universe became transparent. Scattering causes light to become preferentially oriented in a particular way (it is "polarized", see the end of section 16.1.6). The simplest version of inflation predicts a particular polarization of the microwave background that appears to be seen in the WMAP data. WMAP and Planck scientists will look for the imprint of gravitational waves from inflation which would provide much stronger evidence for the inflation theory.

A much-heralded discovery in March 2014 by the Background Imaging of Cosmic Extragalactic Polarization 2 (BICEP2) experiment at the South Pole of gravitational wave signatures in the microwave background turned out to be the result of an older incorrect model of the microwave emission from the interstellar dust in our galaxy that contaminates the cosmic microwave background. The BICEP2 team released its findings early so the observations could be checked by other research teams, including several others operating at the South Pole and the high elevation of the Atacama Desert in South America. Both places have cold, dry air that is very stable. The Planck team and the BICEP2 team then collaborated together to produce the most accurate model of what signals from the ancient gravitational waves should look like and showed in January 2015 that the earlier announcement was incorrect. The search for the gravitational waves imprint on the microwave background continues!

16.3.2   The Cosmological Constant

Albert Einstein completed his theory of General Relativity in 1915. When he applied his theory to the spacetime of the universe, he found that gravity would not permit the universe to be static. Over a decade before Hubble's discovery of an expanding universe, Einstein made the reasonable assumption that the universe is static and unchanging (the perfect cosmological principle). He introduced a term called the **cosmological constant** that would act as a repulsive form of gravity to balance the

cosmological constant

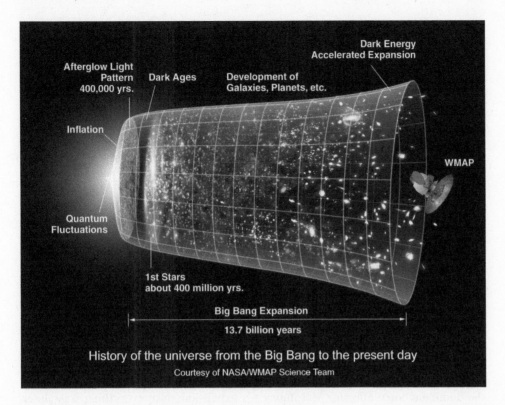

Afterglow Light
Pattern
400,000 yrs.

Dark Ages

Development of
Galaxies, Planets, etc.

Dark Energy
Accelerated Expansion

Inflation

WMAP

Quantum
Fluctuations

1st Stars
about 400 million yrs.

Big Bang Expansion

13.7 billion years

History of the universe from the Big Bang to the present day

Courtesy of NASA/WMAP Science Team

attractive nature of gravity. The cosmological constant is an exotic form of energy filling empty space, the *vacuum energy* discussed above. The vacuum energy creates a repulsive gravitational force that does not depend on position or time; it truly is a constant. When Einstein learned of Hubble's discovery, he realized that he should have had more faith in his original General Relativity. He discarded the cosmological constant as the "biggest blunder of his life".

vacuum energy

Recent observations are indicating that the cosmological constant should be brought back. Astronomers are finding that even when they include the maximum amount of dark matter allowed by the observations, there is not enough matter (luminous or dark) to flatten the universe—the universe is open with negative curvature if the cosmological constant is zero. The inflation theory predicts that the universe should be flat to very high precision. An extra energy called **dark energy** is needed to make the universe curvature flat overall beyond what ordinary and dark matter can do. This dark energy is probably the cosmological constant (vacuum energy) described above. Recent observations of the cosmic microwave background show that the combined efforts of matter and dark energy flatten space as much as that predicted by inflation theory.

flat curvature requires "dark energy"

dark energy

One major stumbling block in the theory of the cosmological constant is that quantum theory predicts that the total vacuum energy should be on the order of 10^{120} times larger than what is observed. The cosmological constant predicted from quantum theory would cause the universe to expand so fast that you would not be able to see your hand in front of your face because the light would not be able to reach your eyes! In reality we can see to billions of light years. Physicists are trying to figure out why there is such a big discrepancy between the quantum theory's prediction and observation. Some cosmologists are exploring the idea of a dark energy that varies with space and time called "quintessence". Stay tuned for developments!

quantum theory predicts too large cosmological constant

A crucial set of observations of very distant ("high-Z") Type Ia supernovae by two independent teams showed that the expansion rate is slower than expected from

Type Ia supernova

a flat universe. Type Ia supernovae are very luminous and can be used as standard candles to measure very large distances because they form from the collapse of a stellar core of a particular mass (1.4 solar masses). By measuring very large distances, astronomers can determine the geometry of the universe. The supernovae were fainter than expected. After exploring and then disproving ordinary possibilities like intergalactic dust, gravitational lensing effects, and metallicity effects, the two teams were forced to conclude that either the universe has negative curvature (is open) or that the supernovae are farther away than the Hubble-Lemaître Law says they are—their redshifts are "too small" because the universe expanded more slowly in the past than expected. What was surprising about the supernova observations was that they showed that the expansion is *accelerating!* This surprising result would have been discounted at the start if it was found by just one team of astronomers. The fact that two independent, highly-competitive teams (eager to prove the other team wrong) found the same surprising result that was the *opposite of their expectations* meant that the accelerating universe conclusion could not be discounted. The two teams eventually got the Nobel Prize in Physics (in 2011) for their discovery. Since then other teams have confirmed that the universe's expansion has been accelerating for the past several billion years.

accelerating universe

Accelerating expansion is impossible without a repulsive cosmological constant to overcome the slowing down effect of gravity. An accelerating universe will increase the derived age of the universe because the expansion rate long ago was *slower* than the expansion rate is now. The galaxies needed more time to get to their large distances than the original decelerating universe model said. Long ago gravity was the dominant force affecting the universe's expansion since everything was closer together. As the universe expanded the effect of gravity got diluted. Eventually, the strength of gravity dropped below the amount of the dark energy. Recent observations of how the expansion rate has changed over the history of the universe show that the dark energy began to dominate over gravity about 4 billion to 6 billion years ago but its presence began to be felt up to about 9 billion years ago.

fate of universe with dark energy

The far future of the universe depends on the form that dark energy takes. If the dark energy is the cosmological constant, then the expansion of the universe will continue long after all of the stars have died out many trillions of years in the future. If the dark energy is one of the possible forms of "quintessence", the acceleration rate increases and the galaxies, stars, even atoms are torn apart in a "big rip" on a time scale before all of the stars die out (but after our Sun dies). Other forms of the dark energy could cause the universe to re-collapse after its current period of acceleration.

Detailed studies of the microwave background and further observations of supernovae with better detectors such as the Dark Energy Survey and new larger space telescopes in the future will tell us if the dark energy is a cosmological constant or a quintessence form. Results from the WMAP and Planck missions and refined measurements of Hubble Constant with the Hubble Space Telescope lean toward the cosmological constant form. However, we have learned enough from the past few years of surprising observations to say that Einstein's greatest blunder was saying that he made a blunder!

disagreement about Hubble Constant

The Planck data has created a significant tension with measurements of the Hubble Constant. The Hubble Constant found from careful measurement of the distance scale ladder finds the Hubble Constant to be 73.5 ± 1.6 km/sec/Mpc. The Planck derivation from measurements of the cosmic microwave background radiation is just 67.4 ± 0.5 km/sec/ Mpc. Although they are close to each other, the 6.1 km/sec/Mpc difference is much larger than the uncertainties. That might be telling us of unexpected complexities in the dark energy or some new exotic particle (besides whatever is the dark matter) that needs to be added to the standard model of cosmology and particle physics or there's some peculiarity in our part of the universe that affects the expansion rate in a way we haven't accounted for. Unfortunately, changes to the standard model would throw off the excellent fit of the standard model to other features of the microwave background. The discrepancy will be resolved in the typical way of science: cross-checking of the analyses, gathering more data, and creative modifications to our understanding of the underlying physics.

Vocabulary

cosmological constant   dark energy   inflation

Review Questions

1. What is the "flatness" problem in the standard Big Bang theory? How is it a fine-tuning problem?

2. What is the "horizon" problem in the standard Big Bang theory?

3. What is the **inflation** extension of the Big Bang theory and when is thought to have occurred in the universe's history?

4. How does the **inflation** extension of the Big Bang theory explain the "flatness" and "horizon" problems that are part of the standard Big Bang theory?

5. How do we know that quantum fluctuations - virtual particles exist?

6. What is the "**cosmological constant**" and why did Einstein invent it? Why did Einstein say that was a mistake? Why do cosmologists now say it was not a mistake?

7. How does **dark energy** affect the expansion of the universe?

Chapter 17

Life Beyond the Earth

This chapter covers the concept of a habitable zone and the types of stars to focus on in the search for suitable planets. The basic definitions of life and the kind of planet where we think life would likely arise are covered next. At the end of the chapter the frequencies used in the Search for Extra-terrestrial Intelligence (S.E.T.I.) is discussed. The vocabulary terms in the text are in boldface.

17.1 Habitable Zones and Suitable Stars for E.T.

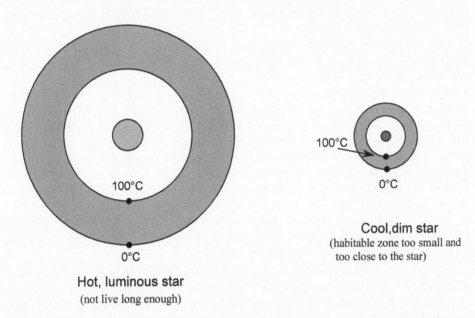

Hot, luminous star
(not live long enough)

Cool, dim star
(habitable zone too small and
too close to the star)

Habitable zones (life zones) for two different luminosity stars. The hot, luminous star has a large, wide habitable zone while the cool, dim star has a small, thin habitable zone. Stars with masses between 0.7 and 1.5 solar masses will live long enough for intelligent life to develop and have habitable zones that are far enough from the star.

For reasons explained elsewhere in this chapter, our search for inhabited exoplanets is focusing on those that have *water-based* life existing on the *surface* of the exoplanet. The **habitable zone**, or life zone, is the distance from a star where the temperature *on the surface* is between the freezing point (0° C) and boiling point (100° C) of water. If you consider a planet with the same reflectivity (clouds and surface material) as the Earth, reradiates the solar energy it absorbed as efficiently

habitable zone

539

as the Earth does, and rotates as quickly as the Earth does, then the habitable zone for the Sun (a G2 main sequence star) is between approximately 0.63 and 1.15 A.U. Calculations that include the effects of the greenhouse effect and whether or not there is a runaway process and ultraviolet dissociation of water like what happened on Venus shift the Sun's habitable zone outward so that the Earth is nearer the inside edge of the habitable zone. Climate research is still at the beginning stages of development, so the habitable zone boundaries are a bit uncertain. Note that the discussion in this section ignores the effect of internal heating that could create liquid water places at much greater distances from the star (e.g., tidal heating of a jovian planet's moon as described in section 9.7.2).

The habitable zone of a hotter main sequence star will be farther out and wider because of the hotter star's greater luminosity. Using the same line of reasoning, the habitable zone of a cooler main sequence star will be closer to the star and narrower. You can use the inverse square law of light brightness to determine the extent of the habitable zones for different luminosity stars. The boundary distance is

$$\text{star boundary} = \text{Sun boundary} \times \sqrt{(\text{star luminosity})/(\text{Sun luminosity})}.$$

For example, if the Sun's habitable zone boundaries are 0.9 and 1.5 A.U, the inner and outer bounds of the habitable zone for a star like Vega, an A0-type main sequence star with (Vega luminosity/Sun luminosity = 53) are 6.6 to 10.9 A.U., respectively. For a cool star like Kapteyn's Star. a M0 main sequence star with (Kapteyn's star luminosity/Sun luminosity = 0.004), the habitable zone stretches from only 0.056 to 0.095 A.U.

Gliese 581c

One of the first exoplanets discovered that orbits in its star's habitable zone is "Gliese 581c". "Gliese 581c" orbits in the habitable zone of an M3-type star, Gliese 581, about 20.4 light years from us. Gliese 581 has a luminosity = 0.013 solar luminosities (even though it is a cooler spectral type than Kapteyn's star). That would put the habitable zone of Gliese 581 between 0.1 AU and 0.17 AU. What is even more intriguing is that Gliese 581c has a mass of just five times the Earth (though that is a minimum derived mass), so it should have a solid surface that liquid water could collect upon as well as enough gravity to hold onto an atmosphere. This planet and the another slightly more massive planet (at a minimum of 8 Earth masses) orbiting Gliese 581 will certainly be studied a lot over the coming years! A major problem with the planet's habitability is its very close distance to the star as described in the next section. Since its discovery, many other exoplanets have been discovered in the habitable zones of their planetary systems, especially by the Kepler mission as described in section 10.9.1.

The much-heralded conclusion that 1 in 5 sun-like stars have an Earth-sized planet (1 to 2 Earth diameters in size) orbiting in their habitable zone is for stars of spectral type G and K and uses an optimistic estimate of the habitable zone boundaries where the inner boundary is the planet receiving up to four times the flux of energy from its star than the Earth receives from the Sun and the outer boundary is the planet receiving as little as 0.25 times (one-fourth) the flux of energy from its star than the Earth receives from the Sun. For a star like the Sun, that corresponds to 0.5 to 2 A.U. Both Venus and Mars would fit within that definition of the habitable zone. More conservative (pessimistic) estimates of the habitable zone that narrow the region drop the fraction of sun-like stars with an Earth-sized planet in the habitable zone down to 6 to 9%. Even with this smaller fraction, though, the potential Earth-analogues in our galaxy alone would number in the hundreds of millions for just the sun-like stars. As explained in the next section, it is possible that suitable stars with habitable planets orbiting them could be much more than just the sun-like stars.

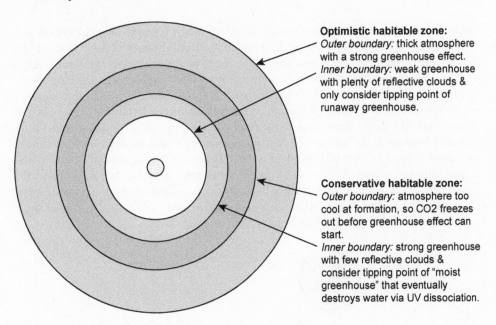

Optimistic habitable zone:
Outer boundary: thick atmosphere with a strong greenhouse effect.
Inner boundary: weak greenhouse with plenty of reflective clouds & only consider tipping point of runaway greenhouse.

Conservative habitable zone:
Outer boundary: atmosphere too cool at formation, so CO2 freezes out before greenhouse effect can start.
Inner boundary: strong greenhouse with few reflective clouds & consider tipping point of "moist greenhouse" that eventually destroys water via UV dissociation.

17.1.1 Suitable Stars

Despite the fact that hotter, more massive stars have wider habitable zones, astronomers are focusing their search on main sequence stars with masses of 0.5 to 1.4 solar masses. Why are these types of stars more likely to have intelligent life evolve on planets around them? You will need to include the main sequence lifetime and the distance and width of the star's habitable zone in any consideration of suitable stars.

First consider the lifetime of a star. Let's assume that it takes 3 billion years for intelligence to evolve on a planet (note, though, that Earth took about 4.5 billion years). The star must last at least 3 billion years! Use lifetime = (mass/luminosity) $\times$ 10 billion years = $1/M^3 \times$ 10 billion years if the star's mass is in units of solar masses. The most massive star's (1.4 solar masses) lifetime = 3.6 billion years (a 1.5-solar mass star with a lifetime = 3.0 billion years would just barely work too). *star must last long enough*

The less massive stars have longer lifetimes but the habitable zones get narrower and closer to the star as you consider less and less massive stars. At the outer boundary of the habitable zone the temperature is 0° C for all of the stars and the inner boundary is at 100° C for all of the stars. You can use the observed mass-luminosity relation $L = M^4$ in the habitable zone boundary relation given above to put everything in terms of just the mass. Substituting M^4 for the luminosity L, the 1.4-solar mass star's habitable zone is between 1.76 A.U. and 2.94 A.U. from the star (plenty wide enough). The 0.5-solar mass star's habitable zone is only 0.23 A.U. to 0.38 A.U. from the star. Planets too close to the star will get their rotations tidally locked so one side of planet always faces the star (this is what has happened to the Moon's spin as it orbits the Earth, for example). On such a planet the night side temperature could drop so much that the atmosphere froze out. This actually happens for 0.7-solar mass stars, but if the planet has a massive moon close by, then the tidal locking will happen between the planet and moon. This lowers the least massive star limit to around 0.5 solar masses. The "super-Earths" of Gliese 581 would be tidally-locked to their star (Gliese 581 has a mass of only 0.31 solar masses). *tidal locking of planet rotation* *M-stars not good?*

On the other hand, if the planet has a thick carbon-dioxide atmosphere, the atmosphere could circulate enough heat between the day and night sides to keep the surface temperatures uniform (like Venus). Most small, cool M stars have *closer look at M-stars* frequent stellar flares with more energy than our Sun's flares that could kill off any complex life. Perhaps a planet with thick enough atmosphere to keep the surface temperatures uniform could also provide enough of a shield from the flares. Also, a planet larger than Earth might be able generate a strong enough magnetic shield to protect the atmosphere. The very narrow habitable zone of the small, cool stars would mean a small chance of finding a nice planet in the habitable zone. On the other hand, the sheer number of M stars in the Galaxy (recall from section 11.2.5 that the M stars make up the greatest proportion of stars) means that there could be many habitable worlds around M stars. Based on the census of stars by the Kepler mission, about 50% or so of the M stars have a planet between 0.5 to 1.4 Earth diameters orbiting within their habitable zone. That statistic means that the closest Earth-size exoplanet having its orbit aligned just right with our line of sight so the exoplanet transits its star is just 29 light years away.

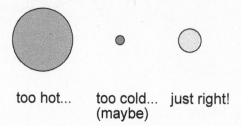

too hot...   too cold...   just right!
             (maybe)

need metal-rich star

Any life forms will need to use some of the elements heavier than helium (e.g., carbon, nitrogen, oxygen, phosphorus, sulfur, chromium, iron, and nickel) for biochemical reactions. This means that the gas cloud which forms the star and its planets will have to be enriched with these heavy elements (called "metals" by astronomers as a catch-all term) from previous generations of stars. If the star has a metal-rich spectrum, then any planets forming around it will be enriched as well. This narrows the stars to the ones of Population I—in the disk of the Galaxy. Now that the Kepler mission has built up enough planet detections, researchers have been able to separate out enough stars with small planets from those with larger jovian planets to have decent statistics from which to draw valid conclusions. They find that smaller planets can form around stars with metallicities as low as just a quarter that of the Sun while the jovian planets require more metal-enriched environments. This result means that small terrestrial-sized planets could be more common in the galaxy (and the rest of the universe) than previously thought. Most searches are focusing on the stars more like the Sun that are not too hot nor too cool—those with masses between 0.5 and 1.4 solar masses. Some searches are including the M stars but they will need to look at a *large* number of M stars to improve their chances of finding the ones with habitable planets.

metal-rich Pop I star with mass 0.5–1.4 solar masses

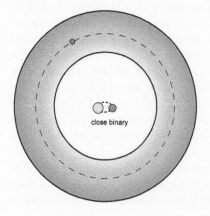

close binary

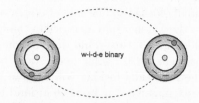

w-i-d-e binary

Habitable zones for stable planet orbits in binary systems
Left: A *circumbinary planet* (orbiting both stars in a close binary system).
    Stable planet orbit is very large in comparison to binary star separation.
Right: A wide binary system, where star-star distance remains very large in
    comparison to stable orbits of the planets.
(These drawings are NOT to scale!)

Most stars in the Galaxy have at least one stellar companion—binary or multiple star systems. Stars like our Sun with no stellar companion are in the minority. It would probably be difficult for there to be stable, only slightly elliptical planet orbits in a binary or multiple star system. Complex life (multi-cellular) will need to have a stable temperature regime to form so the planet orbit cannot be too eccentric. Simple life like bacteria might be able to withstand large temperature changes on a planet with a significantly elliptical orbit but complex life is the much more interesting case. Suitable binary stars would be those systems where either the binary stars orbit very close to each other with the planet(s) orbiting both of them at a large distance (called a "circumbinary planet") or the binary stars orbit very far from each other so the planet(s) could reside in stable orbits near each of the stars—the one star's gravity acting on a planet would be much stronger than that of the other star.

binary stars?

The first discovery of a binary star system with a planet is the first case (orbiting both of them—circumbinary planet): the Kepler-16 stars are a K-type star with 69% the mass of the Sun and a M-type star with 20% the mass of the Sun orbiting each other every 41 days. The planet, Kepler-16b, about the mass of Saturn, orbits them both every 229 days, well outside the habitable zone of the combined stars. The planet was discovered using the transit technique (see section 10.9.1). Since Kepler-16's discovery in 2011, several other circumbinary planets have been discovered, so we now know that Kepler-16 is not an unusual or rare case. Kepler 47 is a circumbinary planet system that has at least two planets, one of which is in the habitable zone. In October 2012, a circumbinary planet in a quadruple star system was announced. The planet named PH1 is slightly larger than Neptune and has less than half a Jupiter mass. It orbits the two inner stars every 138.5 days and well outside PH1's orbit is a binary star system that orbits the first binary (primary pair) at about 1000 AU. The habitable zone of the primary pair is outside the orbit of PH1. Might there be other planets in this system?

Kepler-16b

Kepler 47

PH1: exoplanet in a quadruple star system

Also in October 2012 was the announcement of a planet in the Alpha Centauri trinary system, the closest star system to us. Using the doppler shift technique, the research team claimed they found a planet with a minimum mass of just 1.13 times the Earth orbiting Alpha Centauri B at only 6 million kilometers with a period of 3.24 days. The size of the doppler wobble at just 0.51 meter per second (or about the speed of a baby crawling) was at the limit of detection by the doppler shift technique, so verification of the claim by independent research teams were definitely required as is standard for the science process. Three years later a different research team found that the faint signal of the planet was actually a statistical artifact of how the original data was processed and analyzed. No planet.

In August 2016 a more promising claim was made of an exoplanet orbiting Proxima Centauri, the third star of the Alpha Centauri system. At 1.38 meters per second, Proxima Centauri's wobble is almost three times the size of the one claimed for Alpha Centauri B in 2012. The brighter two stars, Alpha Centauri A and B are a spectroscopic binary—orbiting close enough to each other that to the naked eye, they appear as one object with a combined brightness that makes them the third brightest star in the sky after Sirius and Canopus. Alpha Centauri A is a G2-type star, slightly hotter than the Sun and Alpha Centauri B is a K1-type star, slightly cooler than the Sun. Alpha Cen A and B orbit each other in an elliptical orbit that brings them as close as 11.2 AU and as far as 35.6 AU. The third star of the system, Proxima Centauri is a small red dwarf M6-type star that orbits very far from the central pair at a distance of about 15,000 AU.

Proxima Centauri b

Proxima Centauri's planet has a minimum mass of about 1.3 Earth masses and orbits the star at just 0.05 AU in 11.2 days. That close distance is within Proxima Centauri's habitable zone! Although the star is a moderately active star, during the quiet periods, its activity and X-ray output are comparable to those of the Sun. The "habitability of Proxima Centauri b" website (see textbook's website for the link) discusses the habitability of the exoplanet under two possible rotation scenarios: a synchronous one (rotation period equals orbit period) and a 3:2 spin-orbit resonance (3 spins for every 2 orbits like Mercury has). The discovery has certainly made a number of science fiction fans (including those who are also astronomers!) very excited since the Alpha Centauri system has been the subject of numerous stories. Stay tuned!

free floater planets

Finally, what about all of the possible "free floater" planets—those that probably formed around a star but were later ejected through gravitational interactions with other planets in the system? There may be more free floaters than there are normal stars in the Galaxy according to a recent estimate. It is possible that the free floater planets could harbor life but such planets would be too hard to investigate because they are too dim and small. Such planets are found only when by chance they pass nearly in front of some distant star and they distort the light of the distant star in a microlensing effect (see section 10.9.1). The technique allows us to find the mass of the free floater planets but not much else. Therefore, we will focus our attention on the planets orbiting stars because those planets can be repeatedly observed over an extended length of time and probed with various analytical techniques.

17.2   Life Characteristics

origins of life

As part of our search for life beyond the Earth, we try to understand how life began on the Earth, i.e. the origins of life on Earth, so that we can figure out how life might arise on another planet or moon. There is also the question of what will be the future of life on the Earth and the universe. However, whether you are looking for now-existing life or for how life began or at how the environment will affect life in the far future, you need to know what life is. Unfortunately, we don't have an universally agreed-upon definition of life. A couple of approaches that complement each other try to answer what is alive vs. not alive in the origins of life research: the

top-down vs. bottom-up

"*top-down*" and "*bottom-up*" approaches. The *top-down* approach looks at all sorts of living and fossil life forms to figure out the most primitive forms that are or were alive. Unfortunately, all the life forms we know of are already very sophisticated. There is a big gap between the life forms we know of (either current or fossilized) and the never living material and reactions. The *bottom-up* approach uses laboratory experiments to mimic the emergent chemical processes of environments of ancient Earth or of current conditions on another planet (e.g., Mars) or moon (e.g., Europa or Titan) in order to create a self-reproducing chemical system. But debate still rages on what self-reproducing system would be considered truly alive.

We are limited by a sample size of one—the Earth—in figuring out what life is. All of the life forms on Earth share many common processes and features and

how we know all Earth life has common ancestor

therefore, seem to have evolved from a common ancestor. These common processes and features include such things as: (a) all life on Earth uses the "left-handed" version of amino acids to build the proteins it needs for carrying out the processes of life (look up "chirality" in a search engine for more on this); (b) all living cells use adenosine triphosphate (ATP) to store and release energy; and (c) the same genetic code is used by nearly all cells in reading the information stored in the deoxyribonucleic acid (DNA) to build the proteins. These commonalities among all living things on Earth presents a challenge to us in looking for Life without an Earth bias.

Although an universally agreed-upon definition of life does not yet exist, there are some necessary characteristics of life (life as we know it). The following list of characteristics are necessary but not sufficient to define life. Many counterexamples of non-living things can be given for the characteristics.

1. *Organization*. All living things are organized and structured at the molecular, cellular, tissue, organ, system, and individual level. Organization also exists at levels beyond the individual, such as populations, communities, and ecosystems. Possible counterexamples could be rock crystals, machines, and electronics. However, it is a nice characteristic because it is visible in a short amount of time and it can also be used with past life.

2. *Maintenance/Metabolism*. To overcome entropy (the tendency of a system to become more disorganized and less complex), living things use energy to maintain *homeostasis* (i.e., maintain their sameness; a constant, structured internal environment). Metabolism is a collective term to describe the chemical and physical reactions that result in life. Although non-living things such as electrical or gas appliances use energy too, this characteristic is easy to observe in a short amount of time and the reactions could leave residues or changes in the environment that would tell us of past life.

3. *Growth*. Living things grow. The size and shape of an individual are determined by its genetic makeup and by the environment. Items 2 and 3 are related. Life grows by creating more and more order. Since entropy is decreased (the amount of structure and complexity is increased), life requires an input of energy. Life gains local structure at the expense of seemingly chaotic surroundings on a large scale. Possible counterexamples could be fire and crystals. Looking for growth in living things might be hard to do if the life form grows slowly or has stopped growing and this characteristic cannot be used on past life.

4. *Response to Stimuli*. Living things react to information that comes from outside or inside themselves. Counterexamples include rivers, clouds forming, or thermostats. While it is possible to see responses on a short time scale, we would need to know what the particular response is ahead of time to look for it and this characteristic would not be helpful in looking for past life.

5. *Reproduction*. Individuals reproduce themselves. Life also reproduces itself at the sub-cellular and cellular levels. In some instances, genetic information is altered. These mutations and genetic recombinations give rise to variations in a species. Some possible counterexamples include some types of robots or computer codes or definite living things like mules that are the sterile offspring of a mated female horse and male donkey. "In between" cases like viruses and prions cause debates among biologists about whether they are truly alive. Viruses can reproduce only by infesting other life forms. Prions are infectious proteins that make copies of themselves by causing existing, properly formed proteins to change into the prion form rather than by actually replicating themselves (examples include "mad cow disease" BSE, and CJD in humans). The act of reproduction in truly living things is not always convenient to observe at a given time and it certainly will not work for past life.

6. *Variation*. Living things are varied because of mutation and genetic recombinations. Variations may affect an individual's appearance or chemical makeup and many genetic variations are passed from one generation to the next (*heredity*). Looking for heredity, though, requires a whole series of the organisms and perhaps a long time to see what trait is passed on vs. random chance, as well as, the inherited trait might not be readily visible.

7. *Adaption*. Living things adapt to changes in their environment. Items 5, 6, and 7 are related. Life reproduces—complex structures reproduce themselves.

Life changes itself in response to natural selection on the macroscopic level and to changes in DNA on the microscopic level. On the positive side, it is possible to use this characteristic when examining past life but on the negative side, it would take a long observation time to look for adaptation and evolution by natural selection.

17.2.1 Evolution by Natural Selection

natural selection

Evolution was not a new thing in the time of Charles Darwin—there were scientists writing about evolution a hundred years before Darwin and there were ancient Greek thinkers such as Anaximander and Empedocles who thought that life forms change over time. Evolution is usually thought to have started with Charles Darwin because he developed a plausible materialistic mechanism for evolution called **natural selection**. In the modern view of natural selection, individuals carrying genes (units of heredity consisting of a sequence of DNA bases) that better suit them to the current environment leave more offspring than individuals carrying genes that make them less adapted. Actually, the idea of natural selection was first formally published by Charles Darwin and Alfred Russell Wallace at the same time in 1858 but Charles Darwin had been developing the idea for over twenty years before then and sharing it informally with a few colleagues. After receiving an early draft of a paper from Wallace about Wallace's studies in the South Pacific that led Wallace to discover the process of natural selection, Darwin finally wrote up his own studies of evolution by natural selection in a formal paper that was presented to the public at the same time as Wallace's. Darwin then followed up the paper about a year later with a more complete and convincing argument for natural selection in his book, *On the Origin of Species by Natural Selection*. There are three basic observations and three basic conclusions leading to the idea of natural selection:

- Observation#1: There is variation among individuals of a species (item 6 above).

- Observation#2: Some of this variation is heritable. Darwin did not understand how heredity worked. The idea of heredity via genes was developed by the Austrian monk, Gregor Mendel, in the 1860s, but it wasn't until the 1940s that natural selection and Mendelian genetics were combined into the modern theory of evolution that guides the science of biology today.

- Observation#3: In general, more offspring are produced by species that can survive.

- Conclusion#1: Because of observation#3, there is competition among individuals for resources available to them to grow, survive and reproduce.

- Conclusion#2: Some variations will be more successful than others in allowing individuals to take advantage of these resources in a particular environment. These more successful individuals will be more likely to survive and to reproduce, leaving more offspring that share those successful adaptations for that environment. They are selected by the environment.

- Conclusion#3: Over time, for those traits that are heritable (we now know via genes), natural selection will cause species to evolve adaptations that are particularly well-suited for survival and reproduction in the given environment.

The theory of evolution gives a very plausible explanation for what we see in the fossil record of how organisms have changed over long periods of time and the sequence of those changes, for what we see of the developmental and structural remnants of past ancestry found in living species, and for what we see in the geographic distribution of plants and animals, especially in the case of oceanic islands. Of all the scientific theories, the theory of evolution, is the most controversial among the general public because of what it says about the development of Homo Sapiens, i.e., humans, and our relationship to the rest of the world. These controversies arise most often among those of particular religious views, but as I discuss in the first chapter, it is possible for religion and science to be compatible, even in the area of biological evolution. One possible way to mesh religion and science while honoring the truths of both is given in the Science-Religion Interface Resources section of the textbook's website.

17.2.2 Working Definition of Life

With the understanding that an universally agreed-upon definition of life does not exist, we can at least come up with a working definition to guide current research. One working definition from Gerald Joyce that guides NASA's research in astrobiology is "life is a self-contained chemical system capable of undergoing Darwinian evolution". Another similar definition from Max Coleman at NASA/JPL states "Life is a self-organized system capable of processing energy sources to its advantage." The focus on chemical systems and chemical energy rules out computer programs and robots or other electronic entities and it is more easily measurable. The first definition includes evolution because of the primacy of evolution in modern biology but it is very difficult (at best) to measure evolution in the time length of a typical space mission or grant. The second working definition focuses on the characteristics that can be easily measured quickly. Coleman notes that life usually processes energy at a different rate than its surrounding environment; that life must process energy more efficiently than its environment does or it will be outcompeted by non-biological processes; and that self-organization separates life from its surroundings, isolating its chemical processing abilities from its environment.

Although we have always been aware that our knowledge of life is limited, the discovery of life surviving, even thriving, under conditions not usually studied in high school or undergraduate biology classes, made us confront our biases of what life should be like. Organisms that survive in extreme environments are called **extremophiles**. There are life forms that live in the "dry valleys" of Antarctica when the ice thaws for a few hours a day in the summer and in the sub-surface waters of Lake Vostok miles below the ice of Antarctica. There are life forms growing in boiling hot springs on the surface and miles beneath the ocean surface in pitch blackness near submarine volcanic vents. Bacteria have been found living in rock miles below the surface in deep mines where water has percolated into pores or cracks in the rock. In fact, the total mass of all the microbes living in the rocks miles underground (called *endoliths*) could be greater than the total mass of life forms on the surface!

extremophile

Very hot conditions (up to $120°$ C), very cold conditions, very salty conditions, very acidic (low pH) conditions, very basic (high pH) conditions, and very high pressures: life is possible under all of these conditions as long as there is some liquid water. Other forms of life might be able to use another liquid but liquid water does have some advantages over other liquids as discussed in the next section. Current searches for extra-terrestrial life are focusing on places where liquid water could exist but our experience with extremophiles has taught us that life can be more creative than we can imagine with our biases.

17.3   Habitable Planets

Now that you know what kinds of stars would be good to explore further and what criteria should be used for distinguishing lifeforms from other physical processes, let us hone in on the right kind of planet to support life. Unfortunately, our information about life is limited to one planet, Earth, so the Earth-bias is there. However, scientists do know of the basics of what life needs and what sort of conditions would probably destroy life. With these cautionary notes, let's move forward.

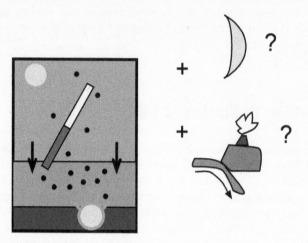

The habitable planet should have:

- a *stable temperature* regime provided by an energy source external to the life forms such as the star the planet orbits or planetary heating from some sort of geological activity and

- a *liquid milieu.* Liquid `water` is best for biochemical reactions and could be very abundant but liquid methane and/or ethane, like what is found on Saturn's moon Titan might work. Since liquid water dissolves other compounds better than liquid methane/ethane and biochemical sort of reactions work better in liquid water than liquid methane/ethane, liquid water will probably be a requirement for a habitable planet. Water is liquid at a wide temperature range. Bio-chemical reactions will not happen in solids and they would be very inefficient in a gas. Water is liquid at a higher temperature than methane, ethane, and ammonia so chemical reactions will happen more quickly in the liquid water than in the other liquids. Also, frozen water floats! The hydrogen bonds of water make water *less dense* when it freezes. The frozen water ice could form a protective layer insulating the liquid water below it. The other types of liquids sink when they freeze and could lead to a runaway freezing process where all of the liquid freezes. Finally, water in some form (mostly either gas or solid) is actually quite abundant in the Galaxy so we are not limiting ourselves too much with the water bias. The liquid milieu is needed to mix...

- the *essential building block elements* together (carbon, hydrogen, nitrogen, oxygen, phosphorus, sulfur, and transition metals like iron, chromium, and nickel). Since the building block elements are only created in the stars, the best places to look for life is around stars formed from processed gas, i.e., look at metal-rich stars. `Carbon` will probably be the base of life because its great versatility to form compounds with other elements and even with itself. Carbon is more likely to *share* its electrons with other atoms rather than donate its electrons to other atoms or steal electrons from other atoms.

why liquid water is best

reactions faster in liquid water
water ice floats— provides insulation

why carbon

Carbon has the highest degree of *"catenation"* (ability to form chemical bonds to itself) of all the elements. There are far more types of organic compounds (molecules containing carbon and usually also hydrogen) known than all the other types of compounds combined. On a planet with carbon-based life and life using carbon's closest competitor, silicon, as a base, the carbon-based chemical reactions would be far more efficient than the silicon-based ones, so the carbon-based life would quickly overrun any silicon-based life present on the planet.

carbon better than silicon

- The planet should have a *solid surface* to concentrate the building block elements together in the *liquid on top*. The more concentrated the solution of water and molecules is, the more likely the molecules will react with each other. If the molecules were fixed in a solid, they would not be able to get close to each other and react with each other. If the molecules were in a gaseous state, they would be too far apart from each other to react efficiently. Though the reactions could conceivably take place, they would be rare!

solid surface concentrates the liquid

- The planet should also have *enough gravity to keep an atmosphere* (see chapter 9). An atmosphere would shield lifeforms on the surface from harmful radiation (charged particles and high-energy photons) and moderate the changes in temperatures between night and day to maintain a stable temperature regime. The atmosphere would also provide the surface pressure needed for the liquid (most likely liquid water) to exist on the surface.

gravity keeps atmosphere around

- A *relatively large moon nearby* **may** be needed to keep the planet's rotation axis from tilting too much and too quickly. This prevents large differences in temperatures over short timescales (life needs sufficient time to adapt to temperature changes).

large moon stabilizes spin axis

- *Plate tectonics* **may** be needed to: 1) regulate the surface temperature of the planet via its crucial role in the carbon cycle (see chapter 9); 2) create a magnetic field to shield the planet from the deadly stellar winds; 3) create dry land on a water-covered world; and 4) promote a high level of biodiversity across the planet by creating new environments that organisms would have to adapt to.

plate tectonics needed?

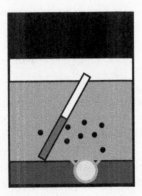

On planets or moons without an atmosphere and/or that are far from their parent star, it may be possible to have life existing below the surface if the planet or moon have a planetary heating source. An example of this would be Jupiter's moon Europa (section 9.7.2). It has a water ice crust and a liquid water ocean below and is kept warm despite its great distance from the Sun because of tidal heating from Jupiter's large gravity.

17.3.1   Methane-based Life

Although the rest of this chapter focuses on water-based life, the existence of methane lakes and rivers on Titan in our solar system compels us to consider life that could use liquid methane as the solvent to mix the organic chemicals about in its biochemistry. Another reason to consider methane-based life is that there are likely more very cold places where liquid methane could exist in our galaxy (and others as well) than liquid water places. For example, methane-based life could exist on exoplanets much further out from the very abundant cool K and M stars than what water-based life would be able to withstand—the habitable zone for methane-based life would be further out than that for water-based life. Planets in a "methane habitable zone" of a cool K and M star would not have their rotations tidally locked to the star.

With regard to Titan, methane-based life would have a ready supply of food from the acetylene and ethane raining down to the surface as a result of the photochemistry of ultraviolet light in sunlight breaking apart the methane vapor in Titan's atmosphere. Using the hydrogen also present in Titan's atmosphere, methanogens (organisms producing methane) would combine hydrogen with acetylene and ethane (and other hydrocarbons) to produce methane and energy. Titan life would need to develop special enzymes to extract oxygen from the water-ice rocks but the other essential elements such as carbon, hydrogen, and nitrogen would be easy to come by in the environment of Titan's surface. See Chris McKay's talk in the Silicon Valley Astronomers Lecture Series for more on the possibilities of life on Titan (see the textbook's website for the link).

A recent study of the reflectivity of the surfaces of the lakes on Titan suggests that frozen methane ice might be able to float if the conditions are just right: if the temperatures were in a narrow range just below the freezing point of methane (like in Titan's winters) and if the ice were composed of at least 5% nitrogen gas that is quite abundant in Titan's atmosphere. However, if the temperature drops by a few more degrees, the ice will sink. An atmosphere of different composition on a cold exoplanet might get the frozen methane to float with a different temperature range. One last thing to note about methane-based life on a cold world is that the metabolic life cycles of an organism could be measured in time intervals of tens of thousands of years instead of the hours or days we are used on Earth, making it even more difficult to detect the metabolic processes. Also, it is very likely that any methane-based life is going to be microbial only. A complex, multi-cellular intelligent organism is much more likely to use oxygen in its metabolism with water as its liquid medium of choice.

17.4   Bio-Markers

While it may be possible for life to exist on a planet or moon below its surface, we will not be able to detect its presence from a great distance away (e.g., if it is in another star system beyond our solar system). In our fastest rocket-propelled spacecraft, it would take us over 70,000 years to travel to the next star system (Alpha Centauri). The type of inhabited planet we will be able to detect outside of our solar system is life that has changed the chemistry of the planet's atmosphere, i.e., the life will have to be on the surface. By analyzing the spectrum of the planet's atmosphere, we may be able to detect **bio-markers**—spectral signatures of certain compounds in certain proportions that could not be produced by non-biological processes. Bio-markers are also called *"biosignatures"*.

bio-marker = biosignature

Spectral lines from water would say that a planet has a vital ingredient for life but it does not mean that life is present. If oxygen, particularly ozone (a molecule of three oxygen atoms), is found in the atmosphere, then it would be very likely

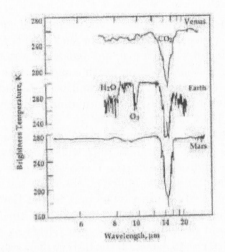

that life is indeed on the planet. Recall from chapter 9 that molecular oxygen quickly disappears if it is not continually replenished by the photosynthesis process of plants and cyanobacteria. However, it is conceivably possible for a few non-biological processes (e.g., the runaway greenhouse effect with the photodissociation of carbon dioxide and water) to create an atmosphere rich in molecular oxygen and ozone. This is especially true for stars that produce proportionally more short-wavelength ultraviolet (far UV) light than long-wavelength ultraviolet (near UV) light. Many red dwarf stars, including the nearby ones such as Gliese 832 with super-Earth-size planets orbiting them, produce a lot more far UV than near UV, so a strong oxygen spectral line could be a "false-positive" sign of life.

Molecular oxygen does not produce absorption lines in the preferred infrared band that would be used by the James Webb Space Telescope and the proposed Terrestrial Planet Finder mission. Ozone does. If we take into account the ultraviolet environment of the exoplanet, then ozone existing along with nitrous oxide and methane in particular ratios with carbon dioxide and water, all of which produce absorption lines in the infrared, would be strong evidence for an inhabited world.

Ozone is a key indicator

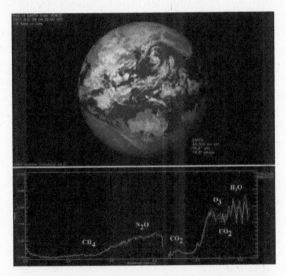

Venus Express spacecraft looks for bio-markers from Earth while orbiting Venus 78 million kilometers from Earth. Earth was just the size of a single pixel in its camera. The side of the Earth facing the spacecraft is shown in the simulated image above the spectrum. Image courtesy of ESA/VIRTIS/INAF-IASF/Obs. de Paris-LESIA + NASA/JPL

The ratios would need to be "off-kilter", not in chemical equilibrium, i.e., not in ratios made by normal geological processes. For such worlds found with these bio-markers, further modeling of what strange non-biological water cycles and volcanic activity very different from that found on Earth could produce the large amount of ozone would need to be done before we could definitively conclude that the exoplanet had life on it. It is a very big step to go from finding a planet that *could* support life to saying that the planet *does* support life!

One recent test of this concept was when the Venus Express spacecraft pointed its spectrometer at the Earth in August 2007 while the spacecraft was orbiting Venus 78 million kilometers from the Earth. The near-infrared spectra of the Earth is shown on the previous page for two different observing sessions. Earth was just the size of a single pixel in its camera. The part of the Earth facing the Venus Express spacecraft is shown in the simulated image above the spectra.

An exoplanet will need to have enough oxygen (either as molecular oxygen or ozone) in its atmosphere for us to detect. If the history of an exoplanet's atmosphere is anything like ours, then life on the exoplanet's surface might not be detectable for a large fraction of the exoplanet's history. Photosynthetic life developed on the Earth at least 3.5 billion years ago (Gya) but it took another 1.2 billion years or so (i.e., 2.3 Gya) for the oxygen levels in the atmosphere to rise up to significant quantities because the oxygen was combining with land and ocean minerals (to make iron oxide and other oxides). Only after 1.2 billion years or so did the surface and ocean minerals get too saturated to suck up any more of the oxygen, allowing the oxygen to build up in our atmosphere.

One example of the research into how the spectrum of an exoplanet can change through time is shown in the figure on the next page from Kaltenegger, et al's paper on the Earth's changing spectrum through time. The light gray curve is what an ultra-high resolution spectrometer would be able to see (the absorption lines are so numerous and close together that they merge into gray bands at the scale of the graph) and the thick black line is what an actual spectrometer with realistic resolution on the proposed Terrestrial Planet Finder mission would be able to see. This particular set of spectra is for a planet without any clouds in the way. See their paper for how clouds in the atmosphere would affect the spectrum and also for the spectrum in the visible and near-infrared bands (link on the textbook's website).

Could life exist on a planet without oxygen? Yes. Photosynthesis might be able to use another element such as sulfur instead of oxygen. The planet's life might use another liquid besides water. Maybe the planet's life would use a different element besides carbon as its base (such as silicon). The first missions that will hunt for life beyond the Earth will focus on biochemical processes that we are more familiar with (carbon-based life using liquid water) because it makes sense to start with what we know (or think we know) and then branch out to finding more exotic life after we have had some practice with the "ordinary" life.

Earth's changing spectrum through time (infrared)

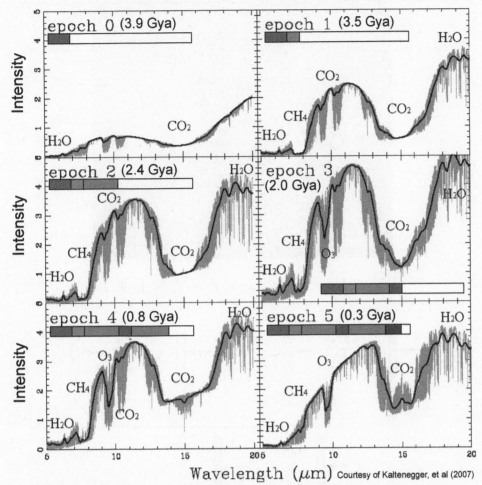

Wavelength (μm) Courtesy of Kaltenegger, et al (2007)

Light gray curve is what an ultra-high resolution spectrometer would see (the absorption lines are so numerous and close together that they merge into gray bands at the scale of the graph). Thick black curve is what a realistic resolution spectrometer on the proposed TPF would see. This set is for the planet without clouds (see the journal article for spectra with clouds and spectra in the visible and near-infrared bands).

17.5 Drake Equation: How Many of Them Are out There?

The **Drake Equation** is a way to estimate the number of communicating advanced civilizations (N) inhabiting the Galaxy. It is named after Frank Drake who first summarized the things we need to know to answer the question, "how many of them are out there?" The equation breaks this big unknown, complex question into several smaller (hopefully manageable) parts. Once you know how to deal with each of the pieces, you can put them together to come up with a decent guess.

Drake Equation

R_* = average star formation rate (number of stars formed each year). If you average over the history of star formation in the Milky Way, you find roughly 200 billion stars in the Galaxy / 10 billion years of Galaxy's lifetime = 20 stars/year (note that this is just a rough average!). The Milky Way's current star formation rate is now only about 2 stars/year, so its early star formation rate was much higher than 20 stars/year.

Frank Drake
September 2009

$$N = R_* \times f_p \times n_E \times f_l \times f_i \times f_c \times L$$

Lots of stars... but only a few with E.T.'s

$f_p =$ average *fraction* of stars with planets. Astronomers are focusing on single
star systems because planets would more likely have stable orbits. With our
current technology it is also easier to find planets around single star systems,
though we have found planets in binary and multiple star systems. The recent
discovery of planets in stable orbits in binary and multiple star systems was
certainly a surprise for planetary dynamicists who model planet orbits and
boosts the f_p term from what we originally thought. Astronomers are looking
at stars where the star is not too hot (hence, short life) nor too cold (hence,
narrow habitable zone and tidal locking of rotation). Also, we should look at
stars that have signatures of "metals" (elements heavier than helium) in their
spectra—stars in the galactic disk and bulge. Leftover "metal" material from
the gas/dust cloud that formed the star may have formed Earth-like planets.
The census of stars by the Kepler mission has shown that *at least* 70% of
ordinary stars including those hotter than the Sun and the great majority
cooler than the Sun have a planet of some size orbiting them (the percentage
will only increase as the Kepler and TESS teams process their data). See the

end of chapter 10 for a discussion about finding exoplanets and web links in the textbook's website to up-to-date information about them.

n_E = average number of Earth-like planets per suitable star system. The planet has a solid surface and liquid medium on top to get the chemical elements together for biochemical reactions. The planet has strong enough gravity to hold onto an atmosphere. Current statistics from the Kepler mission show that 23% of sun-like stars have a planet less than 3 Earth diameters in size. However, the dividing line of size between a rocky planet and a more gaseous one like Neptune is about 1.75 Earth diameters.

f_l = average *fraction* of Earth-like planets with life. Extrasolar life will probably be carbon-based because carbon can bond in so many different ways and even with itself. Therefore, carbon can make the large and complex molecules needed for any sort of biological processes. Also, carbon is common in the galaxy. Many complex organic molecules are naturally made in the depths of space and are found in molecular clouds throughout the Galaxy. The rarer element silicon is often quoted as another possible base, but there are problems with its chemical reactions. When silicon reacts with oxygen, it forms a solid called silica. Carbon oxidizes to form a gas. Silicon has a much lesser ability to form the complex molecules needed to store and release energy. See the previous section and Raymond Dessy's article at Scientific American's "Ask the Experts – Astronomy" website for further discussion of the limitations of silicon chemistry (use the link on the textbook's website). The habitable zone idea would be contained either in this term or put in the nE above.

f_i = average *fraction* of life-bearing planets evolving at least one intelligent species. Is intelligence necessary for survival? Will life on a planet naturally develop toward more complexity and intelligence? Those are questions that must be answered before "reasonable" guesses can be put in for f_i. Take note that on the Earth, there is only one intelligent (self-aware) species among millions of other species. (Perhaps, whales, dolphins, and some apes should be considered intelligent too, but even still, the number of intelligent species is extremely small among the other inhabitants of our planet.) Sharks have done very well for hundreds of millions of years and they are stupid enough to eat tires! Bacteria have thrived on the Earth for *billions* of years. Being intelligent enough to read an astronomy textbook is very nice but it is not essential for the mandates of life.

Bacteria and other simple forms of life have been found in some very extreme conditions on the Earth. Simple forms of life can even survive long passages through space. However, we will not be talking with such simple forms of life. We are more interested in *complex life*—multi-cellular animal and plant life. Complex life is more fragile than simple life, so while new research seems to increase the f_l term, the f_i term might be smaller than was initially thought. If the rise of intelligence is accidental, then the f_i term will be nearly zero. If intelligence is an *emergent property* of any biological system, then intelligence would be an expected result of complex life, boosting the f_i term. An *emergent property* is a property that arises when a simple system with a sufficient number of interacting parts spontaneously becomes more complex. The property cannot be seen in individual members of a system but can be seen only in large assemblages of them—complex behaviors of a collective that are more than just the sum of the individual members.

complex life vs. simple life

emergent property

f_c = average *fraction* of intelligent-bearing planets capable of interstellar communication. The intelligent life we will be able to talk to will have to use some sort of symbolic language. Will intelligent life want to communicate to beings of a different species? The anthropologists, psychologists, philosophers, and theologians will have a lot of input on this term in the Drake Equation.

$L =$ average lifetime (in years) that a civilization remains technologically active. How long will the civilization use radio communication? Will they be around long enough to send messages and get a reply? Even if we manage to take better care of the Earth and each other, our technology is changing, so we may not use radio communication. It used to be that our television and music/talk broadcasts were "over the air" using radio and microwaves. Some of that radio/microwave energy leaked out into interstellar space (that may be why all of the extraterrestrials are staying away). Those broadcasts are now happening mostly via cable. Now the voice communication that used to be via cable is now happening mostly with radio/microwaves (land lines vs. cellular phones). There is also the fact (yes, I use "fact") that individual species have changed and died out as their environment changed. Humans will be very different in a million years from now (if we survive that long). Because of the huge interstellar distances in the Galaxy, the L term is the most significant constraint on communicating with an extraterrestrial.

Another version of the Drake Equation (used by Carl Sagan, for example) replaces R_* with N_*—the number of stars in the Milky Way Galaxy and L with f_L—the fraction of a planetary lifetime graced by a technological civilization. Once you have found N, the average distance between each civilization d can be found from $N \times d^3 =$ volume of the Galaxy $= 5.65 \times 10^{12}$ light years^3. The average distance between each civilization $d = ($volume of the Galaxy$/N)^{1/3}$ light years.

The certainty of the values of the terms in the Drake Equation decreases substantially as you go from R_* to L. Astronomical observations will enable us to get a handle on R_*, f_p, n_E, and f_l. Our knowledge of biology and biochemistry will enable us to make some decent estimates for f_l and some rough estimates for f_i. Our studies in anthropology, social sciences, economics, politics, philosophy, and religion will enable us to make some rough guesses for f_i, f_c, and L but those terms involve sociological factors (behaviors of alien civilizations) and we have a hard enough time trying to understand how our own human societies interact (our predictions often fail miserably). Furthermore, numerical analysis is not used in philosophy and religion.

Some astronomy authors are so bold as to publish their guesses for all of the terms in the Drake equation even though estimates of f_l are only rough and values quoted for the last three, f_i, f_c, L, are just wild guesses. I will not publish my values for the last few terms because I do not want to bias your efforts in trying come up with a value for N. We do know enough astronomy to make some good estimates for the first three terms.

Rare Earth

The authors of the book *Rare Earth*, Don Brownlee and Peter Ward got the astrobiology/SETI community to re-examine its assumptions about extra-terrestrial life when they laid out their case for why complex life (life beyond the microbial level) may be very rare in the universe in their book. Needless to say there is disagreement, but it is a healthy debate in the determination of what it takes to make a habitable planet that can support complex, intelligent (self-aware) life.

17.6 "Hailing Frequencies Open, Captain"

The section title is a bit misleading—astronomers are only trying to eavesdrop on conversations already going on. Astronomers are searching for messages carried via electromagnetic radiation (light) because it is the speediest way to send a message.

It travels at about 300,000 kilometers/second or about 9.5 trillion kilometers/year (remember that this is equal to one light year?). In particular, the radio band part of the electromagnetic radiation spectrum is searched for messages because radio can get through all of the intervening gas and dust easily. Radio also does not require that much energy to produce it so it should be easier for extraterrestrials to make. The lowest interference from background natural sources is between frequencies of 1 to 20 gigahertz. Our atmosphere narrows this range to 1 to 9 gigahertz. The optimum range is 1 to 2 gigahertz. This is also where the 21-cm line of neutral atomic hydrogen and the slightly smaller wavelength lines of the hydroxide molecule (OH) are found. Because the water molecule H_2O is made of one hydrogen atom + one hydroxide molecule, the optimum range to use for our searches is called the *water hole*.

why radio is better

"magic frequencies"

the water hole

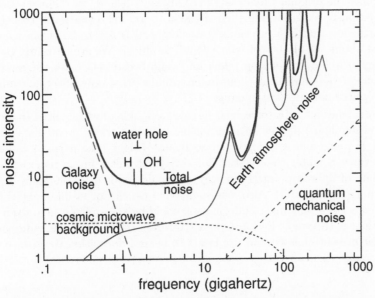

The "water hole" is where the background interference (noise) is the smallest, not only for us, but for anyone else in the Galaxy. The universal noise sources are given by the dashed curves. The noise from the oxygen and water molecules in our atmosphere are shown with the bottom solid curve.

Complicating the search is the doppler effect. Beings on planets orbiting stars will have their transmissions doppler shifted by ever-changing amounts because of their planet's orbital motion (and the Earth's motion around the Sun). Also, their star is moving with respect to our solar system as they orbit the Galaxy. While radio emission from natural objects (i.e., not from intelligent life technology) is over a wide range of frequencies, radio signals from an extra-terrestrial intelligence are expected to be in a very narrow frequency range, just like the narrow radio frequencies used by human technology because that would be a more energy efficient way to communicate. The radio astronomers must therefore search many different frequency intervals to be sure to pick up the one interval in which the other civilization happens to be at that time. Current searches scan several billion frequency intervals at once, each just 1 Hertz wide.

Another key feature of any signal we intercept is that it must be repeatable—it must be confirmed by others as being extra-terrestrial before any announcement to the press is made. With all of the various sources of radio interference possible, S.E.T.I. scientists want to be sure they have not picked up someone's microwave oven, garage door opener, or one of our satellites, etc. The famous "Wow!" signal of

August 15, 1977 in a S.E.T.I. project at Ohio State University was not repeatable. It was a narrowband radio signal that was potentially from beyond Earth but it lasted for only 72 seconds and it has not been detected again.

A message was sent on November 16, 1974 to the globular cluster M 13. Unfortunately, since M 13 is about 25,000 light-years away, we will have to wait about 50,000 years for a reply. Messages have been attached to the Pioneer and Voyager spacecraft, but they will take thousands of years to reach the nearest stars. Our main mode of communication is the inadvertent messages we have been transmitting for several decades now: some of the signal in television and radio broadcasts leaks out to space and rushes outward at the speed of light. It takes many years for the radio and television signals to reach the nearest stars because of the great distances to even the nearest stars. So perhaps radio astronomers on other planets are watching the original broadcasts of "Gilligan's Island" or "Three's Company" and are seriously reconsidering their decision to say hello (message for network legal department: that is a facetious statement and is not to be taken as a serious statement about the quality of your clients' product). We are currently in a major technology switch-over between television/radio broadcasts (over the air to cable) and telephone communication (land-line to cellular) that does affect how much noise and the type of noise we are making.

optical SETI

Some searches for extraterrestrial signals are looking for very brief (nanosecond) optical (visible light) flashes because visible light can travel great distances out of the galactic plane and a tightly-focused beam of light (like a laser) can made to be many times brighter than a star (for very brief pulses just a nanosecond long). If the beam of light is pointed our way, we could see it over the glare of the star the extraterrestrials orbit. Also, the higher frequencies of visible light than radio means that a larger amount of information could be transmitted in a given amount of time than with radio. Perhaps the extraterrestrials would use radio signals to make their presence known and use lasers to beam information to us once we have started looking their direction.

17.7   Fermi's Question: Where Are They?

Enrico Fermi (lived 1901–1954)
Image courtesy of The American Institute of Physics

Fermi's Question

Fermi's Question, also called *Fermi's Paradox,* is named after physicist *Enrico Fermi* (lived 1901-1954) who asked in a conversation with fellow physicists in the summer of 1950, "Where are they?" when talking about extraterrestrial life. Consider these facts and reasonable assumptions:

1. There are tens of billions of Earth-size planets in our galaxy alone. There are hundreds of billions of galaxies in the universe, each with millions to trillions of stars. That means there is plenty of real estate for life to arise somewhere else in the universe.

2. Organic compounds and water molecules are found everywhere in the Galaxy. They are produced in natural astrophysical processes found everywhere in the universe.

3. Habitable conditions are found elsewhere in our solar system and should be found in plenty of other places. As part of the Copernican principle, the habitable conditions of Earth are not unique or special.

4. Life arose quickly on Earth once the conditions were right. That means that there is a sort of cosmic imperative: life *will always* arise and although, we don't know how life arises, it is easy for life to arise. As part of this and the previous item, we assume that life arose on Earth through purely natural means, following the same laws of physics and chemistry found everywhere else.

5. If intelligence is an emergent property of biological systems, then there is the high likelihood that the biological system will eventually develop an intelligent species capable of space travel.

6. It has been possible for life to arise somewhere in the Galaxy in the past ten billion years. There are planetary systems that formed from metal-rich molecular clouds long before our solar system formed. Although the distances may be vast between stars and galaxies, a civilization that has been around for many millions of years would have had time to traverse the distances (even going sub-light speeds) or at least to send out a signal.

7. Successful civilizations will eventually need to expand beyond what their home planet can support.

8. If our history is any reasonable guide, technological progress is non-linear with innovations and breakthroughs happening at an ever-increasing rate. What seems impossible for us today may be easily possible a century or a millennium from now.

Given those facts and reasonable assumptions, why haven't we been visited or at least contacted yet? There's a strong likelihood that we are not the only technologically advanced intelligent civilization that has arisen in the universe, SO: where are they? There is no scientifically credible proof that we have been visited—see the "Pseudoscience vs. Science" essay posted on the textbook's website for more about UFOs as alien spaceships and what is required for credible proof of extraterrestrial life visitation. Fermi's Question remains.

17.7.1 Answers to Fermi's Question: Resolutions of Fermi's Paradox

There are many possible ways to answer Fermi's Question, so the list of answers given here is not complete but it does give the more popular answers.

1. **We really are alone.** Even if extra-terrestrial life is present, it is most likely microbial (like bacteria or archaea). Life on Earth was solely microbial for most of the history of life (i.e., the past 3.5 to 3.8 billion years). Complex life (multi-cellular organisms that don't take a microscope to see) like plants and fungi did not arise on Earth until about a billion years ago with land plants not appearing until just 550 million years ago. Animals appeared in the sea soon after the plants and developed on land within a few tens of millions of years after the plants. Complex life on Earth has approximately another 500 million to 1 billion years before conditions on Earth become too hot too exist due to the ever- brightening sun. The window for complex life on Earth is just 1.0-1.5 billion years wide while the window for microbial life is six to seven billion years wide because microbial life is tougher and can handle much more extreme conditions than can complex life. The fragility of complex life coupled with the apparent lack of evolutionary advantage to being intelligent, means that fact/assumption #5 above is wrong—beings with enough intelligence to build radio telescopes and space ships are extremely rare. Furthermore, if the planet is completely covered in water, any intelligent creatures wouldn't be able to create the electronic technology necessary for communication or travel across space (electronics require dry land). So many things had to go just right in the history of life on Earth for us to develop. We are the first technologically advanced civilization to arise to arise in the Milky Way. If ET's exist in other galaxies, they are too far away for us to know about, so we are effectively alone.

2. **Technologically-advanced civilizations self-destruct.** All civilizations that develop the capability for space travel and radio telescopes also develop chemical, biological, and nuclear weapons of mass destruction and destroy themselves or they pollute their home planet so bad that they can't survive beyond that phase in their technological development. We are the only technologically advanced civilization existing now because the other civilizations have come and gone.

3. **Technologically-advanced civilizations capable of interstellar travel are destroyed by the most advanced civilization in existence.** The malevolent ET civilization considers others an existential threat and destroys other emerging civilizations before they have a chance to compete. A civilization capable of harnessing the huge amounts of energy needed to warp spacetime for interstellar travel would not have to use laser or phaser weapons like you see in the movies. Instead they could create a small black hole near the emerging civilization's planet and totally obliterate the planet or create a targeted biological weapon that wipes out the emerging civilization while leaving the natural resources of planet unharmed for extraction by the more advanced civilization. Similar to this is the possibility that when interstellar civilizations come into contact with each other, they destroy each other unwittingly via some sort of virus or other contagious disease.

4. **A technological or biological obstacle makes interstellar travel impossible.** There is some obstacle we are not aware of that makes interstellar travel impossible or impractical. We are already aware of the great biological challenges in sending people to Mars and the obstacles that have to be overcome with lengthy journeys among the planets, including ill-timed solar flares and coronal mass ejections. Stars are hundreds of thousands of times farther apart from each other than are the planets in a planetary system and stars do provide a magnetic bubble/shield around their planetary systems. Perhaps journeys in interstellar space would take much too long for civiliza-

tions to want to voluntarily take the risk. However, these considerations don't prevent civilizations from attempting communication.

5. **There is a "Prime Directive" of non-interference for all emerging civilizations such as ours.** The Galactic civilization is watching us while deliberately avoiding contact until we have become stable and mature enough to make contact, like the "Prime Directive" of Star Trek. Instead of watching us, perhaps the ET civilization is ignoring us and has installed some sort of mechanical sentinel in our solar system or just beyond the boundary of our solar system that will be activated when we finally reach a stage in our space exploration capabilities to cause the sentinel to send a message to the ET civilization (like the black monolith of Arthur C. Clarke's "*2001: A Space Odyssey*"). Perhaps the ET civilization has its own agenda and simply doesn't want to contact us. We humans like to think we are special and worthy of ET's attention but that could be conceit on our part. Some propose that we should look for other signs of these advanced civilizations besides leaked or directed electromagnetic signals. Perhaps we could detect infrared emission from huge mechanical structures such as Dyson spheres (structures enclosing a star to capture all of the star's light) or arrangements of astronomical objects that appear to have been set up artificially (though this runs the risk of being a "ET of the gaps" type of problem where we blame some bizarre natural phenomenon on ET instead of trying to understand the natural cause).

6. **The Galactic civilization is so advanced that we can't recognize it.** Our situation could be like an ice-age human coming across a field scattered with smartphones and thinking they were blocks of obsidian. ET's technology is so far outside of the realm of our experience and intuition to see that the artifacts around us must be artificial. It is much more likely that civilizations coming into contact with each other will be at vastly different levels of technological capability than what you see in the movies—all those aliens look so much like humans with masks and strange make-up and their spacecraft controls look like variations of our fighter plane cockpits! Given the millions or maybe even billions of years difference of when life arises on the different planets in our galaxy, perhaps our situation is more like humans compared to ants. Both have social structures and can manipulate their immediate environment but ants don't recognize us unless we mess with their nest. Perhaps the ET civilizations have been trying to communicate with us in ways that would seem to be obvious to even primitive creatures on ET's home planet but like a human flashing Morse code signals with their flashlight above the ant nest, we don't notice the symbolic language being used. Maybe the other civilizations are so far beyond us that they just don't notice us and our leaked radio broadcasts haven't had enough time to reach them. Maybe we are so different from ET culturally and technologically that we don't recognize them and they don't recognize us.

Vocabulary

bio-marker	Drake Equation	extremophile
Fermi's Question	habitable zone	natural selection

Review Questions

1. Which stars have large **habitable zones** and which ones have small habitable zones?

2. Why should the search for life be narrowed to stars with masses 0.5 to 1.4 solar masses?

3. What spectral types of stars are *excluded* from S.E.T.I.?

4. What is the range of temperatures for stars *included* in S.E.T.I.?

5. Why are binary or multiple star systems usually excluded from S.E.T.I. searches? Which type of binary system might be good ones to check out?

6. What are the characteristics of life?

7. What is the definition of life? How do you know if something is living?

8. Where can life exist?

9. How will we be able to detect if life exists on an exoplanet?

10. Where in the Galaxy should the search be concentrated (bulge, stellar halo, disk, dark matter halo) and why?

11. Where is extraterrestrial intelligent life expected to be found?

12. How do we estimate how many other communicating civilizations we expect to find? What parts of that estimate are fairly well-known, what parts are much more uncertain, and what makes the terms more or less certain?

13. What do you find when you plug in values for the Drake Equation?

14. What frequency or wavelength bands are the focus of current SETI searches and why?

15. What are the facts and assumptions behind Fermi's Question and what are some possible reasons why we haven't found signs of an extra-terrestrial civilization?

Appendix A

Angular Momentum

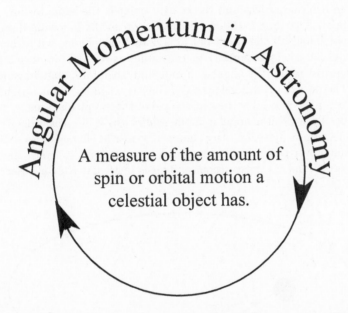

Angular Momentum in Astronomy

A measure of the amount of spin or orbital motion a celestial object has.

To describe how things move you often use the basic quantities of length, mass, and time. Quantities such as velocity, acceleration, force and energy are very powerful ones that help you understand how an object's position will change over time and how it will interact with other things in the universe. *Momentum* and its cousin **angular momentum** are other very powerful quantities.

Ordinary momentum is a measure of an object's tendency to move at constant speed along a straight path. Momentum depends on speed and mass. A train moving at 20 mph has more momentum than a bicyclist moving at the same speed. A car colliding at 5 mph does not cause as much damage as that same car colliding at 60 mph. For things moving in straight lines, momentum is simply mass × speed. Most things move in curved paths, so the more generalized idea of momentum is **angular momentum**. Angular momentum measures an object's tendency to continue to spin. Here, an "object" can be either a single body or a system of two or more bodies acting together as a single group.

angular momentum = mass × velocity × distance (from point object is spinning or orbiting around)

Very often in astronomy, the object (or group of objects) you are observing has no outside forces acting on it in a way to produce **torques** that would disturb the

torque

angular motion of the object (or group of objects). A **torque** is simply a force acting along a line that is off the object's spin axis and would make the object or system spin differently than its current motion. In the case of no net torque, you have **conservation of angular momentum.**

conservation of angular momentum—the total amount of angular momentum does not change with time no matter how the objects interact with one another.

A planet's velocity and distance from the Sun will change but the **combination** of speed×distance will not change unless another planet or star passes close by and provides an extra gravity force.

Applications

Kepler's 2nd law

1) **Kepler's Second Law of orbital motion**: The area swept out by a line connecting an orbiting object and the central point is the same for any two equal periods of times. That line is called a *radius vector* in the following discussion.

The rate of change of the swept-out area does NOT change with time. The line along which gravity acts is parallel to the radius vector. This means that there are no torques disturbing the angular motion and, therefore, angular momentum is conserved. The part of orbital velocity (v-orbit) *perpendicular* (at a right angle) to the radius vector (r) is v_t. The rate of change of the swept-out area $= r \times v_t/2$.

To calculate the orbital angular momentum, use v_t for the velocity. So, the angular momentum $=$ mass $\times v_t \times r =$ mass $\times 2 \times$ rate of change of area. That value does not change over time. So if r decreases, v-orbit (and v_t) must increase! If r increases, v-orbit (and v_t) must decrease. This is just what Kepler observed for the planets!

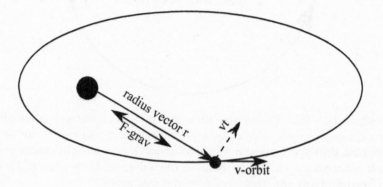

Figure A.1: Kepler's Second Law

Earth-Moon system

2) **Earth-Moon system**: The total angular momentum $=$ spin angular momentum $+$ orbital angular momentum. The total angular momentum is CONSTANT. To find the spin angular momentum, subdivide the object into small pieces of mass and find the angular momentum for each of the small pieces. Then add up the angular momentum for all of the pieces. The Earth's spin speed is decreasing so its spin angular momentum is DEcreasing. Therefore, the Moon's orbital angular momentum must compensate by INcreasing. It does this by increasing the size of the Moon's orbit.

neutron stars

3) **Rapidly spinning neutron stars**: Originally, a big star has a core 10,000's to 100,000's kilometers in radius (the whole star is even bigger!). Here the *radius* is used instead of the diameter, because what is important is how far each piece of the core is from the spin axis that goes through the exact center of the star.

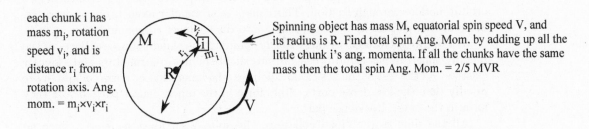

each chunk i has mass m_i, rotation speed v_i, and is distance r_i from rotation axis. Ang. mom. = $m_i \times v_i \times r_i$

Spinning object has mass M, equatorial spin speed V, and its radius is R. Find total spin Ang. Mom. by adding up all the little chunk i's ang. momenta. If all the chunks have the same mass then the total spin Ang. Mom. = 2/5 MVR

Figure A.2: Earth-Moon: Rotation + Revolution

The core spins at 2 to 10 kilometers/second at the core's equator. If no external forces produce torques, the angular momentum is constant. During a supernova the outer layers are blown off and the core shrinks to only 10 kilometers in radius! The core angular momentum is approximately $= 0.4 \times M \times V \times R$ and the mass M has stayed approximately the same. When the radius R shrinks by factors of 10,000's, the spin speed V must increase by 10,000's of times.

Sometimes the neutron star suddenly shrinks slightly (by a millimeter or so) and it spins faster. The neutron star produces radiation from its strong magnetic field. This radiation is produced at the expense of rotational energy and the angular momentum is not strictly conserved—it slowly decreases. Therefore, the neutron star spin speed slowly decreases.

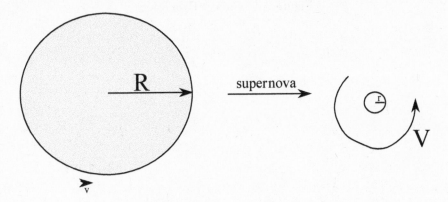

Figure A.3: Neutron Stars – Pulsars

4) **Accretion disk in a binary system**: Gas flowing from one star falls toward its compact companion into an orbit around it. The orbital angular momentum is conserved, so as the gas' distance from the compact companion DEcreases, its orbital speed must INcrease. It forms a rapidly rotating disk-like whirlpool called an *accretion disk*.

accretion disks

Figure A.4: Mass Transfer in Binary System

Over time some of the gas in the disk gas give torques to other parts of the disk's orbital motions through friction. This causes their angular momentum to decrease. Some of that gas, then, eventually falls onto the compact companion.

galaxy formation

5) **Forming Galaxy**: A huge *slowly* spinning gas cloud collapses. Parts of the roughly spherical gas cloud break up into small chunks to form stars and globular clusters. As the rest of the gas cloud collapses, the inner, denser parts collapse more rapidly than the less dense parts. Stars form in the inner, denser parts before they form in the outer, less dense parts.

All the time as the cloud collapses, the spin speed must increase. Since no outside forces produce torques, the angular momentum is conserved. The rapidly spinning part of the gas cloud eventually forms a disk. This is because the cloud can collapse more easily in a direction parallel to the spin axis. The gas that is orbiting perpendicular to the spin axis has enough inertia to resist the inward pull of gravity (the gas feels a "centrifugal force"). The densest parts of the disk will form stars.

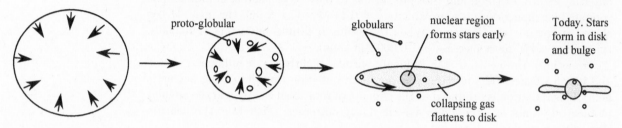

Figure A.5: Galaxy Formation

Appendix B

Mathematics Review

B.1 Fractions and Percentages %

Fractions are a part of every-day life and they are also used in science. A fraction with the same numerator (number on top) as another but with a smaller denominator (number on bottom) is a *larger* number. For example 1/2 is *bigger* than 1/3 which is bigger than 1/4, etc. That is because if you divide 1 by 2, you get 0.5 but 1 divided by 3 is only 0.333 and 1 divided by 4 is only 0.25. The fraction 3/5 (=0.6) is bigger than 3/6 (=0.5) which is bigger than 3/7 (=0.4286).

Fractions are sometimes expressed as a **percent.** To express a fraction as a percentage, find the decimal form and multiply by 100. The percent symbol "%" simply means "divide by 100." For example $1/2 = 0.5 = 0.5 \times 100\% = 50\%$; $3/5 = 0.6 = 0.6 \times 100\% = 60\%$. Some examples on converting percentages to fractions or decimals: $5.8\% = 5.8/100 = 0.058$; $0.02\% = 0.02/100 = 0.0002$; the Sun is 90% hydrogen means that 90 out of every 100 atoms in the Sun is hydrogen.

B.2 "Times" and "Factor of"

Several homework questions ask you to find some quantity and find out how many "times" smaller or larger it is than something else, e.g., star A is ___ times larger than star B. This means star A = $\alpha\times$ star B, and you must find the number α. Another example: A gallon is equivalent to 4 quarts. This means that 1 gallon is 4 **times** *bigger* than 1 quart since 1 gallon = 4×1 quart, or (1 gallon)/(1 quart) = 4/1. This also means that 1 quart is 4 **times** *smaller* than 1 gallon since 1 quart = $1/4 \times$ (1 gallon), or (1 quart)/(1 gallon) = 1/4. Notice when "times bigger" is used and when "times smaller" is used.

The use of the phrase "factor of" is very similar to the use of "times". For example, 1 quart is a **factor of** 4 *smaller* than 1 gallon, or 1 gallon is a **factor of** 4 *bigger* than 1 quart.

B.3 Exponents

A shorthand way to express a quantity multiplied by itself one or more time is to use a superscript number called an **exponent**. So

$$a = a^1$$
$$a \times a = a^2 \quad (\text{not } 2 \times a!)$$
$$a \times a \times a = a^3 \quad (\text{not } 3 \times a!)$$

$$a \times a \times a \times a = a^4$$
$$a \times a \times a \times a \times a = a^5$$

The quantity "a squared" means a^2, "a cubed" means a^3, and more generally, "a to the nth power" is a^n.

Some special rules apply when you divide or multiply numbers raised to some power. When you have a^n multiplied by a^m, the result is a raised to a power that is the sum of the exponents:

$$a^n \times a^m = a^{n+m}$$

When you have a^n divided by a^m, the result is a raised to a power that is the difference of the exponents—the exponent on the bottom is subtracted from the exponent on the top:

$$\frac{a^n}{a^m} = a^{n-m} \quad (\text{not } a^{m-n}!)$$

When you have a^n raised to a power m, you multiply the exponents:

$$(a^n)^m = a^{n \times m} = a^{nm} \quad (\text{not } a^{n+m}!)$$

Negative exponents are used for reciprocals:

$$\frac{1}{a} = a^{-1}, \quad \frac{1}{a^2} = a^{-2}, \quad \frac{1}{a^3} = a^{-3}, \quad \frac{1}{a^4} = a^{-4}, \quad \text{etc.}$$

Scientific calculators have a "y^x" key or a "x^y" that takes care of raising numbers to some exponent. Some fancy calculators have a ˆ key that does the same thing. Some calculators have "x^2" and "x^3" keys to take care of those frequent squaring or cubing of numbers. Check your calculator's manual or your instructor.

B.4   Roots

The **square root** of a quantity is a number that when multiplied by itself, the product is the original quantity:

$$\sqrt{a} \times \sqrt{a} = a.$$

Some examples: $\sqrt{1} = 1$ because $1 \times 1 = 1$; $\sqrt{4} = 2$ because $2 \times 2 = 4$; $\sqrt{38.44} = 6.2$ because $6.2 \times 6.2 = 38.44$; $\sqrt{25A^2} = 5A$ because $5A \times 5A = 25A^2$. A square root of a number less than 1, gives a number *larger* than the number itself: $\sqrt{0.01} = 0.1$ because $0.1 \times 0.1 = 0.01$ and $\sqrt{.36} = 0.6$ because $0.6 \times 0.6 = 0.36$.

The **cube root** of a quantity is a number that when multiplied by itself two times, the product is the original quantity:

$$\sqrt[3]{a} \times \sqrt[3]{a} \times \sqrt[3]{a} = a.$$

Scientific calculators have a "$\sqrt{x}$" and sometimes "$\sqrt[3]{x}$" keys to take care of the common square roots or cube roots. An expression $\sqrt[n]{a}$ means the nth root of a. How can you use your calculator for something like that? You use the fact that the nth root of a is a raised to a fractional exponent of $1/n$. So we have:

$$\sqrt[n]{a} = a^{1/n}$$
$$\sqrt{a} = \sqrt[2]{a} = a^{1/2}$$
$$\sqrt[3]{a} = a^{1/3}$$

When you raise some nth root to some power m, you simply multiply the exponents as you did above for $(a^n)^m$:

$$(\sqrt[n]{a})^m = (a^{1/n})^m = a^{1/n \times m} = a^{m/n}.$$

So $(a^6)^{1/2} = a^{6 \times (1/2)} = a^3$ and $(a^{1/2})^6 = a^{(1/2) \times 6} = a^3$. But if you have $a^{1/n}$ multiplied by a^m, you add the exponents since you are **not** raising $a^{1/n}$ to some power m: $a^{1/2} \times a^6 = a^{(1/2)+6} = a^{6\,1/2} = a^{13/2}$.

B.5   Powers of 10

For numbers larger than 10, the power of 10 is a positive value and negative for numbers less than 1. For numbers between 0 and 10, the power is a positive fraction. In the examples that follow, notice what happens to the decimal point:

$$10^0 = 1. \quad = \quad \text{1. with the decimal point moved 0 places}$$
$$10^1 = 10. \quad = \quad \text{1. with the decimal point moved 1 place to the right}$$
$$10^2 = 100. \quad = \quad \text{1. with the decimal point moved 2 places to the right}$$
$$10^6 = 1000000. \quad = \quad \text{1. with the decimal point moved 6 places to the right}$$

and

$$10^{-1} = 0.1 \quad = \quad \text{1. with the decimal point moved 1 place to the } \textit{left}$$
$$10^{-2} = 0.01 \quad = \quad \text{1. with the decimal point moved 2 places to the } \textit{left}$$
$$10^{-6} = 0.000001 \quad = \quad \text{1. with the decimal point moved 6 places to the } \textit{left}.$$

The exponent of 10 tells you how many places to move the decimal point to the right for positive exponents or left for negative exponents. These rules come in especially handy for writing very large or very small numbers.

B.6   Scientific Notation

Since you will be working with very large and very small numbers, use scientific notation to cut down on all of the zeroes you need to write. Proper scientific notation specifies a value as a number between 1 and 10 (called the **mantissa** below) multiplied by some power of ten. The power of ten tells you which way to move the decimal point and by how many places. As a quick review:

$\text{mantissa} \times 10^{\text{exponent}}$

$10 = 1 \times 10^1$, $253 = 2.53 \times 100 = 2.53 \times 10^2$, and $15,000,000,000 = 1.5 \times 10^{10}$ which you will sometimes see written as 15×10^9 even though this is not proper scientific notation. For small numbers you have: $\frac{1}{10} = 1 \times 10^{-1}$, $\frac{1}{253} = \frac{1}{2.53 \times 100} = \frac{1}{2.53} \times 10^{-2} \approx 0.395 \times 10^{-2} = 3.95 \times 10^{-3}$

B.6.1   Multiplying and Dividing with Scientific Notation

When you multiply two values given in scientific notation, multiply the mantissa numbers and *add* the exponents in the power of ten. Then adjust the mantissa and exponent so that the mantissa is between 1 and 10 with the appropriate exponent in the power of ten. For example: $(3 \times 10^{10}) \times (6 \times 10^{23})$, you'd have $3 \times 6 \times 10^{10+23} = 18. \times 10^{33} = 1.8 \times 10^{34}$.

When you divide two values given in scientific notation, divide the mantissa numbers and *subtract* the exponents in the power of ten. Then adjust the mantissa and exponent so that the mantissa is between 1 and 10 with the appropriate exponent in the power of ten. For example: $\frac{3 \times 10^{10}}{6 \times 10^{23}} = \frac{3}{6} \times 10^{10-23} = 0.5 \times 10^{-13} = 5 \times 10^{-14}$.

Notice what happened to the decimal point and exponent in the examples. You *subtract* one from the exponent for every space you move the decimal to the *right*. You *add* one to the exponent for every space you move the decimal to the *left*.

B.6.2 Entering Scientific Notation on your Scientific Calculator

Please read this if you have not used a scientific calculator for a while!

Most scientific calculators work with scientific notation. Your calculator will have either an "EE" key or an "EXP" key. That is for entering scientific notation. To enter 253 ($= 2.53 \times 10^2$), punch 2 $\rightarrow$. $\rightarrow$5 $\rightarrow$3 $\rightarrow$EE or EXP $\rightarrow$2. To enter 3.95×10^{-3}, punch 3 $\rightarrow$. $\rightarrow$9 $\rightarrow$5 $\rightarrow$EE or EXP $\rightarrow$3 $\rightarrow$[$\pm$ key].

Note that if the calculator displays "3.53 -14" (a space between the 3.53 and -14), it means 3.53×10^{-14} **NOT** 3.53^{-14}! The value of $3.53^{-14} = 0.00000002144 = 2.144 \times 10^{-8}$ which is vastly different than the number 3.53×10^{-14}. Also, if you have the number 4×10^3 and you enter 4 $\rightarrow$x $\rightarrow$1 $\rightarrow$0 $\rightarrow$EE or EXP $\rightarrow$3, the calculator will interpret that as $4 \times 10 \times 10^3 = 4 \times 10^4$ or ten times greater than the number you really want!

One other word of warning: the EE or EXP key is used only for scientific notation and NOT for raising some number to a power. To raise a number to some exponent use the x^y or y^x key depending on the calculator. For example, to raise 3 to the 4th power as in 3^4 enter 3 $\rightarrow x^y$ or y^x $\rightarrow$4. If you instead entered it using the EE or EXP key as in 3 $\rightarrow$EE or EXP $\rightarrow$4, the calculator would interpret that as 3×10^4 which is much different than $3^4 = 81$.

B.7   Metric System

The metric system is a much more logical and straightforward system than the old english still used in the United States. Every other nation in the world uses the metric system, so in today's global economy, it is very advantageous to learn how to use the system. It is also the system used in science.

B.7.1   Prefixes

The metric system is based on the number 10, for example there are 10 millimeters in one centimeter, 1000 grams in one kilogram, 100 centimeters in one meter, 100 degrees between the freezing and boiling point of water, etc. Contrast this with the english system that has 12 inches to 1 foot, 16 ounces to 1 pound, 5,280 feet to one mile, 180 degrees Fahrenheit between the freezing and boiling point of water, ...egad! All of the units in the metric system use a common set of prefixes:

prefix	meaning	example
pico	$10^{-12} = 1/10^{12}$	1 picosecond $= 10^{-12}$ second
nano	$10^{-9} = 1/10^{9}$	1 nanometer $= 10^{-9}$ meter
micro	$10^{-6} = 1/10^{6}$	1 microgram $= 10^{-6}$ gram
milli	$10^{-3} = 1/1000$	1 millikelvin $= 10^{-3}$ kelvin
centi	$10^{-2} = 1/100$	1 centimeter $= 1/100$th meter
kilo	1000	1 kilogram $= 1000$ grams
mega	10^{6}	1 megasecond $= 10^{6}$ seconds
giga	10^{9}	1 gigakelvin $= 10^{6}$ kelvins
tera	10^{12}	1 terameter $= 10^{12}$ meters

B.7.2   Length

The base unit of length in the metric system is the meter. It is a little over 1 yard long, more precisely 39.37 inches long. Here are some other conversions:

1 meter (m)	= 39.37 inches	= 1.094 yards (about one big step)
1 kilometer (km)	= 1000 meters	0.62137 mile
1 centimeter (cm)	= 1/100th meter	0.3937 inch (1/2.54 inch, about width of pinky)

B.7.3   Mass

The base unit of mass is the gram. Mass is the amount of material in something and is different than weight. See chapter 5 for a explanation of mass, weight and the difference between the two. There are 28.3495 grams in one ounce. A paperclip has a mass of roughly one gram. Here are some other conversions:

1 gram (g)	= 0.0353 ounce	produces 0.0022046 pounds **of weight** on the Earth
1 kilogram (kg)	= 1000 grams	produces 2.205 pounds **of weight** on the Earth
1 metric ton	= 1000 kilograms	produces 2,205 pounds **of weight** on the Earth

B.7.4   Temperature

The base unit of temperature is the kelvin, though the Celsius is also used. The kelvin scale is measured from absolute zero—the temperature at which all motion stops, the absolute coldest temperature possible. The Celsius scale is measured from the freezing point of pure water at sea level, but the intervals of temperature are the same as the kelvin scale. Water freezes at 0° Celsius which is the same as 273 kelvin. Water boils at 100° Celsius which is the same as 373 kelvin. The Fahrenheit scale in common usage in the United States has the freezing point of pure water at 32° Fahrenheit and the boiling point at 212° Fahrenheit at sea level. Below are conversion formulae for Fahrenheit to the metric scales and vice versa. Remember to calculate the values in parentheses first!

To convert Fahrenheit to Celsius use: $°C = \frac{5}{9}(°F - 32)$.

To convert Fahrenheit to kelvin use: $K = \frac{5}{9}(°F - 32) + 273$.

To convert Celsius to Fahrenheit use: $°F = \frac{9}{5}°C + 32$.

To convert kelvin to Fahrenheit use: $°F = \frac{9}{5}(K - 273) + 32$.

See chapter 7 for further discussion of the kelvin, Celsius, and Fahrenheit scales.

Appendix C

Tables

Table C.1: Astronomical Constants

Quantity	Value
astronomical unit (A.U.)	149,597,870.691 kilometers
light year (ly)	$9.460536207 \times 10^{12}$ km = 63,240 A.U.
parsec (pc)	$3.08567802 \times 10^{13}$ km = 206,265 A.U.
sidereal year	365.2564 days
tropical year	365.2422 days
Gregorian year	365.2425 days
Earth mass	5.9736×10^{24} kilograms
Sun mass	1.9891×10^{30} kg = 332,980 $\times$ Earth
mean Earth radius	6371 kilometers
Sun radius	6.96265×10^5 km = 109 $\times$ Earth
Sun luminosity	3.827×10^{26} watts

Table C.2: Physical Constants

Quantity	Value
speed of light (c)	299,792.458 kilometers/second
gravitational constant (G)	6.6726×10^{-11} m^3/(kg sec^2)
Boltzmann constant (k)	1.380658×10^{-23} Joules/Kelvin
Stefan-Boltzmann constant (σ)	5.67051×10^{-8} J/(m^2 K^4 s)
Wien's law constant	2.897756×10^6 nanometers Kelvin
Planck constant (h)	$6.6260755 \times 10^{-34}$ Joules second
electron mass	$9.1093898 \times 10^{-28}$ grams = $5.48579903 \times 10^{-4}$ amu
proton mass	$1.6726231 \times 10^{-24}$ grams = 1.007276470 amu
neutron mass	$1.6749286 \times 10^{-24}$ grams = 1.008664904 amu
deuterium nucleus mass	$3.3435860 \times 10^{-24}$ grams = 2.013553214 amu

Table C.3: Planets: Orbital Properties

Planet	distance (A.U.)	revolution	eccentricity	inclination (deg)
Mercury	0.387	87.969 d	0.2056	7.005
Venus	0.723	224.701 d	0.0068	3.3947
Earth	1.000	365.256 d	0.0167	0.0000
Mars	1.524	686.98 d	0.0934	1.851
Jupiter	5.203	11.862 y	0.0484	1.305
Saturn	9.537	29.457 y	0.0542	2.484
Uranus	19.191	84.011 y	0.0472	0.770
Neptune	30.069	164.79 y	0.0086	1.769
Pluto	39.482	247.68 y	0.2488	17.142

Notes: Distance is the semi-major axis in astronomical units (1 A.U. = 1.496×10^8 km); rotation and revolution are the sidereal rotation period and sidereal orbital period, h = hours, d = days; eccentricity is the orbital eccentricity = 1 − (perihelion/semi-major axis); and inclination is the tilt of the orbit with respect to the Earth's orbit. [Yes, Pluto is a dwarf planet.]

Table C.4: Planets: Physical Characteristics

Planet	Mass ($\times M_E$)	Diameter (km)	density (g/cm^3)	oblateness [=$(D_e - D_p)/D_e$]	rotation	axis tilt (deg)	mag. field ($\times$Earth's)
Mercury	0.0553	4879	5.427	0.000	58.785 d	~ 0	0.0006
Venus	0.815	12,104	5.243	0.000	243.686 d	177.36	0.00
Earth	1.000	12,742	5.515	0.00335	23.9345 h	23.45	1.000
Mars	0.107	6779	3.933	0.00648	24.6229 h	25.19	0.00
Jupiter	317.83	139,822	1.326	0.06487	9.9250 h	3.13	19,519
Saturn	95.159	116,464	0.687	0.09796	10.656 h	26.73	578
Uranus	14.536	50,724	1.270	0.02293	17.24 h	97.77	47.9
Neptune	17.147	49,244	1.638	0.01708	16.11 h	28.32	27.0
Pluto	0.0021	2390	1.750	0.000	6.405 d	122.53	0.00

Notes: Mass is given in Earth masses (1 $M_E = 5.9736 \times 10^{24}$ kg); diameter is the "volumetric mean diameter" that takes into account the planet's oblateness; oblateness measures how much a planet bulges at the equator [= (equatorial − polar diameter)/(equatorial diameter)]; and axis tilt is the tilt of the planet's rotation axis with respect to its orbital plane; magnetic field (mag. field) is the total strength (NSSDC gives strength in #gauss $\times R_{planet}^3$, where R_{planet} is the radius of the planet and the Earth's magnetic field strength = 0.3076 gauss $\times R_{planet}^3 = 7.981 \times 10^{10}$ gauss.

Table C.5: Planets: Atmospheres

Planet	g ($\times g_E$)	v_{esc} (km/s)	distance (A.U.)	albedo (%)	temperature (K)	atm. press. ($\times$ Earth's)	atm. comp.
Mercury	0.378	4.3	0.387	11.9	100 night, 590–725 day	10^{-15}	42% O_2, 29% Na, 22% H_2, 6% He, 0.5% K (note that it is essentially a vacuum)
Venus	0.905	10.36	0.723	75	737	92	96.5% CO_2, 3.5% N_2, 0.015% SO_2, 0.007% Ar, 0.002% H_2O, 0.002% CO, 0.001% He, 0.001% Ne
Earth	1.000	11.186	1.000	30.6	283 night, 293 day	1.000	78.08% N_2, 20.95% O_2, 0.934% Ar, 0.038% CO_2, H_2O highly variable (<1%)
Mars	0.379	5.03	1.524	25.0	184 night, 242 day	0.004–0.009	95.32% CO_2, 2.7% N_2, 1.6% Ar, 0.13% O_2, 0.08% CO, 0.021% H_2O, 0.01% NO
Jupiter	2.530	59.5	5.203	34.3	165	$\gg$1000	89.8% H_2, 10.2% He, 0.3% CH_4, 0.026% NH_3. Clouds made of ammonia ice, water ice, ammonium hydrosulfide
Saturn	1.065	35.5	9.537	34.2	134	$\gg$1000	96.3% H_2, 3.25% He, 0.45% CH_4, 0.0125% NH_3, 0.0110% HD, 0.0007% C_2H_6. Clouds made of ammonia ice, water ice, ammonium hydrosulfide
Uranus	0.905	21.3	19.191	30.0	76	$\gg$1000	82.5% H_2, 15.2% He, 2.3% CH_4, 0.0148% HD. Clouds made of ammonia ice, water ice, ammonium hydrosulfide, methane ice
Neptune	1.14	23.5	30.069	29.0	72	$\gg$1000	80.0% H_2, 19.0% He, 1.5% CH_4, 0.0192% HD, 0.0002% C_2H_6. Clouds made of ammonia ice, water ice, ammonium hydrosulfide, methane ice
Pluto	0.059	1.2	39.482	40 to 60	~50	3×10^{-6}	CH_4, N_2

Notes: Surface gravity g is given in Earth gravities (1 g_E = 9.803 m/s^2); escape velocity is v_{esc}, albedo is the percent of ALL of the Sun's energy hitting the planet that is reflected (100% would be perfect reflection); temperature and surface gravity for Jupiter, Saturn, Uranus, Neptune are given at a depth where the atmospheric pressure = 1 Earth atmosphere; atmospheric pressure (atm. press.) is at the surface ($\gg$100 for the jovian planets).

Table C.6: 100 Nearest Stars

HIP	common name	Vmag	Abs Mag	Distance (pc)	B-V (mag)	Spectral Type
70890	Proxima Centauri	11.01	15.45	1.2948	1.807	M5Ve
71681	α Centauri B	1.35	5.70	1.3475	0.9	K1V
71683	Rigel Kentaurus	-0.01	4.34	1.3475	0.71	G2V
87937	Barnard's Star	9.54	13.24	1.8215	1.57	sdM4
54035		7.49	10.46	2.5484	1.502	M2V
32349	Sirius A	-1.44	1.45	2.6371	0.009	A0m...
92403	Ross 154	10.37	13.00	2.9719	1.51	M3.5Ve
16537	ϵ Eridani	3.72	6.18	3.2180	0.881	K2V
114046	Lacaille 9352	7.35	9.76	3.2906	1.483	M2/M3V
57548	FI Virginis or Ross 128	11.12	13.50	3.3380	1.746	M4.5V
104214	61 Cygni A	5.2	7.49	3.4827	1.069	K5V
37279	Procyon	0.4	2.68	3.4974	0.432	F5IV-V
104217	61 Cygni B	6.05	8.33	3.5036	1.309	K7V
91772		9.7	11.97	3.5152	1.561	K5
91768		8.94	11.18	3.5679	1.504	K5
1475	GX Andromedae	8.09	10.33	3.5680	1.56	M1V
108870	ϵ Indi	4.69	6.89	3.6263	1.056	K5V
8102	τ Ceti	3.49	5.68	3.6474	0.727	G8V
5643	YZ Ceti	12.1	14.25	3.7168	1.85	M5.5Ve
36208	Luyten's Star	9.84	11.94	3.7985	1.573	M5
24186	Kapteyn's Star	8.86	10.89	3.9176	1.543	M0V
105090	AX Microscopii	6.69	8.71	3.9468	1.397	M1/M2V
110893		9.59	11.58	4.0077	1.613	M2V
30920	Ross 614 A	11.12	13.05	4.1171	1.69	M4.5Ve
72511		11.72	13.58	4.2510	1.48	M
80824	Wolf 1061	10.1	11.95	4.2642	1.604	M4
439		8.56	10.36	4.3605	1.462	M2V
15689		12.16	13.94	4.3966		
3829	van Maanen's Star	12.37	14.15	4.4063	0.554	DG
72509		12.07	13.80	4.5086	1.524	M
86162		9.15	10.87	4.5280	1.505	M3.5Vvar
85523		9.38	11.10	4.5366	1.553	K5
114110		12.24	13.92	4.6185		
57367		11.5	13.18	4.6211	0.196	DC:
113020	IL Aquarii or Ross 780	10.16	11.80	4.7017	1.597	M5
54211	Furuhjelm I- 650	8.82	10.40	4.8323	1.491	M2Vvar
49908		6.6	8.16	4.8728	1.326	K8V
82725		11.72	13.26	4.9259		
85605		11.39	12.92	4.9336	1.101	
106440		8.66	10.19	4.9375	1.521	M1V
86214		10.94	12.43	5.0424	1.655	M5
19849	o^2 Eridani A	4.43	5.92	5.0444	0.82	K1V
112460	EV Lacertae	10.29	11.77	5.0487	1.54	M4.5Ve
88601	70 Ophiuchi A	4.03	5.50	5.0860	0.86	K0V SB
97649	Altair	0.76	2.20	5.1430	0.221	A7IV-V
1242		11.49	12.90	5.2121	1.75	M:
57544		10.8	12.14	5.3914	1.572	M4
67155	Wolf 498	8.46	9.79	5.4309	1.435	M3V
103039		11.41	12.71	5.4900	1.653	
21088		10.82	12.11	5.5139	1.17	
33226	Wolf 294	9.89	11.18	5.5151	1.58	K:...

Table C.6: 100 Nearest Stars (cont.)

HIP	common name	Vmag	Abs Mag	Distance (pc)	B-V (mag)	Spectral Type
53020	EE Leo or Wolf 358	11.64	12.89	5.6351	1.679	M4:
25878	Wolf 1453	7.97	9.19	5.6909	1.474	M1V
82817	Wolf 630	9.02	10.23	5.7395	1.553	M3Ve
96100	σ Draconis	4.67	5.87	5.7667	0.786	K0V
29295		8.15	9.34	5.7740	1.487	M1/M2V
26857	Ross 47	11.56	12.75	5.7877	1.675	M5
86990		10.75	11.93	5.8113	1.66	M5
94761	Wolf 1055	9.12	10.28	5.8734	1.464	M3.5V
73184		5.72	6.86	5.9060	1.024	K4V
37766	Ross 882	11.19	12.32	5.9315	1.6	M4.5Ve
76074		9.31	10.44	5.9340	1.524	M0
3821	η Cassiopei or Wolf 24	3.46	4.59	5.9527	0.587	G0V SB
84478	36 Ophiuchi C	6.33	7.45	5.9680	1.144	K5V
117473	BR Piscium	8.98	10.10	5.9698	1.46	M2V
84405	36 Ophiuchi	4.33	5.44	5.9852	0.855	K2:III:
99461		5.32	6.41	6.0518	0.868	K2V
15510	82 Eridani	4.26	5.35	6.0599	0.711	G8V
99240	δ Pavonis	3.55	4.62	6.1076	0.751	G5IV-Vvar
71253	Wolf 1481	11.32	12.39	6.1158	1.633	M4
86961		10.49	11.53	6.1816	1.463	M2V:
86963		11.39	12.43	6.1816	1.439	M2V:
45343		7.64	8.68	6.1885	1.41	M0V
99701		7.97	9.01	6.2046	1.431	M0V
116132	EQ Pegasi	10.05	11.07	6.2477	1.19	M6Ve
74995	HO Librae or Wolf 562	10.57	11.58	6.2688	1.6	M5
120005		7.7	8.71	6.2704	1.42	K2
84140		9.31	10.31	6.3223	1.485	K5
34603	QY Aurigae or Ross 986	11.65	12.63	6.3597	1.7	M5Ve
54298		11.69	12.65	6.4400		
82809	Wolf 629	11.73	12.67	6.4952	1.7	M4
114622		5.57	6.50	6.5257	1	K3Vvar
80459		10.13	11.04	6.5820	1.591	M2
53767	Ross 104	10.03	10.92	6.6243	1.525	M3
72659	37 Bootis	4.54	5.41	6.6997	0.72	G8V + K4V
106106	Ross 775	10.33	11.19	6.7435	1.62	M4
114176		12.28	13.13	6.7590		
113296	Ross 671	8.68	9.49	6.8837	1.507	M2:
84709		5.91	6.69	6.9711	1.082	K4V
103096		8.55	9.31	7.0447	1.483	M2V
12114		5.79	6.50	7.2088	0.918	K3V
51317	Ross 446	9.65	10.35	7.2312	1.507	M2
83945		11.77	12.47	7.2548	1.696	M3
3765	Wolf 25	5.74	6.38	7.4605	0.89	K2V
7981	107 Piscium	5.24	5.87	7.4677	0.836	K1V
2021	β Hydri	2.82	3.45	7.4750	0.618	G2IV
73182		8.01	8.64	7.4833	1.519	K5V
12781	VX Arietis or Ross 556	10.55	11.16	7.5517	1.53	M3.5Ve
5336	μ Cassiopei A	5.17	5.78	7.5529	0.704	G5Vp
65859	Ross 490	9.05	9.64	7.6266	1.493	M1V

Table C.7: 100 Brightest Stars As Seen From Earth

HIP	common name	Vmag	Abs Mag	Distance (pc)	B-V (mag)	Spectral type
32349	Sirius	-1.44	1.45	2.64	0.009	A0m
30438	Canopus	-0.62	-5.53	95.88	0.164	F0Ib
69673	Arcturus	-0.05	-0.31	11.25	1.239	K2IIIp
71683	Rigil Kentaurus	-0.01	4.34	1.35	0.71	G2V
91262	Vega	0.03	0.58	7.76	-0.001	A0Vvar
24608	Capella	0.08	-0.48	12.94	0.795	G5IIIe+G
24436	Rigel	0.18	-6.69	236.97	-0.03	B8Ia:
37279	Procyon	0.40	2.68	3.5	0.432	F5IV-V
7588	Achernar	0.45	-2.77	44.09	-0.158	B3Vp
27989	Betelgeuse	0.45	-5.14	131.06	1.5	M2Ib
68702	Agena	0.61	-5.42	161.03	-0.231	B1III
97649	Altair	0.76	2.20	5.14	0.221	A7IV-V
60718	Acrux	0.77	-4.19	98.33	-0.243	B0.5IV
21421	Aldebaran	0.87	-0.63	19.96	1.538	K5III
65474	Spica	0.98	-3.55	80.39	-0.235	B1V
80763	Antares	1.06	-5.28	185.19	1.865	M1Ib+B2.
37826	Pollux	1.16	1.09	10.34	0.991	K0IIIvar
113368	Fomalhaut	1.17	1.74	7.69	0.145	A3V
62434	Becrux	1.25	-3.92	108.11	-0.238	B0.5III
102098	Deneb	1.25	-8.73	990.1	0.092	A2Ia
71681	α Cen B	1.35	5.70	1.35	0.9	K1V
49669	Regulus	1.36	-0.52	23.76	-0.087	B7V
33579	Adara	1.50	-4.10	132.1	-0.211	B2II
36850	Castor	1.58	0.59	15.81	0.034	A2Vm
61084	Gacrux	1.59	-0.56	26.96	1.6	M4III
85927	Shaula	1.62	-5.05	215.52	-0.231	B1.5IV+B
25336	Bellatrix	1.64	-2.72	74.52	-0.224	B2III
25428	El Nath	1.65	-1.37	40.18	-0.13	B7III
45238	Miaplacidus	1.67	-0.99	34.08	0.07	A2IV
26311	Alnilam	1.69	-6.38	411.52	-0.184	B0Ia
109268	Al Nair	1.73	-0.73	31.09	-0.07	B7IV
26727	Alnitak	1.74	-5.26	250.63	-0.199	O9.5Ib
39953	Alsuhail	1.75	-5.31	257.73	-0.145	WC8+O9I
62956	Alioth	1.76	-0.21	24.81	-0.022	A0p
15863	Algenib	1.79	-4.50	181.49	0.481	F5Ib
90185	Kaus Australis	1.79	-1.44	44.35	-0.031	B9.5III
54061	Dubhe	1.81	-1.08	37.91	1.061	K0IIIa
34444	Wezen	1.83	-6.87	549.45	0.671	F8Ia
67301	Alkaid	1.85	-0.60	30.87	-0.099	B3V
41037	ϵ Car	1.86	-4.58	193.8	1.196	K3III+B2
86228	θ Sco	1.86	-2.75	83.4	0.406	F1II
28360	Menkalinan	1.90	-0.10	25.18	0.077	A2V
82273	α TrA	1.91	-3.62	127.39	1.447	K2IIb-II
31681	Alhena	1.93	-0.60	32.13	0.001	A0IV
42913	Koo She	1.93	-0.01	24.45	0.043	A1V
100751	α Pav	1.94	-1.81	56.18	-0.118	B2IV
11767	Polaris	1.97	-3.64	132.28	0.636	F7:Ib-II
30324	Mirzam	1.98	-3.95	153.14	-0.24	B1II/III
46390	Alphard	1.99	-1.69	54.35	1.44	K3III
9884	Hamal	2.01	0.48	20.21	1.151	K2III
50583	Algieba	2.01	-0.92	38.52	1.128	K0III

Table C.7: 100 Brightest Stars As Seen From Earth (cont.)

HIP	common name	Vmag	Abs Mag	Distance (pc)	B-V (mag)	Spectral Type
3419	Deneb Kaitos	2.04	-0.30	29.38	1.019	K0III
92855	Nunki	2.05	-2.14	68.78	-0.134	B2.5V
68933	θ Cen	2.06	0.70	18.68	1.011	K0IIIb
677	Alpheratz	2.07	-0.30	29.76	-0.038	B9p
27366	Saiph	2.07	-6.98	645.16	-0.168	B0.5Iava
5447	Mirach	2.07	-1.86	61.12	1.576	M0IIIvar
72607	Kochab	2.07	-0.87	38.77	1.465	K4IIIvar
112122	Al Dhanab	2.07	-1.52	52.16	1.61	M5III
86032	Ras Alhague	2.08	1.30	14.32	0.155	A5III
14576	Algol	2.09	-0.18	28.46	-0.003	B8V
9640	Alamak	2.10	-3.08	108.81	1.37	K3-IIb
57632	Denebola	2.14	1.92	11.09	0.09	A3Vvar
4427	Cih	2.15	-4.22	187.97	-0.046	B0IV:eva
61932	γ Cen	2.20	-0.81	39.98	-0.023	A1IV
39429	Naos	2.21	-5.95	429.18	-0.269	O5IAf
45556	Tureis	2.21	-4.42	212.31	0.189	A8Ib
76267	Gemma	2.22	0.42	22.91	0.032	A0V
44816	λ Vel	2.23	-3.99	175.75	1.665	K4Ib-II
65378	Mizar	2.23	0.33	23.96	0.057	A2V
100453	Sadr	2.23	-6.12	467.29	0.673	F8Ib
3179	Schedar	2.24	-1.99	70.08	1.17	K0II-III
87833	Eltanin	2.24	-1.04	45.25	1.521	K5III
25930	Mintaka	2.25	-4.99	280.9	-0.175	O9.5II
746	Caph	2.28	1.17	16.7	0.38	F2III-IV
66657	ϵ Cen	2.29	-3.02	115.21	-0.171	B1III
78401	Dschubba	2.29	-3.16	123.15	-0.117	B0.2IV
82396	ϵ Sco	2.29	0.78	20.06	1.144	K2IIIb
71860	α Lup	2.30	-3.83	168.07	-0.154	B1.5III
71352	η Cen	2.33	-2.55	94.61	-0.157	B1Vn + A
53910	Merak	2.34	0.41	24.35	0.033	A1V
72105	Izar	2.35	-1.69	64.31	0.966	G8II-III
107315	Enif	2.38	-4.19	206.19	1.52	K2Ibvar
86670	κ Sco	2.39	-3.38	142.25	-0.171	B1.5III
2081	Ankaa	2.40	0.52	23.74	1.083	K0III
58001	Phecda	2.41	0.36	25.65	0.044	A0V
84012	Sabik	2.43	0.37	25.79	0.059	A2.5Va
113881	Scheat	2.44	-1.49	61.09	1.655	M2II-III
105199	Alderamin	2.45	1.58	14.96	0.257	A7IV-V
35904	η Cma	2.45	-7.51	980.39	-0.083	B5Ia
45941	κ Vel	2.47	-3.62	165.29	-0.141	B2IV
102488	Gienah	2.48	0.76	22.09	1.021	K0III
113963	Markab	2.49	-0.67	42.81	-0.002	B9.5III
14135	Menkar	2.54	-1.61	67.48	1.63	M2III
81377	Han	2.54	-3.20	140.45	0.038	O9.5V
68002	ζ Cen	2.55	-2.81	117.92	-0.176	B2.5IV
54872	Zosma	2.56	1.32	17.69	0.128	A4V
78820	Acrab	2.56	-3.50	162.6	-0.065	B0.5V
25985	Arneb	2.58	-5.40	393.7	0.211	F0Ib
59196	δ Cen	2.58	-2.84	121.21	-0.128	B2IVne

Appendix D

Glossary

absolute magnitude the brightness of an object that would be measured by an observer if the object was 10 **parsecs** away. It is a measure of the object's **luminosity**.

absorption line spectrum dark lines in a continuous spectrum that are produced by cool, thin (low-pressure) gases in front of a hotter, dense object. Made by **electrons** jumping up farther from the nucleus of the atom.

acceleration a *change* in motion = (the **velocity** change)/(time interval of change). It involves a change in the speed (increase or decrease) OR direction OR both speed and direction.

accretion disk disk of gas that forms around a massive object as material spirals onto the massive object. Accretion disks around **white dwarfs, neutron stars,** and **black holes** form when material is drawn off a nearby normal or giant star. Accretion disks around **neutron stars** and **black holes** can be hot enough to radiate X-rays.

active galaxy luminous galaxy that produces most of its energy from a very compact source at its center. It has a non-thermal continuous spectrum. The energy is coming from an accretion disk of gas around a supermassive black hole at the nucleus of the galaxy.

adaptive optics a technique that compensates for atmospheric turbulence by quickly adjusting the light path in the optics. This removes seeing effects and enables the telescope to achieve much better resolution, closer to its theoretical resolving power.

albedo the fraction of light reflected from an object. Specified as a decimal fraction from 0 (total absorption) to 1 (total reflection).

altitude position on the celestial sphere that is the number of degrees an object is above the nearest horizon. Varies from 0° at horizon to 90° at zenith. Vertical position of an object.

angular momentum a measure of the amount of spin or orbital motion an object has. It is proportional to the mass of the object multiplied by its radius multiplied by its spin or orbital speed.

angular diameter see **angular size**.

angular size the apparent size of an object measured by the angle between two lines of sight along each side of an object. An object's actual linear diameter can be found from the angular size *if* the distance is already known. The linear diameter = $(2\pi/360°) \times$ (its distance × angular size in *degrees*).

annular eclipse a type of **solar eclipse** that happens when the Sun and Moon are exactly lined up but the Moon is too far away from the Earth to totally block the Sun's surface. A ring (annulus) of sunlight is seen around the dark Moon (contrast with **total solar eclipse**).

aphelion point in an object's orbit around the Sun that is *furthest* from the Sun.

apparent magnitude the apparent brightness of an object measured by an observer at an arbitrary distance away.

arc minute a small angle unit = 1/60th of a degree.

arc second a tiny angle unit = 1/3600th of a degree = 1/60th of an **arc minute**.

asteroid boulder to mountain-sized piece of rock remaining from the early solar system. The largest asteroid is only 1000 kilometers across but most are much smaller.

asteroseismology study of the internal structure of stars from their pulsations.

astrology a non-scientific belief system in which the positions of the planets among the stars are thought to hold the key to understanding what you can expect from life.

astrometric technique (planet detection) a method of finding **exoplanets** by looking for a periodic wobbling motion of a star on the plane of the sky.

astronomical unit (A.U.): average distance between the Earth and the Sun (149.6 million kilometers). Used for inter*planetary* distances.

astronomy a discipline that uses the scientific method to understand the physical universe (usually beyond the Earth's atmosphere).

astrophysics a branch of astronomy that deals with the physical properties and interactions of celestial bodies—the application of the principles of physics to celestial bodies and phenomena.

aurora australis aurorae seen in the southern hemisphere.

aurora borealis aurorae seen in the northern hemisphere.

aurorae light displays produced by molecules and atoms high up in an atmosphere. The gas particles are excited by collisions with solar wind particles that were deflected by the planet's magnetic field toward the magnetic poles of the planet.

autumnal equinox specific moment in the year (on September 22) when the Sun is directly on the celestial equator, moving south of the celestial equator.

azimuth position on the celestial sphere that is the number of degrees along the horizon away from the exact north point. Exact North = 0°, exact East = 90°, exact South = 180°, exact West = 270°, exact North = 360° (or 0°). Horizontal position of an object.

Big Bang a theory of the creation of the universe from an ultra-compact volume with very high temperatures about 13.7 billion years ago. The ultra-compact volume began expanding and is responsible for the expanding motion we see today.

bio-marker spectral signatures of certain compounds in certain proportions that could not be produced by non-biological processes. Also called *"biosignature"*.

black hole the collapsed core for the most massive stars. Formed from the total collapse of a core greater than 3 solar masses to an infinitesimal point of infinite density. Gravity in the region surrounding the collapsed core is so strong that the escape velocity is greater than the speed of light. Far beyond that region, black holes obey Newton's **law of gravity**.

blueshift the shift of spectral lines from an object to shorter wavelengths because the object is moving *toward* the observer. The greater the speed of the object, the greater the blueshift will be.

brown dwarf object formed from the gravitational collapse of a gas cloud just as a star is but having too little mass (less than 0.08 solar masses) to undergo nuclear fusion reactions.

carbonaceous meteorite type of stone meteorite containing silicates, carbon compounds (giving them their dark color), around 20% water, and sometimes amino acids (the building blocks of proteins used in biological processes of life).

celestial equator great circle that is a projection of the Earth's equator onto the sky. Always intercepts horizon at exact East and exact West point. Its meridian altitude = (90° − observer's latitude). We see one-half of its circle at a time (12 hours worth).

celestial sphere imaginary sphere of extremely large size around the Earth on which the stars appear to be placed.

center of mass the balance point between two massive objects that is proportionally closer to the more massive object. It is the point where (mass object 1) × (object 1 distance from center of mass) = (mass object 2) × (object 2 distance from center of mass).

centripetal force a force directed inward.

Cepheid (variable star): a type of variable star that changes brightness by changing size and temperature with a period that depends on its average luminosity. More luminous Cepheids have longer pulsation periods. Cepheids are particularly valuable for determining distances to the nearby galaxies in which they reside. Distances to Cepheids are derived from measurements of their pulsation periods and apparent brightnesses and application of the **inverse square law of light brightness**.

chondrule round glassy structure 0.5 to 5 millimeters in diameter embedded in a **primitive** stone **meteorite**. It is a solidified droplet of matter from the early solar nebula and is the very oldest part of the primitive meteorite.

chromatic aberration a defect in the images from refractor telescopes that is caused by different colors of light focusing to different points behind the glass lens. A rainbow of colors is produced around the image.

chromosphere the hot, thin layer of the Sun's atmosphere right above its **photosphere**.

circumpolar when an object is close enough to either the **north celestial pole** or **south celestial pole** (within an angular distance = observer's latitude) such that the object never moves below an observer's horizon or never rises above the horizon as the Earth rotates.

climate long-term average of **weather** (usually 30 years or longer for Earth climate). Can change only on long time scales of decades or more.

closed universe a universe with enough matter (gravity) to eventually stop the expansion and recollapse (it has a "closed future").

color-magnitude diagram a plot of the colors (temperatures) and **magnitudes** of stars. Another name for the **Hertzsprung-Russell diagram**.

coma (comet): large atmosphere around a comet's nucleus that forms when the nucleus nears the Sun and warms up (usually at around Saturn's or Uranus' distance from the Sun).

conservation of angular momentum when an object or system of objects has no net outside forces acting on it, the total amount of its **angular momentum** does not change.

continuous spectrum a spectrum that has energy at all wavelengths (a full rainbow). See also **thermal spectrum**.

convection means of energy transport through the bulk motion of a fluid. Warmer fluid is less dense and rises upward releasing its excess energy to the cooler environment and cool, higher density fluid sinks.

convection zone the region of a star's interior where energy is transported outward using bulk motions of rising hot gas and sinking cool gas. For the Sun, it is the region above the **radiative zone**.

core (stellar): the center of a star where the density and temperature are high enough for nuclear fusion to occur.

Coriolis effect the deflection sideways of an object moving across the surface of a rotating body caused by the rotation of the body. The Coriolis effect makes storms spiral on the Earth and produces the banded cloud layers on the gas giant planets.

correlation a mutual relationship between two properties (usually such that an increase in one property is seen when another property increases).

corona the top layer of the Sun's atmosphere. It is up to a few million degrees in **temperature**, but has very low density so the amount of heat is small. It is the pearly-white "crown" or glow seen around the dark Moon during a total **solar eclipse**.

cosmic microwave background radiation radio (microwave) energy that is nearly uniform in all directions and has a nearly perfect thermal spectrum. It is the greatly redshifted remnant of the early hot universe produced about 380,000 years after the birth of the universe.

cosmic rays extremely high-energy (very fast-moving) sub-atomic particles, mostly protons, in space. Some produced by the Sun. Others produced in star deaths such as supernovae. Highest energy cosmic rays are of unknown origin.

cosmological constant an extra term Albert Einstein put in his equations of **General Relativity** that would act as a repulsive form of gravity to balance the attractive nature of gravity and keep the universe static.

cosmological principle an assumption that the universe is everywhere uniform and looks the same in any direction—it is **homogeneous** and **isotropic**.

cosmology the study of the nature and origin of the universe and how it changes over time.

critical density boundary density between enough mass/volume to eventually stop the expansion of the universe and too little mass/volume to eventually stop the expansion.

dark energy an additional energy needed to make the universe's overall curvature flat. It may be the **cosmological constant**.

dark matter material that does not emit any light (or not detected yet), but has a significant gravitational effect.

declination (dec): position on the celestial sphere that is the number of degrees an object is north or south of the celestial equator. It is a projection of latitude lines onto the sky. An object's declination is *fixed* with respect to the stars. Varies from −90° at the

SCP to 0° at the celestial equator to +90° at the NCP. Vertical position of an object.

degenerate gas super-compressed gas that behaves more like a solid and whose properties must be described by quantum mechanics. The pressure of degenerate gas does *not* depend on the temperature.

density how much material an object has in the space it occupies: *density = mass/volume*.

deuterium an isotope of hydrogen with one proton and one neutron in the nucleus.

differentiated when the interior of a large object has undergone **differentiation** so that denser material lies closer to the object's core.

differential rotation (galaxy): stars closer to a disk galaxy's center complete a greater fraction of their orbit in a given time than stars farther out from the center, so that adjacent parts of the galactic disk do not always stay close to each other.

differentiation the separation of materials in a liquid medium under the influence of gravity such that the denser material collects at the core while the less dense material rises to the surface.

direct imaging technique (planet detection) method of finding **exoplanets** by taking a picture of them.

discrete spectrum a spectrum that is not continuous—an **emission line spectrum** or an **absorption line spectrum**.

dissociation the splitting apart of a molecule into its constituent atoms, e.g., the splitting of water molecules into hydrogen and oxygen when water vapor is struck by ultraviolet light.

doppler effect an apparent change in the wavelength of energy produced by an object that is caused by the object's motion towards or away from the observer (along the line of sight). In astronomical spectra, the doppler effect is seen in the shifting of spectral lines.

doppler shift technique (planet detection) method of finding **exoplanets** by looking for a periodic alternating redshift and blueshift of a star.

Drake Equation an equation that estimates the number of communicating advanced civilizations inhabiting the Galaxy.

dust one component of the **interstellar medium** that is made of thin, highly flattened flakes or needles of graphite and silicates coated with water ice and other frozen gases. It is responsible for the **reddening** and **extinction** of starlight.

dust tail (comet): one of the two tails of a comet made of dust grains that curves away from the Sun from the action of the photons in the sunlight pushing the dust grains away from Sun. It has a yellow-white color from reflected sunlight.

eccentricity measures how far from a circular shape an ellipse is. Numerically, the eccentricity $e = 1 -$ (perihelion / semi-major axis). The eccentricity $e = 0$ for a circle and $e =$ nearly one (1) for very long, skinny ellipses.

eclipsing binary two stars orbiting each other in a plane that is along your line of sight so you see one star periodically pass in front of the other star. They are especially useful for determining the diameters and masses of stars.

ecliptic great circle that is a projection of the Earth's orbit onto the sky, or the path the Sun takes through the stars in its *annual* motion. It is tilted by 23.5° with respect to the celestial equator.

electromagnetic radiation a form of energy made of oscillating electric and magnetic fields. It is a fancy word for "light" and it includes (in order of *increasing* energy) radio, infrared, visible light (optical), ultraviolet, X-rays, and gamma rays.

electron negatively-charged subatomic particle that moves around the atomic nucleus in specific energy levels. It has about 1800 times less mass than the **proton** and **neutron**.

electron degeneracy pressure pressure exerted by a **degenerate gas** made of **electrons**. It is what prevents further collapse of a **white dwarf**.

element a substance that cannot be decomposed by chemical means into simpler substances. All atoms of an element have the same number of **protons** in the nucleus.

ellipse squashed circle that tapers at both ends. The total of the distance between any point on the ellipse and one focus + the distance from the point to the other focus = a constant. It is the shape of bound orbits.

elliptical galaxy a **galaxy** with a smooth, rounded appearance. Early large burst of star formation long ago used up all of their original gas and dust. Star orbits are aligned in more random directions and have greater **eccentricities** than star orbits in **spiral galaxies**.

emission line spectrum bright lines in a spectrum that are produced by hot, thin (low-pressure) gases. Made by **electrons** jumping down closer to the nucleus of the atom.

epicycle a device in Ptolemy's Earth-centered model that makes a planet execute a small circular motion around a point that is itself in a circular orbit around the Earth. It was used to explain **retrograde motion**.

equation of state the relation that describes the state or condition of a material as determined by how the temperature, density, and pressure depend on each other in the material.

Equation of Time a relation that describes the difference in time between the meridian crossings of the **mean Sun** and the actual Sun.

equinox point on the sky where the ecliptic and the celestial equator intercept. When the Sun is at the equinox point, it is on the celestial equator and we have 12 hours of daylight. Vernal (spring) equinox: March 21; autumnal equinox: September 22.

equivalence principle states that there is no experiment a person could conduct in a small volume of space that would distinguish between a gravitational field and an equivalent uniform acceleration. This principle is the foundation of **General Relativity**.

erosion the breaking down or building up of geological structures and transporting of material by ice, liquid, or wind.

escape velocity the *initial* speed an object needs to escape a massive body's gravitational influence and never return.

event horizon the distance from a black hole's center at which the escape velocity equals the speed of light. No information of events occurring inside the event horizon can get to the outside.

exoplanet a planet orbiting another star (other than our Sun) beyond our solar system.

exosphere uppermost layer a planet's atmosphere where the gases escape to space. Very low density gases heated by X-rays and ultraviolet light.

extinction reduction in the intensity of the light (the number of photons) from a celestial body as the light passes through a dust cloud. Dust clouds in space make stars behind the dust clouds appear dimmer than they would be if the dust was not there.

extremophile living organism that survives (even thrives) in extreme environments such as very hot or very cold temperatures, very acidic or very basic conditions, or very high pressures.

Fermi's Question Where are they? Given the vast number of planetary systems, prevalence of the ingredients for life (energy, organic compounds, water), and billions of years of history, why haven't we been contacted yet or found signs of an extra-terrestrial civilization in the Galaxy? Also called *"Fermi's Paradox"*.

filter thin material that is transparent to only a narrow range of wavelengths of light.

flat universe a universe that stop expanding only after an infinite amount of time (a special case of an open universe).

flux the amount of energy passing through a given area (e.g., one square centimeter) in a second. It is the apparent brightness of an object.

focus one of two special points along the long axis of an ellipse such that the addition of the distances (satellite to focus#1) plus (satellite to focus#2) always equals the same numerical value. It is *not* at the center of the elliptical orbit unless the orbit is perfectly circular.

force any action or influence that causes an **acceleration**.

frequency the number of wave crests that pass a point every second. Measured in **hertz** (Hz). For electromagnetic radiation, the frequency is inversely proportional to the wavelength.

galactic cannibalism the swallowing up whole of a small galaxy by a large galaxy (usually a large elliptical galaxy at the center of a galaxy cluster).

galaxy a very large cluster of stars (tens of millions to trillions of stars) gravitationally bound together.

General Relativity a theory invented by Albert Einstein to describe gravity. It says that gravity is a warping or distortion of spacetime around a massive object. Although it applies everywhere in the universe, General Relativity *must* be used instead of Newton's **law of gravity** in regions of strong gravity.

geocentric (universe): model of the universe with the Earth at the center and all other objects moving around it.

giant impact theory explanation about how the Moon was formed from mantle material blown out by the impact of a Mars-sized (or larger) planet with the Earth several billion years ago. The ejected material condensed to form the Moon.

giant molecular cloud large, dense gas cloud (with some dust) that is cold enough for molecules to form. A typical giant molecular cloud has a few hundred thousand to a few million solar masses of material. Stars form in them.

globular cluster spherical cluster of hundreds of thousands to millions of very old stars. The orbits of most globular clusters are very elliptical and oriented in random directions.

granulation bright spots of convection on the Sun's surface 700 to 1000 kilometers across forming a honeycomb pattern. Formed from hot, bright gas rising from below in the center of a granule and cooler, dimmer gas falling back down at the edge of a granule.

gravitational lens the focusing of light from a distant object by the warped spacetime around a massive body (such as a galaxy) between you and the distant object as predicted by **General Relativity**.

gravitational redshift the lengthening of the wavelength of electromagnetic radiation as it moves away from a region of intense gravity.

gravity a fundamental force of nature between two objects that is proportional to the product of their masses and inversely proportional to the *square* of the distance between their respective centers. It depends on nothing else.

greenhouse effect the trapping of heat energy close to a planet's surface by certain types of gases in the atmosphere (e.g., water, methane, and carbon dioxide). These gases allow visible light from the Sun to reach the surface but prevent the infrared light from the heated surface to radiate back to space.

ground state the lowest energy state of an atom—all of the **electrons** are as close to the nucleus as possible.

H II region cloud of ionized hydrogen around a hot, luminous star (usually O or B-type). Produced by the copious ultraviolet light from the hot star(s) causing the hydrogen to fluoresce (atoms are ionized and then when the electron recombine, they produce energy in the visible band).

habitable zone the region around a star where the temperature on a planet's surface is between the freezing point (0° C) and boiling point (100° C) of water.

half-life the time required for one-half of a radioactive material to decay to a more stable material (it is NOT one-half the age of the rock!).

heliocentric (universe): model of the universe with the Sun at the center and all other objects moving around it.

helioseismology the study of the Sun's interior from observations of the Sun's pulsations on its surface.

helium flash in low-mass **red giant** stars, the onset of the fusing of helium in the **core** can be very rapid, almost explosive.

hertz (Hz): unit of frequency. One hertz = 1 wave peak/second.

Hertzsprung-Russell diagram (H-R diagram) a plot of stellar luminosity vs. temperature invented by two astronomers, Hertzsprung and Russell. High temperatures are on the left side and decrease to the right. Low luminosities are on the bottom and increase vertically.

homogeneous everywhere uniform in appearance so that there is no preferred observing position.

Hubble constant slope of the line relating the speed of the galaxies away from each other and their distance apart from each other.

Hubble-Lemaître Law the relationship between a galaxy's recession speed from other galaxies and the distance between them: the recession speed = $H \times$ distance, where H is the **Hubble constant**. The recession speed is derived from the **redshift** of the galaxy spectra and with the Hubble-Lemaître Law, it can be used to find the distance to the farthest galaxies.

hydrostatic equilibrium a balance between the compression from the weight of material above a layer and the expansion of an outward-directed pressure below the layer. In normal stars and planet atmospheres, the outward-directed pressure is supplied by the thermal pressure of warm or hot gases.

hypothesis an unproven or unverified idea or **model**.

ideal gas law the equation of state for simple gases: *pressure = (k × density × temperature)/(molecular weight of the gas)*. If use number density (# particles/volume), pressure = (k × number density × temperature), where "k" is the Boltzmann constant.

impact cratering the process of creating round, bowl-shaped depressions on a surface by the explosion of a large body striking the surface.

inertia the property of an object describing its tendency to stay at the same velocity (or at rest) unless a **force** acts on it.

inflation a brief period of ultra-rapid expansion in the very early universe about 10^{-38} to 10^{-36} seconds after the **Big Bang**.

instrumentalism a way of viewing scientific theories and models that says they are merely tools or calculation devices and are *not* to be interpreted as reality.

intensity the number of waves or **photons** reaching your detector every second.

interferometer an array of telescopes connected electronically to act as one large telescope with much improved resolution. The resolution of the interferometer is equal to a single telescope having a diameter equal to the length of the interferometer.

interstellar medium the gas and dust between the stars.

inverse square law of light brightness an object's apparent brightness decreases with the *square* of the distance. The apparent brightness is the amount of energy flowing through a given area in a given amount of time.

ion a particle with an electrical charge (the number of **electrons** is different than the number of **protons**).

ion tail (comet): one of the two tails of a comet made of ionized particles that points directly away from the Sun from the action of the solar wind. It has a bluish color from the emission lines mostly of ionized carbon monoxide.

irregular galaxy a **galaxy** with no definite structure. Stars are distributed in bunches placed randomly throughout the galaxy. Many irregular galaxies have a lot of gas and dust still left in them from which stars are now forming.

isotope a sub-group of an **element** in which the atomic nucleus has the same number of **neutrons**, as well as, the same number of **protons**. All of the atoms of an element will have very nearly the same chemical properties, but the isotopes can have very different *nuclear* properties.

isotropic exhibiting the same property when looking in any given direction.

Kelvin scale a temperature scale that directly scales with the random motion energy of a substance, such that 0 Kelvin is at absolute zero (state where all random motion ceases) and higher temperatures have non-zero Kelvin values. It scales like the metric system's Celsius scale for increasing temperatures—every degree interval of the Kelvin scale corresponds to the same change in the random motion energy as a degree interval of the Celsius scale: # Kelvin = # Celsius − 273.

Kepler's 1st law orbits are ellipses with the central object at one focus (not the center!). There is nothing at the other focus.

Kepler's 2nd law a line between the satellite and the central object sweeps out equal areas in equal intervals of time. A satellite moves faster when it is closer to the massive body it orbits and moves slower when farther from the massive object.

Kepler's 3rd law for an object in an elliptical orbit around a massive body, the square of the orbital period is proportional to the cube of the average distance of the orbiting object from the massive body. The massive body's mass is proportional to the (average distance)^3/(orbital period)^2. In general, for two objects orbiting a common point between them, their *combined* mass is proportional to: (average distance between them)^3/(their orbital period)^2.

kilogram unit of **mass** in the metric system.

kinetic energy the energy something has because of its motion = $1/2 \times \text{mass} \times \text{velocity}^2$.

Kuiper Belt a disk of comets beyond Neptune's orbit (or 30 to 100+ A.U.) that orbit roughly in the same plane as the planets. Many of the **short period comets** come from the Kuiper Belt.

latitude used to specify position on the Earth, it is the number of degrees north or south of the Earth's equator.

law of gravity (Newton's): the force of mutual attraction between two objects = $G \times$ (mass #1) $\times$ (mass #2) / (distance between the objects)^2. The term G is a universal constant of nature that always = 6.672×10^{-11} meter^3/(kilogram second^2).

life zone the region around a star where the temperature on a planet's surface is between the freezing point (0° C) and boiling point (100° C) of water.

light curve a plot of how an object's brightness changes over time.

light-gathering power the ability of a telescope to collect more light than the human eye in a given amount of time. It depends on the *area* of the telescope's objective, such that the larger the collecting area of the objective, the brighter the image will be.

lighthouse model a model describing how pulsars pulsate: the rapidly rotating neutron star produces a narrow beam of light from its magnetic field and if the magnetic pole is aligned with the Earth, the narrow beam of light sweeps over us periodically like the beam of a lighthouse does for ships at sea.

light year distance light travels in one year (9.461 trillion kilometers, over 63,000 A.U.!). Used for inter*stellar* distances.

line of nodes the intersection of a planet's or the Moon's orbit with the Earth's orbit.

lithosphere the layer of hard rock that includes the crust and the outermost part of the mantle in a terrestrial planet.

local noon when the Sun is on an observer's **meridian**.

long period comet a comet with an orbit period of thousands to millions of years long that comes from the **Oort cloud**.

longitude used to specify position on the Earth, it is the number of degrees east or west of the 0° line going through Greenwich, England.

luminosity the total amount of energy radiated by an object every second.

lunar eclipse when the shadow of the Earth hits the Moon at exactly full phase.

magnetic dynamo a mechanism thought to produce magnetic fields in a planet by the swirling, or circulation, of liquid conducting material in or near the planet's core.

magnifying power the ability of telescope to enlarge images. Can be increased by using an eyepiece with a shorter focal length.

magnitude used to quantify brightness. Based on the ancient system of Hipparchus but refined and quantified for measurements today such that a *ratio* of 100 in brightness corresponds to a magnitude *difference* of 5. Fainter objects have larger, positive magnitudes (closer to positive infinity), while brighter objects have *lower* magnitudes (closer to negative infinity).

main sequence the narrow diagonal band in the **Hertzsprung-Russell diagram** going from upper left to lower right describing the characteristics of 90% of the stars. Stars spend about 90% of their lives in this stage and are fusing hydrogen to create helium.

main sequence turnoff the mass of the most massive main sequence star remaining in a star cluster. Stars more massive than the turnoff have already evolved beyond the main sequence stage. The turnoff mass can be used to determine the age of the star cluster (it equals the lifetime of the most massive star still in the main sequence stage).

mass an *intrinsic* property of an object that measures its resistance to an acceleration. Mass is measured in units of **kilograms**.

mathematical models a set of equations describing the structure and interaction of material in an object or group of objects.

mean Sun imaginary object that moves uniformly eastward along the celestial equator such that it completes one 360° circuit of the sky in one year. The average solar day is the time between successive meridian crossings of the mean Sun.

meridian great circle on the sky that goes through the celestial poles *and* the zenith point. It separates the daytime motions of the Sun into "a.m." and "p.m.". The azimuth of an object on the meridian in the northern sky = 0° and the azimuth of an object on the meridian in the southern sky = 180°.

mesosphere layer of a planet's atmosphere above a **stratosphere** where the temperature decreases with increasing altitude.

metals what astronomers call all of the elements heavier than helium (like carbon, nitrogen, oxygen, sodium, aluminum, chlorine, calcium, iron, etc.).

meteor shower what happens when the Earth passes through the dust trail left by a comet in its orbit. The dust grains are the size of a grain of sand or smaller and produce a large number of meteors in a short time that appear to come from a particular point in the sky.

meteorite a small rock from space that makes it to the surface of a planet without burning up in the planet's atmosphere. This distinguishes it from when it is passing through the atmosphere, glowing hot from the friction with the atmosphere and is called a *meteor*.

microlens technique (planet detection) a method of finding **exoplanets** by looking for the **gravitational lensing** effect from a planet orbiting a foreground star added to the **gravitational lensing** effect of the foreground star on the light from a more distant star.

Milky Way Galaxy the large spiral galaxy in which our Sun and planets reside. Our Sun is one star of several hundred billion in the Milky Way.

model an abstract construct or idea that is a simplified view of reality. It must enable you to make testable predictions of what will happen under new circumstances.

nanometer a very tiny distance equal to one-billionth of a meter (0.000000001 meter).

natural selection the primary mechanism of evolution by which, over time, heritable traits that enhance survival and successful reproduction will become progressively more common in succeeding generations in any local environment. It is a NON-random process that produces adaptations.

neap tide tide that has a *small* change between low and high tide. It occurs at first and third quarter phase, when the Moon's tidal effect is perpendicular with the Sun's tidal effect.

neutrino a sub-atomic particle with very small mass that is produced in nuclear fusion reactions and rarely interacts with ordinary matter. Neutrinos travel at the nearly the speed of light and provide current information about the number of nuclear fusion reactions occurring in a star's core (in the case of the Sun, the information is only about 8.3 minutes old).

neutron subatomic particle with zero charge (neutral charge) that is found in the nucleus of an atom. It is slightly more massive than the positively-charged **proton**.

neutron degeneracy pressure pressure exerted by a **degenerate gas** made of **neutrons**. It is what prevents further collapse of a **neutron star**.

neutron star the collapsed core for an intermediate to high-mass star. The core is more than 1.4 solar masses but less than 3 solar masses and is about the diameter of a city. The pressure from **degenerate neutrons** prevents further collapse.

newton unit of **force** in the metric system. It is used to specify the amount of **weight**.

Newton's 1st law (of motion): a body at rest remains at rest, and one moving in a straight line maintains a constant speed and same direction unless it is deflected by a **force**.

Newton's 2nd law (of motion): the amount of force needed to cause an acceleration depends on an object's mass, such that the force applied = the mass of an object × its acceleration.

Newton's 3rd law (of motion): for every action force ON an object, there is an equal but *opposite* force BY the object.

north celestial pole (NCP): projection of the Earth's north pole onto the sky. The NCP **altitude** = the observer's northern **latitude**.

nova an object that greatly increases in brightness rapidly, so it appears as a "new star". It is caused by the buildup on a white dwarf's surface of hydrogen gas from a companion star to the point where the hydrogen fuses explosively into helium. The super-rapid fusion does not blow up the white dwarf, so the process can repeat itself (contrast with a Type I **supernova**).

nuclear fusion the process used by stars to generate energy: less-massive nuclei are fused together under extremely high temperatures and densities to form more-massive nuclei plus some energy. The energy comes from the transformation of some of the mass into energy.

nucleus (comet): the "dirty iceberg" about the size of a city from which all of the stuff in a comet comes from. Irregularly-shaped it is made of dust and frozen gases.

Occam's Razor a way of approaching the development of a scientific model based on the belief that "the best model is the simplest one—the one requiring the fewest assumptions and modifications in order to fit the observations" (i.e., nature prefers the simplest most elegant solution).

objective the primary optical element of a telescope, it gathers the electromagnetic radiation and does the initial focusing.

Olbers' Paradox the problem that if the universe is infinite in size and age, then the night sky should everywhere be as bright as the Sun because no matter which direction you look, your line of sight will see a star or galaxy.

Oort Cloud a large spherical cloud of billions to trillions of comets surrounding the Sun at distances between roughly 50,000 to 100,000 A.U. from the Sun. It has not been directly observed; its presence is inferred from the behavior and orbits of the **long period comets**.

opacity a measure of a material's ability to absorb or block photons. A material with high opacity prevents most of the photons from passing through (the material is *opaque*).

open universe a universe with too little matter (gravity) to stop the expansion (it has an "open future").

ozone a type of oxygen molecule made of three oxygen atoms bound together (O_3). This molecule absorbs ultraviolet light.

paradigm a general agreement of belief of how the world works; what could be called "common sense".

parallax an apparent shifting of an object's position resulting from observing the object from two different vantage points. Stellar parallaxes are seen when we view nearby stars from opposite sides of the Earth's orbit.

parsec (pc): distance at which an object would have a parallax of one arc second. Equals approximately 3.26 **light years** or about 206,265 **astronomical units**.

penumbra region of partial shadow that is outside the **umbra**; the light source is partially blocked.

perfect cosmological principle an assumption that the universe is everywhere uniform and looks the same in any direction in all space and time—it is the same everywhere and does not change throughout time.

perihelion point in an object's orbit around the Sun that is *closest* to the Sun.

period-luminosity relation how the average luminosity of **Cepheid** variable stars depends on their period of pulsation.

photon a distinct "chunk" or particle of **electromagnetic radiation**.

photosphere the thin layer of the Sun where the gas just becomes thin enough for the photons from the interior can escape to space. It is the "surface" of the Sun.

photosynthesis a process used by plants to convert water, carbon dioxide, and sunlight into carbohydrates and oxygen. The oxygen in the Earth's atmosphere is produced by this process.

planetary nebula final mass-loss stage for a dying low-mass star in which the outer layers are ejected during the core's collapse to form a **white dwarf**.

plate tectonics the scientific theory that describes the process of the movement of pieces of the Earth's lithosphere (called "plates") and how it explains the Earth's surface geology.

poor cluster galaxy cluster with only a few tens of galaxies.

Population I (stars): younger stars including the hot blue stars that have slightly elliptical orbits closely aligned with the disk plane of the **Milky Way Galaxy**. The youngest stars are found in the spiral arms of the galactic disk.

Population II (stars): older, redder stars that have very elliptical orbits randomly oriented and are found in the stellar halo and bulge of the **Milky Way Galaxy**.

precession slow wobble of an object's rotation axis or an object's orbit. The precession of the Earth's rotation axis is caused by the gravitational pulls of the Sun and the Moon on the Earth's equatorial bulge.

pressure amount of force per unit area: *pressure = force/area*.

primitive in studies of the solar system, an object or rock that has remained chemically unchanged since it formed (solidified) about 4.6 billion years ago. The object holds a record of the very early conditions from which the rest of the solar system (Sun, planets, moons) formed.

proper motion angular distance an object moves across the sky (perpendicular to your line of sight) in a given amount of time.

proton positively-charged subatomic particle that is found in the nucleus of an atom. It has about 1800 times more mass than its negatively-charged **electron** counterpart.

proton-proton chain a nuclear fusion chain reaction used by most stars to generate energy. In a chain process involving three or more reactions, the net result is four hydrogen nuclei are fused together to form a helium nucleus plus energy.

protostar collapsing clump of dust and gas that will later become a star. The protostar is warm enough to produce a lot of infrared and some microwave radiation. Microwave energy is produced by the surrounding cocoon cloud.

pulsar young **neutron star** with a strong magnetic field and rapid rotation that produces beams of radiation out of its magnetic poles. If the beams cross our line of sight, we see the star "pulsate" (flash on and off).

Pythagorean paradigm "common sense" belief articulated by Pythagoras about the universe that says all objects move in perfectly circular orbits at perfectly uniform speeds and the Earth is at the center of the motions of celestial bodies.

quasar short for "quasi-stellar radio source". Quasars are the most luminous of active galaxies—they are the extremely active nuclei of otherwise normal galaxies. Quasars generate a huge amount of energy within very tiny volumes. Because they are most luminous things known, quasars can be seen at very large distances. Looking like blue stars, they can be distinguished from stars by the presence of broad **emission lines** instead of the narrow **absorption lines** of normal stars, their large **redshifts** because of their very large distances (see the **Hubble Law**), and many quasars are strong radio sources, unlike stars which have weak radio emission.

radial velocity the velocity along the line of sight.

radial velocity curve a plot of how an object's velocity along the line of sight changes over time.

radiative zone the region of a star's interior where energy is transported outward with photons. For the Sun, it is the region above the core.

radio galaxy usually an **elliptical galaxy** emitting very large amounts of radio energy from the core (up to millions of times a typical galaxy's radio emission) and having strong radio emission from regions extending out several million **light years** from the galaxy nucleus.

radioactive dating a technique that gives absolute ages of a material (rather than merely relative ages) from the number of radioactive active atoms remaining in the material.

realism a way of viewing scientific theories and models that says they truly characterize the way the universe operates; they represent reality (contrast with **instrumentalism**).

recombination process of **electrons** becoming bound to **protons** to make neutral atoms.

reddening the preferential scattering of the shorter wavelengths of light as it passes through a dust cloud, so that a large fraction of the bluer wavelengths of light are scattered away from your line of sight while a large fraction of the redder wavelengths of light make it through the dust cloud unaffected. Dust clouds in space make stars behind the dust clouds appear redder than they would be if the dust was not there.

red giant a dying star that has become large in diameter and cool on the surface while the **core** has shrunk and increased in temperature. **Nuclear fusion** takes place in a shell around the compressing core. They are more luminous than when the star was in the **main sequence** stage, even though their surface is cool, because they have a HUGE surface area. Therefore, they are plotted in the upper right part of the **Hertzsprung-Russell diagram**.

redshift the shift of spectral lines from an object to longer wavelengths because the object is moving *away from* the observer. The greater the speed of the object, the greater the redshift will be.

reflector telescope telescope that uses a large mirror at the back of the telescope to gather and focus the light. It has no size limit and is the type preferred for large research telescopes.

refraction the bending of waves when they pass from one transparent medium (or vacuum) to another (e.g., sunlight bending as it passes through the Earth's atmosphere).

refractor telescope telescope that uses a large glass lens at the front end of the telescope to gather and focus the light. The glass lens has a maximum size limit and suffers to some degree from **chromatic aberration**.

representative sample a collection of objects that includes all parts of the population of the objects in their proper proportions; an unbiased sample that gives accurate results.

resolving power the ability of a telescope to detect very small details and produce sharp images. It depends on the *diameter* of the telescope's objective or the interferometer AND the wavelength of light used to observe, such that the more wavelengths that can be fit across the objective or interferometer, the sharper the image will be.

retrograde motion when a solar system object (e.g., a planet) moves "backward" (westward) with respect to its normal eastward drift against the stars. It happens when the Earth is closest to the object.

rich cluster a cluster of hundreds to thousands of galaxies.

right ascension (RA): position on the celestial sphere measured with respect to the **vernal equinox** position on the celestial equator. It is a projection of longitude lines onto the sky and converted to time units. An object's right ascension is *fixed* with respect to the stars. Varies from 0^h at the **vernal equinox** point to 24^h in a full circle.

rotation curve how the orbital velocities of objects in the disk of a spiral galaxy vary with increasing distance from the center of the galaxy. The rotation curve is used to study the distribution of mass in a galaxy.

RR Lyrae (variable star): a type of low-mass variable stars that all have the same average luminosity. RR Lyrae are valuable for determining distances to star clusters.

runaway greenhouse a process in which the heating of a planet increases the greenhouse effect in a feedback loop resulting in a dramatic change in the atmospheric composition and dramatic rise in the surface temperature. Venus' atmosphere is an example of this process.

runaway refrigerator a process in which the cooling of a planet's surface decreases the greenhouse effect in a feedback loop resulting in a dramatic change in the atmospheric composition and dramatic cooling in the surface temperature. Mars' atmosphere is an example of this process.

Schwarzschild radius the distance from a black hole's center at which the escape velocity equals the speed of light (same as the **event horizon**).

season approximately three-month period bounded by an equinox and a solstice.

seeing a measure of the amount of turbulence of the air. When the seeing is "good", the amount of turbulence is small and the images are steady (little twinkling). "Poor" seeing occurs when the atmosphere is turbulent so the images shimmer and dance around (more twinkling).

seismology the study of a planet's interior from observations of how seismic waves ("earthquake waves") travel through the interior.

semi-major axis the distance between the *center* of an elliptical orbit and one end of the orbit along the long dimension of the elliptical orbit. It equals the *average distance* between two orbiting objects.

Seyfert galaxy a **spiral galaxy** with a compact, very bright nucleus that produces a non-thermal **continuous spectrum** with broad (fat) **emission lines** on top.

shell burning nuclear fusion that is occurring in a layer outside a star's core instead of inside the core as the core compresses. The fusion rate is faster than before and the outer layers are pushed outward to form a **red giant**.

short period comet a comet with an orbit period less than about 200 years long that comes from the **Kuiper Belt**.

sidereal day time between successive meridian crossings of *a star*. It is the true rotation period of a planet (on Earth, one sidereal day = 23 hours 56 minutes 4.09 seconds). Rotation rate of the Earth = 1° every 4 minutes (actually 3.989 minutes). The Earth's sidereal day is four minutes shorter than the solar day our clocks are based on so a star crosses the meridian 4 minutes *earlier* than it did the previous night.

sidereal period the period of revolution of one object around another measured with respect to the stars (e.g., for the Moon, it is 27.3 days).

sidereal year the time required for the Earth to complete an exactly 360° orbit around the Sun as measured with respect to the stars = 365.2564 mean solar days (contrast with **tropical year**).

solar day time between successive meridian crossings of *the Sun*. Our clocks are based on this interval of time (on Earth, one solar day = 24 hours *on average*).

solar eclipse when the shadow of the Moon hits the Earth at exactly new phase. The Moon covers up part or all of the Sun.

solar luminosity unit of power relative to the Sun. One solar luminosity is about 4×10^{26} watts.

solar mass unit of mass relative to the Sun. One solar mass is about 2×10^{30} kilograms.

solar neutrino problem the number of neutrinos observed to be coming from the Sun's core is significantly less than what was predicted by the original solar interior models. Discovery of the oscillation of neutrino types solved the problem.

solar wind fast-moving, charged particles (mostly **protons, electrons**, and helium nuclei) flowing outward from the Sun's upper atmosphere, the **corona**.

solstice point on the sky where the ecliptic is furthest from the celestial equator by 23.5°. When the Sun is at the solstice point we have either the longest amount of daylight (summer: June 21 for northern hemisphere) or the shortest amount of daylight (winter: December 21 for northern hemisphere).

south celestial pole (SCP): projection of the Earth's south pole onto the sky. The SCP **altitude** = the observer's southern **latitude**.

spacetime the four-dimensional combination of space (three dimensions) and time (the fourth dimension). As a consequence of **Special Relativity**, time and space are not independent of each other and are relative to the motion of an observer.

Special Relativity a theory invented by Albert Einstein to describe measurements of length and time for objects moving at constant velocity. Although it applies to all motion at constant velocity, it *must* be used instead of Newton's laws of motion at speeds of greater than about ten percent the speed of light.

speckle interferometry method that compensates for atmospheric turbulence by taking many fast exposures of an object to freeze the effect of **seeing**. Computer processing of the multiple exposures removes atmospheric and instrument distortions to produce high-resolution images at the telescope's theoretical resolving power.

spectral type (also spectral class) the classification of a star according to its temperature as measured from the strengths of its spectral lines. In order of temperatures from hottest to coolest the spectral types are O B A F G K M. This is also the order of luminosity and mass (most luminous and most massive to dimmest and least massive).

spectroscopic binary two stars orbiting a common point at too great a distance away from us to resolve the two stars individually, but whose binary nature is indicated in the periodic shift of their spectral lines as they orbit around each other.

spectroscopic parallax a method of determining distances to stars from knowledge of the **luminosity** of their **spectral types** and measurement of their apparent brightness. The distances are derived from the **inverse square law of light brightness**.

spectroscopy the analysis of an object from its **spectrum**.

spectrum display of the intensity of light at different **wavelengths** or **frequencies**.

spherical aberration a defect seen in images that is caused by the objective not being exactly shaped (e.g., an objective mirror not being exactly parabolic) so that not all of the light is focused to the same point.

spiral galaxy a highly flattened **galaxy** with a disk and a central bulge. The disk has a spiral pattern with slightly more stars and gas than in the rest of the disk. A slow, steady star formation rate means that they still have gas and dust left in them from which stars are still forming. The star orbits are constrained to stay within a small distance from the mid-plane of the disk and have small **eccentricities**.

spring tide tide that has a *large* change between low and high tide. It occurs at new and full phase, when the Moon's tidal effect is aligned with the Sun's tidal effect.

standard candle luminous objects of a known luminosity used to measure large distances via the **inverse square law of light brightness**.

starburst galaxy a **galaxy** undergoing a large burst of star formation usually as a result of a collision or merger of two galaxies. It can produce as much light as several hundred "normal" undisturbed galaxies.

Stefan-Boltzmann law relation between the amount of energy emitted by a unit area on an object producing a **thermal spectrum** and its temperature: energy in Joules emitted by one square meter = $5.67 \times 10^{-8} \times$ temperature^4. The temperature is in **Kelvin**.

stellar nucleosynthesis the creation of more massive nuclei from the fusion of less-massive nuclei inside stars. Just about all of the elements heavier than helium on the Earth were originally created via stellar nucleosynthesis.

stratosphere layer of a planet's atmosphere above a **troposphere** where temperature rises with increasing altitude because of the absorption of ultraviolet light.

subgiant the stage in a star's life between the **main sequence** and the **red giant** stages. The helium core shrinks and the hydrogen shell layer outside the core undergoes **nuclear fusion**. The energy of the **shell burning** is great enough to push the outer hydrogen layers outward and they cool off. During the subgiant stage, the expansion is such that the luminosity remains essentially constant as the outer layers expand.

sublime the turning of a solid directly into a gas without going through the intermediate liquid phase, e.g. the vapor of "dry ice" (the sublimation of frozen carbon dioxide).

sunspot cooler region on the Sun's surface that is a region of intense magnetic fields and is associated with solar activity. Because a sunspot is 1000 to 1500 K cooler, it is dimmer than the surrounding surface. The number of sunspots is greater when the Sun is more active.

supercluster a grouping of galaxy clusters pulled together by their mutual gravitational attraction to produce long, thin structures up to a few hundred mega**parsecs** long with large voids devoid of galaxies between the superclusters.

supergiant a dying star of extremely high luminosity and relatively cool surface temperature. Their diameters are over 100 times that of the Sun.

supernova for *Type II* supernova: final huge mass-loss stage for a dying high-mass star where the outer layers are ejected during the core's collapse to form a **neutron star**. A *Type I* supernova is the result of enough hydrogen accreted onto a **white dwarf**'s surface to put the **white dwarf** beyond the *Chandresekhar limit*. The white dwarf collapses and the super-rapid fusion blows the white dwarf apart (contrast with a **nova**). The **luminosity** of a supernova can temporarily be as much as an entire galaxy of billions of stars.

synodic period the time required for a planet or moon to go from a particular configuration with respect to *the Sun* back to that same configuration (e.g., for the Moon, it is the time to go from a given phase back to the same phase—29.5 days).

tangential velocity the velocity perpendicular to the line of sight.

tectonics any stretching or compression of the **lithosphere**.

telescope device used to gather and focus electromagnetic radiation. A telescope extends the power of human vision by making objects brighter, sharper, and larger, as well as, imaging objects in wavelengths that are not detectable by the human eye.

temperature a measure of the random motion energy (the *average* kinetic energy) of a group of particles in a gas, liquid, or solid. The temperature is higher if the particles are moving faster.

theory a logical, systematic set of principles or explanation that has undergone testing or validation from careful observations and has stood up against attempts to prove it false. A scientific theory can be used to make a variety of predictions of what will happen under different circumstances.

thermal spectrum a spectrum that has energy at all wavelengths (a full rainbow). Produced by solids, liquids, and dense (high-pressure) gases.

thermosphere upper layer a planet's atmosphere where the temperature rises with increasing altitude because the gases absorb X-rays and ultraviolet light. X-rays ionize gas particles. **Aurorae** occur in this layer.

time zone interval of longitudes 15 degrees wide in which every clock is set to the same time (e.g., every clock in the Pacific time zone will give the same time).

total solar eclipse a type of **solar eclipse** that happens when the Sun and Moon are exactly lined up and the Moon is close enough to the Earth to totally block the Sun's surface (contrast with **annular eclipse**).

transit technique a method of finding **exoplanets** by looking for a drop in the brightness of a star as the planet passes in front of the star.

trigonometric parallax a method of determining distances to nearby stars that uses trigonometry to derive the distance from the size of the **parallax** angle and the distance between a planet and the Sun: distance in parsecs = (planet-Sun distance in A.U.)/(parallax angle in arc seconds).

tropical year the time interval between two successive **vernal equinoxes** = 365.2422 mean solar days (contrast with **sidereal year**).

T-Tauri (star) young star that is just beginning **nuclear fusion** and produces strong outflows of particles (winds) that clears away the gas and dust from which the star formed.

21-cm line radiation emission line in the radio band by cool, neutral atomic hydrogen that is used to map the structure of the **Milky Way** and other galaxies because it passes easily through dust in the interstellar medium.

umbra region of total shadow; the light source is totally blocked.

velocity description of an object's motion that includes both its speed AND its direction of travel.

velocity dispersion the spread of the distribution of the velocities.

vernal equinox specific moment in the year (on March 21) when the Sun is directly on the celestial equator, moving north of the celestial equator.

volcanism any eruption of molten lava onto the surface.

wavelength the distance between two crests or two troughs of a wave.

weather the ever-changing combination of winds, clouds, temperature, and pressure at a particular location and time. Short timescale description of an atmosphere in contrast to **climate**.

weight amount of the force of gravity felt by an object. It is measured in units of **newtons**. It depends on the strength of the surrounding gravity field.

white dwarf the collapsed core for a dead low-mass star. The core is less than 1.4 solar masses and is about the diameter of the Earth. The pressure from **degenerate** electrons prevents further collapse.

Wien's law relation between the wavelength of maximum emission in a **thermal spectrum** and its temperature: **wavelength** peak in **nanometers** $= 2.9 \times 10^6$/temperature in **Kelvin**.

zenith point on the celestial sphere that is *always* directly above the observer regardless of his/her location.

zodiac narrow belt of twelve constellation centered on the **ecliptic**.

Index

Illustration Credits

All line art (non-photographic) illustrations and photographs were created by the author, Nick Strobel, and copyrighted by the author unless specifically mentioned otherwise. Color images are available on the Astronomy Notes website www.astronomynotes.com. The following illustrations were produced by other individuals, groups, and institutions:

Chapter 4

Section 4.1: Ancient Greek views of the world is courtesy of Jim Siebold. Website: www.henry-davis.com/MAPS/carto.html.

Section 4.1: Plato and Pythagoras images are courtesy of JJ O'Connor and EF Robertson (University of Saint Andrews, Scotland). Website: www-groups.dcs.st-andrews.ac.uk/~history/index.html.

Section 4.2: Aristotle image is courtesy of JJ O'Connor and EF Robertson (University of Saint Andrews, Scotland). Website: www-groups.dcs.st-andrews.ac.uk/~history/index.html.

Section 4.2.1: Ptolemy's view of the world is courtesy of Jim Siebold. Website: www.henry-davis.com/MAPS/carto.html.

Section 4.2.1: Claudius Ptolemy picture is courtesy of Albert van Helden (Rice University). Website: http://es.rice.edu/ES/humsoc/Galileo/.

Section 4.3: Martin Waldseemüller's world map of 1507 is courtesy of Jim Siebold. Website: www.henry-davis.com/MAPS/carto.html.

Section 4.3.1: Nicolaus Copernicus picture is courtesy of JJ O'Connor and EF Robertson (University of Saint Andrews, Scotland). Website: www-groups.dcs.st-andrews.ac.uk/~history/index.html.

Section 4.3.2: Tycho Brahe picture is courtesy of Joseph Dauben (Lehman College - CUNY). Website: http://www.cuny.edu/multimedia/arsnew/arstitle.html.

Section 4.4.1: Galileo Galilei picture is courtesy of of Albert van Helden (Rice University). Website: http://es.rice.edu/ES/humsoc/Galileo/.

Section 4.4.1: Galileo's telescope picture is courtesy of Joseph Dauben (Lehman College - CUNY). Website: http://www.cuny.edu/multimedia/arsnew/arstitle.html.

Section 4.4.1: Galileo's drawing of the Moon is courtesy of Joseph Dauben (Lehman College - CUNY). Website: http://www.cuny.edu/multimedia/arsnew/arstitle.html.

Section 4.5: Johannes Kepler picture is courtesy of JJ O'Connor and EF Robertson (University of Saint Andrews, Scotland). Website: www-groups.dcs.st-andrews.ac.uk/~history/index.html.

Chapter 5

Start: Isaac Newton picture is courtesy of Andrew McNab. Website: www.newton.org.uk/.

Start: Nova orbis tabula by De Wit in 1688 is courtesy of Hargrett Rare Book & Manuscript Library/University of Georgia Libraries. Website: www.libs.uga.edu/darchive/hargrett/maps/maps.html.

Section 5.1: René Descartes picture is courtesy of of Albert van Helden (Rice University). Website: http://es.rice.edu/ES/humsoc/Galileo/.

Chapter 6

Start: Albert Einstein picture is copyrighted © 1996. Courtesy of The Albert Einstein Archives, The Jewish National & University Library, The Hebrew University of Jerusalem, Israel. Photographer: Lucien Chavan. Website: http://sites.huji.ac.il/jnul/einstein/.

Section 6.2: Einstein's Cross picture is courtesy of Space Telescope Science Institute/Association of Universities for Research in Astronomy, Inc. and NASA. Website: www.stsci.edu.

Chapter 7

Section 7.2: Max Planck picture is courtesy of the American Institute of Physics Emilio Segrè Visual Archives, W.F. Meggers Collection. Website: www.aip.org/history/esva.

Section 7.4: Niels Bohr picture is courtesy of the American Institute of Physics Emilio Segrè Visual Archives, W.F. Meggers Collection. Website: www.aip.org/history/esva.

Chapter 8

Section 8.1.2: Picture of Gemini North Telescope courtesy of Gemini Observatory/Association of Universities for Research in Astronomy, Inc. Website: www.gemini.edu.

Section 8.1.2: Pictures of the Hubble Space Telescope and before/after COSTAR images are courtesy of Space Telescope Science Institute/Association of Universities for Research in Astronomy, Inc. and NASA. Website: www.stsci.edu.

Section 8.2.2: Picture of Arecibo Observatory is courtesy of National Astronomy and Ionosphere Center— Arecibo Observatory, a facility of the National Science Foundation; Photo by David Parker. Website: www.naic.edu.

Section 8.2.2: Aerial view of the Very Large Array is courtesy of National Radio Astronomy Observatory/Associated Universities, Inc. Website: www.nrao.edu.

Section 8.2.2: Map of Very Long Baseline Array sites (labels by the author) is courtesy of National Radio Astronomy Observatory/Associated Universities, Inc. Website: www.nrao.edu.

Section 8.3.1: Speckle image of WDS 01017+2518 is courtesy of Keith T Knox at Air Force Research Laboratory.

Section 8.3.2: Earth at night (city lights) picture is courtesy of NASA's Visible Earth Team. Website: http://visibleearth.nasa.gov.

Section 8.3.2: Chandra spacecraft image (labels by author) is courtesy of Chandra X-ray Observatory Center, Operated for NASA by the Smithsonian Astrophysical Observatory. Website: http://chandra.harvard.edu.

Chapter 9

Section 9.1.4: Terrestrial planets montage created by the author from images courtesy of NASA/JPL.

Section 9.1.4: Jovian planets montage created by the author from images courtesy of NASA/JPL.

Section 9.2.7: Jupiter's Great Red Spot image is courtesy of NASA/Jet Propulsion Laboratory. Website: www.jpl.nasa.gov.

9.2.8: Ocean currents image is courtesy of the MODIS Ocean Group, NASA/Goddard Space Flight Center, and the University of Miami. Excerpt and labels by the author. MODIS Ocean Group website: http://modis-ocean.gsfc.nasa.gov/.

Section 9.2.10: Optical band image of Venus by Galileo spacecraft and ultraviolet image of Venus by Pioneer spacecraft are courtesy of NASA/Jet Propulsion Laboratory. Website: www.jpl.nasa.gov.

Section 9.2.10: Earth image is courtesy of NASA. Website: www.nasa.gov.

Section 9.2.10: Mars image is courtesy of Astrogeology Team, U.S. Geological Survey, Flagstaff, Arizona. Website: wwwflag.wr.usgs.gov/USGSFlag/USGSFlag.html.

Section 9.2.10: Jupiter's Great Red Spot image is courtesy of NASA/Jet Propulsion Laboratory. Website: www.jpl.nasa.gov.

Section 9.3.1: Aurorae from Space Shuttle is courtesy of NASA. Website: www.nasa.gov.

Section 9.3.1: Jupiter Aurora courtesy of J. Clarke and G Ballester (University of Michigan), J. Trauger and R. Evans (Jet Propulsion Laboratory) and NASA. Website: http://hubblesite.org.

Section 9.5.1: Tycho Crater courtesy of NASA/Goddard/Arizona State University. Website: www.nasa.gov/mission_pages/LR

Section 9.5.1: Victoria Crater courtesy of NASA/JPL-Caltech/University of Arizona/Cornell/Ohio State Univ. Website: www.jpl.nasa.gov.

Section 9.5.1: Cunitz Crater courtesy of NASA/JPL. Website: www.jpl.nasa.gov.

Section 9.5.2: Shield Volcano vs. Composite Volcano and Pacific Northwest Volcanics lineart courtesy of USGS. Website: www.usgs.gov.

Section 9.5.2: Mercury volcanism erosion courtesy of AAAS/Science. Website from which image came: messenger.jhuapl.edu.

Section 9.5.2: Mt St Helens eruption courtesy of USGS and Austin Pose. Website: www.usgs.gov.

Section 9.5.3: Newton Crater gullies courtesy of NASA/JPL/Malin Space Science Systems. MSSS website: www.msss.com.

Section 9.5.3: Titan canyon system courtesy of NASA/JPL. Website: www.jpl.nasa.gov.

Section 9.5.3: Mars dunes courtesy of NASA/JPL/Maline Space Science Systems. MSSS website: www.msss.com.

Section 9.5.3: Titan dunes courtesy of NASA/JPL. Website: www.jpl.nasa.gov.

Section 9.5.3: Lena River delta courtesy of NASA/GSFC. Website: www.nasa.gov/centers/goddard/home/.

Section 9.5.4: Aine Corona courtesy of NASA/JPL. Website: www.jpl.nasa.gov.

Section 9.5.4: Mars Tharsis Bulge courtesy of NASA/USGS. Website: www.nasa.gov.

Section 9.5.4: Mercury lobate scarps courtesy of NASA/John Hopkins University Applied Physics Laboratory/Carnegie Institution of Washington.

Section 9.5.5: California Shuttle Radar Topography Mission courtesy of NASA/JPL/National Imagery and Mapping Agency. Website: www.jpl.nasa.gov.

Section 9.6.1: Ultraviolet image of Venus by Pioneer spacecraft is courtesy of NASA/Jet Propulsion Laboratory. Website: www.jpl.nasa.gov.

Section 9.6.1: Venus surface imaged by Magellan spacecraft radar is courtesy of NASA/Jet Propulsion Laboratory. Website: www.jpl.nasa.gov.

Section 9.6.1: Venus surface from Venera 13 courtesy of NASA. Website: www.nasa.gov.

Section 9.6.1: Venus craters + Gula Mons from NASA/JPL. Website: www.jpl.nasa.gov.

Section 9.6.2: Mars images are courtesy of NASA/Jet Propulsion Laboratory. Website: www.jpl.nasa.gov.

Section 9.6.2: Mars Nanedi Valles System image is courtesy of NASA/JPL/Malin Space Science Systems. Website: www.jpl.nasa.gov.

Section 9.6.2: Sedimentary conglomerate outcrops image courtesy of NASA/JPL-Caltech/MSSS and PSI. Website: http://photojournal.jpl.nasa.gov.

Section 9.6.2: Gale Crater was a lake images courtesy of NASA/JPL-Caltech/MSSS. Website: http://photojournal.jpl.nasa.gov.

Section 9.6.2: Recurring slope linear in Newton Crater image courtesy of NASA/JPL-Caltech/Univ. of Arizona. Website: mars.jpl.nasa.gov/mro.

Section 9.6.2: Mars surface pictures are courtesy of NASA/Jet Propulsion Laboratory. Website: www.jpl.nasa.gov.

Section 9.6.2: Curiosity's view of Gale Crater panorama courtesy of NASA/JPL-Caltech/MSSS. Website: http://photojournal.jpl.nasa.gov.

Section 9.6.2: Yuty Crater courtesy of NASA/JPL. Website: www.jpl.nasa.gov.

Section 9.6.2: Phoenix Mars Lander trench courtesy of NASA/JPL-Caltech/University of Arizona/Texas A&M Univ. Website: www.jpl.nasa.gov.

Section 9.6.3: Earth image is courtesy of NASA. Website: www.nasa.gov.

Section 9.6.3: Phanerozoic Climate Change graphic from Wikipedia.org.

Section 9.6.3: Carbon dioxide levels plot and global temperature plots with climate models courtesy of Intergovernmental Panel on Climate Change Working Group 1 Assessment Report 5. Website: www.ipcc.ch.

Section 9.6.3: Plots of paleoclimatology generated by author from data at NOAA National Centers for Environmental Information. Website: www.ncdc.noaa.gov.

Section 9.7.2: Galilean satellites montage created by the author from images courtesy of NASA/JPL and UCO/Lick Observatory (for the Moon image).

Section 9.7.2: Io volcanoes courtesy of NASA/John Hopkins University Applied Physics Laboratory/Southwest Research Institute. Website: http://photojournal.jpl.nasa.gov.

Section 9.7.2: Europa surface ice blocks courtesy of NASA/JPL/University of Arizona. Website: www.jpl.nasa.gov.

Section 9.7.2: Europa surface courtesy of NASA/JPL. Website: www.jpl.nasa.gov.

Section 9.7.2: Ganymede detail and Callisto courtesy of NASA/JPL.

Section 9.7.3: Titan montage created by the author from images courtesy of NASA/JPL.

Section 9.7.3: Titan surface pictures courtesy of NASA/JPL/ESA/University of Arizona. Website: http://photojournal.jpl.nasa.gov.

Section 9.7.3: Titan lake glint montage created by the author from images courtesy of NASA/JPL/Space Science Institute and University of Arizona/DLR and USGS. Website: http://photojournal.jpl.nasa.gov.

Section 9.7.4: Enceladus geysers & global view courtesy of NASA/JPL/Space Science Institute. Website: www.jpl.nasa.gov.

Section 9.7.5: Titan, Triton, Moon montage created by the author from images courtesy of NASA/JPL and UCO/Lick Observatory (for the Moon image).

Section 9.7.6: Computer-generated picture of Saturn ring particles is courtesy of NASA/Jet Propulsion Laboratory. Website: www.jpl.nasa.gov.

Section 9.7.6: Saturn back-lit courtesy of NASA/JPL/Space Science Institute. Website: http://photojournal.jpl.nasa.gov.

Section 9.7.6: Saturn's rings detail image is courtesy of NASA/Jet Propulsion Laboratory. Website: www.jpl.nasa.gov.

Section 9.7.6: Propeller feature in ring and Shepherd moons courtesy of NASA/JPL/Space Science Institute. Website: www.jpl.nasa.gov.

Section 9.7.6: Moonlets and Enceladus E-ring courtesy of NASA/JPL/Space Science Institute. Website: www.jpl.nasa.gov.

Chapter 10

Section 10.1: Asteroids visited by spacecraft image courtesy of NASA/JPL-Caltech/JAXA/ESA. Website: http://photojournal.jpl.nasa.gov.

Section 10.1: Itokawa images courtesy of ISAS/JAXA. Website: www.jaxa.jp.

Section 10.1: Toutatis image courtesy of CNSA (China space program). Image downloaded from www.planetary.org.

Section 10.1: Bennu image courtesy of NASA/Goddard/University of Arizona. Website: www.nasa.gov.

Section 10.1: Ceres & Vesta images courtesy of NASA/Jet Propulsion Laboratory/UCLA. Website: www.jpl.nasa.gov.

Section 10.1: Ceres and Occator Crater courtesy of NASA/JPL-Caltech/UCLA/MPS/DLR/IDA. Website: http://photojournal.jpl.nasa.gov.

Section 10.2: Meteorite images are courtesy of NASA/Jet Propulsion Laboratory. Website: www.jpl.nasa.gov.

Section 10.2.1: SNC meteorite image is courtesy of NASA/Jet Propulsion Laboratory. Website: www.jpl.nasa.gov.

Section 10.4: Map of terrestrial impacts is courtesy of Geological Survey of Canada, Natural Resources Canada. Database now at Planetary and Space Science Centre at the University of New Brunswick, Canada. Website: www.passc.net/EarthImpactDatabase/New%20website_05-2018/Index.html.

Section 10.4.1: Meteor crater image is courtesy of David Roddy and Lunar Planetary Institute. Website: http://cass.jsc.nasa.gov/lpi.html.

Section 10.4.1: Chicxulub crater image is courtesy of Virgil L. Sharpton and Lunar Planetary Institute. Website: http://cass.jsc.nasa.gov/lpi.html.

Section 10.5: Comet fear pictures of 1857 and 1066 are not copyrighted and were not made by the author (he's not that old).

Section 10.5.1: Comet Halley nucleus picture taken by the Halley Multicolour Camera on board ESA's Giotto spacecraft. Copyright © 1986, 1996 by Max Planck Institut fuer Aeronomie, Katlenberg-Lindau, Germany. Reprinted by permission of Dr. Horst Uwe Keller. Website: www.linmpi.mpg.de/english/forschung3/hmc.gif.

Section 10.5.1: Comets Borrelly, Wild 2, Tempel 1, Hartley, and Halley montage created by NASA/JPL from images courtesy of NASA/JPL and NASA/JPL/UMD and Max Planck Institut fuer Aeronomie. Churyumov-Gerasimenko added to montage from image courtesy of ESA/Rosetta/MPS for OSIRIS Team MPS/UPD/LAM/IAA/SSO/INTA/UPM/DASP/IDA. Website: http://photojournal.jpl.nasa.gov.

Section 10.5.3: Comet Hale-Bopp picture is copyrighted © Darren Bly.

Section 10.6.2: Earth, Moon, Pluto, Charon montage created by author from images courtesy of NASA and Space Telescope Science Institute. Space Telescope website: www.stsci.edu.

Section 10.6.2: Pluto and Charon courtesy of NASA/John Hopkins University Applied Physics Laboratory/Southwest Research Institute. Website: www.nasa.gov.

Section 10.6.2: Pluto surface images courtesy of NASA/JHUAPL/SwRI (left) and NASA/JHUAPL/SwRI/Lunar and Planetary Institute/Paul Schenk (right). Website: http://pluto.jhuapl.edu.

Section 10.9.1: Fomalhaut System courtesy of NASA, ESA, P. Kalas, J. Graham, E. Chiang, E. Kite (University of California, Berkeley), M. Clampin (NASA Goddard Space Flight Center), M. Fitzgerald (Lawrence Livermore National Laboratory), and K. Stapelfeldt and J. Krist (NASA Jet Propulsion Laboratory). Website: http://hubblesite.org.

Section 10.9.1: Kepler 186 system image courtesy of NASA Ames/SETI Institute/JPL-Caltech. Website: www.nasa.gov.

Section 10.9.1: TRAPPIST-1 system image courtesy of NASA/JPL-Caltech/R. Hurt, T. Pyle (IPAC) and TRAPPIST-1/Solar System comparison image courtesy of NASA/JPL-Caltech. Website: www.spitzer.caltech.edu.

Section 10.9.2: Bar charts from Exoplanet Archive. Website: https://exoplanetarchive.ipac.caltech.edu.

Chapter 12

Section 12.1.2: Sun's photosphere in optical band image is courtesy of NASA/Marshall Space Flight Center. Website: www.msfc.nasa.gov.

Section 12.1.2: Sunspot and surrounding granulation image is courtesy National Solar Observatory/National Optical Astronomy Observatories. Website: www.nso.edu.

Section 12.1.2: Loop prominence picture (left frame) is courtesy of National Solar Observatory/Sacramento Peak, Sunspot, NM, USA. Website: www.sunspot.noao.edu.

Section 12.1.2: Solar flare picture (right frame) is courtesy of NASA. Website: www.nasa.gov.

Section 12.1.4: Solar eclipse picture (top left frame) is copyrighted ©1999 Photo by Fred Espenak. Website: www.mreclipse.com.

Section 12.1.4: Extreme-ultraviolet image of Sun's corona is courtesy of The Solar and Heliospheric Observatory/ Extreme ultraviolet Imaging Telescope. Website: http://umbra.nascom.nasa.gov/eit.

Section 12.3: Neutrino detector in the Homestake Gold Mine image is courtesy of Ray Davis/Brookhaven National Laboratory. Website: www.bnl.gov.

Section 12.3.1: Super-Kamiokande neutrino detector image is courtesy of Institute for Cosmic Ray Research, University of Tokyo. Website: www.icrr.u-tokyo.ac.jp.

Section 12.5.6: Brown dwarf Gliese 229 picture is courtesy of T. Nakajima and S. Kulkarni (Caltech), S. Durrance and D.Golimowski (JHU), NASA. From Space Telescope Science Institute website: www.stsci.edu.

Section 12.5.6: Eta Carinae picture is courtesy of Jon Morse (University of Colorado) and NASA. From Space Telescope Science Institute website: www.stsci.edu.

Chapter 13

Section 13.1.2: Orion Nebula photograph (right frame) is copyrighted © Anglo-Australian Observatory/Royal Observatory, Edinburgh. Photograph from UK Schmidt plates by David Malin. Website: https://images.datacentral.org.au.

Section 13.1.2: Heart of Orion nebula (Trapezium stars) images are courtesy of John Bally, Dave Devine, and Ralph Sutherland. From Space Telescope Science Institute website: www.stsci.edu.

Section 13.1.2: Optical band and infrared image of OMC-1 region is courtesy of Rodger Thompson, Marcia Rieke, Glenn Schneider, Susan Stolovy (University of Arizona); Edwin Erickson (SETI Institute/Ames Research Center); David Axon (STScI), and NASA for the infrared. C. Robert O'Dell, Shui Kwan Wong (Rice University) and NASA for the visible. Website: http://hubblesite.org.

Section 13.1.2: Protostars in the Orion Nebula is courtesy of John Bally, Dave Devine, and Ralph Sutherland and STScI/AURA. From Space Telescope Science Institute website: www.stsci.edu.

Section 13.1.2: Eagle nebula from ground-based telescope (left frame) is copyrighted © Anglo-Australian Observatory, Photograph by David Malin. Website: https://images.datacentral.org.au.

Section 13.1.2: Gaseous pillars of M 16 (right frame) is courtesy of Jeff Hester and Paul Scowen (Arizona State University), and NASA. From Space Telescope Science Institute website: www.stsci.edu.

Section 13.1.2: Jets from young stars image is courtesy of C. Burrows (STScI), J. Hester (ASU), J. Morse (STScI), NASA. From Space Telescope Science Institute website: www.stsci.edu.

Section 13.1.2: Pleiades star cluster image is copyrighted © Anglo-Australian Observatory/Royal Observatory, Edinburgh. Photograph from UK Schmidt plates by David Malin. Website: https://images.datacentral.org.au.

Section 13.1.2: Hubble Space Telescope image of Betelgeuse (right frame) is courtesy of A. Dupree (CfA) and STScI/AURA. From Space Telescope Science Institute website: www.stsci.edu.

Section 13.1.2: NGC 3603 image is courtesy of W. Brandner (JPL/IPAC), E Grebel (UW), Y Chu (UI Urbana-Champaign) and NASA. From Space Telescope Science Institute website: www.stsci.edu.

Section 13.1.2: Ring Nebula image (left frame) is courtesy of Palomar Observatory/California Institute of Technology. Website: http://astro.caltech.edu.

Section 13.1.2: Helix Nebula image (right frame) is copyrighted © Anglo-Australian Observatory, Photograph by David Malin. Website: https://images.datacentral.org.au.

Section 13.1.2: Dumbbell Nebula image (left frame) is copyrighted © IAC/RGO/Malin, Photograph by David Malin. Website: https://images.datacentral.org.au.

Section 13.1.2: NGC 6543 (Cat Eye Nebula) image (right frame) is courtesy of NASA/ESA/HEIC and the Hubble Heritage Team (STScI/AURA). Hubble Heritage website: http://heritage.stsci.edu.

Section 13.1.2: Hourglass Nebula (left frame) is courtesy of R. Sahal & J. Trauger (JPL), the WFPC2 Science Team and NASA. From Space Telescope Science Institute website: www.stsci.edu.

Section 13.1.2: Eskimo Nebula (right frame) is courtesy of NASA, A Fruchter and the ERO Team (STScI). From Space Telescope Science Institute website: www.stsci.edu.

Section 13.1.2: Crab Nebula image is copyrighted © Malin/Pasachoff/Caltech, Photograph from Hale 5m plates by David Malin. Website: https://images.datacentral.org.au.

Section 13.1.2: Part of Large Magellanic Cloud showing SN1987A image is copyrighted © Anglo-Australian Observatory, Photograph by David Malin. Website: https://images.datacentral.org.au.

Section 13.1.3: Vela Supernova remnant image is copyrighted © Anglo-Australian Observatory/Royal Observatory, Edinburgh. Photograph from UK Schmidt plates by David Malin. Website: https://images.datacentral.org.au.

Section 13.3.2: White dwarfs in M 4 image is courtesy of H. Bond (STScI) and NASA. From Space Telescope Science Institute website: www.stsci.edu.

Section 13.3.5: Crab Nebula pulsar detail image is courtesy of J. Hester and P. Scowen (ASU) and NASA. From Space Telescope Science Institute website: www.stsci.edu.

Section 13.3.8 Masses in Stellar Graveyard is courtesy of LIGO/VIrgo/Northwestern Univ./Frank Elavsky. Website: www.ligo.caltech.edu.

Chapter 14

Section 14.1.1: Images of IC 2948 and Barnard 86 are copyrighted © Anglo-Australian Observatory, Photograph by David Malin. Website: https://images.datacentral.org.au.

Section 14.1.2: (top) M 42 (and M 43) and (top right) Trifid Nebula images are copyrighted © Anglo-Australian Observatory, Photograph by David Malin. Website: https://images.datacentral.org.au.

Section 14.1.2: (top left) Lagoon Nebula image is copyrighted © Anglo-Australian Observatory/Royal Observatory, Edinburgh. Photograph from UK Schmidt plates by David Malin. Website: https://images.datacentral.org.au.

Section 14.2: NGC 891 image is copyrighted © IAC/RGO/Malin, Photograph by David Malin. Website: https://images.datacentral.org.au.

Section 14.2.1: Harlow Shapley portrait is courtesy of the American Institute of Physics Emilio Segrè Visual Archives, Shapley Collection. Website: www.aip.org/history/esva.

Section 14.2.1: Light curves for Type I and Type II Cepheids are from The Hipparcos and Tycho Catalogues (published by the European Space Agency). Website: http://astro.estec.esa.nl/hipparcos.

Section 14.2.2: Globular clusters M5 and 47 Tucanae images are copyrighted © Anglo-Australian Observatory, Photograph by David Malin. Website: https://images.datacentral.org.au.

Section 14.2.5: NGC 2997 (left frame) image is copyrighted © Anglo-Australian Observatory, Photograph by David Malin. Website: https://images.datacentral.org.au.

Section 14.2.5: M 33 (right frame) image is copyrighted © IAC/RGO/Malin, Photograph by David Malin. Website: https://images.datacentral.org.au.

Section 14.2.7: Galactic center radio images are courtesy of National Radio Astronomy Observatory/Associated Universities, Inc. Website: www.nrao.edu.

Section 14.2.7: Star orbits around central black hole courtesy of Andrea Ghez and her research team at UCLA and are from data sets obtained with the W.M. Keck Telescopes.
Website: www.astro.ucla.edu/~ghezgroup/gc/index.shtml

Chapter 15

Start: Edwin Hubble and Milton Humason portraits are Image courtesy of The Observatories of the Carnegie Institute of Washington. Website: www.ociw.edu.

Section 15.1.1: (top left) M 32 image is copyrighted © National Optical Astronomy Observatory/Association of Universities for Research in Astronomy/National Science Foundation (NOAO/AURA/NSF), all rights reserved. Website: www.noao.edu.

Section 15.1.1: (top right) M 110 image is copyrighted © Bill Schoening, Vanessa Harvey/REU Program/ AURA/NOAO/NSF. Website: www.noao.edu.

Section 15.1.1: (bottom) Leo I and M 87 images are copyrighted © Anglo-Australian Observatory, Photograph by David Malin. Website: https://images.datacentral.org.au.

Section 15.1.1: (top left) Andromeda Galaxy image is copyrighted © Jason Ware. Website: www.galaxyphoto.com.

Section 15.1.1: (top right) Triangulum Galaxy image is copyrighted © IAC/RGO/Malin, Photograph by David Malin. Website: https://images.datacentral.org.au.

Section 15.1.1: (center left) M 81 image is copyrighted © National Optical Astronomy Observatory/Association of Universities for Research in Astronomy/National Science Foundation (NOAO/AURA/NSF), all rights reserved. Website: www.noao.edu.

Section 15.1.1: (center right and bottom) NGC 2997, NGC 1365, NGC 3351 images are copyrighted © Anglo-Australian Observatory, Photograph by David Malin. Website: https://images.datacentral.org.au.

Section 15.1.1: (top) Large and Magellanic Cloud and Small Magellanic Cloud images are copyrighted © Anglo-Australian Observatory/Royal Observatory, Edinburgh. Photograph from UK Schmidt plates by David Malin. Website: https://images.datacentral.org.au.

Section 15.1.1: (middle and bottom left) NGC 6822, IC 5152, and NGC 1313 images are copyrighted © Anglo-Australian Observatory, Photograph by David Malin. Website: https://images.datacentral.org.au.

Section 15.1.1: (bottom right) M 82 image is courtesy of NASA/ESA/Hubble Heritage Team (STScI/AURA). Website: http://heritage.stsci.edu.

Section 15.1.6: Virgo cluster image is copyrighted © Anglo-Australian Observatory, Photograph from UK Schmidt plates by David Malin. Website: https://images.datacentral.org.au.

Section 15.1.6: Coma cluster and Hercules cluster images are copyrighted © National Optical Astronomy Observatory/Association of Universities for Research in Astronomy/National Science Foundation (NOAO/AURA/NSF), all rights reserved. Website: www.noao.edu.

Section 15.1.7: Abell 1689 image courtesy of NASA, N. Benitez (JHU), T. Broadhurst (The Hebrew University), H. Ford (JHU), M. Clampin(STScI), G. Hartig (STScI), G. Illingworth (UCO/Lick Observatory), the ACS Science Team and ESA. Website: www.hubblesite.org.

Section 15.1.8: 2dF GRS slice map is courtesy of the 2dF Survey team at the Anglo-Australian Observatory. Website: http://www2.aao.gov.au/2dFGRS/.

Section 15.1.8: Sloan Digital Sky Survey slice map courtesy of M. Blanton and SDSS. Website: www.sdss.org.

Section 15.1.9: Spiderweb Galaxy courtesy of NASA, ESA, G Miley & R Overzier (Leiden Observatory), and the ACS Science Team. From Space Telescope Science Institute website.

Section 15.1.9: Dark Matter map and visible/dark matter cross section courtesy of NASA, ESA, and R Massey (California Institute of Technology). From Space Telescope Science Institute website.

Section 15.1.9: Colliding galaxies NGC 4038 & NGC 4039 image is courtesy of B. Whitmore (STScI) and NASA. From Space Telescope Science Institute website: www.stsci.edu.

Section 15.1.9: Cartwheel Galaxy courtesy of Kirk Borne (STScI), and NASA. From Space Telescope Science Institute website: www.stsci.edu.

Section 15.1.9: Hubble Ultra Deep Field image is courtesy of NASA, ESA, S. Beckwith (STScI) and the HUDF Team. From Space Telescope Science Institute website: www.stsci.edu.

Section 15.2.1: Quasar vs. regular star image is courtesy of Charles Steidel (California Institute of Technology, Pasadena, CA) and STScI/AURA/NASA. From Space Telescope Science Institute website: www.stsci.edu.

Section 15.2.1: Quasar host galaxies image is courtesy of John Bahcall (Institute for Advanced Study, Princeton) Mike Disney (University of Wales) and NASA. From Space Telescope Science Institute website: www.stsci.edu.

Section 15.2.2: NGC 1566 image is copyrighted © Anglo-Australian Observatory, Photograph by David Malin. Website: https://images.datacentral.org.au.

Section 15.2.2: Radio Galaxy 3C219 (left frame) is copyrighted © National Radio Astronomy Observatory/ Associated Universities, Inc., 1999. Website: www.nrao.edu.

Section 15.2.2: Quasar 3C334 (right frame) is copyrighted © National Radio Astronomy Observatory/Associated Universities, Inc., 1996. Website: www.nrao.edu.

Section 15.2.3: Radio galaxy NGC 4261 radio image-optical and core montage created by author using images courtesy of H. Ford and L. Ferrarese (Johns Hopkins University) and NASA. Images from Space Telescope Science Institute website: www.stsci.edu.

Section 15.2.3: Gas disk in nucleus of M 87 image (jet label by author) is courtesy of Holland Ford, Space Telescope Science Institute/Johns Hopkins University; Richard Harms, Applied Research Corp.; Zlatan Tsvetanov, Arthur Davidsen, and Gerard Kriss at Johns Hopkins; Ralph Bohlin and George Hartig at Space Telescope Science Institute; Linda Dressel and Ajay K. Kochhar at Applied Research Corp. in Landover, Md.; and Bruce Margon from the University of Washington in Seattle and NASA. From Space Telescope Science Institute website: www.stsci.edu.

Section 15.2.3: Event Horizon Telescope image of M87 black hole comparison with model courtesy of the EHT Collaboration and the American Astronomical Society. Website: https://eventhorizontelescope.org.

Section 15.2.4: M 51 image (left frame) is copyrighted © National Optical Astronomy Observatory/Association of Universities for Research in Astronomy/National Science Foundation (NOAO/AURA/NSF), all rights reserved. Website: www.noao.edu.

Section 15.2.4: Core of M 51 (right frame) is courtesy of Space Telescope Science Institute/Association of Universities for Research in Astronomy, Inc. and NASA. Website: www.stsci.edu.

Section 15.4: Sombrero Galaxy picture is courtesy of Space Telescope Science Institute/Association of Universities for Research in Astronomy, Inc. and NASA. Website: http://heritage.stsci.edu.

Chapter 16

Section 16.1.6: COBE DMR maps of the microwave background are courtesy of NASA/Goddard Space Flight Center. The COBE datasets were developed by the NASA Goddard Space Flight Center under the guidance of the COBE Science Working Group and were provided by the NSSDC. Website: http://space.gsfc.nasa.gov/astro/cobe.

Section 16.1.6: COBE DMR map of microwave background with the WMAP map of microwave background is courtesy of the NASA/WMAP Science Team at Goddard Space Flight Center. Website: http://map.gsfc.nasa.gov/.

Section 16.1.6: Reionization Era and first galaxies schematic from NASA, ESA, P. Oesch & B. Robertson (UC Santa Cruz), and A Feild (STScI). Website: http://hubblesite.org.

Section 16.2.5: Geometry of the Universe from the microwave background is courtesy of the NASA/WMAP Science Team at Goddard Space Flight Center. Website: http://map.gsfc.nasa.gov/.

Section 16.2.5: Angular spectrum graph from Planck Collaboration, 2018 data release. Website: http://sci.esa.int/planck/ .

Section 16.3.1: Universe history is courtesy of NASA/WMAP Science Team at Goddard Space Flight Center. Website: http://map.gsfc.nasa.gov/.

Chapter 17

Section 17.4: Venus Express spectrum is courtesy of ESA/VIRTIS/INAF-IASF/Obs. de Paris-LESIA (Earth views: Solar System Simulator JPL-NASA). Website: www.esa.int/esaMI/Venus_Express/index.html

Section 17.4: Earth's changing spectrum through time is courtesy of L. Kaltenegger, W. Traub, & K. Jucks and the American Astronomical Society. Website: https://iopscience.iop.org.

Section 17.7: Enrico Fermi portrait is courtesy of the American Institute of Physics. Website: https://history.aip.org/phn/ .